RAC Inspected

Hotels and
Bed & Breakfast 2001

Great Britain & Ireland

RAC Inspected

Hotels and
Bed & Breakfast 2001

Great Britain & Ireland

The Swallow George Hotel, Chollerford, Northumberland

RAC

First published 2001
Copyright © RAC 2001

Published by BBC Worldwide Limited
Woodlands, 80 Wood Lane, London W12 OTT
Telephone: 020 8433 2000
Fax: 020 8433 3752

ISBN 0-563-53770-1

Publisher: Adam Waddell
Group Advertising Sales Manager: Phil Greenaway
Commissioning Editor: Ben Dunn

Editorial, production and repro: Thalamus Publishing
    Toby Marsden
    Warren Lapworth
    Neil Williams
Regional maps: Roger Kean
Map illustrations: Oliver Frey
Front cover photography: William King

This book contains mapping sourced from Ordnance Survey

Set in 8pt Helvetica Neue 55
Printed and bound in Spain by Cayfosa-Quebecor, Barcelona

A CIP catalogue record for this book is available from
the British Library

RAC Motoring Services
1 Forest Road
Feltham
Middlesex
TW13 7RR
RAC Hotel Services
Tel: 020 8917 2840

Contents

Shetland
Islands

Orkney
Islands

Hebrides

Isles of
Scilly

How to use this guide

How to find a property

Town, County ——————————————

Property name, Gold/Blue Ribbon Award —————
for hotels, if given, or RAC Little Gem Award
for Guest Accommodation (below), if given

Dorstan Hotel | Little Gem
◆◆◆◆◆ ——————————————

Classification, RAC Dining Awards (see page 15) ——

Address and contact details ——————————

Brief description of the property
with a picture (not all properties listed ——————
have opted for these two items)

Details of prices for rooms ——————————
Details of prices for meals ——————————
Credit cards accepted by the property ——————
Information on property,
bedrooms and general facilities
How to find the property ——————————

Indicates there is an advertisement ——————
nearby with more detail

Ashford, Kent

Eastwell Manor

★★★★ 🍴🍴🍴🍴
Eastwell Park, Boughton Lees, Ashford, Kent,
TN25 4HR
Tel: **01233 213000** Fax: **01233 635530**
Email: **eastwell@btinternet.com**

A 4-star country house hotel set in acres of
grounds offering 62 bedrooms, restaurant, bar
& brasserie, 2x20m heated pools, state of the
art gymnasium, 12 beauty treatment rooms and
hairdressing salon.

SB **£150** DB **£180** HBS **£180** HBD **£210**
B **£11** L **£16.50** D **£30.**
CC: **MC Vi Am DC Swi Delt**

🔥♨🛇🛏🐾⊘☕☐☎📞🅿🎳🎠🐕🎿🚣
🐾👥👤 SPA 🎯🔍🎲🚶

How to get there: **Leave M20 at J-9. Take A28
to Canterbury, then follow A251 towards
Faversham. Hotel is 2½ miles on left-hand side.**

See advert on this page

Notes

This guide is broken down into 12 regional sections:
London, Southeast, Southwest, East Anglia,
East Midlands, West Midlands, Northeast, Northwest,
Wales, Scotland, Northern Ireland & Republic of
Ireland, Channel Islands & Isle of Man. Within each
region towns are listed alphabetically.

Properties are arranged first by classification rating
from 5–1 Star Hotels and 5–1 Diamond Guest
Accommodation and then alphabetically within the
classification.

The final entries for each town list those few properties
which, because of pressure of time, we have been
unable to complete an inspection for Harmonised
Quality Standards this year.

Dialling Ireland from UK
In this guide, telephone and fax numbers for the
Republic of Ireland are shown with the international
dialling code – 00353 (0), but without the 00, like this:

Tel: **+353 (0)1 9876543** Fax: **+353 (0)1 3456789**

Within the Republic, drop the +353 from the number.

Explanation of the listings and symbols

Property information

The listing for each property starts with its name, followed by its classification, RAC awards, address, telephone and fax numbers, email and internet addresses, details of any seasonal closures and any minimum age restrictions for children, if relevant.

★ Hotel classification (from 1 to 5 Stars)

♦ Guest Accommodation classification (from 1 to 5 Diamonds)

✤ A small number of properties in this guide have a provisional classification denoted by this symbol. This means that either we have been unable to confirm their new classification or the property may be awaiting an inspection.

Awards

For further information on all RAC awards, please see page 15.

  Gold Ribbon
         Blue Ribbon
R Dining Award (from 1 to 5)
Little Gem RAC Little Gem
✕ RAC Sparkling Diamond
✓ RAC Warm Welcome

Facilities at the property

🐕 Dogs welcome (where not shown, please contact the property for its guide dog policy)
|↑↑ Lift
⊗ Non-smoking rooms available (the guide does not indicate 100% non-smoking properties, so smokers are advised to find out in advance whether smoking rooms are available)
P Off-street parking
P● Secure off-street parking
♦♦♦ Conference facilities
👁 Beauty salon
△ Licensed for the performance of wedding ceremonies

Bedroom information

♿ Bedrooms with wheelchair access
☕ Tea/coffee-making facilities
📺 TV
📞 Telephone
⌨ Computer connection available
❄ Air conditioning
🛏 Four-poster beds available

Children

👶 Children welcome (any minimum age restrictions are shown beneath contact details)
🎠 Creche facility
📻 Baby listening service
♂ Children's meal menu
👪 Family bedrooms

Sporting facilities

⌧ Indoor swimming pool
⌇ Outdoor swimming pool
'Y' Gymnasium
SPA Health spa
/⦂ Billiards/Snooker/Pool
🎱 Games room
Q Tennis/Squash
⚑ Golf
🐎 Horse riding
🎣 Fishing

Licensing information

♦♦♦ Full licence
♦♦ Restaurant or table licence – the sale of alcohol is restricted to customers taking meals
♦ Residential licence – the sale of alcohol is restricted to residents and to their friends entertained at their expense
▮▮ Club licence
▮✕ Restricted Club licence (Scotland)

Information on room prices

SB Rate for Single Room & Breakfast
DB Rate for Double/Twin Room (double occupancy) & Breakfast
HBS Rate for Half Board Single Room
HBD Rate for Half Board Double/Twin Room
B Price of breakfast
L Price of table d'hôte lunch
D Price of table d'hôte dinner
CC: Credit cards accepted as listed. If no credit cards are listed under the property's entry, only cash payments, or cheques to a given amount supported by credit card or cheque guarantee card, will be acceptable. Travellers' cheques may be accepted, but please check in advance. The major credit cards are abbreviated as shown here:
MC MasterCard
Vi Visa
Amex American Express
DC Diners Club
Swi Switch
Delta Delta

All prices quoted in this guide should include VAT where applicable, and may or may not include a service charge. Prices may range from that for a Standard room in low season to that for Superior rooms in high season, and are based on what hoteliers have told us they expect to charge in 2001. Double rates are shown per room based on two people sharing. However, please check before booking. Although properties in the Republic of Ireland have been asked to quote their charges in £ sterling, there may be some which have quoted in Irish punts, and it is advisable to ascertain which currency is being quoted before booking.

RAC Inspection Scheme

Reassurance with the RAC

With increasing use of new technology to source information and book accommodation, there is greater need than ever for independent and reliable assessment. The RAC Hotels scheme provides the reassurance that guests are looking for to help make the right choice.

By visiting each property within the scheme on a regular basis our trained professionals, working to exacting standards, are able to provide an objective assessment of the establishment, awarding the appropriate rating and awards. Our team of Hotel Inspectors are trained to assess all aspects of the operation of serviced accommodation – from the smallest bed and breakfast to the largest hotel.

The process begins well before the Hotel Inspector has driven up the drive or walked through the gate; with the first impression being formed at the time of booking, every aspect of customer service contributes towards the overall quality assessment of the hotel or guest accommodation.

The Inspection process is carefully controlled to ensure consistency, and a quality assurance programme operates to ensure that a uniform approach is applied to all inspections in the United Kingdom and Republic of Ireland.

Of course, every property is different and the Inspector is trained to adapt to these differences. The needs of a wide range of guests are taken into account throughout the inspection and it is as much a question of how other guests are dealt with as the service that the Inspector receives.

Who would want to be an Inspector?

That's a question that many hoteliers and occasionally RAC Hotel Inspectors ask!

The requirements of the role include a strong background in the hospitality industry, an enquiring mind, obviously good attention to detail and the ability to get on with people, not to mention the days and nights away from home.

But it's not all travelling and being paid to be a guest. The role is that of a consultant, analysing the property and providing a full and detailed report in person to the owner or manager – not an easy task if the stay didn't live up to expectation!

Trends and guest expectations change and the Inspector needs to keep up to date with the latest developments in the industry, being able to advise on a range of subjects, from menu selection to improvements in technology, so helping the proprietor to improve standards at their property.

The most rewarding part of the job is discussing the findings during the de-brief with the owner or manager who views the inspection process as a valuable learning tool. These industry professionals are those who are constantly striving to meet and exceed their guests' expectations and welcome an objective assessment and honest account of the Inspector's visit.

How often are RAC properties inspected?

All properties are inspected on an annual basis, within the time frames agreed by the three main accreditation bodies and the industry. For hotels an overnight visit is undertaken every other year and for the Guest Accommodation sector, every third year. In the intervening years a consultation as a day visit is held. Some establishments value the feedback so much that they elect to have more than one visit each year.

Visits to RAC hotels and guest accommodation are carried out as mystery guests — visits deliberately do not fall on the same day or even the same month each year in order that we can view the establishments with different clientele. Visits are unannounced, Inspectors booking and staying as would guests. Only after the bill has been settled next morning do Inspectors present themselves to discuss their visit.

On day visits, the Inspector again arrives un-announced and if food is served, takes a meal to observe the running of the establishment before a full tour of the guest areas is undertaken with the management.

Continued over the page

RAC Inspection Scheme

What types of property are there?

Serviced accommodation falls into four main types of property:

Hotels – rated from 1 to 5 Stars
Town Houses – rated 4 and 5 Stars only
Guest Accommodation – rated from
1 to 5 Diamonds
Travel Accommodation – no symbol used

How do the ratings differ?

Hotels – Stars

★

Hotels in this classification are likely to be small and independently owned with a family atmosphere. Services may be provided by the owner and family on an informal basis. There may be a limited range of facilities and meals may be fairly simple. Lunch may not be served. Some of the bedrooms may not have an ensuite bath/shower room. Maintenance, cleanliness and comfort should, however, always be of an acceptable standard.

★★

In this classification hotels will typically be small- to medium-sized and offer more extensive facilities than at one-Star level. Some business hotels come into two-Star classification and guests can expect comfortable well-equipped overnight accommodation, usually with an ensuite bath/shower room. Reception and other staff aim for a more professional presentation than at a one-Star level and offer a wider range of straightforward services, including food and drink.

★★★

At this level, hotels are usually of a size to support higher staffing levels, and a significantly greater quality and range of facilities than at the lower Star classifications. Reception and the other public rooms are more spacious and the restaurant also usually caters for non-residents. All bedrooms have fully ensuite bath and shower rooms and offer a good standard of comfort and equipment, such as a hairdryer, direct-dial telephone and toiletries in the bathroom. Some

room service can be expected and some provision for business travellers.

★★★★

Expectations at this level include a degree of luxury, as well as quality in furnishings, décor and equipment, in every area of the hotel. Bedrooms usually offer more space than at the lower star levels, with well-designed, co-ordinated furnishings and décor. Ensuite bathrooms have both bath and fixed shower. There is a high enough ratio of staff to guests to provide services such as porterage, 24-hour room service, laundry and dry-cleaning. The restaurant will demonstrate a serious approach to cuisine.

★ ★ ★ ★ ★

Here you should find spacious and luxurious accommodation throughout the hotel, matching the best international standards. Interior design should impress with its quality and attention to detail, comfort and elegance. Furnishings should be immaculate. Services should be formal, well supervised and flawless in attention to guests' needs, without being intrusive. The restaurants demonstrate a high level of technical skill, producing dishes to the highest international standards. Staff are knowledgeable, helpful and well-versed in all aspects of customer care, combining efficiency with courtesy.

Town House Accommodation

The classification denotes small, personally run town or city centre hotels which afford a high degree of privacy and concentrate on luxuriously furnished bedrooms and suites with high private room service, rather than public rooms or formal dining rooms usually associated with hotels; they are usually in areas well served by restaurants. All fall broadly within the four- and five-Star classification.

Continued on page 13

COUNTRY HOTELS OF DISTINCTION

EXERCISING MIND AND SOUL

Our three magnificent hotels enjoy spectacular settings in the south of England. Each displays individual charm and character and offers discerning guests spacious and exquisitely furnished accommodation and extensive leisure facilities. The award winning restaurants at all the hotels boast two rosettes and offer the finest cuisine and wine selections.

The Grand Hotel
★★★★★

King Edwards Parade, Eastbourne,
East Sussex BN21 4EQ
Telephone +44 (0)1323 412345
Facsimile +44 (0)1323 412233
E-mail reservations@grandeastbourne.com
Website www.grandeastbourne.com

Ashdown Park
Hotel and Country Club
★★★★

Wych Cross, Nr Forest Row,
East Sussex RH18 5JR
Telephone +44 (0)1342 824988
Facsimile +44 (0)1342 826206
E-mail reservations@ashdownpark.com
Website www.ashdownpark.com

Tylney Hall
★★★★

Rotherwick, Hook,
Hampshire RG27 9AZ
Telephone +44 (0)1256 764881
Facsimile +44 (0)1256 768141
E-mail reservations@tylneyhall.com
Website www.tylneyhall.com

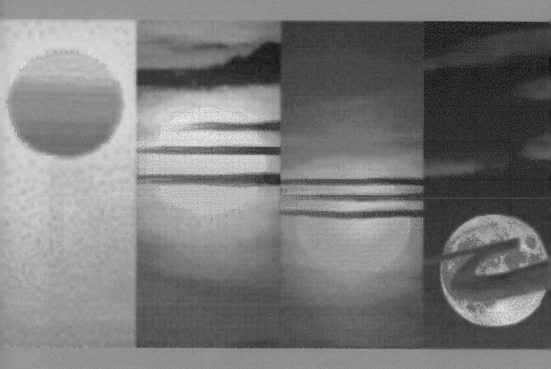

At the end of the day, make sure you're in the right hotel.

Whether you're looking for dependable comfort, reliable quality, great value budget accommodation or something a little different, we can offer you a real choice. Choice Hotels have over 100 hotels throughout the UK and Ireland and more than 5000 worldwide, making us the second largest hotel operator in the world. Located everywhere from rural beauty spots to vibrant city centres, they're great places to stay, great places to do business and great value. And all bookable through a single free telephone number or at our website. At the end of the day what more could you ask?

Book from the UK on 0800 44 44 44. Book from Ireland on 1-800 500 600

CHOICE HOTELS
EUROPE

RAC Inspection Scheme

Guest Accommodation – Diamonds

The term Guest Accommodation comprises guest houses, farmhouses, small private hotels, inns, restaurants with rooms and bed and breakfast properties, which in the UK and Ireland offer a style and warmth of accommodation envied around the world.

The Guest Accommodation scheme assesses establishments at five levels of quality from one Diamond at the simplest, to five Diamonds at the luxury end of the spectrum.

All Guest Accommodation must provide sufficient quality in all areas of operation covered under the following headings to merit a minimum classification of one out of five Diamonds. If they do not achieve sufficient quality in any one of these areas they cannot be awarded an RAC rating at all:

- Cleanliness and Housekeeping
- Service and Hospitality (Guest Care)
- Bathroom, Shower, WC and ensuite facilities
- Food Quality and Service
- Public Rooms
- Safety and Security, Exterior and Interior Appearance
- Up-keep (General Requirements)

The rating takes into account the level of general cleanliness, the comfort and degree of style and quality of furnishings and décor throughout the property; the levels of service and hospitality displayed by owners and staff; the friendliness of the atmosphere; and last but not least, the quality of the meals.

At all Diamond levels, cleanliness and good housekeeping are of the highest importance and the emphasis of the assessment for a Diamond rating is on guest care and quality, rather than the provision of extra facilities.

Travel Accommodation

This classification denotes budget or lodge accommodation suitable for an overnight stay, usually in purpose-built units close to main roads and motorways but could also include city centre locations. They provide consistent levels of accommodation and service, matching today's expectations.

Does the Hotel have to pay to be in the RAC scheme?

Yes, as the accreditation scheme is a voluntary one, the property decides to put themselves forward for assessment. There is a joining fee and then an annual fee, paid each year irrespective of when the inspection was carried out. The fee the property pays covers the cost of the inspection, including the amount the Inspector pays to stay at the property on an overnight visit, as well as an entry in this guide and a range of other benefits that assist with the running of the property.

Have all properties in this guide been inspected?

It is our aim to provide as wide a choice as possible with the relevant rating to provide the reader with as much information as possible to make a decision. However, there are some properties that joined the scheme just before the guide closed and these carry the symbol ❖ which means 'Awaiting Inspection'.

Is that it?

No, there's a lot more to the RAC Hotel scheme; the inspection programme, how Inspectors are trained, the detailed criteria for each type of property and RAC awards – see pages 15–18.

However, to enjoy your stay at a hotel, bed and breakfast, inn or any of the other places covered by this guide, you do not need to train to be a Hotel Inspector. The fact that the property is in this guide or displays an RAC sign means that one of our team has visited that Hotel or Guest Accommodation, slept in that bed and eaten the breakfast, as well as all the other elements that go to make an inspection – our reassurance to you!

Awards for Hotels & Guest Accommodation

To reflect the increasing standards being achieved in the hotel industry and to indicate the quality that can be found at many of the properties in this guide, RAC has a range of awards that covers both the Guest Accommodation and Hotel categories.

Hotels

Gold Ribbon

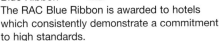

The RAC Gold Ribbon is awarded to those hotels which consistently demonstrate a commitment to superlative standards of customer care, service and accommodation.

Blue Ribbon

The RAC Blue Ribbon is awarded to hotels which consistently demonstrate a commitment to high standards.

A full listing of winners for 2000 can be found on pages 16–18

Guest Accommodation

Quality of service is not only the province of the larger hotel; many tourists and business people prefer to stay at smaller, more intimate properties from the Guest Accommodation sector and we have devised a range of awards that recognises the key attributes important to guest care.

Little Gem

Presented to those Guest Accommodation properties that really 'hit the spot' and excel in the all-round quality they show in hospitality, cleanliness, welcome and attention to detail that makes every stay memorable.
A full listing can be found on pages 18 and 19

RAC Sparkling Diamond

This award is made to those properties that achieve excellent standards of cleanliness, hygiene and attention to detail in guest comfort.

RAC Warm Welcome Award

As the name implies, this award is made to those establishments that make the guest feel 'at home', from the minute they arrive to the time they depart; the hospitality of the host is the key determinant in giving this award.

RAC Dining Award

This award is given to Hotels and Guest Accommodation alike, demonstrating that good food and dining atmosphere can be found at all styles of accommodation.

With more people dining out, either as a guest of a hotel or just using the facilities of the property, we feel that it is important to assess the whole meal experience – not just the food. For that reason, this award requires an overnight visit; dinner is taken into account, as is breakfast the next morning. Not only is breakfast one of the great institutions of the countries covered by this volume, but it is the last meal that the guest experiences, and so forms a large part of the impression of their visit.

In addition to the two meals, room service (where available) is also taken into account, in order that a full impression of the standard of catering can be formed. But it doesn't stop at the food: the ambience, service and knowledge of those on duty are some of the other attributes that comprise the RAC Dining Award.

This award is made at five levels, with a five-level dining award representing a superlative dining experience. However, the standards have been set to challenge the best establishment and the attainment of one level is success in itself.

Look out for this symbol throughout the guide.

RAC Award Winners for

Gold Ribbon Hotels

England

Athenaeum Hotel & Apartments, London
Berkeley, London
Buckland Manor, Broadway
Capital Hotel, London
Castle Hotel, Taunton
Chewton Glen Hotel, New Milton
Claridge's, London
Cliveden Hotel, Taplow
Congham Hall Hotel, King's Lynn
Connaught Hotel, London
Four Seasons Hotel, London
Gidleigh Park, Chagford
Gilpin Lodge Country House, Windermere
Goring Hotel, London
Gravetye Manor Hotel, East Grinstead
Hartwell House Hotel, Restaurant & Spa,
   Aylesbury
Hintlesham Hall Hotel, Ipswich
Holbeck Ghyll Country House Hotel,
   Windermere
Langshott Manor, Horley
Le Manoir aux Quat'Saisons, Great Milton
Lords of the Manor, Upper Slaughter
Lower Slaughter Manor, Lower Slaughter
Lucknam Park Hotel, Colerne
Mandarin Oriental Hyde Park, London
Manor House Hotel, Castle Combe
Middlethorpe Hall Hotel, York
New Hall, A Country House Hotel,
   Sutton Coldfield
Queensberry Hotel, Bath
Sharrow Bay Hotel, Ullswater
Stapleford Park Hotel, Melton Mowbray
Stock Hill House Hotel, Gillingham
Summer Lodge, Evershot
The Dorchester Hotel, London
The George, Yarmouth, Isle of Wight
The Halkin Hotel, London
The Landmark London, London
The Lanesborough Hotel, London
The Lygon Arms, Broadway
The Ritz, London
The Savoy, London
The Vineyard at Stockcross, Stock Cross
Thornbury Castle Hotel, Thornbury
Tylney Hall Hotel, Basingstoke

Ireland

Caragh Lodge, Kerry
Cashel House Hotel, Cashel
Glenlo Abbey, Galway
Hayfield Manor, Cork
Kildare Hotel & Country Club, Straffan
Marlfield House Hotel, Gorey
Mount Juliet Hotel, Thomastown
Park Hotel, Kenmare
Sheen Falls Lodge, Kenmare
The Merrion Hotel, Dublin
Tinakilly Country House Hotel, Rathnew

Scotland

Inverlochy Castle Hotel, Fort William
Kinnaird, Dunkeld

Wales

Bodysgallen Hall Hotel, Llandudno
Maes-y-Neuadd Hotel, Talsarnau
St Tudno Hotel, Llandudno
The Old Rectory Country House Hotel, Conwy
Ynyshir Hall Hotel, Machynlleth

Channel Islands

Chateau la Chaire Hotel, Jersey
Longueville Manor Hotel, Jersey

Town Houses

Castle House, Hereford
The Covent Garden Hotel, London
The Milestone Hotel & Apartments, London

Blue Ribbon Hotels

England

Alexander House, Turners Hill
Ashdown Park Hotel, Forest Row
Bath Priory, Bath
Beechleas, Wimborne Minster
Belmore Hotel, Manchester
Bindon Country House, Wellington
Boscundle Manor House, Tregrehan
Broad Oak Country House, Windermere
Brockencote Hall, Chaddesley Corbett
Calcot Manor, Tetbury
Cavendish Hotel, Baslow
Charingworth Manor, Chipping Campden
Chester Grosvenor, Chester
Cotswold House, Chipping Campden
Crathorne Hall, Crathorne
Devonshire Arms, Bolton Abbey
Donnington Valley, Newbury
Eastwell Manor, Ashford
Farlam Hall, Brampton
Fredrick's, Maidenhead
Hob Green, Harrogate
Hotel on the Park, Cheltenham
Island Hotel, Isles Of Scilly
Lainston House, Winchester
Leeming House, Ullswater
Lindeth Fell Country House Hotel,
    Bowness-on-Windermere
Linthwaite House Hotel,
    Bowness-on-Windermere
Little Barwick, Barwick Village
Maison Talbooth, Dedham
Mill at Harvington Hotel, Harvington
Netherfield Place, Battle
New Inn At Coln, Coln St-Aldwyns
Northcote Manor, Umberleigh
Oaks Hotel, Porlock
Old Vicarage, Bridgenorth
One Aldwych, London
Pear Tree at Purton, Swindon
Pennyhill Park, Bagshot
Priory Hotel, Wareham
Redworth Hall, Newton Aycliffe
Rose & Crown, Romaldkirk
Rosevine, Portscatho
Royal Crescent, Bath
St Martins on The Isle, Isles of Scilly

Soar Mill Cove, Salcombe
South Lodge, Lower Beeding
Ston Easton Park, Ston Easton
Swinside Lodge, Newlands
The George, Stamford
The Grange, York
The Greenway, Shurdington
The Stafford, London
Vermont, Tyne & Wear

Ireland

Aghadoe Heights, Killarney
Glin Castle, Glin
Gregans Castle, Ballyvaughan
Harvey's Point Country Hotel, Donegal Town
Herbert Park, Dublin
Killarney Park, Killarney
Longueville House, Mallow
Moyglare Manor, Maynooth
The Lodge & Spa at Inchydoney Island,
    Inchydoney Island

Scotland

Balbirnie Hotel, Markinch
Banchory Lodge, Banchory
Darroch Learg, Ballater
Kirroughtree House, Newton Stewart
Ladyburn, Maybole
Loch Torridon, Torridon
Norton House, Edinburgh
Turnberry Hotel, Turnberry
Well View, Moffat

Wales

Celtic Manor Resort, Newport
Portmeirion Hotel, Portmeirion
St Davids Hotel and Spa, Cardiff
The Lake Country House, Llangammarch Wells

Channel Islands

Atlantic Hotel, Jersey

Continued over the page

RAC Award Winners for 2000

Blue Ribbon Town Houses

22 Jermyn Street, London
51 Buckingham Gate, London
The Cliveden Townhouse, London
Dorset Square Hotel, London
Durley House, London
The Pelham Hotel, London

Little Gems

England

Cambridge Lodge Hotel, Cambridge
Clow Beck House, Darlington
Coniston Lodge Private Hotel, Coniston
Cooke House, Sheffield
Croyde Bay House Hotel, Croyde
D'isney Place Hotel, Lincoln
Hanchurch Manor Country House,
    Stoke-on-Trent
Langcliffe Country Guest House, Kettlewell
Lower Brook House, Lower Blockley
May Cottage, Thruxton
Moor View House, Okehampton
Northam Mill, Taunton
Number Twenty Eight, Ludlow
Rowanfield Country House, Ambleside
Sawrey House Country Hotel & Restaurant,
    nr. Sawrey
Shallowdale House, Ampleforth
Tasburgh Hotel, Bath
Tavern House, Tetbury
The Ayrlington, Bath
The Briary, Sheffield
The Cobbles Restaurant with Rooms, Mildenhall
The County Hotel, Bath
The Moorlands, Pickering
The Nurse's Cottage, Sway
Widbrook Grange, Bradford-on-Avon

Northern Ireland

Beech Hill Country House, Newtownards

Republic of Ireland

Ahernes Seafood Restaurant
    & Accommodation, Youghal
Coursetown Country House, Athy
Earls Court Guest House, Killarney
Ivyleigh House, Portlaoise
Mal Dua House, Clifden
Mount Royd Country Home, Carrigans
The Castle Farm, Cappagh
Trinity Lodge, Dublin

Scotland

Brown's Hotel, Haddington
Dorstan Hotel, Edinburgh
Kirkton House, Cardross
The Pines, Grantown-on-Spey

Wales

Buttington Country House, Welshpool
The Lighthouse, Llandudno

Le MERIDIEN

the way hotels should be

LE MERIDIEN WALDORF • LE MERIDIEN PICCADILLY • LE MERIDIEN HEATHROW
LE MERIDIEN GROSVENER HOUSE • LE MERIDIEN LONDON GATWICK

Join RAC from £39

Free £10
Marks and Spencer voucher on joining

- Membership covers you as the driver or passenger, 24 hours a day, 365 days a year

- Our average call out time is under 40 minutes, and our patrols fix 80% of breakdowns at the roadside

- For free travel and motoring information visit us at www.rac.co.uk

- Membership can be paid for monthly

- It's easy to join; call now for instant cover, or visit your local BSM shop, Lex Autocentre or visit our website

For instant cover call
0800 029 029

Quoting HOTEL1

A to B – we RAC to it

The British Hospitality Association

Rac

In an age of growing consumerism, guests are becoming increasingly demanding, with ever-higher expectations. Hoteliers recognise this. Indeed, one of the primary roles of the British Hospitality Association – the hotel industry's trade association – is to promote the importance of quality at all levels.

In this, hotel classification and grading plays a unique part. Grading schemes are a key marketing tool for most hotels. They tell the prospective guest what facilities and what standard of comfort a hotel offers. So, for many hotels, a rating is essential. Little surprise, therefore, that the RAC and the British Hospitality Association have worked together for many years to provide the public with a hotel guide which is fair and comprehensive and which, moreover, encourages hoteliers to maintain the highest standards of facilities and service within their grade.

The new, harmonised rating scheme for Hotels and Guest Accommodation in England, which allows RAC to make its own highly regarded quality awards, was a major step forward in this direction. In the coming years, the scheme will be developed and refined but the co-operation between The British Hospitality Association and RAC will continue – and always with the same twin objectives: To encourage higher standards and to make the guide increasingly useful to the travelling public.

BRITISH
Hospitality
ASSOCIATION

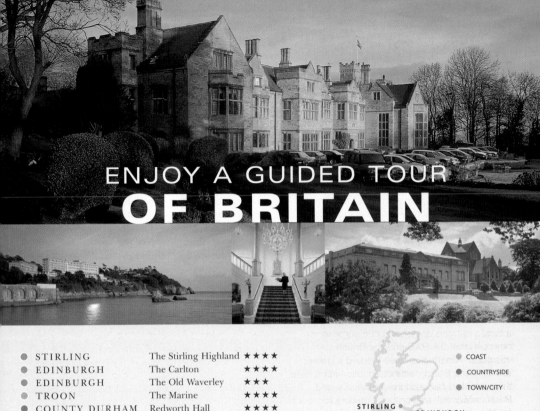

ENJOY A GUIDED TOUR
OF BRITAIN

STIRLING	The Stirling Highland	★★★★
EDINBURGH	The Carlton	★★★★
EDINBURGH	The Old Waverley	★★★
TROON	The Marine	★★★★
COUNTY DURHAM	Redworth Hall	★★★★
HARROGATE	The Majestic	★★★★
BLACKPOOL	The Imperial	★★★★
SOUTHPORT	The Prince of Wales	★★★★
CHESHIRE	Shrigley Hall	★★★★
SOUTH YORKSHIRE	Hellaby Hall	★★★★
BUXTON	The Palace	★★★★
OXFORD	The Oxford	★★★
CHELTENHAM	The Cheltenham Park	★★★★
CARDIFF	The Angel	★★★★
BRIGHTON	The Old Ship	★★★
TORQUAY	The Imperial	★★★★★

● COAST
● COUNTRYSIDE
● TOWN/CITY

STIRLING ● ● EDINBURGH
● TROON
COUNTY DURHAM ●
● HARROGATE
BLACKPOOL ●
SOUTHPORT ●   SOUTH YORKSHIRE
CHESHIRE ●   ● BUXTON
CHELTENHAM ●
CARDIFF ●   ● OXFORD
TORQUAY ●   ● BRIGHTON

With Paramount Group of Hotels, you're never far away from a warm welcome in luxurious surroundings. We give you the choice of 16 stunning hotels in city, town, country and coastal locations. Distinguished by their quality and characterised by their friendliness, all hotels in the Paramount group provide excellent facilities and offer superb value for money. Whether you want to get away from it all, relax in the pool, play a few rounds of golf, or enjoy an event-filled break in a stimulating city, a Paramount group hotel has all you need.

PARAMOUNT
GROUP OF HOTELS

FOR MORE INFORMATION OR TO BOOK, CALL FREE ON
0500 342543
quoting reference number RAC2001

Fountain Court 12 Bruntcliffe Way
Morley Leeds LS27 0JG
Telephone 0113 238 0033 Fax 0113 238 0022
e-mail stay@paramount-hotels.co.uk
www.paramount-hotels.co.uk

General Information

RAC Hotel Reservations

If you're looking for somewhere to stay, why not ask the experts? RAC Hotel Reservations is your free booking service. With just the cost of a local phone call, you can make reservations at any of the RAC Inspected properties listed in this guide – that's over 3,000 hotels, townhouses, B&Bs, farmhouses and inns throughout the UK and Ireland. RAC Hotel Reservations will source the best possible price, facilities and location to suit your needs. And once you have made your booking, we will send you confirmation of the details straight away.

To make a booking call 0870 603 9109 and quote: Guide 2001.

RAC website – www.rac.co.uk

RAC's website www.rac.co.uk serves your motoring and travel needs from products to advice including a free pan-European route planner with live UK traffic news, personal travel insurance, UK and Irish RAC inspected hotels and guest accommodation, international driver's permit, European motoring advisor, European roadside assistance and much more.

Disabled Access at RAC Hotels & Guest Accommodation

RAC currently recommends that disabled guests contact the national charity Holiday Care, for information about accessible accommodation in the UK. Holiday Care is the country's leading source of holiday and travel information for disabled people and inspects and categorises accommodation against agreed national standards according to the degree of accessibility offered. In addition to providing information about facilities, Holiday Care also offers an accessible accommodation reservations service:

Holiday Care, 2nd Floor, Imperial Buildings, Victoria Road, Horley RH6 7PZ
Tel: Information   01293 774 535
Tel: Reservations 01293 773 716
Fax: 01293 784 647
Email: holiday.care@virgin.net
Internet: www.holidaycare.org.uk

Complaints

In cases of dissatisfaction or dispute with a hotel or guest accommodation, readers will find that discussion with their management at the time of the problem/incident will normally enable the matter to be resolved promptly and amicably. Should the personal approach fail, RAC will raise comments with the hotelier at the time of the next inspection.

Please write to:
RAC Hotel Services
1 Forest Road
Feltham TW13 7RR

Please submit details of any discussion or correspondence involved when reporting a problem to RAC.

London

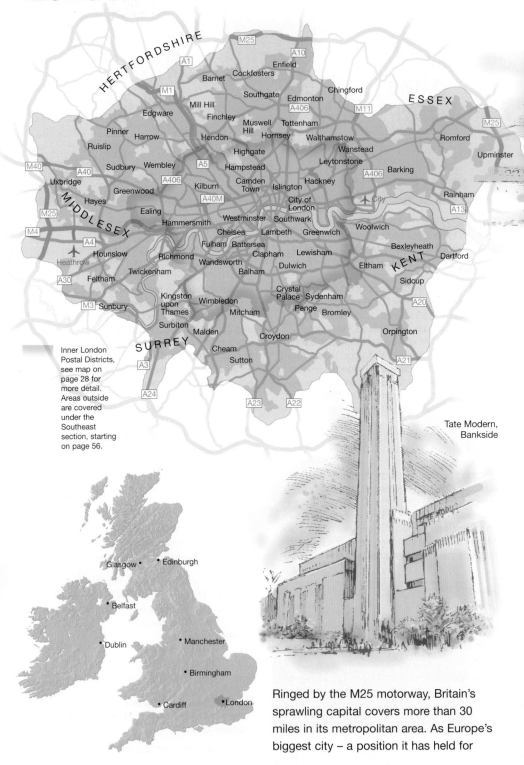

HERTFORDSHIRE

M25
A1
Enfield
Barnet
Cockfosters
A10
Southgate
Edmonton
Chingford
Mill Hill
Finchley
Edgware
Muswell Hill
Tottenham
Hornsey
Walthamstow
Wanstead
A406
M11
ESSEX
M25
Romford
Pinner
Harrow
Hendon
Highgate
Leytonstone
Upminster
Ruislip
Sudbury
Wembley
A5
Hampstead
A406
Barking
M40
A40
Kilburn
Camden Town
Islington
Hackney
A40M
A406
Uxbridge
Greenwood
City of London
City
Rainham
Hayes
Ealing
Hammersmith
Westminster
Southwark
A13
M25
MIDDLESEX
Woolwich
M4
Chelsea
Lambeth
Greenwich
Bexleyheath
A4
Fulham
Battersea
Lewisham
Dartford
Hounslow
Richmond
Clapham
Eltham
KENT
Heathrow
Twickenham
Wandsworth
Dulwich
Sidcup
A30
Feltham
Balham
Crystal Palace
Sydenham
A20
M3
Sunbury
Kingston upon Thames
Wimbledon
Mitcham
Penge
Bromley
Orpington
Surbiton
Malden
Croydon
A21
SURREY
Cheam
Sutton
A3
A24
A23
A22

Inner London Postal Districts, see map on page 28 for more detail. Areas outside are covered under the Southeast section, starting on page 56.

Tate Modern, Bankside

Glasgow
Edinburgh
Belfast
Dublin
Manchester
Birmingham
Cardiff
London

Ringed by the M25 motorway, Britain's sprawling capital covers more than 30 miles in its metropolitan area. As Europe's biggest city – a position it has held for

Tower Bridge

that rich historical atmosphere just by wandering through the older parts and looking at the splendid buildings which survived the 1666 Great Fire's ravages. One of the finest examples was actually erected to replace one of the burnt-out churches: St Paul's Cathedral, whose architect was Sir Christopher Wren.

Older still are such landmarks as the Tower of London – once a grim prison – begun in the 11th century, and Westminster Abbey. Further to the west the grandeur of Buckingham Palace dominates the Mall and nearby Green Park, a refuge for the weary on fine days.

London also boasts some of the finest galleries and museums in the world. From Kensington's Exhibition Road (Science, Natural History, and the Victoria & Albert museums being among the most popular) to the National Maritime Museum in Greenwich, there is much in between to suit all tastes. Of the many art collections, the recently opened Tate Modern, housed in a converted power station on the south bank of the Thames opposite St Paul's, has become a major attraction.

But for those who want to buy rather than look, London's bustling streets offer many famous shopping areas in the West End such as Bond Street, Oxford Street, Regents Street and Covent Garden. Then there is fashionable Knightsbridge to the west; the trendy street markets of Kensington and Camden are worth visiting, while in the East End Petticoat Lane and Brick Lane markets are enduringly popular.

London really comes into its own in the evening, with a huge array of top class restaurants from which to choose and almost limitless entertainment opportunities. Cinemas, theatres, opera, ballet, clubs and pubs ensure that no one need find themselves at a loose end.

centuries – for many of its seven million inhabitants, London is the only place that matters, an attitude that understandably irritates the rest of the country.

It is easy to see why Londoners have always held their city in such high esteem. Despite the recent devolution of many powers to Scotland and Wales, London remains Britain's political centre and, in the square mile known simply as 'The City', the country's financial centre.

Since the Romans founded Londinium in the first century AD on the north bank of the River Thames, the city's position as a capital of international standing has grown steadily over the centuries. Today's visitor is uniquely placed to experience something of a working museum.

From the 12th century, the two separated urban centres of London and Westminster began to expand sideways into each other. While Westminster became the seat of government, London's merchants created a financial hub in The City. Since then, the London we know today has filled in, overflowing the original centres. It's possible to sample some of

London Hotels

Because of the size of London, in addition to the Hotel Directory which follows, an index of London Hotels and Guest Accommodation is provided below. Each property is shown with its postcode, followed by the page on which it is located and the column on the page. The postcode map on page 28 will allow you to identify the area you wish to stay in.

London

La Gaffe	NW3	49	1
The Landmark London	NW1	34	2
The Lanesborough	SW1	33	1
Langdorf Hotel & Apartments	NW3	49	1
Le Meridien Grosvenor House	W1	33	1
Le Meridien Piccadilly	W1	33	1
Le Meridien Waldorf	WC2	33	1
Lincoln House	W1	52	2
London Bridge	SE1	37	2
London Marriott	W1	37	2
London West Hampstead Marriott	NW6	39	1
Lowndes Hyatt Hotel	SW1	43	1
Mandarin Oriental Hyde Park	SW1	33	2
Mandeville Hotel	W1	44	2
Mayfair Inter-Continental London	W1	33	2
Merlyn Court	SW5	54	1
Milestone Hotel & Apartments	W8	35	2
Millennium Gloucester	SW7	39	1
Millennium Mayfair	W1	39	1
Mitre House Hotel	W2	49	1
The Montague	WC1	41	2
Montcalm	W1	39	2
New England	SW1	49	2
Novotel London Waterloo	SE1	44	2
Novotel London West	W6	44	2
One Aldwych	WC2	33	2
Paragon	SW6	44	2
Park Lane Hotel	W1	39	2
Park Lodge	W2	50	1
Parkwood	W2	50	1
The Pelham	SW7	43	1
Quality Hotel Westminster	SW1	44	2
Raj Hideaway Bed & Breakfast	N6	54	2
Ramsees Hotel	SW5	52	2
Rasool Court	SW5	53	1
Regent Palace	W1	47	1
Regents Park	NW1	45	2
Rembrandt	SW7	39	2
The Ritz	W1	34	1
Royal Garden	W8	34	1
Royal Horseguards	SW1	39	2
Royal Lancaster	W2	40	1
Rubens at The Palace	SW1	40	1
Saint George's	W1	40	1
The Savoy	WC2	34	2
The Shaftesbury	W1	47	1
Sheraton Park Tower	SW1	34	2
Sidney Hotel	SW1	50	1
Sleeping Beauty Motel	E10	45	2
The Stafford	SW1	40	2
Strand Palace	WC2	45	1
Swallow International	SW5	40	2
Swiss Cottage Hotel	NW3	50	1
Swiss House	SW5	50	2
Trochee Hotel	SW19	53	1
The Victoria Inn	SW1	51	1
Washington	W1	41	2
The Westbury	W1	42	1
Westland	W2	45	2
White Lodge	N8	51	1
Willett Hotel	SW1	47	1
Wigmore Court	W1	51	1
Wimbledon Hotel	SW19	53	1
The Winchester	SW1	51	1
Windermere	SW1	47	1
Worcester House Hotel	SW19	51	1

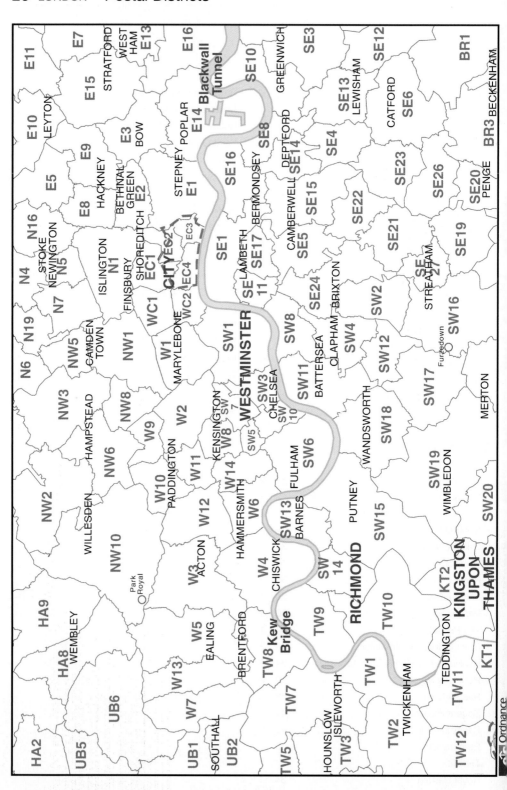

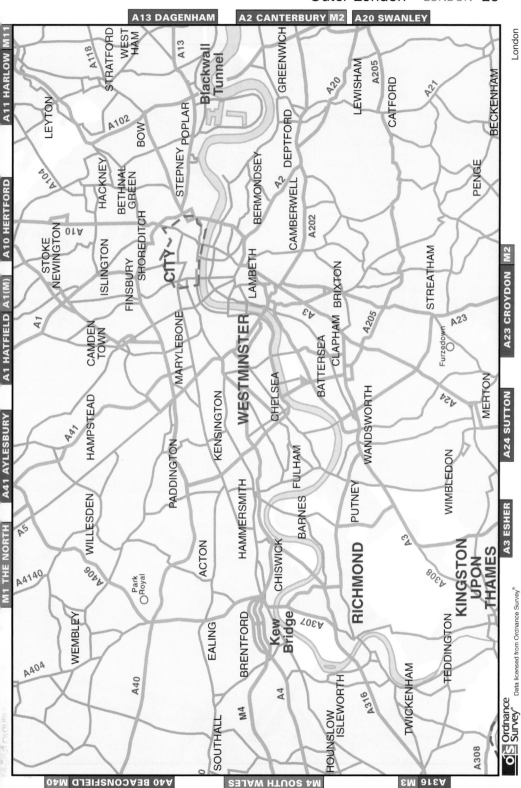

The Berkeley

★ ★ ★ ★ ★ ♖ ♖ ♖ ♖

Wilton Place, London, SW1X 7RL
Tel: 020 7235 6000 Fax: 020 7235 4330
Email: info@the-berkeley.co.uk
Web: www.savoy-group.co.uk
B £16 L £18 D £21. CC: MC Vi Am DC

How to get there: 200 yards down
Knightsbridge from Hyde Park Corner, on left
hand side.

Claridge's

★ ★ ★ ★ ★ ♖ ♖ ♖

Brook Street, Mayfair, London, W1A 2JQ
Tel: 020 7629 8860 Fax: 020 7499 2210
Email: info@claridges.co.uk
Web: www.savoygroup.com
SB £365 DB £445 CC: MC Vi Am DC Swi Delt

The Connaught

★ ★ ★ ★ ★ ♖ ♖ ♖ ♖

16 Carlos Place, London, W1Y 6AL
Tel: 020 7499 7070 Fax: 020 7495 3262
Email: info@the-connaught.co.uk

The Dorchester

Consistently ranked one of the world's
best, this opulent 1931 hotel offers the
friendliest, almost telepathic levels of service,
an outstanding choice of restaurants and a
glorious Spa.

Park Lane, London W1A 2HJ
Tel: 020 7629 8888   Fax: 020 7409 0114
Email: info@dorchesterhotel.com
Website: www.dorchesterhotel.com

Web: www.savoy-group.co.uk
CC: MC Vi Am DC Swi Delt

Conrad International London

★ ★ ★ ★ ★ ♖ ♖

Chelsea Harbour, London, SW10 0XG
Tel: 020 7823 3000 Fax: 020 7351 6525
Email: lonch_gm@hilton.com
B £16 L £17 D £22. CC: MC Vi Am DC Swi Delt

How to get there: A4 Earl's Court Road going
south. Right into King's Road, left down Lot's
Road and hotel straight ahead over roundabout.

Dorchester

★ ★ ★ ★ ★ ♖ ♖ ♖ ♖

Park Lane, London, W1A 2HJ
Tel: 020 7629 8888 Fax: 020 7409 0114
Email: martine@dorchesterhotel.com
Web: www.dorchesterhotel.com
L £29.50 D £39.50. CC: MC Vi Am DC Swi Delt

How to get there: Located on Park Lane,
opposite Hyde Park, approximately halfway
between Marble Arch and Hyde Park Corner.
See advert below left

Four Seasons

★ ★ ★ ★ ★ ♖ ♖ ♖

Hamilton Place, Park Lane, London, W1A 1AZ
Tel: 020 7499 0888 Fax: 020 7493 1895/6629
Web: www.fourseasons.com

With distinctive charm and warmth, set back
from Park Lane, and in the heart of Mayfair
overlooking Hyde Park, the Four Seasons Hotel
is unrivalled in its service and setting. The result
– a highly acclaimed hotel with handsomely
appointed spacious rooms.
SB £335 DB £406 B £16 L £35 D £38.
CC: MC Vi Am DC Swi JCB

How to get there: Set back from Park Lane in Hamilton Place. Closest tubes are Hyde Park Corner and Green Park. Well situated for Victoria and Paddington stations.

Four Seasons Canary Wharf
★★★★★ 🐾🐾
Westferry Circus, Canary Wharf, London, E14 8RS
Tel: 020 7510 1999 Fax: 020 7510 1998

Hyatt Carlton Tower
★★★★★ 🐾🐾
On Cadogan Place, London, SW1X 9PY
Tel: 020 7235 1234 Fax: 020 7235 9129

The Lanesborough
★★★★★ 🐾🐾🐾
Hyde Park Corner, London, SW1X 7TA
Tel: 020 7259 5599 Fax: 020 7333 7033
B £17.50 L £15 D £30.
CC: MC Vi Am DC Swi Delt

How to get there: In theatreland on The Strand. Undergound station Covent Garden (Piccadilly Line).

Mandarin Oriental Hyde Park
★★★★★ 🐾🐾🐾
66 Knightsbridge, London, SW1X 7LA
Tel: 020 7235 2000 Fax: 020 7235 4552
Web: www.mandarinoriental.com
B £16 CC: MC Vi Am DC Swi Delt

How to get there: In the heart of Knightsbridge.

Mayfair Inter-Continental London
★★★★★ 🐾🐾🐾
Stratton Street, London, W1A 2AN
Tel: 020 7915 2803 Fax: 020 7629 1459
Email: mayfair@interconti.com
Web: www.interconti.com
SB £340 DB £340 B £12.50 L £12 D £24.
CC: MC Vi Am DC Swi Delt

How to get there: From London Heathrow, M4/A4 into London. Signs to Piccadilly Circus, turn left at Green Park Station.

Le Meridien Grosvenor House
★★★★★ 🐾🐾🐾🐾
86–90 Park Lane, London, W1A 3AA
Tel: 020 7499 6363 Fax: 020 7493 3341
Web: www.grosvenorhouse.co.uk
B £17 L £42.50 D £42.50. CC: MC Vi DC Swi

How to get there: Situated on Park Lane, in the heart of Mayfair, overlooking Hyde Park.

Le Meridien Piccadilly
★★★★★ 🐾🐾🐾🐾
21 Piccadilly, London, W1V 0BH
Tel: 020 7734 8000 Fax: 020 7437 3574
Email: lmpiccrcs@forte-hotels.com
Web: www.lemeridien-hotels.com
SB £369 DB £430 HBS £394 HBD £480
B £22 L £25 D £30. CC: MC Vi Am DC Swi Delt

How to get there: From M4, directly to Cromwell Road, through Knightsbridge, on to Piccadilly. Underground – Piccadilly Circus (Piccadilly & Bakerloo Lines), 2 mins walk.

Le Meridien Waldorf
★★★★★ 🐾🐾
Aldwych, London, WC2B 4DD
Tel: 0870 400 8484 Fax: 020 7836 7244
Web: www.lemeridien-hotels.com
SB £341 DB £352 B £18 L £30 D £30.
CC: MC Vi Am DC Swi Delt

One Aldwych
★★★★★ 🐾🐾🐾
1 Aldwych, London, WC2B 4BZ
Tel: 020 7300 1000 Fax: 020 7300 1001
Email: rebeccaevans@onealdwych.co.uk
Web: www.onealdwych.co.uk

Poised where the City of London meets the West End, One Aldwych incorporates sleek contemporary design, cutting-edge technology and professional, friendly service.
B £12.50 L £15.75 D £15.75.
CC: MC Vi Am DC Swi Delt JCB

How to get there: Where Aldwych meets Strand, opposite Waterloo Bridge, close to Covent Garden.

The Ritz

★★★★★ ♞♞♞
150 Piccadilly, London, W1V 9DG
Tel: 020 7300 2240 Fax: 020 7300 2245
Email: enquiry@theritzlondon.com
Web: www.theritzlondon.com
SB £387 DB £438 B £23.50 L £36 D £52.
CC: MC Vi Am DC Swi Delt JCB, Enroute
⬟ ♿ ⚏ ⊗ ▭ ☎ ❄ ☎ P ⚕ ⊂ ♞ ♩ ❧ 👁
👥 👥 ❦

How to get there: On Piccadilly, next to Green
Park, a few steps from Bond Street.

Royal Garden

★★★★★ ♞♞♞
2–24 Kensington High Street, London, W8 4PT
Tel: 020 7937 8000 Fax: 020 7361 1991
Email: sales@royalgardenhotel.co.uk
Web: www.royalgardenhotel.co.uk
SB £293.63 DB £381.63
B £13.50 L £9.50 D £25.
CC: MC Vi Am DC Swi Delt JCB
⬟ ♿ ⚏ ⊗ ▭ ☎ ❄ ☎ P ⚕ ⊂ ♞ ♩ ❧ 👥
👥 SPA ❦

How to get there: On Kensington High Street
(A315), between Kensington Church Street and
Kensington Palace Gardens.

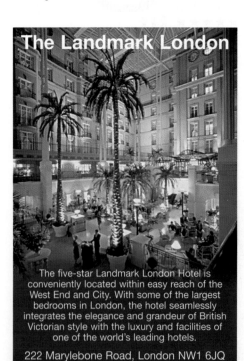

The Landmark London

The five-star Landmark London Hotel is
conveniently located within easy reach of the
West End and City. With some of the largest
bedrooms in London, the hotel seamlessly
integrates the elegance and grandeur of British
Victorian style with the luxury and facilities of
one of the world's leading hotels.

222 Marylebone Road, London NW1 6JQ
Tel: (0)20 7631 8000   Fax: (0)20 7631 8080
Email: reservations@thelandmark.co.uk
Website: www.landmarklondon.co.uk

The Savoy

★★★★★ ♞♞♞♞
The Strand, London, WC2R 0EU
Tel: 020 7836 4343 Fax: 020 7240 6040

Sheraton Park Tower

★★★★★ ♞♞♞
101 Knightsbridge, London, SW1X 7RN
Tel: 020 7235 8050 Fax: 020 7235 8231

The Landmark London

★★★★★ ♞♞♞♞
222 Marylebone Road, London, NW1 6JQ
Tel: 020 7631 8000 Fax: 020 7631 8080
Email: reservations@thelandmark.co.uk
Web: www.landmarklondon.co.uk
B £18.50 L £21 D £32.
CC: MC Vi Am DC Swi Delt Connect JCB
⬟ ♿ ⚏ ✉ ⊗ ▭ ☎ ❄ ☎ P ⚕ ⊂ ♞ ♩ ❧
👁 👥 👥 SPA ❦ 💲

How to get there: In front of Marylebone main
line station and underground.
See advert below left

22 Jermyn Street

★★★★★ Town House
22 Jermyn Street, St James's, London,
SW1Y 6HL
Tel: 020 7734 2353 Fax: 020 7734 0750
Email: office@22jermyn.com
Web: www.22.jermyn.com
DB £205.18 B £11.55
CC: MC Vi Am DC Swi Delt JCB
♿ ⚏ 🐾 ▭ ☎ ❄ ☎ P ⚕ ⊂ ♩ ❧ 👁 👥 ⅼ SPA
❦ 🛁 💲

How to get there: From Hyde Park Corner take
underpass to Piccadilly. Turn right at King St,
through St James's Square to Charles II St. Turn
left into Regent St and left again into Jermyn St.

51 Buckingham Gate

★★★★★ Town House ♞♞
Buckingham Gate, London, SW1E 6AF
Tel: 020 7769 7766 Fax: 020 7963 8385

Cliveden Town House

★★★★★ Town House ♞
26 Cadogan Gardens, London, SW3 2RP
Tel: 020 7730 6466 Fax: 020 7730 0236
Email: reservations@clivedentownhouse.co.uk
Web: www.clivedentownhouse.co.uk
SB £202.50 DB £346.25 B £14.50
CC: MC Vi Am DC Swi Delt
⚏ ✉ 🐾 ⊗ ▭ ☎ ❄ ⊂ ♞ ♩ ❧ 👥 👥

How to get there: From M4, signs to Central
London. After Natural History Museum, road
veers left, becoming Brompton Rd. Take fourth

right turn at lights into Beauchamp Place. Right into Cadogan Square and fifth left into Gardens. See advert below

Covent Garden Hotel
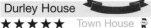

★ ★ ★ ★ ★ Town House 🛡
10 Monmouth Street, London, WC2H 9HB
Tel: 020 7806 1000 Fax: 020 7806 1100
Email: covent@firmdale.com
Web: www.firmdale.com
SB £240 DB £316 CC: MC Vi Am Swi Delt
⊔ 🖿 🕲 ▭ ☎ ❄ ☕ 🔥 ⟡ 🐴 🐾 🏛 👬 'Y'
How to get there: Nearest tube is Covent Garden. Walk to the end of Neal Street (opposite tube) and turn left onto Monmouth Street. Hotel is on right.

Durley House

★ ★ ★ ★ ★ Town House 🛡
115 Sloane Street, London, SW1X 9PJ
Tel: 020 7235 5537 Fax: 020 7259 6977
Email: durley@firmdale.com
Web: www.firmdale.com
SB £307.35 CC: MC Vi Am Swi Delt
⊔ 🕲 ▭ ☎ ❄ ☕ 🔥 ⟡ 🐴 🐾 🏛 👬 🔍
How to get there: From Knightsbridge turn down Sloane St, away from Hyde Park, Durley House is on right 100yds before Sloane Square.

Milestone Hotel & Apartments

★ ★ ★ ★ ★ Town House 🛡🛡🛡
1 Kensington Court, London, W8 5DL
Tel: 020 7917 1000 Fax: 020 7917 1010
Email: mfernandes@milestone.
redcarnationhotels.com
Web: www.redcarnationhotels.com
B £14 L £25 D £30. CC: MC Vi Am DC Swi Delt
♿ ⊔ 🖿 🔥 🕲 🕲 ▭ ☎ ❄ ☕ 🔥 ⟡ 🐴 🐾 🏛 👬 SPA 'Y'
How to get there: Directly opposite Kensington Palace, 1 mile East of Hammersmith flyover (A4) and located ¼ mile west of Royal Albert Hall and Albert Memorial.

The Athenaeum

★ ★ ★ ★ 🛡🛡🛡
116 Piccadilly, London, W1J 7BJ
Tel: 020 7499 3464 Fax: 020 7493 1860
Email: info@athenaeumhotel.com
Web: www.athenaeumhotel.com
SB £315 DB £360 CC: MC Vi Am DC Swi Delt
♿ ⊔ 🕲 🕲 ▭ ☎ ❄ ☕ 🔥 ⟡ 🐴 🐾 👁 🏛 👬 SPA 'Y'
How to get there: Positioned on Piccadilly overlooking Green Park.

Berkshire Hotel

★★★★ ☕☕☕

350 Oxford Street, London, W1N 0BY
Tel: 020 7629 7474 Fax: 020 7629 8156

Berners Hotel

★★★★ ☕

Berners Street, London, W1A 3BE
Tel: 020 7666 2000 Fax: 020 7666 2001
Email: berners@berners.co.uk
Web: www.thebernershotel.co.uk
SB £185 DB £236 HBS £201 HBD £273
B £11.95 L £12.95 D £10.25.
CC: MC Vi Am DC Swi Delt

How to get there: Just off Oxford Street opposite
Wardour Street and between Oxford Circus and
Tottenham Court Road underground stations.

Brown's Hotel

★★★★

Albemarle Street, London, W1X 4BP
Tel: 020 7518 4100 Fax: 020 7518 4063
Email: jasonlewis@brownshotel.com
Web: www.brownshotel.com
SB £278 DB £308 B £14.50 L £19 D £36.
CC: MC Vi Am DC Swi

How to get there: Located on Albermarle and
Dover Street, off Piccadilly and parallel to Old
Bond Street in Mayfair. Nearest tube station
Green Park (Jubilee, Victoria and Piccadilly lines).

Cavendish St James's

★★★★ ☕☕

81 Jermyn Street, St James, London, SW1Y 6JF
Tel: 020 7930 2111 Fax: 020 7839 4551
SB £200 DB £250 HBS £220 HBD £290
B £14.95 L £16.50 D £16.50.
CC: MC Vi Am DC Swi Delt JCB

How to get there: Near Green Park and
Piccadilly underground stations, directly behind
Fortnums on corner of Duke and Jermyn streets.

Chesterfield Mayfair

★★★★ ☕☕

35 Charles Street, Mayfair, London, W1J 5EB
Tel: 020 7514 5609 Fax: 020 7409 1726
Email: bcrawford@chesterfield.
　　　　redcarnationhotels.com
Web: www.redcarnationhotels.com
SB £245 DB £268.60 HBS £257.50 HBD £281
B £13.50 L £12.50 D £12.50.
CC: MC Vi Am DC Swi Delt JCB

How to get there: From Green Park station, turn
to Berkeley Street, straight to Berkeley Square.
The first street on the left is Charles Street.

Clifton Ford

★★★★ ☕

Welbeck Street, London, W1M 8DN
Tel: 020 7486 6600 Fax: 020 7486 7492
Email: michelle_mchale@jurys.com
Web: www.jurysdoyle.com
SB £221 DB £237 HBS £248 HBD £291
B £14 L £18 D £25. CC: MC Vi Am DC Swi

How to get there: From Bond Street
underground station, hotel is behind
Debenhams at the far end of Welbeck Street.

Copthorne Tara London

★★★★

Scarsdale Place, Kensington, London, W8 5SR
Tel: 020 7872 2405 Fax: 020 7872 2940
Email: douglas.greenwood@mill-cop.com
Web: www.stay.with-us.com
SB £216 DB £216 HBS £235 HBD £235
B £11 L £19 D £19. CC: MC Vi Am DC JCB

How to get there: Scarsdale Place is just off
Kensington High Street.

Crowne Plaza London St James

★★★★ ☕☕

Buckingham Gate, London, SW1E 6AF
Tel: 020 7834 6655 Fax: 020 7630 7587

The Cumberland

★★★★

1A Gt Cumberland Place, Marble Arch, London,
W1A 4RF
Tel: 0870 400 8701 Fax: 020 7724 4621
Email: jane.hills@forte-hotels.com
Web: www.thecumberland.co.uk
SB £130 DB £160 HBS £145 HBD £190
B £12 L £14 D £14.95.
CC: MC Vi Am DC Swi Delt

How to get there: Situated on Oxford Street
overlooking Marble Arch and Hyde Park.
Underground: Central Line, Marble Arch Station.

Flemings Mayfair

★★★★ ☕

Half Moon Street, Mayfair, London, W1Y 7RA
Tel: 020 7499 2964 Fax: 020 7629 4063

London

Forum Hotel
★★★★

Cromwell Road, London, SW7 4DN
Tel: 020 7370 5757 Fax: 020 7373 1448
Email: forumlondon@interconti.com
Web: www.interconti.com
B £9.95 L £15 D £25.
CC: MC Vi Am DC Swi Delt

🚹 ♨ ⊗ ⍩ 🖥 ☎ ❄ 🔌 **P** 🎿 ♨ 🐴 🎎 🎴 🛏
♨♨♨ 🎾

Goring Hotel
★★★★ 🥄🥄🥄

Beeston Place, Grosvenor Gardens, London,
SW1W 0JW
Tel: 020 7396 9000 Fax: 020 7834 4393
Email: reception@goringhotel.co.uk
Web: www.goringhotel.co.uk

Third-generation, family owned hotel offering
traditional standards of service to satisfy the
demands of the international traveller. Situated
in a quiet haven behind Buckingham Palace,
convenient for the theatre and shopping.
SB £234 DB £297 B £12.50 L £27 D £39.
CC: MC Vi Am DC Swi

♒ 🚹 ⊗ 🖥 ☎ ❄ 🔌 **P** 🎿 ♨ 🐴 🎴 🛏 ♨♨♨

The Halkin
★★★★ 🥄🥄🥄

Halkin Street, Belgravia, London, SW1X 7DJ
Tel: 020 7333 1000 Fax: 020 7333 1100
Email: sales@halkin.co.uk
Web: www.halkin.co.uk
SB £260 DB £260 CC: MC Vi Am DC Swi Delt
🚹 🖥 ☎ ❄ 🔌 ♨ 🎿 🐴 🎴 🛏 ♨♨♨ 🎾
How to get there: Located between Belgrave
Square and Grosvenor Place. Access via
Chapel Street into Headfort Place and left into
Halkin Street.

Looking for great dining? Look for RAC Hotels
and Guest Accommodation displaying the
RAC Dining Award symbol in this Guide.

Harrington Hall
★★★★ 🥄

5–25 Harrington Gardens, London, SW7 4JW
Tel: 020 7396 9696 Fax: 020 7396 9090
Email: harringtonsales@compuserve.com
Web: www.harringtonhall.co.uk
SB £197.75 DB £219.50 B £9.75 L £15 D £20 .
CC: MC Vi Am DC Swi Delt

🚹 ♨ ⊗ ⍩ 🖥 ☎ ❄ 🔌 ♨ 🎿 🐴 🎴 🛏
♨♨♨ 🎾
How to get there: 100yds from Gloucester Road
underground station.
See advert on following page

Hotel Russell
★★★★

Russell Square, London, WC1B 5BE
Tel: 020 7837 6470 Fax: 020 7837 2857
Web: www.principalhotels.co.uk
SB £189 DB £219 HBS £204 HBD £249
B £12.95 L £14.94 D £19.95.
CC: MC Vi Am DC Swi Delt

🚹 ♨ ⊗ ⍩ 🖥 ☎ ♨ 🎿 🐴 🎴 ♨♨♨ ♨♨♨
How to get there: 2 minute walk from Russell
Square tube station, within 1 mile of Euston.

Jurys Kensington
★★★★

109–113 Queen's Gate, South Kensington,
London, SW7 5LR,
Tel: 003531 6070055 Fax: 003531 6609625
Email: dorothy_cusack@jurysdoyle.com
Web: www.jurysdoyle.com
CC: MC Vi Am DC

🚹 ⍩ 🖥 ☎ ❄ 🔌 **P** 🎿 ♨ 🐴 🎴 🛏 ♨♨♨ ♨♨♨

Kingsway Hall
★★★★ 🥄🥄

Great Queen Street, Covent Garden, London,
WC2B 5BZ
Tel: 020 7309 0909 Fax: 020 7309 9696
Email: kingswayhall@compuserve.com
Web: www.kingswayhall.co.uk
SB £225 DB £250
CC: MC Vi Am DC Swi Delt JCB

🚹 ♨ ⊗ ⍩ 🖥 ☎ ❄ 🔌 ♨ 🎿 🐴 🎴 ♨♨♨ ♨♨♨ 🎾
See advert on following page

London Bridge
★★★★ 🥄🥄🥄

8–18 London Bridge Street, London, SE1 9SG
Tel: 020 7855 2200 Fax: 020 7855 2233

London Marriott
★★★★

Grosvenor Square, London, W1A 4AW
Tel: 020 7493 1232 Fax: 020 7491 3201

London

London West Hampstead Marriott

★★★★

Plaza Parade, Maida Vale, London, NW6 5RP
Tel: 020 7543 6000 Fax: 020 7543 2100

Millennium Gloucester

★★★★

4-18 Harrington Gardens, London, SW7 4LH,
Tel: 020 7373 6030 Fax: 020 7373 0409
Email: tracey.hatton@mill-cop.com
Web: www.stay.with-us.com

Conveniently located in the heart of Kensington,
you'll find a relaxing and calm environment at
the Millennium Gloucester Hotel, offering superb
service and excellent facilities.
SB £253 DB £253 CC: MC Vi Am DC Swi JCB

How to get there: From Heathrow, M4 towards
London, then A4. Along Cromwell Road, turn
into Gloucester Road and hotel is on right.

Millennium Mayfair

★★★★ ♔♔

Grosvenor Square, London, W1K 2HP
Tel: 020 7629 9400 Fax: 020 7629 7736
Email: reservations@mill-cop.com
Web: www.millennium-hotels.com

The elegant and luxurious Millennium Mayfair is
situated in London's prestigious Grosvenor
Square. The hotel is just 5 minutes walk from
Oxford Street and Hyde Park.
SB £225 DB £325 B £21 L £20 D £25.
CC: MC Vi Am DC Swi Delt JCB

How to get there: On Grosvenor Square,
reached via Park Lane or Berkeley Square.

Montcalm

★★★★ ♔♔

Great Cumberland Place, London, W1A 2LF
Tel: 020 7402 4288 Fax: 020 7724 9180
Email: montcalm@montcalm.co.uk
Web: www.nikkohotels.com
B £15.95 L £20 D £20.
CC: MC Vi Am DC Swi JCB

How to get there: Heathrow Express Service,
Paddington and Baker Street stations all within
a mile radius. Two-minute walk from Marble
Arch underground station.

Park Lane

★★★★

Piccadilly, London, W1Y 8BX
Tel: 020 7499 6321 Fax: 020 7499 1965

Rembrandt

★★★★ ♔

11 Thurloe Place, London, SW7 2RS
Tel: 020 7589 8100 Fax: 020 7225 3476
Email: kshelford@sarova.co.uk
Web: www.sarova.com
SB £188.75 DB £213.75 B £12 L £10.95
D £16.95.
CC: MC Vi Am DC Swi Delt

How to get there: Follow A4 (Cromwell Road)
into Central London. Rembrandt is opposite
Victoria & Albert Museum. Nearest tube South
Kensington.

Royal Horseguards

★★★★ ♔♔

Whitehall Court, London, SW1A 2EL
Tel: 020 7839 3400 Fax: 020 7930 4010
Email: royal.horseguards@thistle.co.uk
SB £242 DB £276 HBS £267 HBD £326
B £15.50 L £19.50 D £26.50
CC: MC Vi Am DC Swi Delt

How to get there: Two minutes from Charing
Cross and 10 minutes from Victoria and
Waterloo stations. Nearest underground station
is Embankment.

See advert on following page

Royal Lancaster

★★★★ ♙♙♙
Lancaster Terrace, London, W2 2TY
Tel: 020 7262 6737 Fax: 020 7724 3191

Rubens at The Palace

★★★★ ♙♙
39 Buckingham Palace Road, London,
SW1W 0PS
Tel: 020 7834 6600 Fax: 020 7828 5401
Email: jraggett@rubens.redcarnationhotels.com
Web: www.redcarnationhotels.com
SB £170 DB £225 HBS £185 HBD £255
CC: MC Vi Am DC Swi Delt
⊔⊔ 🖋🐾⊗⊜🖵📞☎❄ℒ♨℃🐎🎵🕱🦮
♨♨♨ ♙♙♙
How to get there: 3 minutes walk from Victoria
tube station. From Gatwick airport, take
Gatwick Rail Express to Victoria and then a
short walk to the hotel.
See advert on facing page

Saint George's

★★★★ ♙
Langham Place, Regent Street, London,
W1N 8QS
Tel: 020 7580 0111 Fax: 020 7436 7997
Email: stgeorgeshotel@talk21.com

SB £177 DB £209 CC: MC Vi Am DC Swi Delt
◑ ⊔⊔ 🦮⊗⊜🖵📞☎🅿♨℃🐎🎵🕱🦮 ♨♨♨ ♙♙♙
How to get there: M40, Euston Road, turn right
at Regents Park into Portland Place. This leads
onto Langham Place with the hotel on the left.

The Stafford

★★★★ ♙♙♙
St James's Place, London, SW1A 1NJ
Tel: 020 7493 0111 Fax: 020 7493 7121

Swallow International

★★★★ ♙♙
147c Cromwell Road, London, SW5 0TH
Tel: 020 7973 1000 Fax: 020 7244 8194
Email: international@swallow-hotels.co.uk
Web: www.swallowhotels.com
To become Marriott, Summer 2001.
CC: MC Vi Am DC
⊔⊔ ⊜🖵📞☎❄🅿♨℃🐎🎵🕱🦮 ♨♨♨ 🍴🗲
How to get there: By Underground – Earls Court
(Piccadilly/District Lines) 5 minutes walk.
Gloucester Road (Circle/District/Piccadilly Lines)
7 minutes walk.

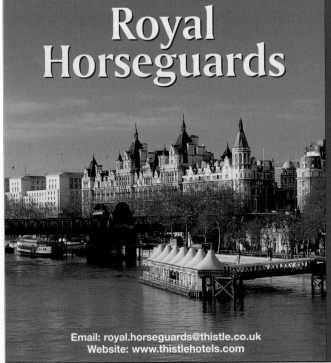

The Capital

★★★★ ⋒⋒⋒⋒⋒

22–24 Basil Street, Knightsbridge, London, SW3 1AT

Tel: 020 7589 5171 Fax: 020 7225 0011

The original luxurious town house in fashionable Knightsbridge, 50 yards from Sloane Street with beautifully furnished, air-conditioned bedrooms, offering a superb restaurant of worldwide renown.

B £12.50 L £24.50 D £60.

CC: MC Vi Am DC Swi Delt

How to get there: Heading west, turn left by side of Harrods, left again and straight on into Basil Street.

The Montague

★★★★

15 Montague Street, London, WC1B 5BJ

Tel: 020 7637 1001

Washington

★★★★

5–7 Curzon Street, London, W1Y 8DT

Tel: 020 7499 7000 Fax: 020 7409 7183

Web: www.washington-mayfair.com

SB £188 DB £188 B £11.95 L £11.95 D £13.95.

CC: MC Vi Am DC Swi Delt

How to get there: Nearest underground station is Green park, 200yds away.

Rubens at the Palace Hotel

★ ★ ★ ★

Located in one of the premier sites in London opposite the Royal Mews at Buckingham Palace. The Rubens at the Palace has recently been extensively refurbished to 4 star Deluxe standard, with 174 Superior bedrooms. This includes a range of 13 signature suites, and 70 king bedded rooms, with air conditioning.

In addition, a range of business traveller rooms boast large workstations with enhanced lighting and fax and modem points. Room safes, Satellite TV, iron and ironing board, tea and coffee making facilities and hairdryer are included in all rooms.

The Cavalry Bar and Palace Lounge provide warm and welcoming surroundings for a relaxing drink or traditional afternoon tea. The Old Master's Restaurant serves an excellent carvery buffet both at lunch and early dinner.

The Library Restaurant offers more intimate surroundings for à la carte dining in the evening.

The Flemish Suites can cater for conferences, meetings and functions from 20 to 120 persons.

Rubens at the Palace Hotel, Buckingham Palace Road, London SW1W 0PS

Tel: 020 7834 6600   Fax: 020 7828 5401

The Westbury

★★★★ ♔ ♔ ♔
Bond Street, London, W1S 2YF
Tel: 020 7629 7755 Fax: 020 7495 1163
Email: westburyhotel@compuserve.com
Web: www.westbury-london.co.uk
SB £275 DB £309 HBS £320 HBD £342 B £11.75
L £ 16.50 D £19.50. CC: MC Vi Am DC Swi Delt
♿ ♨ ⊙ ⊚ ☐ ☎ ❄ ☏ 🅿 ⚿ ℃ ⚘ ♫ ✦ ♨♨♨
♦♦♦ 'Y'
How to get there: On Bond Street, Mayfair.
Underground: Bond Street, Green Park, Oxford
Circus, Piccadilly Circus.
See advert below

The Beaufort

★★★★ Town House
33 Beaufort Gardens, Knightsbridge, London,
SW3 1PP
Tel: 020 7584 5252 Fax: 020 7589 2834
Email: thebeaufort@nol.co.uk
Web: www.thebeaufort.co.uk
SB £182.12 DB £252.63
♨ ⊙ ☐ ☎ ❄ ☏ ⚘ ℃ ⚘ ♫ ✦ ♦
How to get there: Off Brompton Road,
Knightsbridge, between Harrods and
Beauchamp Place.

Dorset Square Hotel

★★★★ Town House ♔
39 Dorset Square, London, NW1 6QM
Tel: 020 7723 7874 Fax: 020 7724 3328
Email: dorset@firmdale.com
Web: www.firmdale.com
SB £128.95 DB £243 CC: MC Vi Am Swi Delt
♨ ⚿ ⊙ ☐ ☎ ❄ ☏ 🅿 ⚘ ℃ ⚘ ♫ ✦ ♦♦♦
How to get there: Nearest tube is Baker Street.
Or, M40, A40 (Euston Road), left lane off flyover.
Left on Gloucester Place. Dorset Square first left.

The Fox Club

★★★★ Town House
46 Clarges Street, Mayfair, London, W1Y 7PJ
Tel: 020 7495 3656 Fax: 020 7495 3656
Email: foxclub@clubhaus.com
Web: www.clubhaus.com
SB £217.38 DB £285.50 B £4 L £6 D £6.
CC: MC Vi Am Swi Delt
⚘ ☐ ☎ ❄ ☏ ⚘ ℃ ⚘ ♫ ✦ ♨
How to get there: From Green Park
underground station, turn right towards Hyde
Park. Take third street on right.

Lowndes Hyatt Hotel

★★★★ Town House ♙
21 Lowndes Street, London, SW1X 9ES
Tel: 020 7823 1234 Fax: 020 7235 1154
Email: rdomingos@hytlondon.co.uk
Web: www.london.hyatt.com
SB £244 DB £262 B £13 L £17.50 D £25.
CC: MC Vi Am DC Delt JCB

⏩ 🐾⊗⌨☎❄🔌🅿️🐎🎋🦮♨️👥
SPA 🍴💈
See advert below right

The Pelham

★★★★ Town House ♙
15 Cromwell Place, London, SW7 2LA
Tel: 020 7589 8288

Academy Hotel

★★★
17–21 Gower Street, London, WC1E 6HG
Tel: 020 7631 4115 Fax: 020 7636 3442

Basil Street Hotel

★★★ ♙
Knightsbridge, London, SW3 1AH
Tel: 020 7581 3311 Fax: 020 7581 3693
Email: info@thebasil.com
Web: www.thebasil.com

Situated in Knightsbridge – a few steps from
Harrods, this 80-bedroom hotel offers a traditional
style and service that draws people back time
after time. Restaurant open every day.
SB £160.40 DB £243.25 B £10 L £14.50 D £18.
CC: MC Vi Am DC Swi Delt

⏩ 🐾⊗⌨☎❄🔌🅿️🐎🎋🦮♨️👥
How to get there: The Hotel is located between
Harrods and Sloane Street.

Bonnington in Bloomsbury

★★★
92 Southampton Row, London, WC1B 4BH
Tel: 020 7242 2828 Fax: 020 7831 9170
Email: sales@bonnington.com
Web: www.bonnington.com

Recently refurbished, independent, ideally
situated for London's major attractions, this
hotel offers a warm welcome to all guests.
'Waterfalls' restaurant. 'Malt' bar and extensive
conference facilities.
SB £117 DB £149 B £7.85 L £12 D £20.75.
CC: MC Vi Am DC Swi Delt

♿⏩🐾⊗⌨☎❄🔌🅿️🐎🎋🦮♨️👥
How to get there: M40 Euston Road, opposite
station. Turn south into Upper Woburn Place,
past Russell Square into Southampton Row.
Bonnington on left.

The Hogarth

★★★ 🛎🛎

Hogarth Road, Kensington, London, SW5 0QQ
Tel: 020 7370 6831 Fax: 020 7373 6179
Email: hogarth@marstonhotels.com
Web: www.marstonhotels.co.uk

MARSTON HOTELS

SB £110 DB £142 B £11 D £20.
CC: MC Vi Am DC Swi Delt
How to get there: Two-minute walk from Earls Court underground station.

Jurys London Inn

★★★

60 Pentonville Road, Islington, London, N1 9LA
Tel: 020 7282 5500 Fax: 020 7282 5511
Email: beatrice.lee@jurys.com
Web: www.jurysdoyle.com
SB £92 DB £100 B £6 L £3 D £6.
CC: MC Vi Am DC Swi Delt
How to get there: From A1 (east) turn right onto A501, then turn right again (north) onto

Pentonville Road. Nearest underground station is Angel, nearest railway station is King's Cross. See advert below left

Mandeville Hotel

★★★

Mandeville Place, London, W1M 6BE
Tel: 020 7935 5599 Fax: 020 7935 9588

Novotel London Waterloo

★★★

113–127 Lambeth Road, Waterloo, London, SE1 7LS
Tel: 020 7793 1010 Fax: 020 7793 0202
Email: H1785@accor-hotels.com
Web: www.novotel.com
SB £142 DB £174 HBS £160 HBD £110 B £12 L £17.95 D £17.95. CC: MC Vi Am DC Swi Delt
How to get there: On Lambeth Road, opposite Lambeth Palace.

Novotel London West

★★★

Hammersmith International Centre, 1 Shortlands, Hammersmith, London, W6 8DR
Tel: 020 8741 1555 Fax: 020 8741 2120
Email: h0737@accor-hotels.com
Web: www.novotel.com
CC: MC Vi Am DC Swi Delt

Paragon

★★★

47 Lillie Road, London, SW6 1UD
Tel: 020 7385 1255 Fax: 020 7381 4450
Email: sales@paragonhotel.co.uk
Web: www.paragonhotel.co.uk
SB £135 DB £165 HBS £150 HBD £195 B £9.50 L £12.50 D £14.50. CC: MC Vi Am DC Swi Delt
How to get there: M4, A4 into London. After crossing Hammersmith flyover move into right lane. Right at 2nd lights, left at mini-roundabout.

Quality Hotel Westminster

★★★

82–83 Eccleston Square, London, SW1V 1PS
Tel: 020 7834 8042 Fax: 020 7630 8942
Email: admin@gb614.u-net.com
Web: www.qualityinn.com/hotel/gb614

Quality Hotel

B £5.75 L £9.75 D £12.50.
CC: MC Vi Am DC Swi Delt

How to get there: Situated close to Victoria rail, coach and tube stations.

Strand Palace
★★★
372 The Strand, London, WC2R 0JJ
Tel: 0870 400 8702 Fax: 020 7936 2077
SB £124 DB £138 HBS £141 HBD £172
B £10.95 L £8.95 D £10.95.
CC: MC Vi Am DC Swi Delt

How to get there: On The Strand. Closest station is 5 minutes walk – Charing Cross.

The Grosvenor Court
★★★
27 Devonshire Terrace, Paddington, London, W2 3DP
Tel: 020 7262 2204 Fax: 020 7402 9351

Clarendon Hotel
★★
8–16 Montpelier Row, Blackheath, London, SE3 0RW
Tel: 020 8318 4321 Fax: 020 8318 4378
Email: relax@clarendonhotel.com
Web: www.clarendonhotel.com

Overlooking historic Greenwich and Blackheath.
SB £65 DB £79 HBS £82.50 HBD £114
L £10.50 D £17.50. CC: MC Vi Am DC Swi Delt

How to get there: Situated just off the A2 on Blackheath. Close to major motorways (M2/M25/A20) – M25 J-2 and J-3.
See advert on following page

Comfort Inn Kensington
★★
22–32 West Cromwell Road, Kensington, London, SW5 9QJ
Tel: 020 7373 3300 Fax: 020 7835 2040
Email: admin@gb043.u-net.com
Web: www.choicehotelseurope.com

SB £100 DB £140 B £9.75 D £18.
CC: MC Vi Am DC Swi Delt JCB

How to get there: On West Cromwell Road, continuation of A4(M) into London from West.

Commodore
★★
50–52 Lancaster Gate, London, W2 3NA
Tel: 020 7402 5291 Fax: 020 7262 1088

Regents Park
★★
154–156 Gloucester Place, London, NW1 6DT
Tel: 020 7258 1911 Fax: 020 7258 0288

Westland
★★
154 Bayswater Rd, London, W2 4HP
Tel: 020 7229 9191 Fax: 020 7727 1054

Sleeping Beauty Motel
Travel Accommodation
543 Lea Bridge Road, Leyton, London, E10 7EB
Tel: 020 8556 8080 Fax: 020 8556 8080
Children minimum age: 4
SB £45 DB £50 CC: MC Vi Am DC Swi Delt

How to get there: Ten minutes' walking distance from Walthamstow Central underground station.

Regent Palace

Piccadilly Circus, London, W1A 4BZ
Tel: 0870 400 8703 Fax: 020 7734 6435

The Shaftesbury

65–73 Shaftesbury Avenue, London, W1V 7AA
Tel: 020 7434 4200 Fax: 020 7437 1717

Claverley

◆◆◆◆

13–14 Beaufort Gardens, Knightsbridge,
London, SW3 1PS
Tel: 020 7589 8541 Fax: 020 7584 3410

Willett Hotel

◆◆◆◆

32 Sloane Gardens, Sloane Square, London,
SW1W 8DJ
Tel: 020 7824 8415 Fax: 020 7730 4830
Email: willett@eeh.co.uk
Web: www.eeh.co.uk
SB £79 DB £117 CC: MC Vi Am DC Swi Delt
🕹 💻 ☎ 🐎 ɕC 🐎 ♬ ♨
How to get there: Take A315 Knightsbridge to
Sloane Street. Hotel is in Sloane Square.

Windermere

◆◆◆◆ 📻 ⚲

142–144 Warwick Way, Victoria, London,
SW1V 4JE
Tel: 020 7834 5163 Fax: 020 7630 8831
Email: windermere@compuserve.com
Web: www.windermere-hotel.co.uk

Small, well-maintained hotel with restaurant and
bar within a welcoming atmosphere. Well
equipped, individually designed bedrooms,
offering home comforts in an elegant setting.
SB £80 DB £99 CC: MC Vi Am Swi Delt JCB
🌐 🕹 💻 ☎ 📞 P🐾 🐎 ɕC 🐎 ♬ ♨ ♀♀ ♀
How to get there: Left opposite Victoria coach
station, first right into Hugh Street. Proceed
along to Alderney St. Hotel is directly opposite
on corner of Alderney St and Warwick Way.

Anchor Hotel

◆◆◆

10 West Heath Drive, London, NW11 7QH
Tel: 020 8458 8764 Fax: 020 8455 3204
Email: res@anchor-hotel.co.uk
Web: www.anchor-hotel.co.uk
SB £33.50 DB £50.70 CC: MC Vi Am Swi Delt
🕹 🚲 💻 ☎ 📞 L P 🐎 ɕC 🐎 ♬ ♨
How to get there: One minute walk from
Golders Green tube station, or by car take North
Circular Road (A406) onto A598 Finchley Road.
At tube turn left, then take first right.

Atlas-Apollo

◆◆◆

18–30 Lexham Gardens, Kensington, London,
W8 5JE
Tel: 020 7835 1155 Fax: 020 7370 4853
Email: keithfenton@atlas-apollo.com
Web: www.atlas-apollo.com
SB £30 DB £100 CC: MC Vi Am Swi Delt JCB
⊞ 💻 ☎ 📞 🐎 ɕC 🐎 ♬ ♨ ♀♀♀
How to get there: Equidistant between Earls
Court and Gloucester Road underground
stations, between Sainsbury's and the Cromwell
Hospital on the A4.

Averard

◆◆◆

10 Lancaster Gate, Hyde Park, London, W2 3LH
Tel: 020 7723 8877 Fax: 020 7706 0860

Excellently located, friendly family hotel in an
interesting Victorian building with original public
rooms and period style paintings, sculptures
and other features.
SB £75 DB £100 CC: MC Vi Am DC Swi Delt
⊞ 💻 ☎ 🐎 ɕC 🐎 ♬ ♨ ♀
How to get there: From Lancaster Gate
undergound station, turn right onto Bayswater
Road, cross main traffic lights. After Swan pub,
turn right to Lancaster Gate.

Central

◆◆◆

35 Hoop Lane, London, NW11 8BS
Tel: 020 8458 5636 Fax: 020 8455 4792
SB £55 DB £75 CC: MC Vi Am DC Swi Delt

How to get there: From M1, take North Circular
Road East, turn right onto A598. After 1 mile,
turn into Hoop Lane at Golders Green.

Craven Gardens

◆◆◆

16 Leinster Terrace, London, W2 3EU
Tel: 020 7262 3167 Fax: 020 7262 2083

Crystal Palace Tower

◆◆◆

114 Church Road, Crystal Palace, London,
SE19 2UB
Tel: 020 8653 0176 Fax: 020 8653 5167
Email: manager@crystalpalacetowerhotel.
freeserve.co.uk
SB £45 DB £51 CC: MC Vi Swi Delt

How to get there: On the A212 in Crystal
Palace. Crystal Palace is the nearest station.

The Diplomat

◆◆◆

2 Chesham Street, Belgravia, London,
SW1X 8DT
Tel: 020 7235 1544 Fax: 020 7259 6153
Email: diplomat.hotel@btinternet.com
Web: www.btinternet.com/~diplomat.hotel

The Diplomat is situated in Belgravia, the most
exclusive and sought-after neighbourhood in
London. It is within easy walking distance of
Harrods and the fashionable Knightsbridge and
Chelsea shops.
SB £95 DB £140 L £6 D £6
CC: MC Vi Am DC Swi JCB
How to get there: Victoria, Knightsbridge and
Sloane Square underground stations all within
10 minutes walk.

Four Seasons

◆◆◆

173 Gloucester Place, London, NW1 6DX
Tel: 020 7724 3461 Fax: 020 7402 5594

Garth Hotel

◆◆◆

64–76 Hendon Way, Cricklewood, London,
NW2 2NL
Tel: 020 8209 1511 Fax: 020 8455 4744

Georgian House Hotel

◆◆◆

87 Gloucester Place, London, W1H 3PG
Tel: 020 7486 3151 Fax: 020 7486 7535
Email: sam@georgian-hotel.demon.co.uk
Web: www.londoncentralhotel.com
SB £70 DB £90 CC: MC Vi Am Swi

How to get there: Parallel to Baker Street, north
of Oxford Street. Two blocks before Marylebone
Road. Few minutes walk from Baker Street tube.

Grange Lodge

◆◆◆

48–50 Grange Road, Ealing, London, W5 5BX
Tel: 020 8567 1049 Fax: 020 8579 5350
Email: enquiries@londonlodgehotels.com
Web: www.smoothhound.co.uk/hotels/gran.html
SB £35 DB £48 B £ Inclusive
CC: MC Vi DC Swi Delt
How to get there: 10 minutes from M4 J-2. Just
off the A406 (North Circular Road) at crossroads
of A4020 (Ealing Common).

Grove Hill

◆◆◆

38 Grove Hill, South Woodford, London,
E18 2JG
Tel: 020 8989 3344 Fax: 020 8530 5286
SB £41 DB £55 B £5
CC: MC Vi Am DC Swi Delt
How to get there: The hotel is close to South
Woodford underground station, and directly off
the A11 London Road.

Hart House

◆◆◆

51 Gloucester Place, London, W1H 3PE
Tel: 020 7935 2288 Fax: 020 7935 8516
Email: reservations@harthouse.co.uk
Web: www.harthouse.co.uk
A highly recommended, clean and
comfortable family-run B&B hotel in the heart
of London's West End – ideal for shopping,

theatres, tourist attractions and business.
SB £68 DB £98 CC: MC Vi Am Swi Delt

How to get there: Just off Oxford Street, behind
Selfridges. Close to Marble Arch and Baker
Street underground stations.

Henley House

♦♦♦

30 Barkston Gardens, Earls Court, London,
SW5 0EN
Tel: 020 7370 4111 Fax: 020 7370 0026

La Gaffe

♦♦♦

107–111 Heath Street, Hampstead, London,
NW3 6SS
Tel: 020 7435 8965 Fax: 020 7794 7592
Email: la-gaffe@msn.com
Web: www.lagaffe.co.uk
SB £65 DB £90 B £2 L £5 D £7.
CC: MC Vi Am Swi Delt

How to get there: Hotel three minutes from
Hampstead underground, three miles from
Kings Cross and 18 miles from Heathrow.
See advert on the right

Langorf Hotel and Apartments

♦♦♦

20 Frognal, Hampstead, London, NW3 6AG
Tel: 020 7794 4483 Fax: 020 7435 9055
Email: langorf@aol.com
Web: www.langorfhotel.com
SB £77 DB £95 CC: MC Vi Am DC Swi Delt

How to get there: Three miles north of Oxford St.
Three miles south of M1 J-1. Off A41 Finchley
Road.

Mitre House Hotel

♦♦♦

178–184 Sussex Gardens, Hyde Park,
London, W2 1TU
Tel: 020 7723 8040 Fax: 020 7402 0990
Email: reservations@mitrehousehotel.com
Web: www.mitrehousehotel.com
SB £60 DB £80 CC: MC Vi Am DC Delt JCB

How to get there: One block north of Hyde Park
and Paddington Station (access to Heathrow
Airport in 15 minutes).
See advert on back cover of this Guide

New England

♦♦♦

20 St Georges Drive, Victoria, London,
SW1V 4BN
Tel: 020 7834 8351 Fax: 020 7834 9000
Email: stay@newenglandhotel.com
Web: www.newenglandhotel.com
SB £65 DB £99
CC: MC Vi Am DC Swi Delt Electron JCB Solo

How to get there: From Victoria station onto
Wilton Road and turn right at the Warwick Way
junction. Second left onto St Georges Drive and
the New England is on your left.
See advert on following page

Park Lodge

73 Queensborough Terrace, Bayswater, London, W2 3SU
Tel: 020 7229 6424 Fax: 020 7221 4772

Parkwood

4 Stanhope Place, London, W2 2HB
Tel: 020 7402 2241 Fax: 020 7402 1574
Email: prkwd@aol.com
Web: www.parkwoodhotel.com
CC: MC Vi Swi Delt Eurocheque

How to get there: Nearest tube: Marble Arch.

Sidney Hotel

68/76 Belgrave Road, Victoria, London, SW1V 2BP
Tel: 020 7834 2738 Fax: 020 7630 0973

Swiss Cottage Hotel

4 Adamson Road, London, NW3 3HP
Tel: 020 7722 2281 Fax: 020 7483 4588
Email: reservations@swisscottagehotel.co.uk
Web: www.swisscottagehotel.co.uk

SB £95 DB £110 CC: MC Vi Am DC Delt

How to get there: A41 to Swiss Cottage. Turn into Adelaide Road, then into Wincheester Street. At Swiss Cottage tube take exit 2.

Swiss House

171 Old Brompton Road, South Kensington, London, SW5 0AN
Tel: 020 7373 9383 Fax: 020 7373 4983
Email: recep@swiss-hh.demon.co.uk
Web: www.swiss-hh.demon.co.uk

"Excellent value for money" has always been our motto. This hotel knows guests' priorities and aims to meet them all. Clean

and friendly atmosphere.
SB £50 DB £85 CC: MC Vi Am DC Swi Delt

How to get there: From M4 turn right into Earls
Court Road. Down the road, turn left onto Old
Brompton Road and hotel is after first set of
lights on right hand side.

The Victoria Inn
◆◆◆
65–67 Belgrave Road, Victoria, London,
SW1V 2BG
Tel: 020 7834 6721

White Lodge
◆◆◆
1 Church Lane, Hornsey, London, N8 7BU
Tel: 020 8348 9765 Fax: 020 8340 7851
SB £30 DB £38 CC: MC Vi Eurocheque

How to get there: Church Lane faces Tottenham
Lane. Hotel next door to police station.

Wigmore Court
◆◆◆
23 Gloucester Place, London, W1H 3PB
Tel: 020 7935 0928 Fax: 020 7487 4254
Email: info@wigmore-court-hotel.co.uk
Web: www.wigmore-court-hotel.co.uk
SB £60 DB £90 CC: MC Vi Swi Delt JCB

How to get there: Nearest tube Marble Arch.
Turn left on Oxford Street. Hotel is
approximately 400yds on left.

The Winchester
◆◆◆
17 Belgrave Road, London, SW1 1RB
Tel: 020 7828 2972 Fax: 020 7828 5191
Children minimum age: 4
DB £75

How to get there: 5 minute walk from Victoria
rail station.

Worcester House Hotel
◆◆◆
38 Alwyne Road, London, SW19 7AE
Tel: 020 8946 1300 Fax: 020 8946 9120
Email: janet@worcesterhouse.demon.co.uk
Web: www.worcesterhousehotel.co.uk
SB £49.50 DB £70 CC: MC Vi Am Swi Delt JCB

How to get there: From A3 at Wimbledon take
A219. Follow road through village. Turn left off
Wimbledon Hill Road. Hotel at end on left-hand
corner.

Abbey Lodge
◆◆
51 Grange Park, Ealing, London, W5 3PR
Tel: 020 8567 7914 Fax: 020 8579 5350
Email: enquiries@londonlodgehotels.com
Web: www.smoothhound.co.uk/
             hotels/abbeylo1.html
SB £45 DB £57 B £inc CC: MC Vi DC Swi Delt

How to get there: From M4 junction 2, A406 to
second set of lights. Turn left into A4020,
following Ealing Common to end, turn left, third
right into Grange Park.

Acton Park Hotel
◆◆
116 The Vale, Acton, London, W3 7JT
Tel: 020 8743 9417 Fax: 020 8743 9417

Ashley Hotel
◆◆
15 Norfolk Square, Paddington, London,
W2 1RU
Tel: 020 7723 3375 Fax: 020 7723 0173
Email: ashhot@btinternet.com

Quiet, secure & sensibly priced. The Ashley
Hotel has a superb location for both tourists
and business people alike. Most reservations
are return bookings or recommendations.
SB £35.50 DB £73 CC: MC Vi Swi Delt

How to get there: Use Paddington Station as
your landmark: hotel is 2 mins walk away.

Barry House

◆◆

12 Sussex Place, Hyde Park, London, W2 2TP
Tel: 020 7723 7340 Fax: 020 7723 9775
Email: bh-hotel@bigfoot.com
Web: www.barryhouse.co.uk

Providing family-like care. Friendly, comfortable B&B with ensuite bedrooms. English breakfast included in competitive rates. Central location close to Paddington Station.
SB £37 DB £75
CC: MC Vi Am DC Swi Delt Solo

How to get there: From Paddington station, into London St to traffic lights. Cross to Sussex Place.

Caswell

◆◆

25 Gloucester Street, London, SW1V 2DB
Tel: 020 7834 6345
Email: manager@hotellondon.co.uk
Web: www.hotellondon.co.uk
Children minimum age: 6
SB £65 DB £75 CC: MC Vi Swi Delt JCB Solo

How to get there: Hotel is approximately 8 mins walk Victoria Station – just off Belgrove Road.

Dylan Hotel

◆◆

14 Devonshire Terrace, Lancaster Gate, London, W2 3DW
Tel: 020 7723 3280 Fax: 020 7402 2443

Edward Lear

◆◆

30 Seymour Street, London, W1H 5WD
Tel: 020 7402 5401 Fax: 020 7706 3766

Haddon Hall

◆◆

39–40 Bedford Place, Russell Square, London, WC1B 5JT
Tel: 020 7636 2474 Fax: 020 7580 4527

Hamilton House

◆◆

60 Warwick Way, London, SW1V 1SA
Tel: 020 7821 7113 Fax: 020 7630 0806

Hotel Orlando

◆◆

83 Shepherds Bush Road, London, W6 7LR
Tel: 020 7603 4890 Fax: 020 7603 4890
SB £35 DB £52 CC: MC Vi Am Swi Delt

How to get there: Situated between Hammersmith Underground Station and Shepherds Bush Undergound Station. Five minutes walk either way.

Lincoln House

◆◆

33 Gloucester Place, Marble Arch, London, W1U 8HY
Tel: 020 7486 7630 Fax: 020 7486 0166
Email: reservations@lincoln-house-hotel.co.uk
Web: www.lincoln-house-hotel.co.uk

Georgian B&B hotel in London, with modern comforts and ensuite rooms. Close to Oxford Street shopping, theatreland and nightlife. Recommended by famous guide books.
SB £69 DB £89
CC: MC Vi Am DC Swi Delt Solo

How to get there: Out of Marble Arch station, turn left, then second turning on left into Portman St. Continuation is Gloucester Place.

Ramsees Hotel

◆◆

32–36 Hogarth Road, Earls Court, London, SW5 0PU
Tel: 020 7370 1445 Fax: 020 7244 6835
Email: ramsees@rasool.demon.co.uk
Web: www.ramseeshotel.com
SB £33 DB £45 CC: MC Vi Am DC Swi Delt

How to get there: The hotel is located off Earls

Court Road. It is about 2 minutes walk from Earls Court Underground station.

See advert on the right

Rasool Court

◆◆

19–21 Penywern Road, Earls Court, London, SW5 9TT
Tel: 020 7373 8900 Fax: 020 7244 6835
Email: rasool@rasool.demon.co.uk
Web: www.rasoolcourthotel.com
SB £36 DB £48 CC: MC Vi Am DC Swi Delt Solo

How to get there: The hotel is located off Earls Court Road. It is about 2 minutes walk from the Earls Court underground station.

See advert below right

Trochee Hotel

◆◆

52 Ridgway Place, Wimbledon, London, SW19 4SW
Tel: 020 8946 9425 Fax: 020 8946 1579
Web: www.trocheehotel.co.uk
SB £41 DB £57 CC: MC Vi Am

How to get there: From Wimbledon station, turn right and take second left into Worple road. Take third right into Ridgway Place.

See advert on following page

Wimbledon Hotel

◆◆

78 Worple Road, Wimbledon, SW19 4HZ
Tel: 020 8946 9265 Fax: 020 8946 9265
SB £55 DB £65 CC: MC Vi Am DC Swi Delt

How to get there: From M25, take A3 to London, Kingston. Take Merton, exit turn left at next traffic lights, keep to right in U-turn.

Forest View

◆

227 Romford Road, Forest Gate, London, E7 9HL
Tel: 020 8534 4844 Fax: 020 8534 8959
Children minimum age: 2
SB £35.85 DB £63.45 HBS £48.65 HBD £76.25 D £12.80.
CC: MC Vi Swi Delt Solo Maestro JCB

How to get there: From North Circular Road, turn off at Ilford and turn left into Romford Road (A118). Follow road to Forest Gate.

Merlyn Court

◆

2 Barkston Gardens, London, SW5 0EN
Tel: 020 7370 1640 Fax: 020 7370 4986
Email: london@merlyncourt.demon.co.uk
Web: www.smoothhound.co.uk/
hotels/merlyn.html

Comfortable, good value, family-run hotel in a central location off a quiet Edwardian square in Kensington. Family rooms are available. Easy access to Olympia and Earls Court exhibition halls, train stations and motorways.

SB £30 DB £50
CC: MC Vi Swi Delt JCB

How to get there: Very central, easy links to airports and motorways (M4, M40, M1). Nearest underground station is Earl's Court.

Kandara Guest House

❖

68 Ockendon Road, Islington, London, N1 3NW
Tel: 020 7226 5721 Fax: 020 7226 3379
Email: admin@kandara.co.uk
Web: www.kandara.co.uk
SB £37 DB £49 CC: MC Vi Delt

How to get there: Ockendon Road is 5th turning on right after Essex Road rail station.

Raj Hideaway Bed & Breakfast

❖

67 Highgate High Street, Highgate Village,
London, N6 5JX
Tel: 020 8348 8760

Trochee Hotel RAC
Wimbledon

The Trochee is a private bed and breakfast hotel offering a warm and homely atmosphere in a delightful part of London.

52 Ridgway Place

21 Malcom Road

Situated in quiet tree-lined streets, the hotel is in two buildings, each with own lounge and dining room. All bedrooms have colour TV, hair dryer and tea/coffee making facilities, some ensuite rooms available. Close to Wimbledon town centre and the All England Tennis Club.

52 Ridgway Place, London SW19 4SW
Tel: 020 8946 9425 Fax: 020 8946 1579
21 Malcolm Road, London SW19 4AS
Tel: 020 8946 1579 Fax: 020 8746 1579

Open and
shut case

Don't get caught out by unexpected legal costs

The availability of Legal Aid in all types of cases has all but disappeared. So what do you do if you or members of your family suffer injury after an accident? Visit a high street solicitor hoping that financial assistance will be available?

'No win No fee agreements' Many solicitors and claims recovery firms may offer this facility but at what cost? In some instances they may ask you to pay up front for out of pocket expenses for reports and court fees. A GP's report may be just £50 but a specialist medical report may be £450. If your claim proceeds to court, Court fees may cost in excess of £100 and Barrister's fees commence at £100 per hour!

A hefty insurance premium to underwrite your claim may be payable. And as much as 30% may be deducted from the compensation awarded to you in lieu of their fees! That means if you were awarded £5000 for your injuries, you would receive only £3500! RAC's Legal Expenses Insurance ensures you receive your damages in full.

RAC Legal Expenses Insurance is personal based and will cover you irrespective of the vehicle you are travelling in. Further Cover may be obtained to protect your partner or your family!

Does your existing policy cover the following benefits?

Consider the alternatives and ask yourself whether you would take the same comfort and peace of mind from these that RAC legal expenses insurance will provide you with?

Call now! Immediate cover is available from just £15

08705 533533

- Up to £50,000 legal expenses cover for non-fault accidents
- Up to £10,000 legal expenses cover for the defence of certain road traffic offences
- 24 hour legal helpline providing advice on most legal matters
- Cover driving/travelling in any vehicle
- Cover for passengers travelling with you
- Cover for you as a pedestrian

A to B - we RAC to it

Southeast

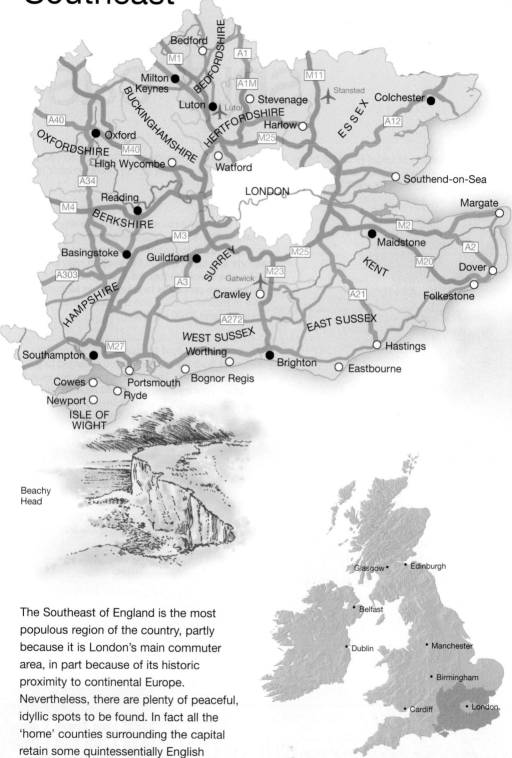

Bedford

Milton Keynes

Luton

Stevenage

Colchester

Oxford

High Wycombe

Watford

Reading

Basingstoke

Guildford

Maidstone

Dover

Crawley

Folkestone

Southampton

Worthing

Hastings

Cowes

Portsmouth

Bognor Regis

Brighton

Eastbourne

Newport

Ryde

ISLE OF WIGHT

Beachy Head

BEDFORDSHIRE
BUCKINGHAMSHIRE
HERTFORDSHIRE
ESSEX
OXFORDSHIRE
BERKSHIRE
SURREY
KENT
HAMPSHIRE
WEST SUSSEX
EAST SUSSEX

M1
A1
A1M
M11
Stansted
Luton
Harlow
A12
A40
M40
M25
A34
M4
M3
A303
A3
Gatwick
M23
M25
A272
M2
A2
M20
A21
M27
LONDON
Southend-on-Sea
Margate

Glasgow
Edinburgh
Belfast
Dublin
Manchester
Birmingham
Cardiff
London

The Southeast of England is the most populous region of the country, partly because it is London's main commuter area, in part because of its historic proximity to continental Europe. Nevertheless, there are plenty of peaceful, idyllic spots to be found. In fact all the 'home' counties surrounding the capital retain some quintessentially English villages, much agricultural countryside and a relaxed lifestyle to match.

Closest to the Continent, Kent is the main thoroughfare for heavy road traffic and yet enjoys a rural nature befitting its title of 'the garden of England'. Canterbury is a prime destination for visitors, its Cathedral serving as the seat of the Church of England and the county's number one tourist attraction. A walled city similar in many ways to its historical contemporaries Chester and York, the centre is a pleasant place to explore and relax in. A short drive away lies Dover, the main ferry gateway to Europe. Despite

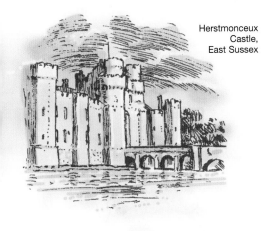

Herstmonceux Castle, East Sussex

being a busy port, Dover is worth a visit to see its famous white cliffs and its magnificent Norman castle.

Surrey is known these days as a commuter county for London, and for its two theme parks, Chessington World of Adventures and Thorpe Park. But Surrey has several more traditional attractions such as the North Downs, Sandown Park and Epsom racecourses, and the county town of Guildford with its 20th-century cathedral.

Sussex is now split into two counties, East and West. Due south of London, Brighton has been a popular seaside resort since early Victorian days. Today, its large student population gives what could otherwise be a sleepy town a young, vibrant atmosphere. Sussex is famous for its dramatic coastal cliffs, Beachy Head being the best known, and it abounds in places of historical interest – for at Hastings and the nearby town of Battle, William the Conqueror invaded with his Norman fleet in 1066. There are also many quaint villages such as Deal and Rye, part of the so-called Cinque Ports, England's primary medieval mercantile and naval centres facing the nearby French coast.

The county of Hampshire possesses such diverse sights as the New Forest, Winchester Cathedral, the ocean docks of Southampton and the naval base of Portsmouth. Separated from the mainland by the Solent (popular with sailing enthusiasts), the Isle of Wight offers excellent coastal paths for walking holidays. Among the island's many attractions, don't miss a visit to Queen Victoria's residence of Osborne House and, if you are there at the right time of year, one of the world's greatest sailing events, the Cowes Regatta, held annually at the end of July and start of August.

Although more heavily industrialised, the northern counties surrounding London – Oxfordshire, Berkshire, Buckinghamshire, Bedfordshire, Hertfordshire and Essex – have much to offer the visitor. See the superb Roman mosaics at St Albans' Verulamium Museum, stroll through the beautiful Chiltern Hills in Buckinghamshire – especially the marvellous Whiteleaf Cross cut into a hillside near Princes Risborough – enjoy the picturesque areas around Chipping Ongar in Essex, visit Oxford to see the wonderful University buildings and perhaps treat it as a springboard for touring the delightful Cotswolds to the northwest.

Abingdon, Oxfordshire

Abingdon Four Pillars

★★★

Marcham Road, Abingdon, Oxfordshire,
OX14 1TZ
Tel: 01235 553456 Fax: 01235 554117

Heritage Hotels – The Upper Reaches

★★★

High Street Abingdon, Thames Street,
Abingdon, Oxfordshire, OX14 3JA
Tel: 0870 400 8101 Fax: 01235 555182
Email: heritagehotels_abingdon.upper_reaches
@forte-hotels.com
Web: www.heritage-hotels.com
SB £131.95 DB £158.90 HBS £151.95
HBD £198.90 B £11.95 L £15 D £18.
CC: MC Vi Am DC Swi Delt

How to get there: On reaching Abingdon town
centre, turn from Stratton Way into Stert Street
(A415). Follow road towards Dorchester. Stop
just before bridge and turn left.

Looking for great dining? Look for RAC Hotels
and Guest Accommodation displaying the
RAC Dining Award symbol in this Guide.

Aldershot, Hampshire

Potters International Hotel

★★★

1 Fleet Road, Aldershot, Hampshire, GU11 2ET
Tel: 01252 344000 Fax: 01252 311611
SB £105 DB £120 L £14 D £17.50.
CC: MC Vi Am DC Swi Delt

Alfriston, East Sussex

Heritage Hotels – The Star Inn

★★★

High Street, Alfriston, East Sussex,
BN26 5TA
Tel: 0870 400 8102 Fax: 01323 870922
Web: www.heritage-hotels.com
SB £70 DB £140 HBS £85 HBD £170
B £12 L £7 D £17.
CC: MC Vi Am DC Swi Delt

How to get there: Located in the centre of
Alfriston, which is accessed via the A27
between Brighton and Eastbourne.

Fifehead Manor Hotel

Set in the midst of the Wallops, Nether and Over, with
a history recorded in the Domesday Book, Fifehead
Manor is the quintessential of English country house
hotels. The 16th-century manor house, lovingly restored
to its former glory, offers superb cuisine, fine wine,
and impeccable service and hospitality.

Middle Wallop,
Stockbridge,
Hampshire SO20 8EG

Tel: 01264 781565
Fax: 01264 781400

Alton, Hampshire

Alton Grange

★★★ ♨

London Road, Alton, Hampshire, GU34 4EG
Tel: 01420 86565 Fax: 01420 541346
Email: info@altongrange.co.uk
Web: www.altongrange.co.uk
Children minimum age: 5. Closed Dec 23 to Jan 3
SB £76 DB £92.50 B £8.95 L £15 D £22.95.
CC: MC Vi Am DC Swi Delt JCB Solo

How to get there: M3 J-4. A331 then A31 in
Farnham/Winchester direction. Turn right after
7 miles at roundabout (signed B2004 to
Alton/Holybourne). Hotel 350yds on left.

Amersham, Buckinghamshire

Heritage Hotels – The Crown

★★★ ♨♨

16 High Street, Amersham, Buckinghamshire,
HP7 0DH
Tel: 01494 721541 Fax: 01494 431283
Email: heritagehotels_amersham.crown
@forte-hotels.com
Web: www.heritage-hotels.com
SB £60 DB £120 B £11.50 L £13.95 D £20.95.
CC: MC Vi Am DC Swi Delt

How to get there: M25 J-18, take A404. Signs
for Old Amersham. At Tesco roundabout, go
straight ahead, past pelican crossing. The
Crown is on left.

Andover, Hampshire

Esseborne Manor

★★★ ♨

Hurstborne Tarrant, Andover, Hampshire,
SP11 0ER
Tel: 01264 736444 Fax: 01264 736725
Email: essebornemanor@compuserve.com

An intimate county house hotel set in attractive
gardens surrounded by open countryside. All
bedrooms are individually furnished and
comfortable public areas abound with fresh fruit
and flowers.
SB £95 DB £112 HBS £115 HBD £152
B £8 L £12 D £20. CC: MC Vi Am DC Swi Delt

How to get there: Halfway between Andover
and Newbury on A343. Twenty minutes M4 J-13
and M3 J-8.

Fifehead Manor

★★★

Middle Wallop, Stockbridge, Hampshire,
SO20 8EG
Tel: 01264 781565 Fax: 01264 781400
SB £75 DB £120 HBS £90 HBD £150
B £8.50 L £13.50 D £27.50.
CC: MC Vi Am Swi Delt

How to get there: Located on A343, 6 miles
from Andover and 12 miles from Salisbury.
See advert on facing page

Quality Hotel Andover

★★★

Micheldever Road, Andover, Hampshire,
SP11 6LA
Tel: 01264 369111 Fax: 01264 369000
Email: andover@quality-hotels.co.uk
Web: www.quality-hotels.co.uk
SB £74 DB £90 B £3.99 D £ 6.50.
CC: MC Vi Am DC Swi Delt Solo JCB

How to get there: From A303, take A3093. At
first roundabout, first exit. At second
roundabout first exit, then follow signs to
Quality Hotel.

White Hart

★★★

12 Bridge Street, Andover, Hampshire,
SP10 1BH
Tel: 01264 352266 Fax: 01264 323767

Southeast

May Cottage `Little Gem`

◆◆◆◆ ✕ ⛵

Thruxton, nr Andover, Hampshire, SP11 8LZ
Tel: 01264 771241 Fax: 01264 771770
Children minimum age: 7

Georgian house set in picturesque tranquil village with old inn. Stonehenge, Salisbury, Winchester and stately homes and gardens all nearby. Pretty, secluded garden with private parking. A non-smoking establishment.
DB £50

⊗ ⊚ ▢ P ☼ ℃ ☎ ♫ ⤢

How to get there: From A303, take turning marked 'Thruxton (village only)'. May Cottage is located almost opposite The George Inn.

Arundel, West Sussex

Arundel Swan

★★★ ℞

27–29 High Street, Arundel, West Sussex, BN18 9AG
Tel: 01903 882314 Fax: 01903 883759
Email: info@swan-hotel.co.uk
Web: www.swan-hotel.co.uk
SB £65 DB £70 HBS £80 HBD £50 B £6.25
L £16 D £16. CC: MC Vi Am DC Swi Delt

⊜ ⊗ ⊚ ▢ ☎ P ☼ ℃ ☎ ♫ ⤢ ⋔ ⋔⋔

How to get there: On the A27 between Worthing and Chichester, the Swan Hotel is at the bottom of the High Street, close to the river.

Comfort Inn Arundel

★★

Junction A27/A284, Crossbush, Arundel, West Sussex, BN17 7QQ
Tel: 01903 840840 Fax: 01903 849849
Email: admin@gb642.u-net.com
Web: www.choicehotels.com

SB £62.75 DB £68.50 HBS £73.50 HBD £90
B £8 D £11. CC: MC Vi Am DC Swi Delt

♿ ✕ ⊗ ⊚ ▢ ☎ P ☼ ℃ ☎ ♫ ⤢ ⋔ ⋔⋔

How to get there: Go to junction of A27/A284 trunk road to the east of Arundel.

Ascot, Berkshire

Heritage Hotels – The Berystede

★★★★ ℞

Bagshot Road, Ascot, Berkshire, SL5 9JH
Tel: 01344 623311 Fax: 01344 872301
Email: heritagehotels_ascot.berystede
        @forte-hotels.com
B £14 L £18 D £28. CC: MC Vi Am DC Swi

◁ ♿ ⊞ ✉ ✕ ⊗ ⊚ ▢ ☎ ☏ P ☼ ℃ ☎ ♫
⤢ ⋔ ⋔⋔ ⛲

How to get there: From Ascot, take A330 for Brockenhurst.

Ashford, Kent

Eastwell Manor

★★★★ ℞℞℞

Eastwell Park, Boughton Lees, Ashford, Kent, TN25 4HR
Tel: 01233 213000 Fax: 01233 635530
Email: eastwell@btinternet.com

A 4-star country house hotel set in glorious acres, offering 62 bedrooms, a 3 AA rosette restaurant, bar & brasserie, 2x20yds heated pools, state-of-the-art gymnasium, 12 beauty treatment rooms and hairdressing salon.
SB £150 DB £180 HBS £180 HBD £210
B £11 L £16.50 D £30.
CC: MC Vi Am DC Swi Delt

◁ ♿ ⊞ ✉ ✕ ⊗ ⊚ ▢ ☎ ☏ P ☼ ℃ ☎ ♫
⤢ ⛲ ⋔ ⋔⋔ 🐎 ⛳ ✗ ⚲ ⊡ ⛲

How to get there: Leave M20 J-9. Take A28 to Canterbury, then follow A251 towards Faversham. Hotel is 2½ miles on left-hand side.

Southeast

Croft Hotel

♦♦♦

Canterbury Road, Kennington, Ashford, Kent,
TN25 4DU
Tel: 01233 622140 Fax: 01233 635271
Email: crofthotel@btconnect.com

Small family-run hotel set in 2 acres of grounds
near to Canterbury, Leeds Castle, Ashford
International and Channel Tunnel. Dover 20
mins.
SB £45 DB £58 HBS £56 HBD £80 D £11.
CC: MC Vi Am Swi Delt Solo
ᴅ ⚕ ⊗ ⊜ ⬜ ☎ ⬛ P ⬛ ⬛ ⬛ ⬛ ⬛ ⬛ ⬛
How to get there: M20 J-9 or J-10, follow A28
signs to Canterbury. Croft Hotel is on right.

Warren Cottage

♦♦♦

136 The Street, Willsborough, Ashford, Kent,
TN24 0NB
Tel: 01233 621905 Fax: 01233 623400
Email: general@warrencottage.co.uk
Web: www.warrencottage.co.uk
SB £39.90 DB £50 HBS £50 HBD £72 B £5 L £5
D £11. CC: MC Vi DC Swi Delt
⬛ ⚕ ⊜ ⬜ P ⬛ ⬛ ⬛ ⬛ ⬛ ⬛ ⬛
How to get there: M20 J-10, take B2164.
First turn right into 'The Street'. Travel past
Blacksmith's Arms. Warren Cottage is third
cottage on left.
See advert on the right

Ashurst, Hampshire

Busketts Lawn

★★

174 Woodlands Road, Woodlands, Ashurst,
Hampshire, SO4 2GL
Tel: 023 80292272 Fax: 023 80292487

Avon, Hampshire

Tyrrells Ford Country House

★★★

Avon, Hampshire, BH23 7BH
Tel: 01425 672646 Fax: 01425 672262

Aylesbury, Buckinghamshire

Hartwell House

★★★★ 🐾🐾🐾

Oxford Road, nr Aylesbury, Buckinghamshire,
HP17 8NL
Tel: 01296 747444 Fax: 01296 747450
Email: info@hartwell-house.com
Web: www.hartwell-house.com
Children minimum age: 8
SB £151.90 DB £248.80 HBS £160 HBD £160
B £12.50 L £22 D £45. CC: MC Vi Swi Delt

How to get there: In Aylesbury, take A418 to
Oxford. Hartwell House two miles on the right.

Horse and Jockey

★★

Buckingham Road, Aylesbury, Buckinghamshire,
HP19 3QL
Tel: 01296 423803 Fax: 01296 395142
SB £66 DB £73 B £7 L £2.45 D £4.95.
CC: MC Vi Am DC Swi

How to get there: North on A413 Buckingham
Road. Hotel one mile from Aylesbury town
centre on left, adjacent to roundabout.

B and B at 103

♦♦♦

103 London Road, Aston Clinton, Aylesbury,
Buckinghamshire, HP22 5LD
Tel: 01296 631313 Fax: 01296 631616
Children minimum age: 12. Closed Easter
SB £32 DB £48 CC: MC Vi Swi Delt JCB Solo

How to get there: On A41 trunk road, M25 J-25.
4 miles from Aylesbury in Aston Clinton.

Bagshot, Surrey

Pennyhill Park

★★★★★ 🐾🐾🐾

London Road, Bagshot, Surrey, GU19 5EU
Tel: 01276 471774 Fax: 01276 475570
Email: debbie@pennyhillpark.co.uk
Web: www.exclusivehotels.co.uk
HBD £240 B £15 L £18.95 D £25.

CC: MC Vi Am DC Swi Delt

How to get there: From M4 J-10 onto A329(M)
for Wokingham/Bracknell/Reading, through
Bracknell, signs for A322 Camberley onto A30.

Banbury, Oxfordshire

Heritage Hotels – Whately Hall

★★★

Banbury Cross, Banbury, Oxfordshire,
OX16 0AN
Tel: 0870 400 8104 Fax: 01295 271736

Lismore Hotel

★★

61 Oxford Road, Banbury, Oxfordshire,
OX16 9AJ
Tel: 01295 267661 Fax: 01295 269010
SB £55 DB £75 HBS £70 HBD £90
B £7.50 D £8.95. CC: MC Vi Am DC Swi Delt

How to get there: From Banbury Cross in town
centre, follow road south. Take 4th turn left into
Old Parr Road, then first right into car park.

La Madonette Country Guest House

♦♦♦♦

North Newington Road, Banbury, Oxfordshire,
OX15 6AA
Tel: 01295 730212 Fax: 01295 730363
Email: lamadonett@aol.com

17th-century millhouse, peacefully situated in
rural surroundings on outskirts of Banbury. Well
located for Cotswolds, Stratford-upon-Avon,
Oxford and Silverstone. Licensed. Gardens,
outdoor pool.
SB £42 DB £62 CC: MC Vi DC Swi Delt

How to get there: M40 J-11, follow signs to
Banbury Cross. Take B4035 for approximately
2 miles, turn right for North Newington, then
¼ mile on right before village.

Easington House

◆◆◆

50 Oxford Road, Banbury, Oxfordshire,
OX16 9AN
Tel: 01295 270181 Fax: 01295 269527

Barton-on-Sea, Hampshire

Cliff House

★★ ℞

Marine Drive West, New Milton, Barton-on-Sea,
Hampshire, BH25 7QL
Tel: 01425 619333 Fax: 01425 612462
Children minimum age: 10
SB £40 DB £80 HBS £55 HBD £55 B £9.50
L £14.95 D £20. CC: MC Vi Am Swi Delt

How to get there: Turn off A35 on B3058 to New
Milton. Right at roundabout on A337, then left
onto Sea Road at Barton-on-Sea. Hotel is at
end of Sea Road on cliff top.

Basildon, Essex

Chichester Hotel

★★★

Old London Road, Wickford, Basildon, Essex,
SS11 8UE
Tel: 01268 560555 Fax: 01268 560580
SB £77 DB £86 B £5.95 L £9.50 D £10.75.
CC: MC Vi Am DC

How to get there: M25 J-29. Turn east on
A127 (sign Southend on Sea). After 13 miles,
turn north on A130, after 1 mile turn west on
A129, after ¼ mile turn right at hotel sign.

Campanile Hotel

Travel Accommodation

Burches, Basildon, SS14 3AE
Tel: 01268 530810 Fax: 01268 286710

Campanile hotels offer comfortable and

convenient budget accommodation and a
traditional French style Bistro providing freshly
cooked food for breakfast, lunch and dinner. All
rooms ensuite with tea/coffee making facilities,
DDT and TV with Sky channels.
SB £46.90 DB £51.85 B £4.95 L £4.95 D £5.95.
CC: MC Vi Am DC Swi Delt

How to get there: M25 J-29. After 6 miles, exit
onto A176. Head for Basildon and follow brown
tourist sign.

Basingstoke, Hampshire

Hanover International Basingstoke

★★★★ ℞℞℞

Scures Hill, Nately Scures, Hook, Hampshire,
RG27 9JS
Tel: 01256 764161 Fax: 01256 764412
Closed December 24 to January 1

HANOVER INTERNATIONAL

Surrounded by mature woodland, this elegant
hotel with superb leisure club is conveniently
located within a mile of the M3.
SB £136.25 DB £157.50 B £11.25 L £15 D £19.
CC: MC Vi Am DC Swi Delt JCB

How to get there: M3 J-5, take A287 to
Basingstoke/Newnham. Turn left at crossroads
onto the A30, and the hotel is 400yds on the right.

Southeast

Hampshire Centre Court

★★★ ℞

Centre Drive, Chineham, Basingstoke,
RG24 8FY
Tel: 01256 816664 Fax: 01256 816727
Email: hampshirec@marstonhotels.com
Web: www.marstonhotels.co.uk

MARSTON HOTELS

SB £110 DB £142 HBS £79.50 HBD £159
B £11 L £14 D £21.
CC: MC Vi Am DC Swi Delt
⛰ ♨ 🖎 🛏 🖥 ☎ 📞 🅿 🐎 ⚗ 🕯 🐕 🍴 🐴 🏊 ♨ 🐎 🎣 ♨ 'ĭ' 🔍 ⛳

How to get there: M3 J-6. A33 for Reading.
Right at Chineham Centre roundabout. Hotel
¼ mile on left.

Red Lion

★★★

London Street, Basingstoke, Hampshire,
RG21 7NY
Tel: 01256 328525 Fax: 01256 844056

Romans
Country House Hotel

Country House set in the tranquil village of
Silchester, ideal for conferences and short
break holidays. Gourmet restaurant. Real log
fire in the oak panelled lounge. Leisure centre
with Tennis, Gymnasium, Sauna and unique
outdoor pool heated to a steaming 30° C year
round.

Little London Road, Silchester,
Basingstoke, Hampshire RG7 2PN
Tel: 0118 9700421   Fax: 0118 9700691
Email: romanhotel@hotmail.com

Ringway

★★★

Aldermaston Roundabout, Ringway North,
Basingstoke, Hampshire, RG24 9NU
Tel: 01256 320212 Fax: 01256 842835

Romans Country House

★★★ ℞℞

Little London Road, Silchester, Basingstoke,
Berkshire, RG7 2PN
Tel: 0118 970 0421 Fax: 0118 970 0691
Email: romanhotel@hotmail.com
SB £95 DB £105 B £7.50 L £10 D £19.50.
CC: MC Vi Am DC Swi Delt
⛰ ♨ 🖎 🛏 🖥 ☎ 📞 🅿 🐎 ⚗ 🕯 🐴 🏊 🎣 🍴 🐕 🍴 🏊 SPA 'ĭ' 🔍 🐕

How to get there: M3 J-6, signs on A340 to
Tadley/Aldermarston. At Pamber end, follow
hotel signs to Silchester.
See advert below

Battle, East Sussex

Netherfield Place

★★★ ℞℞℞

Netherfield, Battle, East Sussex, TN33 9PP
Tel: 01424 774455 Fax: 01424 774024
Email: reservations
                @netherfieldplace.demon.co.uk
Web: www.netherfieldplace.demon.co.uk
Closed Christmas to New Year
SB £75 DB £135 HBS £100 HBD £180
B £15 L £18 D £35. CC: MC Vi Am DC Swi Delt
⛰ 🖎 🛏 🖥 ☎ 🅿 🐎 ⚗ 🐴 🍴 🐕 🏊 🍴 🔍

How to get there: A2100 signs for Battle. After
2½ miles, take Netherfield Road turning on
right. Hotel 1½ miles on left.

Powder Mills

★★★ ℞

Powdermill Lane, Battle, East Sussex,
TN33 0SP
Tel: 01424 775511 Fax: 01424 714540
Email: powdc@aol.com
Web: www.powdermills.co.uk
SB £75 DB £95 HBS £87.50 HBD £65 B £10
L £14.95 D £25. CC: MC Vi Am DC Swi Delt
⛰ ♨ 🖎 🛏 🖥 🖥 ☎ 🅿 🐎 ⚗ 🐴 🍴 🐕 🏊 🍴 🐕 🎣

How to get there: Through the town of Battle,
towards Hastings. First turn left after Battle
Abbey, Powder Mills 1 mile down lane.

Southeast

Little Hemingfold

♦ ♦ ♦ 🦢

Telham, Battle, East Sussex, TN33 0TT
Tel: 01424 774338 Fax: 01424 775351
Closed January 2 to February 11
SB £54 DB £88 HBS £74 HBD £128
B £10.50 D £23.50. CC: MC Vi Am DC Swi Delt

🛋️🐎🦢🖥️☎️🅿️♨️ℭ🐴🎠⛪️🍴🔍⚓️🚣

How to get there: 1½ miles south of Battle on
A2100 towards Hastings. Look out for blue
Hotel sign adjacent to sign depicting sharp
bend. Turn down track to left of road for ½ mile.

Beaconsfield, Buckinghamshire

Chequers Inn

★★ 🦢

Kiln Lane, Wooburn Common, Beaconsfield,
Buckinghamshire, HP10 0JQ
Tel: 01628 529575 Fax: 01628 850124
Email: info@chequers-inn.com
Web: www.chequers-inn.com
SB £97.50 DB £102.50 B £7.50 L £17.95
D £21.95. CC: MC Vi DC Swi

🛋️🦢🖥️☎️🅿️♨️ℭ🐴🎠⛪️🍴🚻👨‍👩‍👧

How to get there: M40 J-2. Follow signs to
Beaconsfield. A40 towards High Wycombe, left
into Broad Lane, stay on road. Hotel on left.
See advert on the right

Beaulieu, Hampshire

Beaulieu Hotel

★★★

Beaulieu Road, Beaulieu, Hampshire, SO42 7YQ
Tel: 023 80293344 Fax: 023 80292729
Email: info@carehotels.co.uk
Web: www.carehotels.co.uk
DB £120 HBD £163 B £7.50 D £7.50.
CC: MC Vi Am DC Swi Delt

♨️🦢🖥️☎️🅿️♨️ℭ🎠⛪️🍴🚻👨‍👩‍👧🔗

How to get there: From M27, follow signs to
Lyndhurst, then Beaulieu on B3056. Beaulieu
Hotel is approximately 3 miles along the road.

Master Builders House

★★★ 🦢 🦢

Bucklers Hard, Beaulieu, Hampshire, SO42 7XB
Tel: 01590 616253 Fax: 01590 616297

Bedford, Bedfordshire

Bedford Swan Hotel

★★★

The Embankment, Bedford, Bedfordshire,
MK40 1RW
Tel: 01206 210001 Fax: 01206 212167
Email: sales@patenhotels.co.uk
Web: www.bedfordswanhotel.co.uk
SB £84.95 DB £102.40 HBD £58 B £8.95
L £11.50 D £16.50. CC: MC Vi Am DC Swi Delt

♿️🛗♨️🦢🖥️☎️📞🅿️♨️ℭ🐴🎠⛪️🍴🚻👨‍👩‍👧🔗

How to get there: Off M1, A421, A6 to Bedford
centre. Cross River Ouse; hotel just to the right.

Woodlands Manor

★★★ 🦢

Green Lane, Clapham, Bedford, Bedfordshire,
MK41 6EP
Tel: 01234 363281 Fax: 01234 272390
Email: woodlands.manor@pageant.co.uk
Web: www.pageant.co.uk
SB £59.50 DB £77.50 HBS £45 HBD £90 B £7.50
L £7.95 D £25.95. CC: MC Vi Am Swi Delt

⚓️♿️🛋️🐎♨️🦢🖥️☎️🅿️♨️ℭ🐴🎠⛪️🍴🚻👨‍👩‍👧

How to get there: M1 J-13, J-14 or J-15 to
Bedford, A6 towards Kettering. 2 miles outside
Bedford, into Clapham, first right into Green Lane.
See advert on following page

The Chequers Inn

Lovely 17th-century country inn with 17 pretty
ensuite bedrooms. Exceptional award winning
restaurant and delicious bar meals. Close to
Marlow, Henley and Windsor and ideal for
exploring the Thames Valley or visiting
London. 3 miles from M40 (J2) and 6 miles
from M4 (J7). Conference Room • Weekend
Breaks • Horse Racing Weekends

Kiln Lane, Wooburn Common,
Beaconsfield, Bucks HP10 0JQ
Tel: 01628 529575   Fax: 01628 850124
Email: info@chequers-inn.com
Website: www.chequers-inn.com

Knife & Cleaver

◆◆◆◆

The Grove, Houghton Conquest, Bedford,
Bedfordshire, MK45 3LA
Tel: 01234 740387 Fax: 01234 740900

Bexhill-on-Sea, East Sussex

Park Lodge

◆◆◆

16 Egerton Road, Bexhill-on-Sea, East Sussex,
TN39 3HH
Tel: 01424 216547

Bexleyheath, Kent

Bexleyheath Marriott

★★★★
1 Broadway, Bexleyheath, Kent, DA6 7JZ
Tel: 020 8298 1000 Fax: 020 8298 1234
SB £126 DB £152 B £9.75 L £14 D £19.75.
CC: MC Vi Am DC Swi Delt

How to get there: Just off A2 and only minutes
from M25 J-2.

Bicester, Oxfordshire

Westfield Farm

◆◆◆◆

The Fenway, Steeple Aston, Bicester,
Oxfordshire, OX6 3SS
Tel: 01869 340591 Fax: 01869 347594
Email: info@westfieldmotel.u-net.com
Web: www.oxlink.co.uk/accom/westfield-farm/
SB £50 DB £65 CC: MC Vi Am DC Swi Delt

How to get there: Eight miles south of Banbury
on A4260, turn first left into Steeple Aston.
Hotel ½ mile, entrance on right.

The Swan

◆◆◆

13 Church Street, Bicester, Oxfordshire,
OX6 7AY
Tel: 01869 369035 Fax: 01869 369035

Bickley, Kent

Glendevon House

◆◆◆

80 Southborough Road, Bickley, Kent, BR1 2EN
Tel: 020 8467 2183

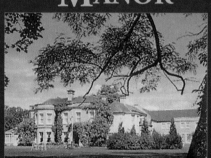

Bishop's Stortford, Hertfordshire

Down Hall Country House

★★★★ ⍾

Hatfield Heath, nr Bishop's Stortford,
Hertfordshire, CM22 7AS
Tel: 01279 731441 Fax: 01279 730416
Email: reservations@downhall.demon.co.uk
Web: www.downhall.co.uk
CC: MC Vi Am DC Swi Delt

How to get there: M11 J-8. A1250 through
Bishops Stortford, A1060 to Hatfield Heath.
Follow signs to Down Hall.
See advert on facing page

The Cottage

♦♦♦♦

71 Birchanger Lane, Birchanger, Bishop's
Stortford, Hertfordshire, CM23 5QA
Tel: 01279 812349 Fax: 01279 815045
Closed Christmas to New Year

17th-century listed house set in large mature
garden. Quiet and peaceful village setting yet near
M11 J-8, Stansted airport and Bishop's Stortford.
SB £35 DB £63 CC: MC Vi Swi Delt Eurocard JCB

How to get there: M11 J-8. A120 west for 1 mile,
B183 north for Newport, first right into Birchanger
Lane.

George Hotel

♦♦♦

North Street, Bishop's Stortford, Herts,
CM23 2LQ
Tel: 01279 504128 Fax: 01279 655135

Botley, Hampshire

Botley Park

★★★★ ⍾

Winchester Road, Boorley Green, Botley,
Hampshire, SO32 2UA
Tel: 01489 780888 Fax: 01489 789242
Email: info@botleypark.macdonald-hotels.co.uk
Web: www.macdonald-hotels.co.uk
SB £97 DB £107 HBS £117 HBD £147 B £12.50
L £13.75 D £24.50. CC: MC Vi Am DC Swi Delt

How to get there: M27 J-7. A334 for Botley. Left
at fourth roundabout into Woodhouse Lane. Left
at T-junction. Hotel ½ mile right.

Bracknell, Berkshire

Coppid Beech

★★★★ ⍾

John Nike Way, Bracknell, Berkshire, RG12 8TF
Tel: 01344 303333 Fax: 01344 301200
Email: welcome@coppid-beech-hotel.co.uk
Web: www.coppidbeech.com
SB £105 DB £185 B £9.50 L £12.95 D £23.95.
CC: MC Vi Am DC Swi Delt

How to get there: M4 J-10. A329(M) to
Wokingham. After 3 miles 1st exit to Coppid
Beech roundabout. First exit, hotel 300yds on
right.

Brentwood, Essex

Marygreen Manor

★★★★ ⍾⍾

London Road, Brentwood, Essex, CM14 4NR
Tel: 01277 225252 Fax: 01277 262809
Web: www.marygreenmanor.co.uk

Located 2 miles from J-28 of the M25. Guests
can choose from our air-conditioned 'Garden

Suite', situated around the courtyard garden, or our new 'Country House' extension.

B £11 L £15 D £26. CC: MC Vi Am Swi Delt

How to get there: M25 J-28. Take A1023. Hotel two minutes on right.

See advert below

Heybridge Hotel

★★★

Roman Road, Ingatestone, Essex, CM4 9AB

Tel: 01277 353288

SB £103 DB £124 B £11 L £16 D £16.
CC: MC Vi Am DC Swi

Marygreen Manor Hotel

RAC
★★★

In the warm and friendly atmosphere of this genuine Tudor House you can enjoy the traditional comfort of log fires in oak-panelled lounges then sample the extensive menus in our elegant Baronial Hall-style restaurant. We offer highly professional service, full à la Carte menu plus Fixed Price selections and our award winning wine list. All-day Snack Menu and Afternoon teas also available in our lounges or the tranquil garden.

London Road, Brentwood, Essex

Tel: 01277 225252   Fax: 01277 262809

Website: www.marygreenmanor.co.uk

Brighton, East Sussex

Kings Hotel

★★★

139–141 Kings Road, Brighton, East Sussex, BN1 2NA

Tel: 01273 820854 Fax: 01273 828309

Email: kingshotel@vienna-group.co.uk

Web: www.viennagroup.co.uk

SB £70 DB £110 HBS £80 HBD £130

B £7 D £12. CC: MC Vi Am DC Swi Delt

How to get there: M23/A23 to Brighton. Signs for seafront. At Brighton Pier roundabout take 3rd exit. Hotel is opposite West Pier.

Old Ship

★★★

Kings Road, Brighton, East Sussex, BN1 1NR

Tel: 01273 329001 Fax: 01273 820718

Email: admin@oldshiphotel.co.uk

Web: www.paramount-hotels.co.uk

SB £85 DB £110 HDB £150

CC: MC Vi Am DC Swi Delt

How to get there: On Brighton seafront, 10 minutes walk train station.

See advert on page 22

Quality Hotel Brighton

★★★

West Street, Brighton, East Sussex, BN1 2RQ

Tel: 01273 220033 Fax: 01273 778000

Email: admin@gb057.u-net.com

Web: www.choicehotels.com

SB £97.25 DB £117 HBS £110.25 HBD £143

B £9.75 L £2.25 D £14.75.

CC: MC Vi Am DC Swi Delt

How to get there: A23 into Brighton. Signs Seafront/town centre. A259 to Hove/Worthing. Hotel off seafront, right into West Street.

Adelaide

♦♦♦♦

51 Regency Square, Brighton, East Sussex, BN1 2FF

Tel: 01273 205286 Fax: 01273 220904

Email: adelaide@pavilion.co.uk

SB £41 DB £68 CC: MC Vi Am DC Swi Delt

How to get there: Signs town centre/seafront. Right at Palace Pier roundabout. Regency Square on right opposite West Pier.

Arlanda

◆◆◆◆

20 New Steine, Brighton, East Sussex, BN2 1PD
Tel: 01273 699300 Fax: 01273 600930
Email: arlanda@brighton.co.uk
Closed Christmas
SB £28 DB £40 CC: MC Vi Am DC Swi Delt

How to get there: From Palace Pier, 400yds east on Marine Parade. Hotel in New Steine on left.

Ascott House

◆◆◆◆

21 New Steine, Marine Parade, Brighton, East Sussex, BN2 1PD
Tel: 01273 688085 Fax: 01273 623733
Email: ascotthouse@supanet.com
Children minimum age: 2
SB £36 DB £66
CC: MC Vi Swi Delt Electron Maestro

How to get there: A23 to seafront. Left at Palace Pier roundabout. Ninth left off Marine Parade.

Fyfield House

◆◆◆◆

26 New Steine, Brighton, East Sussex, BN2 1PD
Tel: 01273 602770 Fax: 01273 602770
Email: fyfield@aol.com
Web: www.brighton.co.uk/hotels/fyfield
Closed Christmas
SB £20 DB £45 CC: MC Vi Am DC Swi Delt JCB

How to get there: At Palace Pier, A259 east. 8th turning into square, which is one-way system.

Hotel Twenty One

◆◆◆◆

21 Charlotte Street, Marine Parade, Brighton, East Sussex, BN2 1AG
Tel: 01273 686450 Fax: 01273 695560
Email: the21@pavilion.co.uk
Web: www.smoothhound.co.uk/hotels/21.html
SB £35.50 DB £60 CC: MC Vi Swi Delt
How to get there: From Palace Pier left onto A259. After ³/₄ mile, turn left onto Charlotte Street. Hotel Twenty One is on left-hand side.

Paskins Town House

◆◆◆◆

18–19 Charlotte Street, Brighton, BN2 1AG
Tel: 01273 601203 Fax: 01273 621973

Email: welcome@paskins.co.uk
Web: www.paskins.co.uk
SB £30 DB £70 B £7.75
CC: MC Vi Am DC Swi Delt

How to get there: At Brighton Pier, turn left. Paskins Hotel is on 11th road on right.

Regency

◆◆◆◆

28 Regency Square, Brighton, East Sussex, BN1 2FH
Tel: 01273 202690 Fax: 01273 220438
Email: enquiries@regencybrighton.co.uk
Web: www.regencybrighton.co.uk
Children minimum age: 6

Once the home of Jane, Dowager Duchess of Marlborough, this 1820 townhouse is now a small, smart hotel. Direct sea views. Car parking (500) under square. London 1 hour (train).
SB £55 DB £90 CC: MC Vi Am DC Swi Delt
How to get there: Regency Square is off coast road (Kings Road) directly opposite West Pier.

Trouville

◆◆◆◆

11 New Steine, Marine Parade, Brighton, East Sussex, BN2 1PB
Tel: 01273 697384
Closed January
SB £25 DB £57 CC: MC Vi Am Delt
How to get there: A23 to Palace Pier. Left onto A259. New Steine is first square 300yds on left.

Allendale

◆◆◆

3 New Steine, Brighton, East Sussex, BN2 1PB
Tel: 01273 675436 Fax: 01273 602603

Book with RAC Hotel Reservations and check the latest offers available. Call 0870 603 9109 and quote 'RAC Guide 2001'

Southeast

Brighton Marina House

♦♦♦

8 Charlotte Street, Marine Parade, Brighton,
East Sussex, BN2 1AG
Tel: 01273 605349 Fax: 01273 679484
Email: rooms@jungs.co.uk
Web: www.s-h-systems.co.uk/hotels/brightma
SB £25 DB £45 HBS £45 HBD £75 D £15.25.
CC: MC Vi Am DC

How to get there: From Palace Pier left into
Marine Parade (A259). Pass two traffic lights
and Charlotte Street is fifth on left.
See advert on facing page

Cavalaire House

♦♦♦

34 Upper Rock Gardens, Brighton, East Sussex,
BN2 1QF
Tel: 01273 696899 Fax: 01273 600504
Email: cavalaire.hotel@virgin.net
Web: business.virgin.net/cavalaire.hotel
Children minimum age: 5.
Closed mid-January to mid-February
SB £25 DB £50
CC: MC Vi Am DC Swi Delt

How to get there: At Brighton Pier roundabout,
take A259 Rottingdean. At second set of lights,
turn left into Lower Rock Gardens. Hotel up hill.

Genevieve

♦♦♦

18 Maderia Place, Brighton, East Sussex,
BN2 1TN
Tel: 01273 681653

Rowland House

♦♦♦

21 St George's Terrace, Kemp Town, Brighton,
Sussex, BN2 1JJ
Tel: 01273 603639 Fax: 01273 603639
Web: www.brightoninuk.com/
          rowlandhouse.html
Closed Christmas
SB £20 DB £40 CC: MC Vi Am

How to get there: Train station 20 minutes, bus
station 10 minutes.

The Lanes

♦♦♦

70–72 Marine Parade, Brighton, East Sussex,
BN2 1AE
Tel: 01273 674231

Melford Hall

♦♦

41 Marine Parade, Brighton, East Sussex,
BN2 1PE
Tel: 01273 681435 Fax: 01273 624186

Broadstairs, Kent

Devonhurst Hotel

♦♦♦♦

Eastern Esplanade, Broadstairs, Kent,
CT10 1DR
Tel: 01843 863010 Fax: 01843 868940
Email: info@devonhurst.co.uk
Web: www.devonhurst.co.uk
Children minimum age: 5
SB £29 DB £51 HBS £41 HBD £75 D £12.
CC: MC Vi

How to get there: High Street to bottom, left
into Albion Street. Third right Dickens Road,
then Eastern Esplanade.

Oakfield Private Hotel

♦♦♦♦

11 The Vale, Broadstairs, Kent, CT10 1RB
Tel: 01843 862506 Fax: 01843 600659
Email: oakfield.hotel@lineone.net
Web: www.smoothhound.co.uk
Children minimum age: 5
SB £25 DB £50 HBS £35 HBD £70
CC: MC Vi Am DC Swi Delt JCB

How to get there: Halfway down High Street,
right into Queens Road, then third right. Hotel is
25 yards on right.

Bay Tree

♦♦♦

12 Eastern Esplanade, Broadstairs, Kent,
CT10 1DR
Tel: 01843 862502 Fax: 01843 860589
Children minimum age: 10
SB £26 DB £52 HBS £38 HBD £76 D £12.
CC: MC Vi Swi Delt

How to get there: On clifftop Eastern Esplanade.
Follow main road through town, turning right
into Rectory Road on leaving Broadstairs.

Brockenhurst, Hampshire

New Park Manor Hotel

★★★ ⋒⋒⋒
Brockenhurst, Hampshire, SO42 7QH
Tel: 01590 623467 Fax: 01590 62268
Email: enquiries@newparkmanorhotel.co.uk
Web: www.newparkmanorhotel.co.uk

Gracious country house hotel, formerly a hunting lodge for Charles II, surrounded by acres of parkland and ancient forest.
SB £85 DB £110 HBS £95 HBD £70 B £9.50 L £14 D £27.50.
CC: MC Vi Am DC Swi Delt

How to get there: M27 J-1. A337 to Lyndhurst and Brockenhurst. Hotel sign and drive on right midway between Lyndhurst and Brockenhurst.

Rhinefield House

★★★ ⋒⋒⋒
Rhinefield Road, Brockenhurst, Hampshire, SO42 7QB
Tel: 01590 622922 Fax: 01590 622800
Web: www.arcadianhotels.co.uk
SB £110 DB £145 HBS £105 HBD £175
CC: MC Vi Am DC Swi Delt

How to get there: From Lyndhurst via A35 to Christchurch. Left after 3 miles into Ornamental Drive, sign Rhinefield. Hotel 1½ miles on right.

Whitley Ridge Country House

★★★ ⋒⋒
Beaulieu Road, Brockenhurst, Hampshire, SO42 7QL
Tel: 1590 622354

Watersplash

★★ ⋒
The Rise, Brockenhurst, Hampshire, SO42 7ZP
Tel: 01590 622344 Fax: 01590 624047

Cottage Hotel

♦♦♦♦ ⋩
Sway Road, Brockenhurst, Hampshire, SO42 7SH
Tel: 01590 622296 Fax: 01590 623014
Email: terry@compuserve.com
Web: www.cottage-hotel-new-forest.co.uk
Children minimum age: 10. Closed Dec-Feb

A delightfully converted 300-year-old oak-beamed forester's cottage with pretty gardens and residents' cosy 'snug bar'. In summer, cream teas are served on the terrace.
SB £60 DB £75 CC: MC Vi Swi Delt

How to get there: From Lyndhurst on A337, right at Carey's Manor into Grigg Lane. Continue ½ mile to crossroads, straight over and Cottage is next to war memorial.

Bromley, Kent

Bromley Court

★★★
Bromley Hill, Bromley, Kent, BR1 4JD
Tel: 020 8464 5011 Fax: 020 8460 0899
Email: bromleyhotel@btinternet.com
Web: www.bromley-hotel.co.uk
SB £94 DB £100 B £6.95 L £12 D £15.
CC: MC Vi Am DC Swi Delt

How to get there: M25 J-4, A21 Orpington/Bromley. Follow for 6 miles to Bromley. Via A21 to London Road for 1 mile. Hotel drive on left.

Buckingham, Buckinghamshire

Villiers

★★★ ⋒
3 Castle Street, Buckingham, Buckinghamshire, MK18 1BS
Tel: 01280 822444 Fax: 01280 822113

Email: villiers@villiershotel.demon.co.uk
SB £105 DB £120 B £6.95 L £12 D £25.
CC: MC Vi Am DC Swi Delt

How to get there: M40 J-9 or M1 J-13, A421 to Buckingham. Hotel is in Castle Street.

Burford, Oxfordshire

Bird In Hand

♦♦♦♦

Hailey, Burford, Oxfordshire, OX8 5XP
Tel: 01993 868321 Fax: 01993 868702

Maytime Inn

♦♦♦

Asthall, Burford, Oxfordshire, OX18 4HW
Tel: 01993 822068 Fax: 01993 822635

Burley, Hampshire

Moorhill House

★★★

Burley, nr Ringwood, Hampshire, BH24 4AG
Tel: 01425 403285 Fax: 01425 403715
Email: info@carehotels.co.uk
Web: www.carehotels.co.uk
SB £60 DB £120 HBS £81.50 HBD £163
B £7.50 D £21.50. CC: MC Vi Am DC Swi Delt

How to get there: From M27, A31 and follow signs to Burley. Bear left at war memorial, right past Queens Head. Hotel signposted on right.

Burnham-on-Crouch, Essex

Ye Olde White Harte

♦♦

The Quay, Burnham-on-Crouch, Essex,
CM0 8AS
Tel: 01621 782106 Fax: 01621 782106

17th-century building overlooking River Crouch.

Exposed brickwork and fireplaces in bars, restaurant and rooms. Private jetty over river.
SB £45 DB £65 B £5.50 L £13 D £13.
CC: MC Vi Swi Delt

How to get there: High Street in Burnham. Right before clocktower, then right into hotel car park.

Cadnam, Hampshire

Bartley Lodge

★★★ ♨

Lyndhurst Road, Cadnam, Hampshire,
SO40 2NR
Tel: 01703 812248 Fax: 01703 812075
Email: information@carehotels.co.uk
CC: MC Vi Am DC

See advert below

Camberley, Surrey

Heritage Hotels – Frimley Hall

★★★

Lime Avenue, off Portsmouth Road, Camberley, Surrey, GU15 2BG
Tel: 0870 4008224 Fax: 01276 691253
SB £65 DB £90 HBS £75 HBD £110 B £13.50
L £7.50 D £19.50. CC: MC Vi Am DC Swi Delt

How to get there: M3 J-3, A30 for Camberley for 1 mile, then A325 for Farnham. Conifer Drive 1 mile on right.

Camberley Guest House

♦♦♦

116 London Road, Camberley, Surrey, GU15 3TJ
Tel: 01276 24410 Fax: 01276 65409
Closed Christmas
SB £50 DB £65 CC: MC Vi DC

How to get there: Hotel in town centre.

Canterbury, Kent

Heritage Hotels – The Chaucer

★★★ ®

Ivy Lane, Canterbury, Kent, CT1 1TT
Tel: 0870 400 8106 Fax: 01227 450397
SB £15.80 DB £112.60 HBS £100 HBD £120
B £12 L £6.95 D £15.
CC: MC Vi Am DC Swi Delt

How to get there: M2 J-7. Signs to Canterbury. At 5th roundabout turn right. Hotel is on left.

Canterbury Hotel

★★

71 New Dover Road, Canterbury, Kent, CT1 3DZ
Tel: 01227 450551 Fax: 01227 780145
Email: canterbury.hotel@btinternet.com
Children minimum age: 6

Elegant Georgian-style hotel, 10 minutes from city centre, providing high standards of personal service and comfort. Executive rooms and apartments. 'La Bonne Cuisine' French restaurant.
SB £55 DB £75 HBS £66 HBD £102
L £14 D £17. CC: MC Vi Am DC Swi Delt

How to get there: On A2 – New Dover Road.

Ebury

★★ ®

65-67 New Dover Road, Canterbury, Kent, CT1 3DX
Tel: 01227 768433 Fax: 01227 459187
Email: info@ebury-hotel.co.uk
Web: www.ebury-hotel.co.uk
Closed December 17 to January 8
SB £50 DB £79 HBS £60 HBD £94 B £6.95
D £9.95. CC: MC Vi Am DC Swi Delt Solo

How to get there: London-bound A2, Canterbury turn off. Ring road around city. At fifth roundabout signs to Dover. Hotel 2 miles on left.

Pointers Hotel

★★

1 London Road, Canterbury, Kent, CT2 8LR
Tel: 01227 456846 Fax: 01227 831131

Thanington Hotel

♦♦♦♦♦

140 Wincheap, Canterbury, Kent, CT1 3RY
Tel: 01227 453227 Fax: 01227 453225
Email: thanington@lineone.net
Web: www.thanington-hotel.co.uk
Children minimum age: 8. Closed Christmas
SB £50 DB £68 CC: MC Vi Am DC Swi Delt

How to get there: Just outside city walls, on A28 Canterbury to Ashford road.

Waltham Court

♦♦♦♦

Kake Street, Petham, Canterbury, Kent, CT4 5RY
Tel: 01227 700413 Fax: 01227 700127

Three Tuns Hotel

♦♦♦

24 Watling Street, Canterbury, Kent, CT1 2UD
Tel: 01227 456391 Fax: 01227 785962
DB £53.50 B £5.50 L £5.45 D £5.45.
CC: MC Vi Am DC Swi Delt

How to get there: In heart of Canterbury. Come around ring road. Turn into town at police station, down into Watling Street.

Chelmsford, Essex

Atlantic
★★★
New Street, Chelmsford, Essex, CM1 1PP
Tel: 01245 268168 Fax: 01245 268169
Email: book@atlantichotel.co.uk
Web: www.atlantichotel.co.uk
SB £55 DB £60 B £5.95 L £10 D £20.
CC: MC Vi Am DC Swi Delt
♿☯☕🖥☎📞🅿🛏🎠🏇Ħ🍴♨♨♨
How to get there: A1016 to Chelmsford and
signs to station. Over two mini-roundabouts, turn
left then right. At traffic lights left into New St.
See advert below right

County Hotel
★★★ ℞
29 Rainsford Road, Chelmsford, Essex,
CM1 2QA
Tel: 01245 455700 Fax: 01245 492762
Email: sales@countyhotel-essex.co.uk
Web: www.countyhotel-essex.co.uk
SB £75 DB £85 B £10.50 L £20 D £20.
CC: MC Vi Am DC Swi Delt
♿♿☕🖥☎📞🅿🛏🎠🏇Ħ🍴♨♨♨
How to get there: M25 J-28, A12 to Chelmsford.
From town centre to rail station. Pass station,
under bridge, hotel on left after traffic lights.

Ivy Hill
★★★
Writtle Road, Margaretting, Essex, CM4 0EH
Tel: 01277 353040 Fax: 01277 355038
Email: sales@ivyhillhotel.co.uk
Web: www.ivyhillhotel.co.uk
B £6.50 L £22.95 D £22.95.
CC: MC Vi Am DC Swi Delt
♿♿🗄☕🖥☎🅿🛏🎠🏇Ħ🍴♨♨♨
🔍🏊
How to get there: Eight miles east of M25 on
A12. Take 2nd exit on B1002 for Margaretting.

Pontlands Park
★★★
West Hanningfield Road, Great Baddow,
Chelmsford, Essex, CM2 8HR
Tel: 01245 476444 Fax: 01245 478393
Email: sales@pontlandsparkhotel.co.uk
Web: www.pontlandsparkhotel.co.uk
SB £100 DB £145 HBS £119.80 HBD £184.60
B £6.60 L £17.05 D £17.05.
CC: MC Vi Am DC Swi Delt JCB
♿♿🗄☕🖥☎🅿🛏🎠🏇Ħ🍴♨♨♨
🍸🔍🏊
How to get there: From A12, take A1114 to
Chelmsford. Take first left to Great Baddow,
then first left and first left again.

Beechcroft Private Hotel
♦♦♦
211 New London Road, Chelmsford, Essex,
CM2 0AJ
Tel: 01245 352462 Fax: 01245 347833
Email: beechcroft.hotel@btinternet.com
SB £36 DB £59 CC: MC Vi Swi Delt
🔔☯☕🖥🅿🛏🎠🏇Ħ🍴♨
How to get there: From A12 take B1007 into
Chelmsford. Hotel is 3 miles from A12.

Tanunda
♦♦♦
217–219 New London Road, Chelmsford,
Essex, CM2 0AJ
Tel: 01245 354295 Fax: 01245 345503
SB £36 DB £60 CC: MC Vi Am DC Swi Delt
♿☕🖥☎🛏🎠🏇Ħ🍴♨♨

Millstream Hotel
Hotel and Restaurant, Bosham

RaC ★★★

This quintessentially English country hotel dates from 1701 and nestles in the picturesque quayside village of Bosham, just four miles west of Chichester. The Millstream is renowned for its unique blend of idyllic setting, ambience and superb food.

Bosham, Chichester PO18 8HL
Tel: 01243 573234   Fax: 01243 573459
Email: info@millstream-hotel.co.uk
Website: www.millstream-hotel.co.uk

Aberlands House Hotel

Former Victorian rectory in 2½ acres, close to beaches, harbour and Goodwood. Family run, residential licence with comfortable bar and lounge with log fire. Spacious ensuite family and four poster rooms and private suite. Short breaks available with a selection of interesting menus. Ideally suited for small private functions and parties.

Merston, Chichester, West Sussex
PO20 6DY
Tel: 01243 532675   Fax: 01243 788884

Chenies, Hertfordshire

Bedford Arms

★★★ ?
Chenies, nr Rickmansworth, Hertfordshire, WD3 6EQ
Tel: 01923 283301 Fax: 01923 284825
Email: info@bedfordarms-hotel-chenies.com
SB £157.50 DB £170 B £12.50 L £25 D £25.
CC: MC Vi Am DC Swi

How to get there: 2 miles from M25 J-18 on A404 to Amersham. Signpost Chenies on right.

Chichester, West Sussex

Millstream Hotel

★★★ ? ?
Bosham Lane, Bosham, Chichester, West Sussex, PO18 8HL
Tel: 01243 573234 Fax: 01243 573459
Email: info@millstream-hotel.co.uk
Web: www.millstream-hotel.co.uk

Beautifully appointed country house dating from 1701, set in a picturesque sailing village. Bar, sitting room, restaurant and a bedroom designed for wheelchair access, all on ground floor. Locally renowned award-winning restaurant.
SB £72 DB £115 HBS £70 HBD £140 B £9 L £11.50 D £21.50. CC: MC Vi Am DC Swi Delt

How to get there: A259 Chichester/Havant to Bosham. At Swan roundabout brown signs to hotel.
See advert above left

Ship Hotel
★★★
North Street, Chichester, West Sussex, PO9 1NH
Tel: 01243 778000 Fax: 01243 788000
Email: bookings@shiphotel.com

Southeast

Web: www.shiphotel.com
SB £75 DB £114 HBS £93 HBD £148 B £7.50
L £15.50 D £19.50. CC: MC Vi Am DC Swi Delt
⛄ 🍴 🐾 🎱 🖥 ☎ 🛎 **P** ⛳ 🎯 🐴 🎿 ♨ ⚑ 🏨 🍽
How to get there: Signs to Chichester Festival
Theatre, until Northgate roundabout, then turn
into North Street. Hotel on left, car park at rear.

Aberlands House

♦♦♦♦

Merston, Chichester, West Sussex, PO20 6DY
Tel: 01243 532675 Fax: 01243 788884
SB £37.50 DB £60 HBS £50 HBD £42.50
D £14.50.
CC: MC Vi Swi Delt
♿ 🍴 🎱 🖥 **P** ⛳ 🎯 🐴 🎿 ♨ 🏨 🍽
See advert on facing page

Chinnor, Oxfordshire

Peacock Hotel

★★ 🐾

Henton, Chinnor, Oxfordshire, OX9 4AH
Tel: 01844 353519 Fax: 01844 353891

Chipping Norton, Oxfordshire

Southcombe Lodge

♦♦♦ ✍

Southcombe, Chipping Norton, Oxfordshire,
OX7 5QH
Tel: 01608 643068 Fax: 01608 642948
Email: georgefindlysouthcombelodge
@tinyworld.co.uk
SB £30 DB £50
🎱 🖥 **P** ⛳ 🎯 🐴 🎿 ♨ 🍽
How to get there: A44 Oxford to Chipping
Norton, next to Chipping Norton golf course.

Clacton-on-Sea, Essex

Sandrock Hotel

♦♦♦

1 Penfold Road, Marine Parade West,
Clacton-on-Sea, Essex, CO15 1JN
Tel: 01255 428215 Fax: 01255 428215

Well-presented small hotel in excellent position
very close to sea-front. High standards of
house-keeping and a friendly welcome. Good
home-cooking. Rear car park.
SB £31 DB £53 HBS £43 HBD £77 D £12.
CC: MC Vi Am DC Swi Delt JCB
🐾 🎱 🖥 **P** ⛳ 🎯 🐴 🎿 ♨ 🍽
How to get there: A120 to Clacton. Right at
seafront. Hotel second turn on right, past pier.

Le Vere Private Hotel

⚑

15 Agate Road, Marine Parade West,
Clacton-on-Sea, Essex, CO15 1RA
Tel: 01255 423044 Fax: 01255 423044
SB £30 DB £47.50 HBS £38 HBD £65
B £5 L £6 D £10. CC: MC Vi Am DC JCB
🍴 🐾 🎱 🖥 **P** ⛳ 🎯 🐴 🎿 ♨ 🍽
How to get there: To seafront. Turn right, cross
lights. Agate Road next right (sea on left).

Clanfield, Oxfordshire

The Plough at Clanfield

★★★ 🐾 🐾 🐾

Bourton Road, Clanfield, Oxfordshire,
OX18 2RB
Tel: 01367 810222 Fax: 01367 810596
Email: ploughatcranfield@hotmail.com
Children minimum age: 12
SB £85 DB £125 HBS £117.50 HBD £160 B £10
L £17 D £33. CC: MC Vi Am DC Swi Delt JCB
♿ 🍴 🎱 🖥 ☎ 🛎 **P** ⛳ 🎯 🐴 🎿 ♨ 🏨 🍽
How to get there: The Plough located at
junction of A4095 and B4020 between towns of
Witney and Faringdon, 15 miles west of city of
Oxford.

Colchester, Essex

Five Lakes

★★★★ ⍤ ⍤

Colchester Road, Tolleshunt Knights, Maldon, Essex, CM9 8HX
Tel: 01621 868888 Fax: 01621 869696
Email: enquiries@fivelakes.co.uk
Web: www.fivelakes.co.uk

Set in 320 acres including two golf courses. Spacious and innovative in design, with extensive leisure, health, beauty and sporting facilities. Easily accessible from A12, M25 and M11.
SB £115.95 DB £169.90 HBS £135.45 HBD £208.90 B £10.95 L £13.50 D £19.50.
CC: MC Vi Am DC Swi Delt JCB Eurocard

⚓ ⟐ ⑊ 🗺 🍴 ✪ ▧ ▢ ☎ 📞 🅿 ⚙ ⟡ 🎠 🎋
🐾 👁 ♨ ⑊ SPA ⟟ ⟐ ⚒ ⚲ ⍓ ⎙

How to get there: A12 for Kelvedon, then follow brown 'Five Lakes' tourist board signs.

Butterfly Hotel

★★★

A12/A120 Junction, Old Ipswich Road, Colchester, Essex, CO7 7QY
Tel: 01206 230900 Fax: 01206 231095
Email: colbutterfly@lineone.net
Web: www.butterflyhotels.co.uk
SB £75.45 DB £83.40 HBS £75.45 HBD £48.25 B £7.50 L £10 D £12.
CC: MC Vi Am DC Swi Delt

⟐ 🐾 ✪ ▧ ▢ ☎ 📞 🅿 ⚙ ⟡ 🎠 🎋 🐾 ♨ ⑊

How to get there: North of Colchester by A12/A120 Ardleigh junction.

George

★★★

116 High Street, Colchester, Essex, CO1 1TD
Tel: 01206 578494 Fax: 01206 761732
Email: colcgeorge@aol.com
SB £63.25 DB £72 B £6.95 L £6.95 D £9.95.
CC: MC Vi Am DC Swi Delt JCB

🗺 🐾 ✪ ▧ ▢ ☎ 📞 🅿 ⚙ ⟡ 🎠 🎋 🐾 ♨ ⑊

How to get there: Follow signs for Colchester Town Centre. Hotel ½ mile left on High Street.

Marks Tey Hotel

★★★

London Road, Marks Tey, Colchester, Essex, CO6 1DU
Tel: 01206 210001 Fax: 01206 212167
Email: sales@patenhotels.co.uk
Web: www.marksteyhotel.co.uk
SB £80.95 DB £97.40 HBD £55 B £8.95 L £11.50 D £16.50. CC: MC Vi Am DC Swi Delt

⚓ ⟐ ✪ ▧ ▢ ☎ 📞 🅿 ⚙ ⟡ 🎠 🎋 🐾 👁 ⑊
⑊ SPA ⟟ ⚲ ⎙

How to get there: A12, take A120.
At roundabout, take third exit to Colchester, at next roundabout first exit, Copford/Colchester. Hotel on left.

Rose & Crown

★★★ ⍤ ⍤ ⍤

East Street, Colchester, Essex, CO1 2TZ
Tel: 01206 866677 Fax: 01206 866616

Copythorne, Hampshire

Old Well

◆◆◆

Copythorne, Southampton, Hampshire, SO40 2PE
Tel: 02380 812700
SB £30 DB £38 HBS £37 HBD £52 B £4.50 L £7.95 D £7.95. CC: MC Vi Swi Delt

🐾 ✪ ▧ ▢ 🅿 ⚙ ⟡ 🎠 🎋 🐾 ⑊ ⑊

How to get there: Five minutes M27 J-1, J- 2, close to New Forest, Bournemouth and Southampton.

Crawley, West Sussex

Waterhall Country House

◆◆◆

Prestwood Lane, Ifield Wood, nr Crawley, West Sussex, RH11 0LA
Tel: 01293 520002

Crowborough, East Sussex

Plough and Horses

◆◆◆◆

Walshes Road, Crowborough, East Sussex, TN6 3RE
Tel: 01892 652614 Fax: 01892 652614
SB £28 DB £48 B £3.50 L £5.50 D £8.50.
CC: MC Vi Swi Delt

⚓ 🐾 ✪ ▧ ▢ 🅿 ⚙ ⟡ 🎠 🎋 🐾 ⑊ ⑊

How to get there: A26 Tunbridge Wells to

Crowborough. First left at Boars Head roundabout. Cross junction with Crowborough Hill to end of Tollwood Road.

Croydon, Surrey

Coulsdon Manor
★★★★ ♞ ♞ ♞

Coulsdon Court Road, Old Coulsdon, Croydon, CR5 2LL
Tel: 01303 267441 Fax: 01303 264610
Email: coulsdonmanor@marstonhotels.com
Web: www.marstonhotels.co.uk

MARSTON HOTELS

SB £110 DB £142 HBS £79.50 HBD £159
B £11 L £15 D £26. CC: MC Vi Am DC Swi Delt
🐟 ♨ ⊗ ☕ ⬜ ☎ 📞 P ⚙ ⧖ 🎠 ♃ 🦞 ♨♨♨ ♟ 'Y' ⚲
How to get there: M2 for Croydon, through Coulsdon on A23. Turn right into Stoats Nest Road. Hotel 1 mile on right.

Croydon Park
★★★★

7 Altyre Road, Croydon, CR9 5AA
Tel: 020 8680 9200 Fax: 020 8286 7676
Email: reservations@croydonparkhotel.co.uk
Web: www.croydonparkhotel.co.uk
SB £120 DB £135 HBS £137.95 HBD £170.90
B £10.50 L £17.95 D £17.95.
CC: MC Vi Am DC Swi Delt
🐟 ♿ ♨ ⊗ ☕ ⬜ ☎ ❄ 📞 P ⚙ ⧖ 🎠 ♃ 🦞
♨♨♨ ♟ 🆂🅿🅰 'Y' ⚡
How to get there: Enter Croydon on A235 Brighton Road. Signs to Fairfield Halls. At major roundabout system, first left exit into Fairfield Road. First left into Altyre Road.

Selsdon Park
★★★★ ♞ ♞

Assington Road, Sanderstead, South Croydon, Surrey, CR2 8YA
Tel: 020 8657 8811 Fax: 020 8651 6171
Email: selsdonpark@principalhotels.co.uk
Web: www.principalhotels.co.uk
SB £69 DB £138 HBS £79 HBD £158
CC: MC Vi Am DC Swi Delt JCB
🐟 ♿ ♨ 🎿 ⊗ ☕ ⬜ ☎ 📞 P ⚙ ⧖ 🎠 ♃ 🦞
🌦 ♨♨♨ ♟ 'Y' ⚲ 🍷 🗺 ⚡
How to get there: On A2022 10 minutes from East Croydon railway station, 15 minutes from M25 J-6, 13 miles Central London.

Hayesthorpe
★★

48–52 St Augustine Avenue, South Croydon, CR2 6JJ
Tel: 020 8688 8120 Fax: 020 8680 1099
Email: hayesthorpe@ukonline.co.uk
Web: www.hayesthorpe.co.uk Closed Christmas
SB £50 DB £55 HBS £67.50 HBD £80 D £12.50.
CC: MC Vi Am DC Swi Delt
♿ ⊗ ☕ ⬜ ☎ P ⚙ ⧖ 🎠 ♃ 🦞 ♟
How to get there: A23 to Croydon. Left at Hilton Hotel into Waddon Way. On to roundabout, turn right and first left into St Augustine Avenue.

Markington
★★

9 Haling Park Road, South Croydon, CR2 6NG
Tel: 020 8681 6494 Fax: 020 8688 6530
Email: rooms@markingtonhotel.com
Web: www.markingtonhotel.com
Children minimum age: 5.
Closed Christmas and New Year
SB £50 DB £65 B £6.50 D £10.
CC: MC Vi Swi Delt
⊗ ☕ ⬜ ☎ P ⚙ ⧖ 🎠 ♃ 🦞 ♨♨♨ ♟
How to get there: M25 J-7 onto M23 for Croydon. M23 becomes A23, at Purley A235 Brighton Road. 2 miles on, after bus garage on left, hotel is next on right hand side .

Kirkdale
♦♦♦♦ ♘

22 St Peters Road, Croydon, CR0 1HD
Tel: 020 8688 5898 Fax: 020 8680 6001
Email: enquiries@kirkdalehotel.co.uk
Web: www.kirkdalehotel.co.uk
Closed Christmas to New Year
SB £55 DB £70
CC: MC Vi DC Swi Delt JCB Eurocard
⊗ ☕ ⬜ ☎ 📞 P ⚙ ⧖ 🎠 ♃ 🦞 ♨♨♨ ♟
How to get there: M25 J-7, for Croydon (9 miles). Few minutes East and South Croydon stations.

Guide dogs

If a Hotel or Guest Accommodation does not display this 'dogs welcome' symbol in its listing, the hotelier may still be happy to welcome guests with guide dogs, and you should contact the property to discover whether this will be a problem.

Southeast

Dartford, Kent

Rowhill Grange

★★★★ ☏☏

Wilmington, Dartford, Kent, DA2 7QH
Tel: 01322 615136 Fax: 01322 615137
Email: admin@rowhillgrange.com
Web: www.rowhillgrange.com
Children minimum age: 5

With 9 acres of mature gardens and the finest
health spa in the south, Rowhill Grange is ideal
for business or pleasure – just 2 miles from the
M25.
HBS £134 HBD £99 B £8.95 L £19.95 D £29.95.
CC: MC Vi Am DC Swi Delt

How to get there: M25 J-3 to Swanley. B2175
through 3 roundabouts to Hextable on B258.
Hotel 1½ miles on left opposite garage.

Deal, Kent

Kilgour House

♦♦♦♦

22 Gilford Road, Deal, Kent, CT14 7DJ
Tel: 01304 368311

Dedham, Essex

Maison Talbooth

★★★ ☏☏☏

Stratford Road, Dedham, Colchester, Essex,
CO7 6HN
Tel: 01206 322367 Fax: 01206 322752
Email: mtreception@talbooth.co.uk
Web: www.talbooth.com
SB £120 DB £155 HBD £180 L £16.50 D £22.
CC: MC Vi Am DC Swi Delt

How to get there: A12 for Colchester. Turn for
Stratford St Mary's and Dedham. Right at
junction on left hand bend. Hotel 500yds on right.

Dorchester-on-Thames, Oxfordshire

George

★★★ ☏☏

High Street, Dorchester on Thames,
Oxfordshire, OX10 7HH
Tel: 01865 340404 Fax: 01865 341620

White Hart

★★★

High Street, Dorchester-on-Thames,
Oxfordshire, OX9 8HN
Tel: 01865 340074 Fax: 01865 341082
Email: whitehart.dorchester@virgin.net
SB £70 DB £80 B £10 L £10 D £17.50.
CC: MC Vi Am DC Swi Delt

How to get there: Off A415/A4074 (M40 J-6).
Nearest rail station: Didcot.

Dorking, Surrey

Heritage Hotels – Burford Bridge

★★★★ ☏

At the foot of Boxhill, Dorking, Surrey, RH5 6BX
Tel: 0870 4008283 Fax: 01306 880386
Web: www.heritage-hotels.com
B £13.50 L £15 D £20. CC: MC Vi Am DC Swi

How to get there: M25 J-9, four miles south on
A24. Two miles north of Dorking.

Gatton Manor

★★★ ☏

Standon Lane, Ockley, nr Dorking, Surrey,
RH5 5PQ
Tel: 01306 627555 Fax: 01306 627713
Email: gattonmanor@enterprise.net
Web: www.gattonmanor.co.uk
SB £67.50 DB £105 HBS £82.50 HBD £135
B £8.50 L £8.95 D £15.
CC: MC Vi Am DC Swi Delt

How to get there: Off A24/A29 between
Horsham and Dorking.
See advert on facing page

Heritage Hotels – White Horse

★★★ ☏

High Street, Dorking, Surrey, RH4 1BE
Tel: 0870 400 8282 Fax: 01306 887241
Web: www.heritage-hotels.com
B £12.50 L £5.75 D £14.95.
CC: MC Vi Am DC Swi JCB

How to get there: On High Street in Dorking.

Southeast

Dover, Kent

Churchill

★★★

Dover Waterfront, Dover, Kent, CT17 9BP
Tel: 01304 203633 Fax: 01304 216320
Email: enquiries@churchill-hotel.com
Web: www.churchill-hotel.com
SB £68 DB £97 HBS £76.50 HBD £119
CC: MC Vi Am DC Swi Delt

How to get there: From A20 signs for Hoverport, left onto seafront, hotel 800 yards along.

Wallett's Court Country House

★★★

Westcliffe, St Margaret's Bay, Dover, Kent, CT15 6EW
Tel: 01304 852424 Fax: 01304 853430
Email: wc@wallettscourt.com
Web: www.wallettscourt.com
SB £70 DB £80 HBS £97.50 HBD £67.50 B £6
L £13.50 D £27.50. CC: MC Vi Am DC Swi Delt

How to get there: From M2/A2 or M20/A20, signs A258 Deal. On A258, first right for Westcliffe, St. Margaret's-at-Cliffe. Hotel 1 mile on right.

East Lee Guest House

♦♦♦♦

108 Maison Dieu Road, Dover, Kent, CT16 1RT
Tel: 01304 210176 Fax: 01304 206705
Email: eastlee@eclipse.co.uk
Web: www.eastlee.co.uk
DB £50 CC: MC Vi Swi Delt
How to get there: From M20/A20, at York Street roundabout turn left and straight over next roundabout. Right at Dover town hall. At end of street, right into Maison Dieu Road.

Number One Guest House

♦♦♦♦

1 Castle Street, Dover, Kent, CT16 1QH
Tel: 01304 202007 Fax: 01304 214078
Email: res@number1guesthouse.co.uk
Web: www.number1guesthouse.co.uk
DB £48
How to get there: Off A20, below castle. A2 1 mile, 2 minutes port, 10 minutes Chunnel.

Tower House

♦♦♦♦

Priory Hill, Dover, Kent, CT17 0AE
Tel: 01304 208212 Fax: 01304 208212
Email: enquiries@towerhouse.net
Web: www.towerhouse.net
DB £50 CC: Eurocheque
How to get there: M20/A20, B2011 into Dover. Left at roundabout, third left to top of hill. Tower House is last on right.

Ardmore Private Hotel

♦♦♦

18 Castle Hill Road, Dover, Kent, CT16 1QW
Tel: 01304 205895 Fax: 01304 208229
Email: res@ardmorehh.co.uk
DB £50 CC: MC Vi Swi Delt
How to get there: On A258 by Dover Castle.

Gateway Hovertel

♦♦♦

Snargate Street, Dover, Kent, CT17 9BZ
Tel: 01304 205479 Fax: 01304 211504

Hubert House Guest House

♦♦♦

9 Castle Hill Road, Dover, Kent, CT16 1QW
Tel: 01304 202253 Fax: 01304 210142
Closed October
SB £35 DB £50 CC: MC Vi Swi Delt
How to get there: On A258 Deal road at bottom of Castle Hill, near Dover town centre.

Gatton Manor Hotel

The attractive manor, which was built in 1728, provides eighteen ensuite hotel rooms, a delightful two-tiered dining room, bar, residents' lounge and private conference suites. The well established 18-hole, par 72 championship-length golf course of 6,653 yards is truly a hidden gem with immense character, incorporating natural waters of the River Arun.

Standon Lane, Ockley, Dorking, Surrey RH5 5PQ

Tel: 01306 627555 Fax: 01306 627713
Email: gattonmanor@enterprise.net

Pennyfarthing

◆◆◆

109 Maison Dieu Road, Dover, Kent, CT16 1RT
Tel: 01304 205563 Fax: 01304 204439
Email: pennyfarthing.dover@btinternet.com
SB £24 DB £20

St Martins Guest House

◆◆◆

17 Castle Hill Road, Dover, Kent, CT16 1QW
Tel: 01304 205938 Fax: 01304 208229
Email: res@stmartinsgh.co.uk
Closed Christmas
SB £35 DB £48 CC: MC Vi Swi Delt

How to get there: On A258 Lee of Dover Castle,
link A20/M20, A2/M2.

Whitmore Guest House

◆◆◆

261 Folkestone Road, Dover, Kent, CT17 9LL
Tel: 01304 203080 Fax: 01304 240110
Email: whitmoredover@aol.com
Web: www.smoothhound.co.uk/hotels/whitmore
Closed Christmas
SB £18 DB £32
CC: MC Vi Swi Delt Maestro Solo JCB

How to get there: M20/A20 to B2011. First exit
off roundabout at bottom of slip road (Folkestone Road). Guest house 3 miles on right.

Hanover International Dunstable

★★★

Church Street, Dunstable, Bedfordshire, LU5 4RT
Tel: 01582 662201 Fax: 01582 696422
Email: info@hanover-dunstable.fsnet.co.uk
Closed December 24–26 and 31, January 1

HANOVER INTERNATIONAL

An original hotel with many exquisite features
offering old English charm. Close to Whipsnade,
Woburn and other local attractions.
CC: MC Vi Am DC Swi Delt

How to get there: M1 J-11. Signs to Dunstable
town centre. Under bridge, hotel 200yds further,
opposite the Priory church on the right.

Dymchurch, Kent

Waterside Guest House

◆◆◆◆

15 Hythe Road, Dymchurch, Kent, TN29 0LN
Tel: 01303 872253 Fax: 01303 872253
Email: water.side@cwcom.net
Web: www.smoothhound.co.uk/
hotels/watersid.html
SB £25 DB £40 HBS £32 HBD £54 D £4.50.
CC: MC Vi Swi Delt JCB Solo

How to get there: M20 J-11. Signs to Hythe.
Right onto A259. Hotel approx 7 miles on right.

East Grinstead, West Sussex

Gravetye Manor

★★★ 🏮🏮🏮🏮

nr East Grinstead, West Sussex, RH19 4LJ
Tel: 01342 810567 Fax: 01342 810080
Email: gravetye@relaischateaux.fr
Children minimum age: 7
CC: MC Vi Swi Delt

How to get there: M23 J-10, A264 towards East
Grinstead. After 2 miles, at roundabout, third
exit (B2028) towards Turners Hill.

Woodbury House

★★★

Lewes Road, East Grinstead, West Sussex,
RH19 3UD
Tel: 01342 313657 Fax: 01342 314801
Email: stay@woodbury-house.demon.co.uk
SB £80 DB £95 HBS £95 HBD £120
B £9.50 L £12.50 D £19.50.
CC: MC Vi Am DC Swi Delt

How to get there: M25 then M23 J-10. A264 to
East Grinstead, A22 for Eastbourne. Hotel
½ mile south of town centre.

Eastbourne, East Sussex

The Grand

★ ★ ★ ★ ★ ✿ ✿ ✿
King Edwards Parade, Eastbourne,
East Sussex, BN21 4EQ
Tel: 01323 412345 Fax: 01323 412233
Email: reservations@grandeastbourne.co.uk
Web: www.grandeastbourne.co.uk
SB £125 DB £159 HBS £145 HBD £105
CC: MC Vi Am DC Swi Delt

How to get there: West end Eastbourne seafront.

Chatsworth

★ ★ ★
Grand Parade, Eastbourne, East Sussex,
BN21 3YR
Tel: 01323 411016 Fax: 01323 643270
Email: stay@chatsworth-hotel.com
Web: www.chatsworth-hotel.com
SB £53 DB £83 HBS £57.50 HBD £105 B £9.50
L £7.50 D £17.50. CC: MC Vi Am DC Swi Delt

How to get there: Centre of seafront, near pier.

Cumberland

★ ★ ★
Grand Parade, Eastbourne, East Sussex,
BN21 3YT
Tel: 01323 730342 Fax: 01323 646314

Hydro Hotel

★ ★ ★
Mount Road, Eastbourne, East Sussex,
BN20 7HZ
Tel: 01323 720643 Fax: 01323 641167
Email: sales@hydrohotel.co.uk
Web: www.hydrohotel.co.uk

An elegant traditional hotel offering the highest
standards of cuisine and service. Situated in a
unique garden setting with panoramic sea
views.

SB £35 DB £60 HBS £53 HBD £50
B £6.95 L £8.95 D £15.95. CC: MC Vi Am Swi

How to get there: Along King Edwards Parade
to Grand Hotel. Note sign Hydro Hotel. Up
South Cliff and Hydro Hotel signs are visible.

Lansdowne

★ ★ ★
King Edward's Parade, Eastbourne, East
Sussex, BN21 4EE
Tel: 01323 725174 Fax: 01323 739721
Email: the.lansdowne@btinternet.com
Web: www.lansdowne-hotel.co.uk
Closed January 1–18
SB £55 DB £87 HBS £67.50 HBD £112
B £8.75 L £13.95 D £17.95.
CC: MC Vi Am DC Swi Delt JCB Solo Maestro
Electron

How to get there: Hotel at west end of seafront
(B2103) facing Western Lawns.
See advert below

Princes Hotel

★★★

Lascelles Terrace, Eastbourne, East Sussex,
BN21 4BL

Tel: 01323 722056 Fax: 01323 727469

Email: princes-hotel@btconnect.com

Web: www.smoothhound.co.uk/hotels/princesh.
html

Closed January

A friendly family-run hotel situated in a beautiful
unspoilt Victorian terrace adjacent to seafront,
close to the theatres and a short level walk from
main shopping area.

SB £34 DB £60 HBS £40 HBD £37.50 D £14.50.

CC: MC Vi Am DC Swi Delt

Quality Hotel Eastbourne

★★★

Grand Parade, Eastbourne, East Sussex,
BN21 3YS

Tel: 01323 727411 Fax: 01323 720665

Email: admin@gb610.u-net.com

Web: www.choicehotels.com

SB £35 DB £60 HBS £45 HBD £40 B £9.50
L £5.95 D £14.50. CC: MC Vi Am Swi Delt

How to get there: Seafront, opposite bandstand.

Wish Tower

★★★

King Edward's Parade, Eastbourne,
East Sussex, BN21 4EB

Tel: 01323 722676 Fax: 01323 721474

Looking for great dining? Look for RAC Hotels
and Guest Accommodation displaying the
RAC Dining Award symbol in this Guide.

Congress

★★

31–37 Carlisle Road, Eastbourne, East Sussex,
BN21 4JS

Tel: 01323 732118 Fax: 01323 720016

Closed January-February

Located by main theatres in a level area.
Ramped entrance, so accessible for wheelchair
users. Family owned and managed –
'Service our aim'.

SB £30 DB £60 HBS £33 HBD £66

B £5 L £8 D £10.

CC: MC Vi Swi Delt Solo

How to get there: Opposite Congress Theatre,
approx 150yds from seafront. Signs for 'Theatres'.

Langham

★★

Royal Parade, Eastbourne, East Sussex,
BN22 7AH

Tel: 01323 731451 Fax: 01323 646623

Email: langhamhotel@mistral.co.uk

Web: www3.mistral.co.uk/langhamhotel

Closed January

SB £28 DB £56 HBD £64

B £5.90 L £9.10 D £13.25.

CC: MC Vi Am Swi Delt JCB, Solo

How to get there: Seafront. Langham ½ mile
east of pier, near Redoubt Fortress.

Lathom

★★

Howard Square, Eastbourne, East Sussex,
BN21 4BG

Tel: 01323 641986 Fax: 01323 416405

SB £32 DB £64 HBS £39 HBD £78

CC: MC Vi

How to get there: 25 yards from seafront,
between bandstand and Wish Tower Slopes.
Turn right at TGWU Hotel.

Southeast

New Wilmington

★★

25 Compton Street, Eastbourne, East Sussex, BN21 4DU
Tel: 01323 721219 Fax: 01323 728900

Oban

★★

King Edwards Parade, Eastbourne, East Sussex, BN21 4DS
Tel: 01323 731581 Fax: 01323 721994
Closed December to March
SB £28 DB £56 HBS £43 HBD £98
B £6.95 L £2 D £15.
CC: MC Vi Swi Delt Solo

How to get there: Seafront, facing Wish Tower.

West Rocks

★★

Grand Parade, Eastbourne, East Sussex, BN21 4DL
Tel: 01323 725217 Fax: 01323 720421

York House

★★

Royal Parade, Eastbourne, East Sussex, BN22 7AP
Tel: 01323 412918 Fax: 01323 646238
Email: frontdesk@yorkhousehotel.co.uk
Web: www.yorkhousehotel.co.uk
SB £39 DB £78 HBS £56 HBD £112
B £9 L £12.50 D £17.
CC: MC Vi Am DC Swi Delt JCB Solo

How to get there: Seafront, ¼ mile east of pier.

Bay Lodge

♦♦♦

61-62 Royal Parade, Eastbourne, East Sussex, BN22 7AQ
Tel: 01323 732515 Fax: 01323 735009

Chalk Farm

♦♦♦

Coopers Hill, Willingdon, Eastbourne, East Sussex, BN20 9JD
Tel: 01323 503800 Fax: 01323 520331
SB £43 DB £54.50 B £2.50 L £10.95 D £16.95.
CC: MC Vi Am DC Swi Delt
How to get there: A22 into Eastbourne past Polegate traffic lights. At next major traffic lights right into Coopers Hill. Hotel 200yds on right.

Sheldon

♦♦♦

9–11 Burlington Place, Eastbourne, BN21 4AS
Tel: 01323 724120 Fax: 01323 430406
SB £24 DB £48 HBS £29 HBD £58
CC: MC Vi Am DC Swi Delt

How to get there: From pier, west towards bandstand. Turn right by side of Cavendish hotel. Hotel is 150yds on left.

Sherwood

♦♦♦

7 Lascalles Terrace, Eastbourne, East Sussex, BN21 4BJ
Tel: 01323 724002
SB £20 DB £25 HBS £26 HBD £30
B £3.50 D £7.
How to get there: Lascalles Terrace runs between Devonshire Park and seafront.

Courtlands Hotel

♦♦

68 Royal Parade, Eastbourne, East Sussex, BN22 7AQ
Tel: 01323 726915

Egham, Surrey

Runnymede Hotel & Spa

★★★★ 🍴🍴🍴

Windsor Road, Egham, Surrey, TW20 0AG
Tel: 01784 436171 Fax: 01784 436340
Email: info@runnymedehotel.com
Web: www.runnymedehotel.com
SB £165.50 DB £216 HBS £100 HBD £170
B £13.50 L £17.95 D £26.95.
CC: MC Vi Am DC Swi Delt

How to get there: M25 J-13. A308 to Egham.

Emsworth, Hampshire

Brookfield

★★★ 🍴🍴

Havant Road, Emsworth, Hampshire, PO10 7LF
Tel: 01243 373363 Fax: 01243 376342
SB £65 DB £90 B £7.95 L £13.50 D £13.50.
CC: MC Vi Am DC Swi Delt

How to get there: From A3(M), M27 to Chichester eastbound. At Emsworth turn off onto A259 Havant road.

Jingles Hotel

77 Horndean Road, Emsworth, Hampshire,
PO10 7PU
Tel: 01243 373755 Fax: 01243 373755
SB £26 DB £50 B £6.50 L £12.50 D £14.
CC: MC Vi Am Swi Delt

How to get there: A259 in Emsworth, north on
B2148 towards Rowlands Castle approx 1 mile.

Enfield, Middlesex

West Lodge Park

★★★★ ℞℞
Cockfosters Road, Hadley Wood, Middlesex,
EN4 0PY
Tel: 020 8216 3900 Fax: 020 8216 3937
Email: info@westlodgepark.com
Web: www.westlodgepark.com
B £11 L £22 D £35. CC: MC Vi Am DC Swi Delt

How to get there: M25 J-24. A111 towards
Cockfosters. Hotel one mile on left.

Royal Chace

★★★ ℞℞
The Ridgeway, Enfield, Middlesex, EN2 8AR
Tel: 020 8884 8181 Fax: 020 8884 8150
Email: royal-chace@dial.pipex.com
Web: www.royal-chace.com
SB £99 DB £115 B £9.50 D £19.95.
CC: MC Vi Am DC Swi Delt

How to get there: M25 J-24. A1005 towards
Enfield. Hotel 3 miles along on right-hand side.

Oak Lodge

★★
80 Village Road, Enfield, Middlesex, EN1 2EU
Tel: 020 8360 7082
Web: www.oaklodgehotel.co.uk
SB £79 DB £89.50 HBS £125 HBD £150
B £10.50 L £15 D £20.
CC: MC Vi Am DC Swi Delt

How to get there: M25 J-25. Right at 11th set of
lights south along A10. Right at next lights into
A105. Hotel ¼ mile on right.

Looking for great dining? Look for RAC Hotels
and Guest Accommodation displaying the
RAC Dining Award symbol in this Guide.

Epsom, Kent

Epsom Downs Hotel

9 Longdown Road, Epsom, Surrey, KT17 3PT
Tel: 01372 740643 Fax: 01372 723259
CC: MC Vi Am DC

See advert on facing page

Fareham, Hampshire

Solent Hotel

★★★★ ℞℞
Solent Business Park, Whiteley, Fareham,
Hampshire, PO15 7AJ
Tel: 01489 880000 Fax: 01489 880007
Email: solent@shireinns.co.uk
SB £122 DB £150 HBS £73 HBD £73
B £10.50 L £15 D £28.50.
CC: MC Vi Am DC Swi Delt

How to get there: M27 J-9 to Whiteley. Left at
first roundabout.

Bembridge House

◆◆◆◆
Osborn Road, Fareham, Hampshire, PO16 7DS
Tel: 01329 317050 Fax: 01329 317050
Email: ian@bembridgehouse.freeserve.co.uk
Web: joineme.net/bembridge

Character rooms in Victorian town centre
residence, in own quiet grounds. Gargantuan
breakfasts, luxurious dining room. Immaculately
clean. Cheerful welcome, most needs satisfied!
Packages available.
SB £40 DB £44
CC: MC Vi Swi Delt JCB Electron

How to get there: M27 J-11. Follow signs
to Fareham town centre then Feeneham
Hall. Bembridge House is almost directly
opposite.

Southeast

Avenue House

♦ ♦ ♦

22 The Avenue, Fareham, Hampshire,
PO14 1NS
Tel: 01329 232175 Fax: 01329 232196
Children minimum age: 10
SB £48.50 DB £57 CC: MC Vi Am DC
♿ 🖥 ⊕ 🖱 ▯ ☎ ▯ 🍴 🕯 🐴 ⏰ 🛎

How to get there: M27 J-9 (Fareham West). A27
to Fareham. Fareham village 5 minutes on right,
hotel 300yds further on left.

Faringdon, Oxfordshire

Faringdon Hotel

★★

1 Market Place, Faringdon, Oxfordshire,
SN7 7HL
Tel: 01367 240536 Fax: 01367 243250
SB £60 DB £70 B £5 D £10.
CC: MC Vi Am DC Swi Delt
🖱 🛎 ⊕ 🖥 ☎ ▯ 🍴 🕯 🐴 ⏰ 🛎 ⛲ ⛲

How to get there: Nearest Bus/Railway Stations
Swindon or Oxford. M40 20 miles M4 14 miles.
Faringdon is on A420.

Farnborough, Hampshire

Falcon Hotel

★★★

68 Farnborough Road, Farnborough,
Hampshire, GU14 6TH
Tel: 01252 545378 Fax: 01252 522539

Farnham, Surrey

Bishop's Table

★★★ ☕ ☕

27 West Street, Farnham, Surrey, GU9 7DR
Tel: 01252 710222 Fax: 01252 733494
Email: welcome@bishopstable.com
Web: www.bishopstable.com
Children minimum age: 16.
Closed December 26 to January 4
SB £95 DB £120 B £12.50 L £12.50 D £30.
CC: MC Vi Am DC
⊕ 🖥 🖱 ☎ 🍴 🕯 🐴 ⏰ 🛎 ⛲ ⛲

How to get there: M3 J-4, signs 'Birdworld',
Farnham town centre. Next door to library.

To make an on-line booking at an RAC
inspected Hotel or Guest Accommodation,
visit www.rac.co.uk/hotels

Frensham Pond Hotel

★★★

Bacon Road, Churt, Farnham, Surrey,
GU10 2QB
Tel: 01252 795161 Fax: 01252 792631
SB £95 DB £10 B £6.50 L £14.50 D £18.50.
CC: MC Vi Am DC Swi Delt
♿ ⊕ 🖥 🖱 ☎ 🍴 ▯ 🕯 🐴 ⏰ 🛎 ⛲ ⛲ 🏊
🎾 ⛳

How to get there: M25 J-10, A3 to A287. Turn
right and continue for 5 miles. Left at signpost
'Frensham Pond Hotel'.

Heritage Hotels – The Bush Hotel

★★★

The Borough, Farnham, Surrey, GU10 4QQ
Tel: 0870 400 8225 Fax: 01252 733530
SB £166 DB £176 HBS £55 HBD £55
B £13 L £10 D £20. CC: MC Vi Am DC Swi Delt
♨ ♿ 🖱 🎣 ⊕ 🖥 🖱 ▯ 🍴 🕯 🐴 ⏰ 🛎
⛲ ⛲

How to get there: Follow signs to town centre.
At lights turn left and immediate right into hotel
car park on South Street.

Please mention the RAC Inspected guide
when you make your booking at an RAC
Hotel or Guest Accommodation.

Epsom Downs Hotel

Epsom Downs is a small privately owned hotel
offering comfortable home surroundings. All our
rooms have ensuite facilities with amenities to
ensure your stay is enjoyable. Situated 1 mile
from the town centre, and with excellent train
connections to London, we cater for everyone's
individual requirements.

9 Longdown Road, Epsom,
Surrey KT17 3PT
Tel: 01372 740643   Fax: 01372 723259
Email: e.d.h@dial.pipex.com

♦ ♦ ♦

Fleet, Hampshire

Lismoyne

★★★

Church Road, Fleet, Hampshire, GU13 8NA
Tel: 01252 628555 Fax: 01252 811761
B £7 L £14 D £18. CC: MC Vi Am Swi

How to get there: Approach town on B3013.
Over railway bridge and to town centre. Through
traffic lights, fourth right. Hotel ¼ mile on left.

Folkestone, Kent

Clifton

★★★

The Leas, Clifton Gardens, Folkestone, Kent,
CT20 2EB
Tel: 01303 851231 Fax: 01303 223949
Email: reservations@thecliftonhotel.com
Web: www.thecliftonhotel.com
SB £58 DB £78 HBS £60 HBD £57 B £8.50
L £10.50 D £18. CC: MC Vi Am DC Swi Delt

How to get there: M20 J-13, Hotel ¼ mile west
of town centre on A259.
See advert below

Clifton Hotel

Folkestone's premier hotel occupies a cliff-top
position on the Leas, with views over the
English Channel and minutes from town
centre. Dating back to 1864, the hotel is
tastefully decorated in the Victorian style. Five
well equipped
conference rooms, seating from 5–80. Bar and
restaurant. Channel Tunnel terminus 4 miles.
Dover ferry and Hoverspeed terminals 7 miles.
Folkestone Hoverspeed ½ mile. For further
details call or email us.

The Leas, Folkestone, Kent CT20 2EB
Tel: 01303 851231   Fax: 01303 223949
Email: reservations@thecliftonhotel.com
Website: www.thecliftonhotel.com

Fordingbridge, Hampshire

Ashburn Hotel

★★

Station Road, Fordingbridge, Hampshire,
SP16 1JP
Tel: 01425 652060 Fax: 01425 652150

Forest Row, East Sussex

Ashdown Park

★★★★

Wych Cross, Forest Row, East Sussex,
RH18 5JR
Tel: 01342 824988 Fax: 01342 826206
Web: www.ashdownpark.co.uk
SB £120 DB £152 HBS £135 HBD £195
CC: MC Vi Am DC Swi Delt

How to get there: From north M23 J-10. A264 to
East Grinstead. A22 to Eastbourne through
Forest Row. Turn left after 2 miles at Wych
Cross to Hartfield. Hotel ¾ mile on right.
See advert on page 11

Frimley Green, Surrey

Lakeside International

★★★

Wharf Road, Frimley Green, Surrey, GU16 6JR
Tel: 01252 838000 Fax: 01252 837857

Gatwick Airport, West Sussex

Copthorne Effingham Park

★★★★

West Park Road, Copthorne, West Sussex,
RH10 3EU
Tel: 01342 711733 Fax: 01342 713661
Email: hayley.pratt@mill-cop.com
Web: www.stay.with-us.com

Former stately home set in 40 acres of peaceful parkland. Superb leisure facilities including a nine-hole golf course. Close to many local attractions. Weekend break rates also available.
B £13.50 CC: MC Vi Am DC Swi Delt

How to get there: M23 J-10, A264 towards East Grinstead. At 2nd roundabout, left onto B2028. Hotel is on the right.

Copthorne London Gatwick
★★★★ 🏰🏰
Copthorne Road, Copthorne, West Sussex, RH10 3PG
Tel: 01342 348800 Fax: 01342 348822
Email: hayley.pratt@mill-cop.com
Web: www.stay.with-us.com

Traditional, welcoming country house hotel built around a 16th century farmhouse in 100 acres of gardens. Ideal for many local attractions. Weekend break rates also available.
B £13.50 CC: MC Vi Am DC Swi Delt

How to get there: M23 J-10, A264 towards East Grinstead. At first roundabout, 3rd exit is hotel entrance.

Le Meridien Gatwick
★★★★ 🏰
North Terminal, Gatwick Airport, West Sussex, RH6 0PH
Tel: 0870 400 8494 Fax: 01293 567739
Email: reservations.gatwick
         @lemeridien-hotels.com
Web: www.lemeridien-hotels.com
B £14.50 L £17.50 D £20.
CC: MC Vi Am DC Swi Delt

How to get there: Car: exit M23 J-9, signs to North Terminal Gatwick Airport. Rail: Gatwick Express from Central London. At Gatwick Station take free monorail to North Terminal.

South Lodge
★★★★ 🏰🏰🏰
Brighton Road, Lower Beeding, West Sussex, RH13 6PS
Tel: 01403 891711 Fax: 01403 891766
Email: enquiries@southlodgehotel.co.uk
Web: www.exclusivehotels.co.uk
Children minimum age:
B £12.95 L £18.50 D £35.
CC: MC Vi Am DC Swi Delt

How to get there: From Gatwick, M23 south. Exit to B2110 to Handcross. Follow road to Leonardslee Gardens. Left and hotel is on right.

Alexander House
★★★ 🏰🏰🏰
Fen Place, Turners Hill, West Sussex, RH10 4QD
Tel: 01342 714914 Fax: 01342 717328
Email: info@alexanderhouse.co.uk
Web: www.alexanderhouse.co.uk

Beautiful 17th-century English mansion. Fifteen individually appointed, luxury suites and bedrooms including 2 with four-poster beds.
SB £129 DB £158 HBD £99

Langshott Manor
★★★ 🏰🏰🏰
Langshott, Horley, nr Gatwick, Surrey, RH6 9LN
Tel: 01293 786680 Fax: 01293 783905
Email: admin@langshottmanor.com
Web: www.langshottmanor.com
SB £145 DB £165 HBS £180 HBD £120
B £12.50 L £24.95 D £35. CC: MC Vi Am DC Swi Delt Travellers Cheque

How to get there: From Horley, A23 towards Redhill. At roundabout with Shell petrol station, take third exit into Ladroke Road. Langshott Manor is ³/₄ mile on right.

Stanhill Court

★★★ ®

Stanhill Road, Charlwood, Surrey, RH6 0EP
Tel: 01293 862166 Fax: 01293 862773
Web: www.stanhillcourthotel.co.uk

The Victorians excelled at building baronial mansions and Stanhill Court Hotel is a fine example of their skills. 35 acres of glorious countryside. Restaurant 1881 for fine dining.
B £11.50 L £26.50 D £32.50.
CC: MC Vi Am DC Swi Delt
How to get there: Leaving Charlwood village, pass Rising Sun pub on right, pass TH Gorringe on left. Next right (NOT Gatwick Zoo). Pass 40mph sign. Stanhill Court signposted.

Lawn Guest House

♦♦♦♦

30 Massets Road, Horley, Surrey, RH6 7DE
Tel: 01293 775751 Fax: 01293 821803
Email: info@lawnguesthouse.co.uk
Web: www.lawnguesthouse.co.uk

Luxury Victorian house set in a mature garden, four minutes to Gatwick, two minutes to the centre of Horley, and close to mainline rail station. Holiday parking. No smoking.
DB £50 CC: MC Vi Am Swi Delt JCB
How to get there: M23 J-9. A23 for Redhill. At 3rd roundabout (Esso station) 3rd exit. After 200yds, right to Massetts Rd. Lawn 400yds on left.

Prinsted

♦♦♦

Oldfield Road, Horley, Surrey, RH6 7EP
Tel: 01293 785233 Fax: 01293 820624
Web: www.networkclub.co.uk/prinsted
Closed Christmas week
SB £32 DB £47 CC: MC Vi Am Swi Delt
How to get there: M23 J-9. Airport signs. Straight over 1st roundabout, 4th exit at next, 3rd at next (still A23). Right past Texaco garage onto Woodroyd Avenue. Prinsted on left corner.

Melville Lodge

♦♦

15 Brighton Road, Horley, Surrey, RH6 7HH
Tel: 01293 784951 Fax: 01293 785669
Email: melvillelodge.guesthouse@tesco.net
SB £25 DB £38 CC: MC Vi
How to get there: M25, M23 J-9 to Gatwick. At South Terminal roundabout, 2nd exit, at North Terminal roundabout 4th exit. At 3rd roundabout 3rd exit. Melville Lodge 2nd on left after Texaco.

Godalming, Surrey

Kings Arms and Royal Hotel

★★

High Street, Godalming, Surrey, GU7 1DZ
Tel: 01483 421545 Fax: 01483 415403

Meads

♦♦♦

65 Meadow, Godalming, Surrey, GU7 3HS
Tel: 01483 421800 Fax: 01483 429313

Gosport, Hampshire

Belle Vue

★★★

39 Marine Parade East, Lee-On-The-Solent, Gosport, Hampshire, PO13 9BW
Tel: 023 9255 0258 Fax: 023 9255 2624
Email: information@bellevue-hotel.co.uk
Web: www.bellevue-hotel.co.uk
Closed Christmas
B £6.50 L £18.50 D £18.50.
CC: MC Vi Am Swi Delt
How to get there: From the M27 (J- 9 or J-11), follow signs to Fareham, then Lee-On-The-Solent. Hotel is situated on the seafront on the Gosport side of the village.

Southeast

Great Milton, Oxfordshire

Le Manoir Aux Quat'Saisons
★★★★ ℞℞℞℞
Great Milton, Oxfordshire, OX44 7PD
Tel: 01844 278881 Fax: 01844 278847
Email: lemanoir@blanc.co.uk
Web: www.manoir.com
Head chefs: Raymond Blanc and Gary Jones.
SB £230 DB £230 L £35 D £84.
CC: MC Vi Am DC Swi Delt
How to get there: From London, M40 J-7. Turn towards Wallingford. Le Manoir is signposted on the right 2 miles further on.

Greenford, Middlesex

Whysdyn Guest House

17–21 Sudbury Heights Avenue, Greenford, Middlesex, UB6 0ND
Tel: 020 8903 2016 Fax: 020 8903 4195

Harlow, Essex

Swallow Churchgate
★★★ ℞
Churchgate Street Village, Old Harlow, Essex, CM17 0JT
Tel: 01279 420246 Fax: 01279 420248
Email: churchgate.manor@swallow-hotels.co.uk
Web: www.swallowhotels.co.uk
B £9.75 L £5.50 D £25. CC: MC Vi Am DC Swi
How to get there: M11 J-7. A414 to Harlow. At fourth roundabout turn right, onto B183. Follow signs to Churchgate Street.

Harpenden, Hertfordshire

Hanover International Harpenden
★★★ ℞
1 Luton Road, Harpenden, Hertfordshire, AL5 2PX
Tel: 01582 760271 Fax: 01582 460819
Email: davidhunter9@virgin.net
Web: www.stalbans.gov.uk/gleneagle

HANOVER INTERNATIONAL

An attractive hotel that retains many original features and offers excellent attention to detail. Transport links are superb via the M1 and M25 motorways.
B £8 L £5 D £12. CC: MC
How to get there: Close to town centre on left side of Luton Road if coming from M1 J-9, or right side when coming from J-10.

Harrow, Middlesex

Grim's Dyke
★★★★ ℞℞
Old Redding, Harrow Weald, Middlesex, HA3 6SH
Tel: 020 8954 4227 Fax: 020 8954 4560
Email: enquiries@grimsdyke.com
Web: www.grimsdyke.com
SB £119 DB £145 B £10 L £19 D £19.
CC: MC Vi Am DC Swi Delt
How to get there: From north, M1 J-5. A41 towards A409 Harrow. After Kiln Nursery on right, turn right. Hotel is 300 yards on right.
See advert on following page

Set in 40 acres of gardens and woodland, Grim's Dyke is an attractive 4-star country retreat only 10 miles from London's West End. The 44-bedroom hotel is renowned for its banqeting and wedding facilities, plus fully equipped conference rooms. Entertainment is provided every weekend in our award winning Music Room restaurant. Grim's Dyke was once home to W.S. Gilbert, and costumed operettas, with dinner, are performed on a regular basis.

Old Redding, Harrow Weald HA3 6SH

Tel: 020 8385 3100   Fax: 020 8954 4560
Email: enquiries@grimsdyke.com
Website: www.grimsdyke.com

Cumberland Hotel

A warm welcome awaits you at the Cumberland Hotel. The extensive facilities and friendly, efficient service make it Harrow's leading three-star hotel. Situated in the heart of Harrow, central London is just 20 minutes away. (Harrow-on-the-Hill Metropolitan Line is 3 minutes walk away).

St Johns Road, Harrow HA1 2EF

Tel: 020 8863 4111 Fax: 020 8861 5668
Email: sforsdyke@cumberlandhotel.co.uk
Website: www.cumberlandhotel.co.uk

Cumberland Hotel
★★★
St John's Road, Harrow, Middlesex, HA1 2EF
Tel: 020 8863 4111 Fax: 020 8861 5668
Email: sforsdyke@cumberlandhotel.co.uk
Web: www.cumberlandhotel.co.uk
SB £95 DB £107
CC: MC Vi Am DC Swi Delt Solo
How to get there: M1 J-5. A41 and then A409 to Harrow town centre. Hotel is 1, St John's Road (reach via Lyon Road).
See advert below left

Quality Harrow Hotel
★★★
12–22 Pinner Road, Harrow, Middlesex, HA1 4HZ
Tel: 020 8427 3435 Fax: 020 8861 1370
Email: info@harrowhotel.co.uk
Web: www.harrowhotel.co.uk
SB £98 DB £123 B £11.50 L £15 D £17.95.
CC: MC Vi Am DC Swi Delt
How to get there: At junction of A312/A404 on A404, leaving Harrow towards Pinner and Rickmansworth.
See advert on facing page

Crescent
◆ ◆ ◆
58–62 Welldon Crescent, Harrow, Middlesex, HA1 1QR
Tel: 020 8863 5491 Fax: 020 8427 5965
Email: jivraj@crsnthtl.demon.co.uk
Web: www.crsnthtl.demon.co.uk
SB £50 DB £60 CC: MC
How to get there: In heart of Harrow. Five minutes to underground.

Hindes
◆ ◆ ◆
8 Hindes Road, Harrow, Middlesex, HA1 1SJ
Tel: 020 8427 7468 Fax: 020 8424 0673
Email: reception@hindeshotel.com
Web: www.hindeshotel.com
SB £39 DB £50
CC: MC Vi Am DC Swi Delt
How to get there: M1 J-5, Harrow signs (A409). Or M4/A40 exit A312 and follow signs.

Southeast

Central Hotel

6 Hindes Road, Harrow, Middlesex, HA1 1SJ
Tel: 020 8427 0893 Fax: 020 8424 8797
Email: central@hindeshotel.com
SB £39 DB £48
CC: MC Vi Am DC Swi Delt JCB Eurocard

How to get there: Hindes Road is off Station Road (A409), in Harrow town centre. Hotel opposite entrance to Tesco.

Harwich, Essex

Pier at Harwich

★★★ ♀♀
The Quay, Harwich, Essex, CO12 3HH
Tel: 01255 241212 Fax: 01255 551922
Email: reception@thepieratharwich.com
Web: www.thepieratharwich.com
SB £62.50 DB £80 B £5.50 L £15 D £18.50.
CC: MC Vi Am DC Swi Delt
How to get there: From A12, A120 down to the quay (18 miles). Hotel opposite lifeboat station.

Cliff

★★
Marine Parade, Dovercourt, Harwich, Essex, CO12 3RE
Tel: 01255 503345 Fax: 01255 240358
SB £50 DB £60 HBS £64.95 HBD £89.90
B £4 L £11.95 D £14.95.
CC: MC Vi Am DC Swi Delt JCB
How to get there: Leave A120 at Harwich International. At roundabout last exit to Dovercourt, left at next mini-roundabout. Take 10th turn right to seafront, then right 200 yards on.

Tower

★★
Main Road, Dovercourt, Harwich, Essex, CO12 3PJ
Tel: 01255 504952 Fax: 01255 504952
Email: admin@towerharwich.fsnet.co.uk
SB £50 DB £60 B £6 L £6 D £6.
CC: MC Vi Am DC Swi Delt
How to get there: Main road for Dovercourt and Harwich.

New Farm House

♦♦♦
Spinnel's Lane, Wix, Manningtree, Essex, CO11 2UJ

Tel: 01255 870365 Fax: 01255 87075
Email: barrie.winch@which.net

Modern comfortable farmhouse in 4 acres. Relaxing atmosphere. Good food. Sailing, fishing, bird-watching, walking. Close to Colchester/ Ipswich. 55 minutes by train to London.
SB £32 DB £50 HBS £44 HBD £74
B £7 D £12.
CC: MC Vi Swi Delt JCB Solo
How to get there: Seven miles Harwich, from A120 follow signs to Wix. At village crossroads, take Bradfield Road. Under bridge and next right.

Haslemere, Surrey

Lythe Hill

★★★★ ☃ ☃

Petworth Road, Haslemere, Surrey, GU27 3BQ
Tel: 01428 651251 Fax: 01428 644131
Email: lythe@lythehill.co.uk
Web: www.lythehill.co.uk

Lythe Hill is a traditional and charming 4 star
country hotel. All 41 bedrooms are individually
designed, from 4 poster bed to modern Jacuzzi
bathrooms.
SB £110 DB £144 B £8 L £24 D £40.
CC: MC Vi Am DC Swi Delt JCB

How to get there: One mile east Haslemere on
B2131.

Hastings, East Sussex

Eagle House

◆◆◆◆

12 Pevensey Road, St Leonards, East Sussex,
TN38 0JZ
Tel: 01424 430535 Fax: 01424 437771
Email: eaglehouse@cwcom.net
Web: www.eaglehousehotel.com
A Victorian family house furnished in period
style, with large car park. All ensuite bedrooms,
bar and restaurant overlooking large garden.
Near main London Road but in a quiet
residential area.
SB £33 DB £52 HBS £57.95 HBD £101.90
B £5 L £10.95 D £24.
CC: MC Vi Am DC Swi Delt

How to get there: Follow signs to St Leonards,
Landan Road. At church opposite office building
Ocean House, turn sharp right into Pevensey
Road.
See advert on facing page

Hatfield, Hertfordshire

Quality Hotel Hatfield

★★★

Roehyde Way, Hatfield, Hertforshire, AL10 9AF
Tel: 01707 275701 Fax: 01707 266033
Email: admin@gb055.u-net.com
Web: www.choicehotels.com

SB £105 DB £115 HBS £123 HBD £141
B £7 L £10 D £18.
CC: MC Vi Am DC Swi Delt JCB

How to get there: A1(M) J-3. Follow signs for
university of Hertfordshire. Hotel on Roehyde
Way, half mile from Junction roundabout.

Havant, Hampshire

Langstone

★★★

Northney Road, Hayling Island, Havant,
Hampshire, PO11 0NQ
Tel: 01206 210001 Fax: 01206 212167
Email: sales@patenhotels.co.uk
Web: www.langstonehotel.co.uk
SB £84.95 DB £102.40 HBD £58 B £8.95
L £10.95 D £15.95. CC: MC Vi Am DC Swi Delt

How to get there: Leave A3(M) or A27, signs to
Havant/Hayling Island. A3023 across bridge and
turn immediate left.

Hayes, Middlesex

Comfort Inn Heathrow

★★★

Shepiston Lane, Hayes, Middlesex, UB3 1BL
Tel: 020 8573 6162

Shepiston Lodge Guest House

◆◆◆

31 Shepiston Lane, Hayes, Middlesex, UB3 1LJ
Tel: 020 8573 0266 Fax: 020 8569 2536

Hayling Island, Hampshire

Cockle Warren Cottage

♦♦♦♦
36 Seafront, Hayling Island, Hampshire,
PO11 9HL
Tel: 02392 464961 Fax: 02392 464838
SB £35 DB £60 B £5 CC: MC Vi Swi Delt

How to get there: On Hayling Island, signs to
seafront, through Mengham Village. Road to left
signed with brown signposts.

Haywards Heath, West Sussex

Oakfield Cottage

Brantridge Lane, Staplefield, Haywards Heath,
West Sussex, RH17 6JR
Tel: 01444 401121 Fax: 01444 401121
Email: joyoakfieldcot@aol.com
SB £25 DB £45

How to get there: Handcross (N) take B2110
(Turners Hill), after 2 miles right and right again
into Brantridge Lane. Property 1½ miles on right.

Headcorn, Kent

Four Oaks Bed & Breakfast

♦♦♦
Four Oaks Road, Headcorn, nr Ashford, Kent,
TN27 9PB
Tel: 01622 891224 Fax: 01622 890630
Email: info@fouroaks.uk.com
Web: www.fouroaks.uk.com

Restored, 500 year old farmhouse in quiet rural
location. Close to Leeds Castle, Sissinghurst
gardens and mainline rail services. London
1 hour, Eurolink 30 minutes.
SB £25 DB £36 CC: MC Vi

How to get there: South from Maidstone on
A274, right at Weald of Kent Golf Club. One
mile on right.

Heathrow Airport, Middlesex

Forte Crest Heathrow

★★★★ ®
Sipson Road, West Drayton, Heathrow Airport,
Middlesex, UB7 0JU
Tel: 020 8759 2323 Fax: 020 8897 8659

Le Meridien Heathrow

★★★★ ® ®
Bath Road, Heathrow, Middlesex, UB7 0DU
Tel: 0870 400 8899 Fax: 020 8283 2001
Web: www.lemeridien-hotels.com
B £14.50 L £17 D £19.95.
CC: MC Vi Am DC Swi Delt

How to get there: On A4 (Bath Road) by spur
road to Terminals 1, 2 and 3. M4 J-4.

Novotel London Heathrow

★★★

M4 J-4, Cherry Lane, West Drayton,
UB7 9HB
Tel: 01895 431431 Fax: 01895 431221
Email: h1551@accor-hotels.com
SB £125 DB £135 B £9.95 L £15.50 D £18.50.
CC: MC Vi Am DC Swi Delt

How to get there: M4 J-4, signs for Uxbridge
A408. Keep to left lane and take second exit off
island onto Cherry Lane, signposted West
Drayton. Hotel entrance on left.

Osterley Four Pillars

★★★

764 Great West Road, Isleworth, Middlesex,
TW7 5NA
Tel: 020 8568 7781 Fax: 020 85697819
Email: osterley@four-pillars.co.uk
Web: osterley@four-pillars.co.uk
SB £84 DB £84 HBS £90 HBD £110 B £5.95
L £4.80 D £12.95. CC: MC Vi Am DC Swi Delt

How to get there: At junction of A4 and Wood
Lane, ³/₄ mile past Osterley Underground station
eastbound on A4, ¹/₂ mile past Gillette westbound on A4.

St Giles

Hounslow Road, Feltham, Middlesex,
TW14 9AD
Tel: 020 8817 7000 Fax: 020 8817 7002
Email: book@stgiles.com
Web: www.stgiles.com
B £9.95 L £15 D £15.
CC: MC Vi Am DC Swi Delt

How to get there: 2 miles Heathrow, 600yds
Feltham mainline station, on A244. Easy access
M4, M3 and M25.

Hemel Hempstead, Hertfordshire

Alexandra Guest House

♦♦♦

40–42 Alexandra Road, Hemel Hempstead,
Hertfordshire, HP2 5BP
Tel: 01442 242897 Fax: 01442 211829
Email: alexhous@aol.com
Web: www.alexandraguesthouse.co.uk
Children minimum age: 2. Closed Dec 24 to Jan 2
SB £29.50 DB £40 CC: MC Vi Swi Delt

How to get there: M1 J-8 or M25 J-20. A41 and
signs for Hemel centre. At roundabout take
A4146 to Leighton Buzzard. At 2nd roundabout
turn right and 2nd right into Alexandra Road.

Henfield, West Sussex

Tottington Manor

♦♦♦♦

Edburton, Henfield, West Sussex, BN5 9LJ
Tel: 01903 815757 Fax: 01903 879331

Hertford, Hertfordshire

Heritage Hotels – The White Horse

★★★

Hertingfordbury, Hertford, Hertfordshire,
SG14 2LB
Tel: 0870 400 8114 Fax: 01992 550809

Salisbury Arms

★★

Fore Street, Hertford, Hertfordshire, SG14 1BZ
Tel: 01992 583091 Fax: 01992 552510
SB £40 DB £70 B £5.95 L £9.95 D £12.95.
CC: MC Vi Am DC Swi Delt Electron Solo JCB
Maestro

How to get there: Centre of Hertford, off A414
on Fore Street.

High Wycombe, Buckinghamshire

Bird in Hand

♦♦♦

West Wycombe Road, High Wycombe,
Buckinghamshire, HP11 2LR
Tel: 01494 523502 Fax: 01494 459449
DB £50 B £5.50 L £4.10 D £8.50.
CC: MC Vi DC Swi Delt Solo

How to get there: On A40 West Wycombe to
Oxford road, just minutes from town centre.

Southeast

Clifton Lodge

210 West Wycombe Road, High Wycombe,
Buckinghamshire, HP12 3AR
Tel: 01494 440095 Fax: 01494 536322
Email: hotelaccom@lineone.net
Web: www.cliftonlodgehotel.com

Situated two miles from the M40 and one mile
from High Wycombe on the A40 towards Oxford
and Aylesbury.
SB £69 DB £80 B £6.50 L £10 D £15.
CC: MC Vi Am DC Swi Delt

Drake Court

♦♦

141 London Road, High Wycombe,
Buckinghamshire, HP11 1BT
Tel: 01494 523639 Fax: 01494 472696

Hitchin, Hertfordshire

Firs Hotel & Restaurant

★

83 Bedford Road, Hitchin, Hertfordshire,
SG5 2TY
Tel: 01462 422322 Fax: 01462 432051
Email: enquiries@firshotel.co.uk
Web: www.firshotel.co.uk
SB £47 DB £57 D £6.50.
CC: MC Vi Am DC Swi Delt

How to get there: M1 J-10. A505 to Hitchin.
Signs for Bedford. Hotel just outside Hitchin
town centre on A600.

Redcoats Farmhouse

♦♦♦♦

Redcoats Green, nr Hitchin, Hertfordshire,
SG4 7JR
Tel: 01438 729500 Fax: 01438 723322
Email: sales@redcoats.co.uk
Web: www.redcoats.co.uk

SB £80 DB £90 B £7.50 L £16 D £35.
CC: MC Vi Am DC Swi

How to get there: A1(M) J-8, road to Little
Wymondley. At end of village left at roundabout
into Blakemore End Road (to Redcoats Green).

Tudor Oaks Lodge

♦♦♦

Taylors Road, Astwick, nr Hitchin, Hertfordshire,
SG5 4AZ
Tel: 01462 834133 Fax: 01462 834133
Children minimum age: 6

15th-century lodge around secluded courtyard.
ensuite rooms, fresh food daily from bar snacks
to à la carte. Real Ales.
SB £45 DB £55 B £6 L £8.50 D £10.
CC: MC Vi Am DC Swi Delt

How to get there: By A1, 1 mile north, past J-10.
Near Letchworth, Baldock and Stevenage.
See advert on following page

Hook, Hampshire

Tylney Hall

★★★★ 🐾🐾🐾
Rotherwick, Hook, Hampshire, RG27 9AZ
Tel: 01256 764881 Fax: 01256 768141

White Hart

★★
London Road, Hook, Hants, RG27 9DZ
Tel: 01256 762462 Fax: 01256 768351

Guide dogs

If a Hotel or Guest Accommodation
does not display this 'dogs welcome'
symbol in its listing, the hotelier may
still be happy to welcome guests with guide
dogs, and you should contact the property to
discover whether this will be a problem.

Horsham, West Sussex

Ye Olde King's Head

★★

Carfax, Horsham, West Sussex, RH12 1EG
Tel: 01403 253126 Fax: 01403 242291
SB £77 DB £92 CC: MC Vi Am DC Swi Delt
How to get there: Junction of The Carfax (town centre) and East Street. Brown tourist signs.

Quintrell House

♦♦♦

13 Warnham Road, Horsham, West Sussex, RH12 2QS
Tel: 01403 260929
Children minimum age: 10. Closed Christmas
SB £24 DB £44
How to get there: M23 J-11. A264 to Horsham. Follow bypass (A24 to Worthing), at Robin Hood Roundabout left into Warnham Road (B2237).

Horton-cum-Studley, Oxfordshire

Studley Priory

★★★

Horton-cum-Studley, Oxfordshire, OX33 1AZ
Tel: 01865 351203 Fax: 01865 351613

Tudor Oaks Lodge & Restaurant

Tudor Oaks Lodge is a complex dating back to the 15th century, comprising of Lodge style rooms, all ensuite and with usual facilities, set around a secluded courtyard, with a Free-house and Restaurant.

Fresh food prepared daily, à la carte and bar snacks. We have a wide range of Real Ales from all over the country.

Taylors Road, Astwick, Hitchin, Hertfordshire SG5 4AZ
Tel: 01462 834133

RAC ♦♦♦

Hounslow, Middlesex

Master Robert Hotel

★★★

Great West Road, Hounslow, Middlesex, TW5 0BD
Tel: 020 8570 6261 Fax: 020 8569 4016
Email: masterrobert@fullers.co.uk
B £6.75 CC: MC Vi Am DC Swi Delt

Hove, East Sussex

Courtlands

★★★

15-27 The Drive, Hove, East Sussex, BN3 3JE
Tel: 01273 731055 Fax: 01273 328295

Situated in Hove's premier street, our ensuite rooms are ideal for both business and leisure visitors. Private car park and indoor swimming pool are available.
SB £55 DB £85 HBS £70 HBD £115 B £5.50 L £9.95 D £12.95. CC: MC Vi Am DC Swi Delt
How to get there: From A23 follow signs to Hove. Second turning at roundabout, follow Dyke Road, then Upper Drive and The Drive.

Imperial

★★★

First Avenue, Hove, East Sussex, BN2 2GU
Tel: 01273 777320 Fax: 01272 777310
Email: imperialhotel@pavilion.co.uk
SB £55 DB £95 HBS £67.50 HBD £120 B £7.95 L £15 D £15. CC: MC Vi Am DC Swi Delt
How to get there: Enter Brighton on A23, on to seafront. Right (west) onto A259. First Avenue 2 miles on right.

Please mention the RAC Inspected guide when you make your booking at an RAC Hotel or Guest Accommodation.

Langfords

★★★ ℞

Third Avenue, Hove, East Sussex, BN3 2PX
Tel: 01273 738222 Fax: 01273 779426
Email: langfords@pavilion.co.uk
SB £60 DB £100 B £7.50 L £15 D £18.
CC: MC Vi Am DC Swi Delt

How to get there: From A23 signs to Hove. Left on seafront (A259), east to Third Avenue on left.

Princes Marine

★★★

153 Kingsway, Hove, East Sussex, BN3 2WE
Tel: 01273 207660 Fax: 01273 325913
Email: princemarine@bestwestern.co.uk
Web: www.brighton.co.uk/hotels/princes

Seafront hotel with well-equipped ensuite bedrooms. Rooftop function suites, seaview restaurant and bar. Large private car park. Situated close to all attractions, bowling greens and the King Alfred Leisure Centre. Open for Christmas and New Year.
SB £45 DB £55 HBS £60 HBD £90 B £6.95 L £6.95 D £15.95. CC: MC Vi Am DC Swi Delt

How to get there: From M23, to seafront. Right at Palace Pier, on along seafront road. Hotel 200 yds west of King Alfred swimming pool.

St Catherine's Lodge

★★

Sea Front, Kingsway, Hove, East Sussex, BN3 2RZ
Tel: 01273 778181 Fax: 01273 774949
A traditional seafront hotel, situated opposite the leisure centre, with an abundance of character throughout, particularly in the Regency restaurant.
SB £55 DB £75 HBS £65 HBD £95 B £9.50 L £6 D £14.50.
CC: MC Vi Am DC Swi Delt

How to get there: St Catherine's Lodge is south-

facing on the main A259 Seafront Road in Hove. Near the King Alfred Leisure Centre.

Hungerford, Berkshire

Marshgate Cottage

◆◆◆◆

Marsh Lane, Hungerford, Berkshire, RG17 0QX
Tel: 01488 682307 Fax: 01488 685475
Email: reservations@marshgate.co.uk
Web: www.marshgate.co.uk
SB £36.50 DB £52 CC: MC Vi Swi Delt

How to get there: M4 J-14. From High Street, into Church Street, ½ mile along, right into Marsh Lane. Hotel is at end.

Hythe, Kent

Hythe Imperial

★★★★ ℞℞

Prince's Parade, Hythe, Kent, CT21 6AQ
Tel: 01303 267441 Fax: 01303 264610
Email: hytheimperial@marstonhotels.com
Web: www.marstonhotels.co.uk

MARSTON HOTELS

SB £110 DB £142 HBS £79.50 HBD £159 B £11 L £14.50 D £26. CC: MC Vi Am DC Swi Delt

How to get there: M20 south J-11. A261 to Hythe, then signs to Folkestone. Right into Twiss Rd.

Stade Court

★★★ ⓡ

West Parade, Hythe, Kent, CT21 6DT
Tel: 01303 268263 Fax: 01303 261803
Email: stadecourt@marstonhotels.com
Web: www.marstonhotels.co.uk

MARSTON HOTELS

SB £80 DB £110 HBS £65 HBD £130 B £10
L £10.95 D £20. CC: MC Vi Am DC Swi Delt

⊔⊔ ☇ ☕ ⊑ ☎ ☍ ℙ ☸ ℃ ☕ ♞ ♬ ☙ ☂ ♨ ⛓ ⫴
⛲ ⵊ ℃ ⚲ ⚲ ⵊ ☒

How to get there: M20 southbound J-11. A261
to Hythe, then right into Stade Street (by canal).

Ilford, Essex

Park Hotel

◆◆◆

327 Cranbrook Road, Ilford, Essex, IG1 4UE
Tel: 020 8554 9616 Fax: 020 8518 2700
Email: parkhotelilford@netscapeonline.co.uk
Web: www.the-park-hotel.co.uk
SB £44.50 DB £55 CC: MC Vi Swi Delt

♿ 🐾 ☇ ☕ ⊑ ℙ ☸ ℃ ♞ ♬ ☙ ⫴ ♦

How to get there: Opposite Valentines Park, 5
minutes walk from Gants Hill underground and
Ilford railway stations.

Woodville Guest House

◆◆◆ ✍

10–12 Argyle Road, Ilford, Essex, IG1 3BQ
Tel: 020 8478 3779 Fax: 020 8478 6282
Email: cass@woodville-guesthouse.co.uk

Very friendly family-run business. Comfortable
bedrooms, beamed dining room, garden and
terrace make this a delightful stay. Most rooms
ensuite. All rooms with Sky TV. Families with
children particularly welcome. 2 mins from
station. 20 mins from city.

SB £35.00 DB £40.00

☇ ☕ ⊑ ℙ ☸ ℃ ♞ ♬ ☙

How to get there: M25 for M11 south to A406.
Exit Ilford Junction, past station, 2nd left off
Cranbrook Rd into Beal Rd, 2nd left into Argyle Rd.

Cranbrook Hotel

◆◆ ✍

24 Coventry Road, Ilford, Essex, IG1 4QR
Tel: 020 8554 6544 Fax: 020 8518 1463

Isle of Wight

Bonchurch Manor

★★★

Bonchurch Shute, Bonchurch, Isle of Wight,
PO38 1NU
Tel: 01983 852868

Brunswick

★★★ ⓡ

Queens Road, Shanklin, Isle of Wight,
PO37 6AM
Tel: 01983 863245

Burlington

★★★

Bellevue Road, Ventnor, Isle of Wight,
PO38 1DB
Tel: 01983 852113 Fax: 01983 853862
Children minimum age: 3. Closed Nov-Mar
SB £32 DB £64 HBS £40 HBD £80 B £8 D £15.
CC: MC Vi Swi Delt

🐾 ☕ ⊑ ☎ ℙ ☸ ℃ ♞ ♬ ☙ ⫴ ℃ ⵊ

Country Garden

★★★ ⓡ

Church Hill, Totland Bay, Isle of Wight,
PO39 0ET
Tel: 01983 784821 Fax: 01983 784821
Email: pat.burton@lineone.net
Children minimum age: 12. Closed January

'Simply the best' 3-star hotel in tranquil walking
country of West Wight; near to bustling port of

Southeast

Yarmouth. ensuite, garden and sea-view rooms available.
SB £56 DB £104 HBS £63 HBD £118
B £14 D £17.50. CC: MC Vi Swi Delt
How to get there: 8-minute drive west Yarmouth.

Eversley Hotel
★★★
Park Avenue, Ventnor, Isle of Wight, PO38 1LB
Tel: 01983 852244 Fax: 01983 853948
Email: eversleyhotel@fsbdial.co.uk
Web: www.eversleyhotel.com
Closed January
SB £32 DB £64 HBS £47 HBD £94
B £5.50 D £15. CC: MC Vi Swi Delt

George Hotel
★★★ 🍴🍴🍴🍴
Quay Street, Yarmouth, Isle of Wight, PO41 0PE
Tel: 01983 760331 Fax: 01983 760425
Email: res@thegeorge.co.uk
Children minimum age: 10
SB £90 DB £150 HBS £115 HBD £190
B £12 L £15 D £20. CC: MC Vi Am Swi Delt
How to get there: Yarmouth, between pier and castle.

Holliers
★★★
Church Road, Old Village, Shanklin,
Isle of Wight, PO37 6NU
Tel: 01983 862764 Fax: 01983 867314
Email: holliers@i12.com
Web: www.holliers.i12.com
SB £50 DB £65 CC: MC Vi Am Swi Delt
How to get there: On the main A3055.

Keats Green Hotel
★★★
3 Queens Road, Shanklin, Isle of Wight,
PO37 6AN
Tel: 01983 862742 Fax: 01983 868572
Email: keats_green@netguides.co.uk
Closed November to February

Comfort and enjoyment with a combination of space, location and friendly personal service from Geraldine and Lloyd Newton makes Keats Green Hotel an unbeatable destination for your holiday.
SB £25 DB £50 HBS £31 HBD £62 D £12.
CC: MC Vi DC Swi Delt
How to get there: Driving from Lake take A3055

towards Ventnor (Queens Road). Hotel is situated approx 400 yds on left.

New Holmwood
★★★
Queens Road, Egypt Point, Cowes,
Isle of Wight, PO31 8BW
Tel: 01983 292508 Fax: 01983 295020

Sentry Mead
★★★ 🍴
Madeira Road, Totland Bay, Isle Of Wight,
PO39 0BJ
Tel: 01983 753212 Fax: 01983 753212

Shanklin Manor House
★★★ 🍴
Church Road, Old Village, Shanklin,
Isle of Wight, PO37 6XQ
Tel: 01983 862777 Fax: 01983 863464
Children minimum age: 5
SB £39 DB £72 HBS £49 HBD £88
B £7.50 D £16. CC: MC Vi Swi Delt
See advert on following page

Braemar
★★ 🍴
1 Grange Road, Shanklin, Isle Of Wight,
PO37 6NN
Tel: 01983 863172 Fax: 01983 863172

Clarendon Hotel & Wight Mouse Inn
★★
Newport Road, Chale, Isle of Wight,
PO38 2HA
Tel: 01983 730431 Fax: 01983 730431
Email: wightmouse@aol.com
Web: www.trad-inns.co.uk/clarendon
SB £25 DB £50 HBS £28 HBD £56
B £5 L £10 D £10.
CC: MC Vi Swi Delt
How to get there: On the Military Road B3055.

Farringford

★★ ℞

Bedbury Lane, Freshwater Bay, Isle of Wight,
PO40 9PE
Tel: 01983 752500 Fax: 01983 756575
Email: enquiries@farringford.co.uk
Web: www.farringford.co.uk

Alfred Lord Tennyson's home for almost forty
years, now a well-appointed hotel set in 33
acres of parkland incorporating a 9 hole par 3
golf course and poolside bistro.
SB £47.50 DB £95 HBS £65 HBD £130
B £8 L £12.50 D £19.95.
CC: MC Vi Am Swi Delt

Shanklin Manor House HOTEL

Majestic manor house standing in four and
a half acres of beautiful, secluded gardens.
Offering many leisure facilities including
indoor and outdoor swimming pools, gym
and sauna.

Church Road, Old Village, Shanklin
PO37 6XQ
Tel: 01983 862777   Fax: 01983 863464

How to get there: A3054 towards Freshwater.
Turn left to Norton Green, left at roundabout to
Freshwater Bay, then right onto Bedbury Lane.

Fernbank

★★

Highfield Road, Shanklin, Isle of Wight,
PO37 6PP
Tel: 01983 862790 Fax: 01983 864412
Children minimum age: 7.
Closed Christmas to New Year
SB £29 DB £58 HBS £38 HBD £70
L £7 D £12. CC: MC Vi Swi Delt

Hambledon

★★

11 Queens Road, Shanklin, Isle of Wight,
PO37 6AW
Tel: 01983 862403 Fax: 01983 867894
Email: enquiries@hambledon-hotel.co.uk
Web: www.hambledon-hotel.co.uk
SB £25 DB £50 HBS £34 HBD £68
CC: MC Vi Swi Delt

How to get there: Queens Road joins main
Sandown/Shanklin Road at Five-Ways Junction
(with traffic lights) at foot of Arthur's Hill.

Heatherleigh

★★

17 Queens Road, Shanklin, Isle of Wight,
PO37 6AW
Tel: 01983 862503 Fax: 01983 862503
SB £25 DB £50 HBS £35.50 HBD £71
B £5 D £10.50. CC: MC Vi Swi

How to get there: Enter Shanklin, signs for
Beach Lift. Hotel 100yds from cliff walk and lift.

Hillside

★★

Mitchell Avenue, Ventnor, Isle of Wight,
PO38 1DR
Tel: 01983 852271 Fax: 01983 852271
Email: rac@hillside-hotel.co.uk
Children minimum age: 5. Closed Christmas
SB £23 DB £46 HBS £33 HBD £66
B £2.50 D £10.
CC: MC Vi Swi Delt Connect

How to get there: B2257 off A3055 at junction
between Leeson Hill and St Bonipace Road –
hotel is 500 yards on right, from tennis
courts.

Luccombe Hall

★★

Luccombe Road, Shanklin, Isle of Wight,
PO37 6RL
Tel: 01983 862719 Fax: 01983 863082
Email: reservations@luccombehall.co.uk
Web: www.luccombehall.co.uk
SB £35 DB £70 HBS £43 HBD £86
B £5.95 L £4.95 D £9.95. CC: MC Vi Swi

How to get there: From Shanklin, B3020 for
Ventnor. Take road for Luccombe. Left at top.
Hotel is 100yds on right.

Malton House

★★

8 Park Road, Shanklin, Isle of Wight, PO37 6AY
Tel: 01983 865007 Fax: 01983 865576
Email: couvoussis@totalise.co.uk
SB £26 DB £44 HBS £35 HBD £62 D £9.
CC: MC Vi

How to get there: From Sandown on A3055,
enter Shanklin. At traffic lights (Hope Road), go
straight up hill. Third road on left.

Melbourne-Ardenlea Hotel

★★

Queens Road, Shanklin, Isle of Wight,
PO37 6AP
Tel: 01983 862283 Fax: 01983 862865
Email: melbourne-ardenlea@virgin.net
Web: www.hotel-isleofwight.co.uk
Closed November to February

Long-established, family-run hotel in pleasant
gardens, giving personal service. Centrally
situated in peaceful area, yet close to all of
Shanklin's amenities.
SB £37 DB £74 HBS £44 HBD £88 D £12.
CC: MC Vi Am Swi Delt

How to get there: From Sandown, bear left at

Fiveways Crossroads heading for Ventnor. Hotel
150 yards on right after passing church spire.

Monteagle

★★

Priory Road, Shanklin, Isle of Wight, PO37 6RJ
Tel: 01983 862854

Montrene

★★

Avenue Road, Sandown, Isle of Wight,
PO36 8BN
Tel: 01983 403722 Fax: 01983 405553
Email: montrenehotel@ic24.net
Web: www.montrene.co.uk
Closed January
SB £35 DB £70 HBS £43 HBD £86
CC: Vi Swi Delt
How to get there: From Ryde via Brading, under
railway bridge. Keep to left at roundabout. Hotel
at end on right. Look out for yellow sign.

Orchardcroft

★★

Victoria Avenue, Shanklin, Isle of Wight,
PO37 6LT
Tel: 01983 862133 Fax: 01983 862133
Email: nicklaffan@hotmail.com
Web: www.orchardcroft-hotel.co.uk
Children minimum age: 6 months.
Closed January to March
SB £26 DB £52 HBS £38 HBD £76 B £5 D £12.
CC: MC Vi Swi Delt
How to get there: From Newport on Sandown
road, right to Shanklin through Godshill into
Victoria Avenue. Orchardcroft first hotel on left.

Sandpipers Country House

★★

Entrance through main car park, Freshwater
Bay, Isle of Wight, PO40 9QX
Tel: 01983 758500 Fax: 01983 754364
Email: sandpipers@fatcattrading.demon.co.uk
Web: www.fatcattrading.co.uk
SB £19 HBS £34 B £3 L £3 D £6.75.
CC: MC Vi Swi Delt Solo Electron
How to get there: Enter Freshwater Bay, into
main council park. Drive between two brick
pillars at back to enter private car park.

Villa Mentone

★

11 Park Road, Shanklin, Isle of Wight,
PO37 6AY
Tel: 01983 862346 Fax: 01983 862130
SB £40 DB £60 HBS £55 HBD £90
B £5 L £9 D £15.

How to get there: A3055 to Sandown, then
Shanklin. Follow Beach Lift signs.

Aqua Hotel

♦♦♦♦

17 The Esplanade, Shanklin, Isle of Wight,
PO37 6BN
Tel: 01983 863024 Fax: 01983 864841
Email: info@aquahotel.co.uk
Web: www.aquahotel.co.uk
Closed November to March
SB £25 DB £50 HBS £35 HBD £70
B £5 L £5 D £10.
CC: MC Vi Am DC Swi Delt Solo JCB

How to get there: From Sandown Road left into
Hope Road. Down hill to Esplanade. Aqua Hotel
80yds past clock tower.

Lake Hotel

♦♦♦♦

Shore Road, Lower Bonchurch, Ventnor,
Isle of Wight, PO38 1RF
Tel: 01983 852613
Email: richard@lakehotel.co.uk
Web: www.lakehotel.co.uk
Children minimum age: 3.
Closed November to February
SB £28 DB £50 HBS £35 HBD £70 B £5 D £8.

How to get there: Opposite Bonchurch Pond,
within easy reach of Shanklin.

Rooftree

♦♦♦♦

26 Broadway, Sandown, Isle of Wight,
PO36 9BY
Tel: 01983 403175 Fax: 01983 407354
Web: www.netguides.co.uk
SB £40 DB £30 HBS £46 HBD £36 D £15.
CC: MC Vi Am DC Swi Delt

How to get there: Broadway is the Isle of
Wight's main A-road. Hotel is on the corner of
Melville Street. From the rail station, turn right
and immediately left. Turn right onto the
Broadway, hotel up on left.

St Catherines

♦♦♦♦

1 Winchester Park Road, Sandown,
Isle of Wight, PO36 8HJ
Tel: 01983 402392 Fax: 01983 402392
Email: stcathhotel@hotmail.com
Web: www.isleofwight-holidays.co.uk
SB £24 DB £48 HBS £34 HBD £68 B £3 D £10.
CC: MC Vi Swi Delt Electron Solo

How to get there: By car from Fishbourne to
Sandown, right at mini-roundabout up
Broadway. Hotel top of hill on left, on corner of
Broadway and Winchester Park Road.

St Leonards

♦♦♦♦

22 Queens Road, Shanklin, Isle of Wight,
PO37 6AW
Tel: 01983 862121 Fax: 01983 868895
Email: les@wight-breaks.co.uk
Web: www.wight-breaks.co.uk
SB £22 DB £44 HBS £30 HBD £60
CC: MC Vi Delt Solo

How to get there: Approach Shanklin on A3054.
At Fiveways lights take left hand fork (signed
Ventnor). Hotel on left, after 1/4 mile.

The Lodge

♦♦♦♦

Main Road, Brighstone, Isle of Wight, PO30 4DJ
Tel: 01983 741272 Fax: 01983 741144
Email: thelodgeb@hotmail.com
Web: www.isle-of-wight.uk.com/lodge

Beautiful country house set in 3 acres. Quality
accommodation and value with an excellent
breakfast selection. A relaxing atmosphere,
delightful walks on coast or downs.
DB £50

How to get there: Leave Newport via Caris-
brooke. B3323 then B3399 to Brighstone.
Through village, past Three Bishops Pub. The
Lodge is 1/2 mile on left hand side.

Bay House

◆◆◆

8 Chine Avenue, Shanklin, Isle of Wight,
PO37 6AG
Tel: 01983 863180 Fax: 01983 868934
Email: bay-house@netguides.co.uk
Web: www.bayhouse-hotel.co.uk

Located in a quiet position with one of the finest
views over the bay, this family-run hotel, serving
exceptional cuisine, is just a five-minute walk to
the old village and beach.
SB £25 DB £50 HBS £31 HBD £31 B £5 D £6.
CC: MC Vi Swi

How to get there: Follow Queens Road (B3328)
to end at Chine Avenue, left into Chine Avenue.

Belmore Private Hotel

◆◆◆

101 Station Avenue, Sandown, Isle of Wight,
PO36 8HD
Tel: 01983 404189 Fax: 01983 405942
SB £16 DB £32 HBS £22 HBD £44 CC: MC Vi
Closed Dec 25–26
How to get there: From Fishbourne car ferry, left
at traffic lights, 3055 road to Sandown. Driving
along Broadway, turn left at antique shop.
Belmore is on left, past Conservative Club.

Brackla

◆◆◆

7 Leed Street, Sandown, Isle of Wight,
PO36 9DA
Tel: 01983 403648 Fax: 01983 402887
Email: web@brackla-hotel.co.uk
Web: www.brackla-hotel.co.uk
Children minimum age: 3.
Closed October-March
SB £21 DB £42
CC: MC Vi Swi Delt

How to get there: Leed Street is situated off
main Brading to Shanklin road (A3055).

Denewood

◆◆◆

7 Victoria Road, Sandown, Isle of Wight,
PO36 8AL
Tel: 01983 402980 Fax: 01983 402980
Email: holiday@denewoodhotel.co.uk
SB £21 DB £42 HBS £30 HBD £60 D £9.
CC: MC Vi Swi Delt

Georgian House Guest House

◆◆◆

22 George Street, Ryde, Isle of Wight,
PO33 2EW
Tel: 01983 563588
SB £20 DB £17

How to get there: George Street is opposite
Bus/Railway Station and Hovercraft terminal.
Hotel 100yds up George Street on right .

Glen Islay House

◆◆◆

St Boniface Road, Ventnor, Isle of Wight,
PO38 1NP
Tel: 01983 854095

Little Span Farm

◆◆◆

Rew Lane, Wroxall, Ventnor, Isle of Wight,
PO38 3AU
Tel: 01983 852419 Fax: 01983 852419

Mount House

◆◆◆

20 Arthurs Hill, Shanklin, Isle of Wight,
PO37 6EE
Tel: 01983 862556 Fax: 01983 867551
Closed January
SB £18 DB £36 HBS £25 HBD £50 D £5.
CC: MC Vi Delt

How to get there: On A3055 Sandown to Shanklin, on corner of Clarance Rd and Arthurs Hill.

Richmond

◆◆◆

23 Palmerston, Shanklin, Isle of Wight,
PO37 6AS
Tel: 01983 862874 Fax: 01983 862874
Email: richmondhotel.shanklin@virgin.net
Closed November to February
SB £23 DB £46 HBS £32.50 HBD £65
CC: MC Vi Swi Delt Solo JCB Maestro Electron

How to get there: Turn off Shanklin High Street
opposite Boots. Hotel facing you.

Rowborough Hotel

♦♦♦

32 Arthurs Hill, Shanklin, Isle of Wight,
PO37 6EX
Tel: 01983 866072 Fax: 01983 867703
Email: rowborough@holaccom.co.uk
SB £21 DB £42 HBS £29 HBD £58
CC: MC Vi Am DC Swi Delt

How to get there: On main route entering
Shanklin. Close to clifftop path, buses, rail
station, theatre and main town.

The Nodes Country Hotel

♦♦♦

Alum Bay Road, Totland Bay, Isle of Wight,
PO39 0HZ
Tel: 01983 752859 Fax: 023 92201621

White House

♦♦♦

7 Park Road, Shanklin, Isle of Wight, PO37 6AY
Tel: 01983 862776 Fax: 01983 865980

Channel View

♦♦

4-8 Royal Street, Sandown, Isle of Wight,
PO36 8LP
Tel: 01983 402347 Fax: 01983 404128

Esplanade

♦♦

22 The Esplanade, Shanklin, Isle of Wight,
PO37 6BG
Tel: 01983 863001 Fax: 01983 863001

Lincoln Hotel

♣

30 Wittlestairs Road, Shanklin, Isle of Wight,
PO37 6HS
Tel: 01983 562147 Fax: 01983 562147
Children minimum age: 4.
Closed November to March
SB £16 DB £32

How to get there: Main Newport/Sandown road.
Right for Shanklin. Over bridge, first road on left.

Kingston-upon-Thames, Surrey

Heritage Hotels – The Kingston Lodge

★★★

94 Kingston Hill, Kingston-upon-Thames,
Surrey, KT2 7NP
Tel: 020 8541 4481 Fax: 020 8547 1013
Email: kingstonlodge@forte-hotels.com
Web: www.heritage-hotels.com
SB £159.85 DB £169.70 B £10.50 L £9.95
D £16.95. CC: MC Vi Am DC Swi

How to get there: M25 J-10 to A3, up to Robin
Hood roundabout, after 14½ miles. Sharp left
onto Ringston Hill. Hotel 1½ miles on left.

Hotel Antoinette

★★

26 Beaufort Road, Kingston-upon-Thames,
Surrey, KT1 2TQ
Tel: 020 8546 1044 Fax: 020 8547 2595
Email: hotelantoinette@btinternet.com
Web: www.hotelantoinette.co.uk

Well established family-owned hotel situated
close to London and many tourist attractions.
Comfortable accommodation, inviting
atmosphere and large car park. Brasserie
restaurant. Landscaped gardens.
SB £52 DB £62 B £6.50 D £12.
CC: MC Vi Am Swi

How to get there: M25 J-9, A243 to
Kingston/Surbiton. At Surbiton second right
after railway bridge, Maple Road, then turn left
at third set of traffic lights.

Leatherhead, Surrey

Bookham Grange

★★

Little Bookham Common, Bookham,
Leatherhead, Surrey, KT23 3HS
Tel: 01372 452742 Fax: 01372 450080
Email: bookhamgrange@easynet.co.uk
This Victorian country house hotel, set in two
and a half acres of landscaped gardens, blends
the best of tradition with modern facilities.
Leatherhead, Epsom, Guildford and London are
all within easy reach by train or car.
SB £65 DB £75 HBS £79.50 HBD £89.50
L £15 D £15. CC: MC Vi Am DC Swi

Southeast

⚓ 🐎 🖨 💻 ☎ 🅿 ♿ ⚞ 🐴 ♠ 🦀 ▦ ⦚

How to get there: M25 J-9 into Leatherhead and
A246 towards Guildford. In Bookham, turn right
into High Street, straight on into Church Road
and first right after Bookham Station.
See advert on the right

Lewes, East Sussex

Shelleys Hotel

★★★ ℝ ℝ

High Street, Lewes, East Sussex, BN7 1XS
Tel: 01273 472361 Fax: 01273 483152
Email: info@shelleys-hotel-lewes.com
SB £141 DB £191 B £10.25 L £8.50 D £25.
CC: MC Vi Am DC Swi Delt JCB

⚓ 🖪 ☺ 🖨 💻 ☎ 📞 🅿 ♿ ⚞ 🐴 ♠ 🦀 ▦ ⦚

How to get there: Hotel in Lewes High Street.

White Hart Hotel

★★★

High Street, Lewes, East Sussex, BN7 1XE
Tel: 01273 476694 Fax: 01273 476695
SB £62 DB £89 B £4 L £7.50 D £7.50.
CC: MC Vi Am DC Swi Delt

♿ 🖪 🐎 🖨 💻 ☎ 🅿 ♿ ⚞ 🐴 ♠ 🦀 🚤 ▦ ⦚
🏇 💲

How to get there: Town centre, facing law courts.
See advert below right

Berkeley House

♦ ♦ ♦ ♦　✑

2 Albion Street, Lewes, East Sussex, BN7 2ND
Tel: 01273 476057 Fax: 01273 479575
Email: rp.berkeleyhse@lineone.net
Web: www.berkeleyhousehotel.co.uk

An elegant Georgian townhouse, in a central but
quiet location. Roof terrace with views across
Lewes to the downs. Limited off-street parking –
advance booking recommended. Licensed.
SB £40 DB £50 CC: MC Vi Am DC Swi Delt
🖨 💻 🅿 ♿ ╏　　　　　　Closed Christmas
How to get there: Albion Street is a turning off
'School Hill', part of High Street in town centre.

Bookham Grange

This Victorian country house hotel, set in two
and a half acres of landscaped gardens,
blends the best of tradition with modern
facilities. 21 bedrooms, all ensuite.
Leatherhead, Epsom, Guildford and London
are all within easy reach by train or car.

Little Bookham Common, Bookham,
Leatherhead, Surrey KT23 3HS
Tel: 01372 452742　Fax: 01372 450080
Email: bookhamgrange@easynet.co.uk

White Hart Hotel

A charming 16th-century coaching inn which
has been magnificently extended to comprise
an indoor leisure complex with pool, sauna,
steam room and gym. Accommodation is
available in the main house or in our
contemporary annexe.

This privately owned, family run hotel offers a
friendly and lively though relaxed atmosphere.

High Street, Lewes,
East Sussex BN7 1XE
Tel: 01273 476694　Fax: 01273 476695

Millers

134 High Street, Lewes, East Sussex, BN7 1XS
Tel: 01273 475631 Fax: 01273 486226
Email: millers134@aol.com
Closed Christmas to New Year, Bonfire Night
SB £51 DB £57

How to get there: Situated on High Street – but be aware of the consecutive numbering.

Luton, Bedfordshire

Leaside Hotel & Restaurant

72 New Bedford Road, Luton, Bedfordshire, LU3 1BT
Tel: 01582 417643 Fax: 01582 734961

Lymington, Hampshire

Passford House

★★★
Mount Pleasant, Lymington, Hampshire, SO41 8LS
Tel: 01590 682398 Fax: 01590 683494

Stanwell House

★★★
14–15 High Street, Lymington, Hampshire, SO41 9AA
Tel: 01590 677123 Fax: 01590 677756
Email: sales@stanwellhousehotel.co.uk
Web: www.stanwellhousehotel.co.uk
SB £80 DB £105 HBS £105 HBD £150
B £6.50 L £9 D £25.
CC: MC Vi Am DC Swi Delt

How to get there: M27 J-1, A397 Lyndhurst and Brockenhurst into Lymington High Street. Hotel halfway along.
See advert on facing page (top)

Efford Cottage

Everton, Lymington, Hampshire, SO41 0JD
Tel: 01590 642315 Fax: 01590 641030
Email: effcottage@aol.com
Web: www.bandbnewforest.com
Children minimum age: 14
DB £50

How to get there: Two miles west of Lymington on A337 on the eastern edge of village of Everton.

Lyndhurst, Hampshire

Forest Lodge Hotel

★★★
Pikes Hill, Romsey Road, Lyndhurst, Hampshire, SO43 7AS
Tel: 02380 283677 Fax: 02380 282940
Email: info@carehotels.co.uk
Web: www.carehotels.co.uk
SB £60 DB £120 HBS £81.50 HBD £168
B £4.50 L £4 D £21.50.
CC: MC Vi Am DC Swi Delt

How to get there: M27 J-1 onto A337, then after approx 3 miles turn right into Pikes Hill. Forest Lodge is on left.
See advert on facing page (bottom)

Knightwood Lodge

★
Southampton Road, Lyndhurst, Hampshire, SO43 7BU
Tel: 02380 282502 Fax: 02380 283730
SB £47.50 DB £90 HBS £62.50 HBD £120
L £4.95 D £17.95. CC: MC Vi Am DC Swi Delt

How to get there: M27 J-1, A337 for Lyndhurst. Left at traffic lights in Lyndhurst. Hotel 1/4 mile along A35 Southampton Road.

Little Hayes

43 Romsey Road, Lyndhurst, Hampshire, SO43 7AR
Tel: 02380 283816
DB £56

How to get there: M27 J-1, A337 for Lyndhurst. Little Hayes is on right as you enter village.

Lyndhurst House

35 Romsey Road, Lyndhurst, Hampshire, SO43 7AR
Tel: 02380 282230 Fax: 02380 282230
Email: bcjwood@lyndhouse.freeserve.co.uk
Web: www.newforest.demon.co.uk/lynho.html
Children minimum age: 10
DB £44 CC: MC Vi

How to get there: M27 J-1. A337 to Lyndhurst. Situated 1/4 mile inside 30mph limit, on right.

Southeast

Penny Farthing

Romsey Road, Lyndhurst, Hampshire,
SO43 7AA
Tel: 02380 284422 Fax: 02380 284488

A cheerful small hotel, ideally situated in the village of Lyndhurst. Offering licensed bar, bicycle store, comfortable ensuite rooms with colour TV, telephone and tea/coffee making facilities and large car park. Ideal base for touring New Forest.
SB £39 DB £68 B £6.50
CC: MC Vi Am DC Swi Delt   Closed Christmas
🖥🐾⊗🖱⌨☎P☕🐎♫♿👤
How to get there: M27 J-1, A337 to Lyndhurst. Hotel is on left as you enter village.

Maidenhead, Berkshire

Fredrick's

★★★★ 🍷🍷🍷

Shoppenhangers Road, Maidenhead, Berkshire,
SL6 2PZ
Tel: 01628 581000 Fax: 01628 771054
Email: reservations@fredericks-hotel.co.uk
Web: www.fredericks-hotel.co.uk

The Lösel family ensure the smooth operation of this exceptional hotel and its renowned restaurant. The emphasis is firmly on personal service and warm, friendly hospitality combined

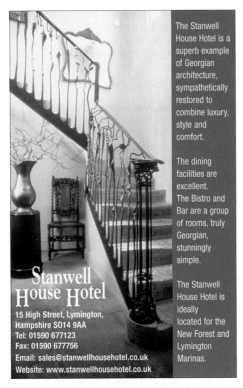

with the highest professional standards.
SB £185 DB £220 B £14.50 L £25.50 D £35.50.
CC: MC Vi Am DC JCB

Monkey Island

★★★★ ♟♟

Bray-on-Thames, Maidenhead, Berkshire,
SL6 2EE
Tel: 01628 23400 Fax: 01628 784732
Email: monkeyisland@btconnect.com
Web: www.methotels.com
SB £117 DB £150 HBS £100 HBD £190
B £8 L £19 D £29.50.
CC: MC Vi Am DC Swi Delt

Thames Hotel

★★★

Raymead Road, Maidenhead, Berkshire,
SL6 8NR
Tel: 01628 628721 Fax: 01628 773921
Email: reservations@thameshotel.co.uk
Web: www.thameshotel.co.uk

Idyllically situated on the banks of the River
Thames. The hotel has 35 ensuite rooms, many
with superb views of the river.
SB £98 DB £116 B £8 D £15.
CC: MC Vi Am DC Swi Delt

How to get there: M4 J-7. Turn left for
Maidenhead, over bridge and right at mini-roundabout. Hotel is 200yds on left.

Inn on The Green

♦♦♦♦ ♟

The Old Cricket Common, Cookham Dean,
Berkshire, SL6 9NZ
Tel: 01628 482638 Fax: 01628 487474
Email: enquiries@theinnonthegreen.com
Web: www.theinnonthegreen.com

Charming country inn, with a renowned gourmet
restaurant, in a secluded setting overlooking the
old cricket common. Sunny courtyard, log fires,
comfortable rooms and friendly service.
SB £60 DB £100 L £12.95 D £16.95.
CC: MC Vi Am Swi Delt

How to get there: First left after Marlow Bridge.
After 1½ miles first right, then first left, first left
again, then left at the war memorial.

Clifton Guest House

♦♦♦

21 Crauford Rise, Maidenhead, Berkshire,
SL6 7LR
Tel: 01628 623572 Fax: 01628 623572
Email: clifton@aroram.freeserve.co.uk
Web: www.cliftonguesthouse.co.uk
SB £30 DB £60 CC: MC Vi Am Swi Delt

How to get there: M4 J-8/9. A308 to Maidenhead, on for Marlow. Crauford Rise off Marlow Rd.

Maidstone, Kent

Grange Moor

★★

St Michael's Road, Maidstone, Kent, ME16 8BS
Tel: 01622 677623 Fax: 01622 678246
Email: reservations@grangemoor.co.uk
Closed Christmas
SB £40 DB £50 B £5.50 D £14.50.
CC: MC Vi Swi Delt

How to get there: A26 Tonbridge Road. Church
on left, hotel on the right.

Southeast

Willington Court

◆◆◆◆

Willington Street, Ashford Road, Maidstone,
Kent, ME15 8JW
Tel: 01622 738885

Margate, Kent

Greswolde

◆◆◆◆

20 Surrey Road, Cliftonville, Kent, CT9 2LA
Tel: 01843 223956 Fax: 01843 223956
Children minimum age: 7
SB £28 DB £40 CC: MC Vi

How to get there: At Margate seafront, left at
clocktower, past harbour for ¹/₂ mile. Surrey
Road on right. Greswolde faces bowling centre.

Marlow, Buckinghamshire

Danesfield House

★★★★ ♟♟♟

Medmenham, Marlow, Buckinghamshire,
SL7 3ES
Tel: 01628 891010 Fax: 01628 484115
Web: www.danesfieldhouse.co.uk

Built at the turn of the century, the hotel stands
in 65 acres of grounds overlooking the River
Thames, with spectacular views.
SB £155 DB £205 B £12.50 L £24.50 D £26.50.
CC: MC Vi Am DC Swi Delt JCB

How to get there: M4 J-8/9 or M40 J-4, A404 to
Marlow. Then take A4155 towards Henley.

Book with RAC Hotel Reservations and check
the latest offers available. Call 0870 603 9109
and quote 'RAC Guide 2001'

Heritage Hotels – The Compleat Angler

★★★★ ♟♟

Marlow Bridge, Marlow, Buckingamshire,
SL7 1RG
Tel: 01628 484444 Fax: 01628 486388
Email: heritagehotels_marlow.compleat_angler
@forte-hotels.com
Web: www.heritage-hotels.com
DB £218.45 B £15.50 L £19.50 D £34.50.
CC: MC Vi Am DC Swi Delt JCB Eurocard

How to get there: From A404, at the first
roundabout follow signs for Bisham. Hotel on
right immediately before Marlow Bridge.

Holly Tree House

◆◆◆◆

Burford Close, Marlow Bottom,
Buckinghamshire, SL7 3NF
Tel: 01628 891110 Fax: 01628 481278
Closed Christmas to New Year
SB £64.50 DB £79.50
CC: MC Vi Am DC Swi Delt

How to get there: M4 J-8/9, A404 for High
Wycombe. Marlow turn to second mini-round-
about. Turn right and on until sign for Marlow
Bottom. Take second on left.

Milford-on-Sea, Hampshire

Westover Hall

★★★ ♟♟♟

Park Lane, Milford-on-Sea, Hampshire,
SO41 0PT
Tel: 01590 643044 Fax: 01590 644490
Email: westoverhallhotel@barclays.net
Web: www.westoverhallhotel.com
SB £70 DB £120 HBS £95 HBD £165
B £12 L £6.50 D £27.50.
CC: MC Vi Am DC Swi Delt

How to get there: M27 J-1. A337 via Lyndhurst,
Brockenhurst, Lymington, Pennington then
Everton. take B3058 to Milford-on-Sea.
See advert on following page

Westover Hall

RAC ★★★ 🐾🐾🐾

A Grade II Listed Victorian Mansion on the edge of the New Forest, 200 yards from the beach with stunning uninterrupted views across to the Needles and Isle of Wight. Magnificent oak panelled interior with stained glass windows and antique furniture. Family owned and run with a relaxed friendly atmosphere. Excellent cuisine. Individually furnished, luxurious bedrooms, many with sea view, all ensuite.
A fascinating and unusual hotel.

Park Lane, Milford-on-Sea, Lymington Hampshire SO41 0PT
Tel: 01590 643044   Fax: 01590 644490
Email: westoverhallhotel@barclays.net
Website: www.westoverhallhotel.com

The Swan Hotel

Well appointed, family-run coaching inn close to steam Watercress line. 23 rooms all ensuite, telephones, colour TV, tea/coffee facilities. Beautiful undercroft, fine dining restaurant catering for weddings, parties, conferences. Buffet snacks available. Children welcome. Open to residents.

11 West Street, New Alresford, Hampshire SO24 9AD
Tel: 01962 732302   Fax: 01962 735274

Milton Keynes, Bedfordshire

Moore Place

★★★ 🐾🐾

The Square, Aspley Guise, Milton Keynes, Bedfordshire, MK17 8DW
Tel: 01908 282000 Fax: 01908 281888
Email: info@mooreplace.co.uk
Web: www.mooreplace.co.uk

Moore Place is a charming Georgian Manor in a delightful village location. The award-winning restaurant overlooks a beautiful courtyard garden with rockery and waterfall.
SB £85 DB £105 B £11 L £14 D £22.
CC: MC Vi Am DC Swi Delt JCB Eurocard
🦢 🛆 🐾 🕾 🖵 🕿 P 🐾 ⅌ 🐴 ⼍ 🐾 ⅲⅲ ⅲⅲ
How to get there: M1 at J-13. A507, signs to Aspley Guise. Moore Place on left in village.

Quality Hotel & Suites Milton Keynes

★★★

Monks Way, Two Mile Ash, Milton Keynes, Buckinghamshire, MK8 8LY
Tel: 01908 561666 Fax: 01908 568303
Email: admin@gb616.u-net.com
Web: www.choicehotels.com

SB £105 DB £125 HBS £131 HBD £147
B £9.95 L £3.50 D £16.
CC: MC Vi Am DC Swi Delt
🦢 🛆 🐾 🐾 🕃 🖵 🕿 ⅃ P 🐾 ⅌ 🐴 ⼍ 🐾
ⅲⅲ ⅲⅲ 🍴 💲
How to get there: M1 J-14, follow until the A5. Go north, take next exit and follow signs for A422, Two Mile Ash.

Southeast

Swan Revived

★★ ℞

High Street, Newport Pagnell, Buckinghamshire, MK16 8AR
Tel: 01908 610565 Fax: 01908 210995
Email: swanrevived@btinternet.com
Web: www.swanrevived.co.uk
SB £42.50 DB £60 HBS £55 HBD £45
B £6.50 L £5 D £14.50.
CC: MC Vi Am DC Swi Delt Solo

How to get there: M1 J-14, A509/B526 to Newport Pagnell. 1¹/₂ miles to hotel (on High Street).

Campanile

Travel Accommodation
40 Penn Road, Fenny Stratford, Bletchley, Milton Keynes, MK2
Tel: 01908 649819 Fax: 01908 649818

Typical Campanile Bistro

Campanile hotels offer comfortable and convenient budget accommodation and a traditional French-style Bistro providing freshly cooked food for breakfast, lunch and dinner. All rooms ensuite with tea/coffee-making facilities, DDT and TV with Sky channels.
SB £45.90 DB £50.85 B £4
CC: MC Vi Am DC Swi Delt Solo

How to get there: A5 south for Dunstable. At Little Chef roundabout, take fourth exit, on right to Fenny Stratford. Take first left turn.

Looking for great dining? Look for RAC Hotels and Guest Accommodation displaying the RAC Dining Award symbol in this Guide.

For your complete reassurance, only RAC Hotels and Guest Accommodation have been assessed on your behalf by our team of independent inspectors for quality, facilities and service.

New Alresford, Hampshire

Swan

★★

11 West Street, New Alresford, Hampshire, SO24 9AD
Tel: 01962 732302 Fax: 01962 735274
Email: swanhotel@btinternet.com

In the 18th century, The Swan was a staging post on the London-Southampton run. The original 17th century gabled building has been well-matched by a new bedroom wing.
CC: MC Vi

See advert on facing page

New Milton, Hampshire

Chewton Glen

★★★★★ ℞℞℞

Christchurch Road, New Milton, Hampshire, BH25 6QS
Tel: 01425 275341 Fax: 01425 272310
Email: reservations@chewtonglen.com
Web: www.chewtonglen.com
Children minimum age: 6
SB £272.50 DB £290 HBS £337.50 HBD £385
B £17.50 L £30 D £47.50.
CC: MC Vi Am DC Swi Delt

How to get there: On A35 from Lyndhurst, drive 10 miles and turn left at staggered junction. Follow brown tourist signs for hotel through Walkford, take second left.

Guide dogs

If a Hotel or Guest Accommodation does not display this 'dogs welcome' symbol in its listing, the hotelier may still be happy to welcome guests with guide dogs, and you should contact the property to discover whether this will be a problem.

Newbury, Berkshire

Donnington Valley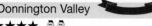

★★★★ ⒭ ⒭

Old Oxford Road, Donnington, Newbury,
Berkshire, RG14 3AG
Tel: 01635 521199 Fax: 01635 551123
Email: general@donningtonvalley.co.uk
Web: www.donningtonvalley.co.uk

A luxurious privately owned 4 star hotel
surrounded by its own 18 hole golf course.
Superb food in the 'Wine Press' restaurant with
an extensive wine list.
SB £148 DB £160 HBS £170 HBD £200
B £12.50 L £16 D £20.
CC: MC Vi Am DC Swi Delt

How to get there: M4 J-13. A34 southbound to
Newbury. Leave at first exit signed Donnington
Castle. First right, then left. Hotel 1 mile on right.

Regency Park

★★★★ ⒭

Bowling Green Road, Thatcham, Newbury,
Berkshire, RG18 3RP
Tel: 01635 871555 Fax: 01635 871571
Email: regencypark@bestwestern.co.uk
Web: www.regencyparkhotel.co.uk

Recently refurbished luxury hotel renowned for
its high standards of service. Extensive indoor
leisure facilities with pool and gymnasium.

Executive standard bedrooms and award-
winning restaurant.
SB £125 DB £170 HBS £145 HBD £105
B £12.50 L £17.50 D £21.50.
CC: MC Vi Am DC Swi Delt

How to get there: From Newbury A4 signed
Thatcham/Reading. At second roundabout
follow signs to Cold Ash. Hotel 1 mile on left.

Vineyard at Stockcross

★★★★ ⒭ ⒭ ⒭ ⒭

Stockcross, Newbury, Berkshire, RG20 8JU
Tel: 01635 528770 Fax: 01635 528398
Email: general@the-vineyard.co.uk
Web: www.the-vineyard.co.uk

To dine and stay at the Vineyard is to experience
excellence at every level. Award winning cuisine
matches an encyclopedic wine list.
SB £146 DB £174 HBD £153 B £15.50 L £18
D £44. CC: MC Vi Am DC Swi Delt

How to get there: M4 J-13. A34 southbound
and exit to Stockross. At roundabout take
second exit. Vineyard is ¼ mile on right.

Newick, East Sussex

The Pilgrims Rest At The Bull Inn

❖

The Bull Inn, The Green, Newick, East Sussex,
BN8 4LA
Tel: 01825 722055

Newport Pagnell, Buckinghamshire

Thurstons

◆◆◆

90 High Street, Newport Pagnell,
Buckinghamshire, MK16 8EH
Tel: 01908 611377 Fax: 01908 611394

SB £48 DB £62 CC: MC Vi Am

How to get there: Located in the middle of town centre in High Street, just off M21 J-14.

Old Harlow, Essex

Green Man
★★★
Mulberry Green, Old Harlow, Essex, CM17 0ET
Tel: 01279 442521 Fax: 01279 626113

Oxford, Oxfordshire

Cotswold Lodge
★★★★ 🍷🍷
66a Banbury Road, Oxford, Oxfordshire,
OX2 6JP
Tel: 01865 512121 Fax: 01865 512490
Web: www.cotswoldhotel.co.uk

Beautiful Victorian building, half a mile from the city centre in a quiet Conservation Area. Recently refurbished to a very high standard. Award winning restaurant. Bar with log fires, ample parking.
SB £125 DB £175 HBS £150 HBD £225 B £9.50
L £12 D £17. CC: MC Vi Am DC Swi Delt

How to get there: A40 Oxford ring road north, A4165 into city. Hotel on Banbury Road, 2 miles into city on left.

Heritage Hotels – The Randolph
★★★★ 🍷🍷
Beaumont Street, Oxford, Oxfordshire, OX1 2LN
Tel: 0870 4008200
Email: heritagehotels_oxford.randolph
@forte-hotels.com
Web: www.heritage-hotels.com
SB £163.95 DB £200 HBS £190 HBD £215
B £15 L £10.95 D £20.
CC: MC Vi Am DC Swi Delt

Oxford Belfry
★★★★ 🍷
Milton Common, Thame, Oxfordshire, OX9 2JW
Tel: 01844 279381 Fax: 01844 279624
Email: oxfordbelfry@marstonhotels.com
Web: www.marstonhotels.co.uk

MARSTON HOTELS

SB £110 DB £142 HBS £79.50 HBD £159 B £11
L £15.95 D £26. CC: MC Vi Am DC Swi Delt

How to get there: M40 northbound J-7, southbound J-8a. Hotel on A40, 1½ miles from either junction.

Heritage Hotels – Eastgate Hotel
★★★ 🍷
Merton Street, Oxford, Oxfordshire, OX1 4BE
Tel: 0870 400 8201 Fax: 01865 791681
Email: heritagehotels_oxford.eastgate
@forte-hotels.com
Web: www.heritage-hotels.com
SB £85 DB £160 HBS £105 HBD £180
B £9.95 L £5.95 D £10.95.
CC: MC Vi Am DC Swi Delt JCB

Balkan Lodge
★★
315 Iffley Road, Oxford, Oxfordshire, OX4 4AG
Tel: 01865 244524 Fax: 01865 251090
SB £62.50 DB £72.50 CC: MC Vi Swi Delt

Foxcombe Lodge
★★
Fox Lane, Boars Hill, Oxford, Oxfordshire,
OX1 5DP
Tel: 01865 730746 Fax: 01865 730628

Palace Hotel
★★
250-250a Iffley Road, Oxford, Oxfordshire,
OX4 1SE
Tel: 01865 727627 Fax: 01865 200478
Web: www.oxlink.co.uk/oxford/hotels/theplace
SB £65 DB £75 HBS £72.50 HBD £90
B £5.80 D £7.50.
CC: MC Vi Am Swi Delt

How to get there: One mile from city centre, on 4158 road southeast of city centre.

Victoria Hotel

★★

180 Abingdon Road, Oxford, Oxfordshire,
OX1 4RA
Tel: 01865 724536 Fax: 01865 794909
Web: www.localhost/hotels/victoria
SB £58 DB £68 CC: MC Vi Swi Delt

Chestnuts Guest House

♦♦♦♦♦

45 Davenant Road, off Woodstock Road,
Oxford, OX2 8BU
Tel: 01865 553375 Fax: 01865 553375
Children minimum age: 10.
Closed Christmas to New Year
SB £44 DB £67

How to get there: Leave A40/A34 at Peartree
roundabout for Woodstock Road, then
Woodstock/A414 second left and A40 West off
Woodstock Road roundabout.

Eltham Villa

♦♦♦♦

148 Woodstock Road, Yarnton, Oxford,
Oxfordshire, OX5 1PW
Tel: 01865 376037 Fax: 01865 376037
Children minimum age: 5.
Closed Christmas to New Year

An immaculately kept small cottage-style guest
house, in countryside village area on the main
A44 between the city of Oxford and the historic
towns of Woodstock and Blenheim Palace.
SB £30 DB £45 CC: MC Vi Swi Delt

How to get there: On A44 between Oxford and
Woodstock, minutes from Blenheim Palace.

Get your personalised route to the Hotel or
Guest Accommodation of your choice with
RAC's free on-line Route Planner facility —
visit www.rac.co.uk

Galaxie

♦♦♦♦

180 Banbury Road, Oxford, Oxfordshire,
OX2 7BT
Tel: 01865 515688 Fax: 01865 556824
Email: info@galaxie.co.uk
Web: www.galaxie.co.uk
SB £52 DB £76 CC: MC Vi Swi Delt

How to get there: One mile north of Oxford on
Banbury Road.

Marlborough House

♦♦♦♦

321 Woodstock Road, Oxford, Oxfordshire,
OX2 7NY
Tel: 01865 311321 Fax: 01865 515329
Email: enquiries@marlbhouse.win-uk.net
Web: www.oxfordcity.co.uk/hotels/marlborough
Children minimum age: 5

This modern purpose-built hotel is located
1½ miles from city centre. Immaculate ensuite
bedrooms with kitchenette, TV, tea/coffee-
making facilities. Parking available.
SB £69 DB £80 CC: MC Vi Am DC Swi Delt
JCB Solo

How to get there: In north Oxford, 6 miles
M40 J-9. 1½ miles from city centre,

Acorn Guest House

♦♦♦

260-262 Iffley Road, Oxford, Oxfordshire,
OX4 1SE
Tel: 01865 247998 Fax: 01865 247998
Children minimum age: 9.
Closed Christmas to New Year
SB £27 DB £48 CC: MC Vi Am Swi Delt JCB

How to get there: From Oxford ring road, follow
A4158 north towards city centre. From
roundabout go 1 mile; hotel on left, just after
Motorworld VW garage on right.

Southeast

Bath Place

◆◆◆

4/5 Bath Place, Holywell Street, Oxford,
Oxfordshire, OX1 3SU
Tel: 01865 791812 Fax: 01865 791834
Email: bathplace@compuserve.com
Web: www.bathplace.co.uk
SB £90 DB £95 CC: MC Vi Am DC Swi Delt

How to get there: Signs to city centre. Hotel is
100yds from Mansfield Road and Parks Road.

Brown's Guest House

◆◆◆

281 Iffley Road, Oxford, Oxfordshire, OX4 4AQ
Tel: 01865 246822 Fax: 01865 246822

Coach and Horses

◆◆◆

Stadhamton Road, Chislehampton, Oxon,
OX44 7UX
Tel: 01865 890255 Fax: 01865 891995
Closed December 26–30

A charming 16th-century oak-beamed inn and
free house set in splendid Oxfordshire
countryside. Excellent reputation for food and
service.
CC: MC Vi Am DC

Conifer Guest House

◆◆◆

116 The Glade, Headington, Oxford,
Oxfordshire, OX3 7DX
Tel: 01865 763055 Fax: 01865 63055

Pickwick's

◆◆◆
15–17 London Road, Headington, Oxford,
OX3 7SP
Tel: 01865 750487 Fax: 01865 742208
Email: pickwicks@x-stream.co.uk
Web: www.pickwicks.oxfree.com
SB £38 DB £60 CC: MC Vi Am DC Swi Delt

How to get there: Oxford ring road, A420 for
Headington at Headington roundabout.
Pickwicks at junction Lowdon/Sandfield roads.

River Hotel

◆◆◆

17 Botley Road, Oxford, Oxfordshire, OX2 0AA
Tel: 01865 243475 Fax: 01865 724306
Closed Christmas and New Year
SB £60 DB £70 CC: MC Vi

How to get there: One mile Oxford Ring Road
West Exit (A420). Near Railway/Coach stations.
Nearest motorway junctions: J-8, J-9, J-13.

Tilbury Lodge

◆◆◆

5 Tilbury Lane, Botley, Oxford, Oxfordshire,
OX2 9NB
Tel: 01865 862138 Fax: 01865 863700

Pagham, West Sussex

Inglenook Hotel

★★★
253–255 Pagham Road, Pagham, West Sussex,
PO21 3QB
Tel: 01243 262495 Fax: 01243 262668
Email: inglenook@btinternet.com
Web: www.btinternet.com/~inglenook

Family owned and run, 16th century hotel,
restaurant and free house. Cosy bars with
inglenook log fireplaces. Attractive restaurant
overlooking and opening onto gardens. Seafood
specialities. Wedding ceremonies & receptions,
conferences. Car parking at rear.
SB £50 DB £90 HBS £60 HBD £115 B £8.50
L £11.95 D £16.95. CC: MC Vi Am DC Swi Delt
How to get there: Ten minutes from A27,
travelling south, signposted Pagham.

Pangbourne, Berkshire

George

★★★

The Square, Pangbourne, Berkshire, RG8 7AJ
Tel: 01189 842237 Fax: 01189 844354
Email: info@georgehotelpangbourne.co.uk
Web: www.georgehotelpangbourne.co.uk
B £6 L £6 D £13. CC: MC Vi Am DC Swi Delt

How to get there: M4 J-12. A340 towards
Pangbourne. In village, right at mini-roundabout.
Hotel 50 yards on left.

Pevensey, East Sussex

Priory Court

♦ ♦ ♦

Castle Road, Pevensey, East Sussex, BN24 5LG
Tel: 01323 763150 Fax: 01323 769030
Email: prioryct@easynet.co.uk
SB £45 DB £60 B £5 L £7 D £7.
CC: MC Vi Swi Delt

How to get there: At the roundabout at junction
of A27 and A259, follow sign for Pevensey.
See advert below

Portsmouth, Hampshire

Queen's Hotel

★★★

Clarence Parade, Southsea, Portsmouth,
Hampshire, PO5 3LJ
Tel: 02392 822466 Fax: 02392 821901
Email: cjgil93131@aol.com
Web: www.queenshotel-southsea.co.uk
SB £59.75 DB £91.50 HBS £74.50 HBD £60.25
B £9.75 L £14.75 D £19.75.
CC: MC Vi Am DC Swi Delt

How to get there: M27/M275 to Portsmouth. To
Southsea seafront. Hotel opposite war memorial.
See advert below

Royal Beach

★★★

South Parade, Portsmouth & Southsea,
Hampshire, PO4 0RN
Tel: 02392 731281 Fax: 02392 817572
SB £69.50 DB £75 HBS £65 HBD £95 B £9
D £11.50. CC: MC Vi Am DC Swi Delt JCB

How to get there: M27 J-12. M275 to Portsmouth. To Southsea main seafront road.

Priory Court Hotel

Character 17th-century hotel in landscaped
gardens adjacent to Pevensey Castle.
Offers 9 well equipped bedrooms, à la carte
restaurant, bar fayre and a traditional free
house bar with secluded gardens. Open all
year including Christmas. Bargain breaks
available Nov–March. Small functions and
private dining.

Castle Road, Pevensey, East Sussex
BN24 5LG
Tel: 01323 763150   Fax: 01323 769030
Email: prioryct@easynet.co.uk

The Queens Hotel

Splendid Edwardian style hotel with
panoramic views of the Solent, offering a
selection of bars and an award winning
restaurant. 72 ensuite bedrooms. Easily
accessible from M275 and continental ferry
port. Ample secure, free parking

Clarence Parade, Southsea,
Portsmouth PO5 3LJ
Tel: 02392 822466   Fax: 02392 821901
Website: www.queenshotel-southsea.co.uk

Sandringham

★★

Osborne Road, Clarence Parade, Southsea,
Hampshire, PO5 3LR
Tel: 023 92826969 Fax: 023 92822330
Email: reception@sandringham-hotel.co.uk
Web: www.sandringham-hotel.co.uk
SB £45 DB £56 HBS £10 HBD £20
B £3.50 D £8. CC: MC Vi Am Swi

How to get there: M27 to Portsmouth.
Southsea seafront. Hotel 200 yards on corner
of amusement park.

Uppermount House

♦♦♦♦

The Vale, off Clarendon Road, Southsea,
Portsmouth, Hampshire, PO5 2EQ
Tel: 0239 282 0456 Fax: 0239 282 0456

An attractive, family-run Victorian villa with
rooms of character, some with four-poster or
canopy beds. Within easy walking distance of
the city centre.
SB £25 DB £42 HBS £37.50 HBD £67
CC: MC Vi Swi Delt Solo Electron JCB Switch

How to get there: Head for D-Day museum.
Down road opposite, across Cross Road to
Debenhams. Right and first right.

Aquarius Court

♦♦♦

34 St Ronan's Road, Portsmouth, Hampshire,
PO4 0PT
Tel: 023 92822872

Abbeville Hotel

♦

26 Nettlecombe Avenue, Portsmouth/Southsea,
Hampshire, PO4 0QW
Tel: 023 92826209

Princes Risborough, Buckinghamshire

Rose & Crown

★★

Wycombe Road, Saunderton, Princes
Risborough, Buckinghamshire, HP27 9NP
Tel: 01844 345299 Fax: 01844 343140
Closed Christmas
SB £69.95 DB £78 CC: MC Vi Am DC Swi Delt

How to get there: On A4010 midway between
High Wycombe and Aylesbury.

Ramsgate, Kent

Grove End Hotel

♦♦♦

2 Grange Road, Ramsgate, Kent, CT11 9NA
Tel: 01843 587520 Fax: 01843 853666

Reading, Berkshire

Millennium Madejski

★★★★ ஜ ஜ ஜ

Madejski Stadium, J-11 M4, Reading, Berkshire,
RG2 0FL
Tel: 0118 925 3500 Fax: 0118 925 3501

Prestigious hotel with superb luxury facilities
ideally located in royal Berkshire for business
trips and leisure weekends. Nearby attractions
include Legoland and Windsor Castle.

Copper Inn

★★★ ஜ ஜ

Church Road, Pangbourne-on-Thames,
Berkshire, RG8 7AR
Tel: 0118 9842244 Fax: 0118 9845542
Email: reservations@copper-inn.co.uk
Web: www.copper-inn.co.uk
B £7.95 L £12.95 D £20. CC: MC Vi Am DC Swi
How to get there: M4 J-12. By parish church.

Hanover International Reading

★★★

Pingewood, Reading, Berkshire, RG30 3UN
Tel: 0118 950 0885 Fax: 0118 939 1996
Email: hihreading.sales@virgin.net
Web: www.hanover-international.com

Stunning modern hotel in a spectacular lakeside setting, convenient for London, Windsor Castle, Legoland, M4, Heathrow and Gatwick.
Extensive indoor and outdoor leisure facilities, including watersports.

The Mill House Hotel

A hotel of elegance and charm, dating back to 1823, set in beautiful gardens beside the River Loddon. Individually designed ensuite bedrooms with all of today's modern facilities. A particular feature of this hotel is the food which has recently been awarded an RAC Grade One Dining Award. Close proximity to M4, M5.

Old Basingstoke Road, Swallowfield, Reading, Berkshire RG7 1PY
Tel: 01189 883124   Fax: 01189 885550
Email: info@themillhousehotel.co.uk
Website: www.themillhousehotel.co.uk

SB £146.50 DB £158 HBS £166 HBD £98.50
B £11.50 L £10 D £19.50.
CC: MC Vi Am DC Swi Delt

How to get there: M4 J-11, A33 south (Basingstoke). Right at first roundabout then second right. Follow lane for 2 miles, through traffic lights. Hotel on left.

Mill House

★★

Old Basingstoke Road, Swallowfield, Reading, Berkshire, RG7 1PY
Tel: 01189 883124 Fax: 01189 885550
Email: info@themillhousehotel.co.uk
Web: www.themillhousehotel.co.uk
Closed December 25 to January 7
SB £67.50 DB £85 HBS £45 HBD £65 B £7.50
D £20. CC: MC Vi Am DC Swi Delt

How to get there: M4 J-11, A33 to Basingstoke. Left at 1st roundabout. Hotel 2 miles on right.
See advert below left

Rainbow Corner

★★

132–138 Caversham Road, Reading, Berkshire, RG1 8AY
Tel: 01189 588140 Fax: 01189 586500
Email: info@rainbowhotel.co.uk
Web: www.rainbowhotel.co.uk
B £2.95 D £11.95. CC: MC Vi Am DC Swi

How to get there: On A329, 1 mile Reading town centre. Signposted Caversham/Henley.

Redhill, Surrey

Ashleigh House

♦♦♦♦

39 Redstone Hill, Redhill, Surrey, RH1 4BG
Tel: 01737 764763 Fax: 01737 780308
Closed Christmas
SB £36.50 DB £52.50 CC: MC Vi

How to get there: 500 yards Redhill rail station on A25. M25 J-6 and J-8 3 miles away.

Dining out

If you are looking for great dining when staying away, look for RAC Hotels and Guest Accommodation displaying the RAC Dining Award symbol in this Guide.

Southeast

Reigate, Surrey

Reigate Manor

★★★
Reigate Hill, Reigate, Surrey, RH2 9PF
Tel: 01737 240125 Fax: 01737 223883
B £11 L £17 D £21. CC: MC Vi Am DC Swi Delt

How to get there: M25 J-8. A217 south. Hotel is
1 mile on right.

Richmond, Surrey

The Bingham Hotel

❖
61/63 Petersham Road, Richmond, Surrey,
TW10 6UT
Tel: 020 8940 0902 Fax: 020 8948 8737

Rochester, Kent

Bridgewood Manor

★★★★ ♟♟♟
Bridgewood Roundabout, Walderslade Woods,
Chatham, Kent, ME5 9AX
Tel: 01634 201333 Fax: 01634 201330
Email: bridgewoodmanor@marstonhotels.com
Web: www.marstonhotels.co.uk

**MARSTON
HOTELS**

SB £110 DB £142 HBS £73 HBD £146
B £11 L £15 D £26.
CC: MC Vi Am DC Swi Delt

How to get there: M2 J-3 or M20 J-6. A229 for
Rochester. At Bridgewood roundabout 3rd exit.

Royal Victoria & Bull

★
High Street, Rochester, Kent, ME1 1PX
Tel: 01634 846266 Fax: 01634 832312
Email: enquiries@rvandb.co.uk
Web: www.rvandb.co.uk
SB £57.50 DB £72.50 B £5.75 L £5.45 D £10.
CC: MC Vi Am DC Swi
How to get there: Follow A2 into Rochester.
Across bridge and into middle lane. After lights,
turn right into Northgate at first dual
carriageway intersection. Turn right into High
Street: hotel is on left.

Rochford, Essex

Hotel Renouf

★★★
Bradley Way, Rochford, Essex, SS4 1BU
Tel: 01702 541334 Fax: 01702 549563
B £3 L £15.50 D £15.50.
CC: MC Vi Am DC Swi Delt   Closed Dec 26–30
How to get there: M25 J-29. A127 for Southend.
Left at Tesco roundabout. To Rochford. Under rail
bridge, right, first left by BP garage. Hotel on right.
See advert below

Romsey, Hampshire

Heritage Hotels – The White Horse

★★★
Market Place, Romsey, Hampshire, SO51 8ZJ
Tel: 0870 400 8123 Fax: 01794 517485

Ruislip, Middlesex

The Barn

★★★
West End Road, Ruislip, Middlesex, HA4 6JB
Tel: 01895 636057 Fax: 01895 638379

Rye, East Sussex

Flackley Ash

★★★

Peasmarsh, nr Rye, East Sussex, TN31 6YH
Tel: 01797 230651 Fax: 01797 230510
Email: flackleyash@marstonhotels.com
Web: www.marstonhotels.co.uk

MARSTON HOTELS

SB £82 DB £123 HBS £76 HBD £152
B £9 L £11 D £24. CC: MC Vi Am DC Swi Delt

How to get there: M25 J-5. A21 to Tunbridge Wells. A268 to Rye. Hotel on left on entering Peasmarsh.

The Mermaid

★★★

Mermaid Street, Rye, East Sussex, TN31 7EY
Tel: 01797 223065 Fax: 01797 225069

Hope Anchor

Watchbell Street, Rye, East Sussex, TN31 7HA
Tel: 01797 222216 Fax: 01797 223796

Benson

♦♦♦♦♦

15 East Street, Rye, East Sussex, TN31 7JY
Tel: 01797 225131 Fax: 01797 225512
Web: www.bensonhotel.co.uk

Situated in the heart of historic Rye, Benson offers sumptuous period-style bedrooms, most four-posters, with all modern conveniences, attractive lounge, conservatory and terrace overlooking the River Rother and Romney Marshes.
SB £50 DB £64 D £16. CC: MC Vi Swi Delt

How to get there: For East Street, follow town centre signs. Pass through landgate and after 300yds first left. Hotel is 75yds up hill on left.

Jeake's House

♦♦♦♦♦

Mermaid Street, Rye, East Sussex, TN31 7ET
Tel: 01797 222828 Fax: 01797 222623
Email: jeakeshouse@btinternet.com
Web: www.s-h-systems.co.uk/hotels/
jeakes.html
Children minimum age: 11
SB £27.50 DB £69 CC: MC Vi Swi Delt

How to get there: Approach Rye from A259 or A2070. Town centre signs. From High Street right into West Street, leading to Mermaid Street.
See advert on facing page

White Vine House

♦♦♦♦♦

High St, Rye, East Sussex, TN31 7JF
Tel: 01797 224748 Fax: 01797 223599
Email: irene@whitevinehouse.freeserve.co.uk

Tudor town house in the heart of ancient Rye with comfortable bedrooms, oak beams, stone fireplaces, books and paintings. Excellent breakfasts. Ideal for antique hunting, castles and gardens.
SB £40 DB £90 B £5 L £4.40
CC: MC Vi Am DC Swi Delt JCB

How to get there: At Rye follow signs to town centre and enter under Landgate Arch. Follow road into High Street and hotel is on right.

Old Borough Arms

♦♦♦♦

The Strand, Rye, East Sussex, TN31 7DB
Tel: 01797 222128 Fax: 01797 222128
Email: oldborougharms@btinternet.com
SB £30 DB £60 CC: MC Vi Swi Delt

How to get there: 20 minutes M20 J-10. Hotel on corner of Mermaid Street, one block away from the A259.

Southeast

Strand House

♦♦♦♦

The Strand, Winchelsea, Rye, East Sussex,
TN36 4JT
Tel: 01797 226276 Fax: 01797 224806
Email: strandhouse@winchelsea.freeserve.co.uk
Web: www.smoothhound.co.uk/hotels/
          strand.html
Children minimum age: 2

Fine old 15th century house with lots of oak
beams and inglenook fireplaces. Ensuite rooms
with TV and drinks tray. Romantic four-poster
available. Residents' bar and lounge. Non-
smoking establishment.
SB £34 DB £48 CC: MC Vi Swi Delt JCB

How to get there: From Rye, A259 for Hastings.
House on left, set back from road, approx
1¹/₂ miles from Rye after Winchelsea town sign.

Magnolia House

♦♦♦

15 Udimore Road, Rye, East Sussex, TN31 7DS
Tel: 01797 222561 Fax: 01797 227525
Web: www.magnoliaguesthouse.co.uk

Licensed premises, situated a few minutes' level
walk to Medieval Rye. A family-run guest house
with spacious accommodation.
SB £25 DB £50 HBS £35 HBD £70
CC: MC Vi DC Swi Delt

Jeake's House

17th-century Jeake's House stands on the
most famous cobbled street in Rye's medieval
town centre. Each stylishly restored bedroom
with brass, mahogany or Four-Poster bed
creates a very special atmosphere, combining
traditional elegance with modern comforts.

Breakfast served in
the galleried dining
room is traditional
or vegetarian and
the roaring fire and
timeless
atmosphere will
combine to make
your stay truly
memorable.

There is a
comfortable
drawing room
and book-lined
bar. Private car
park nearby

RaC

♦♦♦♦♦

Mermaid Street, Rye, East Sussex
TN31 7ET
Tel: 01797 222828   Fax: 01797 222623
Email: jeakeshouse@btinternet.com
Website: www.jeakeshouse.com

⊛ ⌇ ▭ **P** ⅋ ℃ ⅂ ⧖ ⏚ ⊹

How to get there: At roundabout at Strand Quay, go to Rye Centre. Keeping to the left of one-way system, go over rail line onto B2089. Over bridge and house is on right.

Saffron Walden, Essex

Crown House

★★ ♛♛♛

Great Chesterford, Saffron Walden, Essex, CB10 1NY

Tel: 01799 530515 Fax: 01799 530683
Web: www.virtualhotels.com
SB £62.50 DB £85 B £5 L £4.95 D £9.75.
CC: MC Vi Am Swi

⟐ ⅋ ⚑ ⅋ ⌇ ▭ ☎ ✆ **P** ⅋ ℃ ⧖ ⏚ ⊹
♨ ♨♨

How to get there: Close M11 J-9, on B1383 (old A11), 1 mile from Stump Cross roundabout.
See advert below

St Albans, Hertfordshire

Sopwell House

★★★★ ♛♛♛

Cottonmill Lane, St Albans, Hertfordshire, AL1 2HQ

Tel: 01727 864477 Fax: 01727 844741
Email: enquiries@sopwellhouse.co.uk
Web: www.sopwellhouse.co.uk

An elegant Georgian country house hotel, minutes away from M1 and M25 and 20 minutes from London by train. For meetings, accommodation, leisure and dining.
B £12.95 L £15.95 D £25. CC: MC Vi Am DC Swi Delt

⟐ ⌇ ▭ ☎ **P** ⅋ ℃ ⧖ ⏚ ⊛ ♨ ♨♨ SPA
Ψ ⅊

How to get there: M1 north/south, M25 east/west/ Heathrow/Dartford Tunnel. A414 Hatfield direction.

St Michael's Manor

★★★ ♛♛

Fishpool Street, St Albans, Hertfordshire, AL3 4RY

Tel: 01727 864444 Fax: 01727 848909
Email: smmanor@globalnet.co.uk
Web: www.stmichaelsmanor.com

23 individually styled bedrooms enjoy a unique blend of award-winning lakeside gardens, architectural splendour and unparalleled service. Just 10 minutes walk from the Abbey and city centre. Easy access to London, Heathrow and

Luton airports, and the M25 and M1.
SB £110 DB £145 B £13 L £15 D £31.
CC: MC Vi Am Swi Delt Solo

How to get there: M25 J-21a. Through Chiswell
Gn. Left at King Harry pub, right at roundabout. By
Waitrose, right at roundabout, next right then left.

Avalon

★★
260 London Road, St Albans, Hertfordshire,
AL1 1TJ
Tel: 01727 856757 Fax: 01727 856750
Email: hotelavalon@aol.com
Web: www.theavalonhotel.co.uk
SB £59 DB £65 CC: MC Vi Am DC Swi Delt

Quality Hotel St Albans

★★
237 London Road, St Albans, Hertfordshire,
AL1 1JQ
Tel: 01727 857858 Fax: 01727 855666
Email: st.albans@quality-hotels.net
Web: www.quality-hotels.net
SB £72 DB £89 B £6.95 L £2.80 D £14.25.
CC: MC Vi Am DC Swi Delt

How to get there: M25 J-2. A1081 to St Albans.
After 3 miles, hotel on left.

Ardmore House

♦♦♦
54 Lemsford Road, St Albans, Hertfordshire,
AL1 3PR
Tel: 01727 859313 Fax: 01727 859313

Large Edwarian house set in the conservation
area of St Albans. In close proximity to the main
city station for London and easy walking
distance of the town centre.
SB £52.50 DB £75 CC: MC Vi Am Swi Delt Solo

How to get there: M25 J-22. A1081 to St Albans.
London Colney Roundabout, A1081. Past 2 sets
of traffic lights: right at second mini-roundabout.
Hotel 800yds on right, after 2 sets of lights.

St Leonards-on-Sea, East Sussex

Royal Victoria

★★★
Marina, St Leonards on Sea, East Sussex,
TN38 0BD
Tel: 01424 445544 Fax: 01424 721995

Sandwich, Kent

Bell Hotel

★★★
The Quay, Sandwich, Kent, CT13 9EF
Tel: 01304 613388 Fax: 01304 615308

Famed for its excellent cuisine, the Bell offers
individually furnished bedrooms, with views over
the ancient town or the River Stour. Relax in
traditional comfort.
SB £75 DB £100 B £8 L £11.95 D £11.95.
CC: MC Vi Am DC Swi Delt JCB Solo

See advert on following page

Sedlescombe, East Sussex

Brickwall Hotel

★★★
The Green, Sedlescombe, East Sussex,
TN33 0QA
Tel: 01424 870253 Fax: 01424 870785
Email: reception@brickwallhotel.totalserve.co.uk
SB £55 DB £80 HBS £70 HBD £127
B £9 L £12.50 D £20.
CC: MC Vi Am DC Swi Delt JCB Solo Electron

How to get there: Hotel in Sedlescombe on
B2244, 3 miles east of Battle.

Southeast

Sevenoaks, Kent

Moorings Hotel

◆ ◆ ◆

97 Hitchen Hatch Lane, Sevenoaks, Kent,
TN13 3BE
Tel: 01732 452589 Fax: 01732 456462
Email: theryans@mooringshotel.co.uk
Web: www.mooringshotel.co.uk

SB £40 DB £60 HBS £55 HBD £90
B £4 L £4 D £6.50.
CC: MC Vi Am DC Swi Delt JCB Solo Electron
  ♿ ⊗ ⌚ 💻 ☎ 📞 🅿 🐎 💈 🐎 ⌇ 🐟 ⚘ 👥 ♨
How to get there: M25 J-5. To Sevenoaks for
1 mile. At roundabout, right, after one mile left
into Hitchen Hatch Lane opposite rail station.

The Bell Hotel

Situated in the heart of classic championship
golf links country, The Bell Hotel enjoys an
international reputation for its hospitality and
cuisine. Exclusive golf breaks combine the
traditional comforts of this 3-star hotel with
golf at the famous Prince's Golf Club.

The Quay, Sandwich, Kent CT13 9EF
Tel: 01304 613388   Fax: 01304 615308

Sheerness, Kent

Victoriana

❖

103–109 Alma Road, Sheerness, Kent,
ME12 2PD
Tel: 01795 665555 Fax: 01795 580633
SB £17 DB £32 B £4 D £3.50. CC: MC Vi Am
  ♿ 🐟 🐎 ⊗ 💻 🅿 🐎 💈 🐎 ⌇ 🐟 ⚘ 👥 ♨
How to get there: Hotel is corner property on
Alma/Winstanley Road, close town and beach.

Shepperton-on-Thames, Middlesex

Warren Lodge

★ ★ ★
Church Square, Shepperton-on-Thames,
Middlesex, TW17 9JZ
Tel: 01932 242972 Fax: 01932 253883

Sittingbourne, Kent

Coniston Hotel

★ ★
London Road, Sittingbourne, Kent, ME10 1NT
Tel: 01795 472131 Fax: 01795 428056

Hempstead House

◆ ◆ ◆ ◆ ◆   🏆 ⌀
London Road, Bapchild, Sittingbourne, Kent,
ME9 9PP
Tel: 01795 428020 Fax: 01795 436362
Email: info@hempsteadhouse.co.uk
Web: www.hempsteadhouse.co.uk
SB £65 DB £75 HBS £84.50 HBD £57 B £5
L £6.95 D £17.50. CC: MC Vi Am DC Swi Delt
  ⛱ 🐟 🐎 ⊗ 💻 📞 🅿 🐎 💈 🐎 ⌇ ⚘ 👥
👥 ♨ ⚓
How to get there: A2 1½ miles east Sittingbourne.
See advert on facing page

Beaumont

◆ ◆ ◆   ⌀
74 London Road, Sittingbourne, Kent,
ME10 1NS
Tel: 01795 472536 Fax: 01795 425921
Email: beaumont74@aol.com
Web: www.thebeaumont.co.uk
SB £30 DB £50 B £5
CC: MC Vi Am DC Swi Delt
  ♿ 🐟 🐎 ⊗ ⌚ 💻 ☎ 📞 🅿 🐎 💈 🐎 ⌇ ⚘
👥 ♨
How to get there: M2 or M20, take A249 north
towards Sheerness. A2 exit and follow road for
1 mile towards Sittingbourne.

Slough, Berkshire

Copthorne Slough–Windsor

★★★★
Cippenham Lane, Slough, Berkshire, SL1 2YE
Tel: 01753 516222 Fax: 01753 516237

Sonning-on-Thames, Berkshire

French Horn

★★★ 🐎🐎🐎
Sonning on Thames, Berkshire, RG4 6TN
Tel: 01189 692204 Fax: 01189 442210

Southampton, Hampshire

Highfield House

★★★
Highfield Lane, Portswood, Southampton,
Hampshire, SO17 1AQ
Tel: 023 80359955 Fax: 023 80583910
Email: highfield@zoffanyhotels.co.uk
Web: www.zoffanyhotels.co.uk
SB £85 DB £98 HBS £65 HBD £45
B £7.50 L £9 D £14. CC: MC Vi Am DC Swi Delt
🐎🛇🍴🖥📞🅿🛝🎠🐕🎠♻🎱 🎱 'Y'
How to get there: M3 J14. A33 to city centre.
Signs Portswood/Bitterne. Hotel on left 1½ miles.
M27 J-5. A335 to city centre. Signs
Portswood/University. Hotel on right 1 mile.

Novotel Southampton

★★★
1 West Quay Road, Southampton, Hampshire,
SO15 1RA
Tel: 02380 330550 Fax: 02380 222158
Email: h1073@accor-hotels.com
Web: www.novotel.com
SB £79 DB £88.50 B £9.50 L £13.50 D £17.50.
CC: MC Vi Am DC Swi Delt
♿🛗🐎🛇🍴🖥📞❄🔦🅿🛝🎠🐕🎠♻
🎱🎱 'Y'⁄. 🖊
How to get there: M3 to M27 Bournemouth,
M271 J-3 Southampton Docks. At end left on A35.

Elizabeth House

★★
43–44 The Avenue, Southampton, Hampshire,
SO17 1XP
Tel: 023 80224327 Fax: 023 80224327
Email: mail@elizabethhousehotel.com
Web: www.elizabethhousehotel.com
SB £47.50 DB £57.50 B £6 L £3 D £8.
CC: MC Vi Swi Delt Solo JCB Electron
♿🐎🛇🖥📞🅿🛝🎠🐕🎠♻🎱🎱
How to get there: M3 to A33. Hotel 2 miles on left.

The Star Hotel & Restaurant

★★
26 High Street, Southampton, Hampshire,
SO14 2NA
Tel: 023 80339939 Fax: 023 80335291

Hunters Lodge

♦♦♦♦ 🍴
25 Landguard Road, Shirley, Southampton,
SO15 5DL
Tel: 02380 227919 Fax: 02380 230913
Email: hunterslodge.hotel@virgin.net
SB £42 DB £55 CC: MC Vi Am DC Swi Delt
🛇🍴🖥📞🅿🛝🎠🐕🎠♻🎱
How to get there: North of railway station, up
Hill Lane. 4th left, hotel halfway on left.

Landguard Lodge

♦♦♦♦ 🍴
21 Landguard Road, Southampton, SO1 5DL
Tel: 023 80636904 Fax: 023 80632258
Email: landguard.lodge@mail.com
Web: www.landguardlodge.co.uk
Children minimum age: 5
SB £29 DB £45 CC: MC Vi Am Swi Delt
🛇🍴🖥🅿🛝🎠🐕🎠♻
How to get there: North of railway station,
between Hill Lane and Shirley Road.

Nirvana Private Hotel

386 Winchester Road, Bassett, Southampton,
Hampshire, SO16 7DH
Tel: 023 80790087 Fax: 023 80790575

Southend-on-Sea, Essex

Balmoral

32-36 Valkyrie Road, Westcliff-on-Sea, Essex,
SS0 8BU
Tel: 01702 342947 Fax: 01702 337828
Email: balmoralhotel@netscapeonline.co.uk
Web: www.smoothhound.co.uk/
             hotels/balmoral.html
SB £45 DB £69 HBS £55 HBD £89 B £6.95
L £4.95 D £9.95. CC: MC Vi Am Swi Delt
See advert below

Tower Hotel and Restaurant

146 Alexandra Road, Southend-on-Sea, Essex,
SS1 1HE
Tel: 01702 348635 Fax: 01702 433044
Email: tower.rest@virgin.net

Balmoral Hotel

Located in a quiet area of Westcliff-on-Sea, the
Balmoral Hotel offers the discerning business
traveller quality accommodation, high levels of
comfort and service in an environment that is
friendly and welcoming. Ideally positioned for
central Southend and its many commercial
areas, the hotel also offers fully enclosed
off-street parking, cable TV, ensuite rooms,
24-hour room service, exclusive à la carte or
simple table d'hôte menus, and is within easy
reach of major local leisure facilities.

32–36 Valkyrie Road, Westcliff-on-Sea,
Essex SS0 8BU

Tel: 01702 342947   Fax: 01702 337828
Email: balmoralhotel@netscapeonline.co.uk

SB £39 DB £59 B £3.50 D £7.95.
CC: MC Vi Am DC Swi Delt

How to get there: Off A13 into Milton Rd, left into
Cambridge Rd, third right at mini-roundabout into
Wilson Rd. Hotel on right at crossroads.
See advert on facing page top

Mayflower

6 Royal Terrace, Southend-on-Sea, Essex,
SS1 1DY
Tel: 01702 340489

Terrace

8 Royal Terrace, Southend-on-Sea, Essex,
SS1 1DY
Tel: 01702 348143 Fax: 01702 348143
Children minimum age: 3
SB £21 DB £34

How to get there: From seafront up Pier Hill into
Royal Terrace.

Regency

♦

18 Royal Terrace, Southend-on-sea, Essex,
SS1 1DU
Tel: 01702 340747

Southsea, Hampshire

Seacrest

★★

12 South Parade, Southsea, Hampshire, PO5 2JB
Tel: 023 92875666 Fax: 023 92832523

Staines, Middlesex

Heritage Hotels – The Thames Lodge

★★★

Thames Street, Staines, TW18 4SJ
Tel: 0870 400 8121 Fax: 01784 454858

Stanwell Hall Hotel

★★

Town Lane, Stanwell, Staines, Middlesex,
TW19 7PW
Tel: 01784 252292 Fax: 01784 245250
Closed December 24–29
SB £80 DB £100 CC: MC Vi Am DC Swi Delt

How to get there: M25 J-14. To Heathrow Terminal 4. Roundabout, right to Staines. At lights
left to Stanwell. Right at mini-roundabout.

Southeast

Stansted Airport, Essex

Vintage Court

★★★
Puckeridge Corner, Puckeridge, Ware,
Hertfordshire, SG11 1SA
Tel: 01920 409955 Fax: 01920 468016
Email: countyware@msihotels.co.uk
CC: MC Vi Am DC

See advert below right

Stevenage, Hertfordshire

Novotel Stevenage

★★★
Knebworth Park, Stevenage, Hertfordshire,
SG1 2AX
Tel: 01438 346100 Fax: 01438 723872
Email: H0992@accor-hotels.com
Web: www.novotel.com
SB £99 DB £109 CC: MC Vi Am DC Swi

How to get there: On A1(M) J-7. Entrance
Knebworth Park.

Steyning, West Sussex

Old Tollgate

★★★
The Street, Bramber, Steyning, West Sussex,
BN44 3WE
Tel: 01903 879494 Fax: 01903 813399
Email: otr@fastnet.co.uk
Web: www.home.fastnet.co.uk/otr
SB £78.95 DB £85.90 HBS £98.90
HBD £125.80 B £6.95 L £13.95 D £19.95.
CC: MC Vi Am DC Swi Delt JCB

How to get there: From A24 or A27, A283 to
Steyning, then signs to Bramber. Brown tourist
signs advertise hotel.

Penfold Gallery Guest House

♦♦♦♦

30 High Street, Steyning, BN44 3GG
Tel: 01903 815595 Fax: 01903 816686
Email: jturner15@compuserve.com
Children minimum age: 12
A medieval dwelling full of architectural interest,

the Penfold Gallery has the beautiful backdrop of the South Downs. Personal attention to all guests. Creative cooking. Non-smoking.
SB £45 DB £70 HBS £115 HBD £110
CC: MC Vi Swi Delt

How to get there: Exit A27 at A283 for Steyning. House is east of mini-roundabout in High Street.

Springwells Hotel

A former Georgian Merchant House in picturesque village.

All bedrooms are individually furnished with TV and telephone.

The bar and adjoining conservatory lead to a patio and outdoor heated swimming pool.

High Street, Steyning, West Sussex
BN44 3GG
Tel: 01903 812446   Fax: 01903 879823
Email: contact@springwells.co.uk
Website: www.springwells.co.uk

Springwells

♦♦♦♦

9 High Street, Steyning, West Sussex,
BN44 3GG
Tel: 01903 812446 Fax: 01903 879823
Email: contact@springwells.co.uk
Web: www.springwells.co.uk
Closed Christmas to New Year
SB £32 DB £54 B £6.95 CC: MC Vi Am DC

See advert below left

Stockbridge, Hampshire

Carbery

♦♦♦

Salisbury Hill, Stockbridge, Hampshire, SO20 6EZ
Tel: 01264 810771 Fax: 01264 811022
Closed 3 weeks around Christmas

Carbery Guest House is 2 minutes walk from the old market village of Stockbridge overlooking the River Test in one acre of landscaped gardens.
SB £28 DB £54 HBS £42.50 HBD £83 D £14.

How to get there: Hotel at Salisbury end of Stockbridge on A30.

Stokenchurch, Buckinghamshire

Kings Arms

★★★

Oxford Road, Stokenchurch, Buckinghamshire, HP14 3TA
Tel: 01494 609090 Fax: 01494 484582

Southeast

Streatley-on-Thames, Berkshire

Swan Diplomat

★★★★ 🛏 🛏

Streatley-on-Thames, Berkshire, RG8 9HR
Tel: 01491 878800 Fax: 01491 872554
Web: www.diplomathotel.com
SB £117.50 DB £157 HBS £144.50 HBD £211
B £8 L £27 D £27. CC: MC Vi Am DC Swi Delt

How to get there: M4 J-12, towards Theale, then A340 into Pangbourne. Take A329 to Streatley.

Surbiton, Surrey

Pembroke Lodge Guest House

♦ ♦ ♦

35 Cranes Park, Surbiton, Surrey, KT5 8AB
Tel: 020 839 00731

Sutton, Surrey

Thatched House

★★ 🛏

135 Cheam Road, Sutton, Surrey, SM1 2BN
Tel: 020 8642 3131 Fax: 020 8770 0684
SB £65 DB £80 HBS £75 HBD £100 B £7.50
L £10.95 D £13.50. CC: MC Vi DC Swi Delt

How to get there: M25 J-8. A217 Sutton. Right at A232. Hotel 500 yards right, before centre.

Eaton Court

♦ ♦

49 Eaton Road, Sutton, Surrey, SM2 5ED
Tel: 020 8643 6766 Fax: 020 8642 4580
Email: manager@eatoncourthotel.co.uk
Web: www.eatoncourthotel.co.uk
Children minimum age: 3.
Closed 2 weeks over Christmas
SB £35 DB £55 CC: MC Vi Am DC Swi Delt

How to get there: M25 J-8. A217 to Sutton, then B2230. First right after BP station into Cedar Road. Right into Eaton Road.

Guide dogs 🅡🅐🅒

If a Hotel or Guest Accommodation does not display this 'dogs welcome' symbol in its listing, the hotelier may still be happy to welcome guests with guide dogs, and you should contact the property to discover whether this will be a problem.

Sway, Hampshire

The Nurse's Cottage Little Gem

♦ ♦ ♦ ♦ ♦   🛏 🛏 ✿ ✦

Station Road, Sway, Lymington, Hampshire, SO41 6BA
Tel: 01590 683402 Fax: 01590 683402
Email: nurses.cottage@lineone.net
Web: www.hants.gov.uk/tourist/hotels
Children minimum age: 10.
Closed March and November
SB £55 DB £95 L £15 D £17.65.
CC: MC Vi Am Swi Delt

How to get there: Off B3055 in village centre, next to post office.
See advert below

Forest Heath

♦ ♦ ♦

Station Road, Sway, nr Lymington, Hants, SO41 6BA
Tel: 01590 682287

Taplow, Berkshire

Cliveden House

★★★★★ ♕♕♕♕

Taplow, Berkshire, SL6 0JF
Tel: 01628 668561 Fax: 01628 661837
Web: www.clivedenhouse.co.uk
B £18 L £46 D £42. CC: MC Vi Am DC Swi Delt

How to get there: M4 J7. Brown National Trust signs to Taplow. From M40 J-2, signs to Taplow.
See advert below

How to get there: Centre Thame, on A418 between Aylesbury and Oxford. M49 J-6 south, J-8 north. Car park at rear of hotel.

Thame, Oxfordshire

Spread Eagle

★★★ ♕♕

16 Cornmarket, Thame, Oxfordshire, OX9 2BR
Tel: 01844 213661 Fax: 01844 261380
Carefully modernised former Coaching Inn, set in town centre. Large car park. Good centre for visitng Oxford and the Vale of Aylesbury. Hospitality is the speciality.
SB £94.45 DB £55.90 HBS £111.25
HBD £79.80 B £12.50 L £18 D £24.50.
CC: MC Vi Am DC

Tonbridge, Kent

Langley

★★

18-20 London Road, Tonbridge, Kent, TN10 3DA
Tel: 01732 353311 Fax: 01732 771471
Email: the.langley@virgin.net
Web: www.rbhotels.co.uk
SB £75 DB £95 B £9.95 L £12.95 D £15.95.

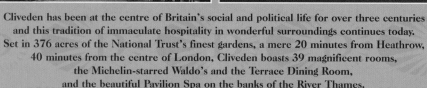

Southeast

CC: MC Vi Am Swi Delt

⚓ ⛰ 🍳 🖥 ☎ **P** 🐎 🚶 🦌 Ħ 🦢 ♨ ⅲ

How to get there: M25 J-5. A21 southbound, then B245 through Hildenborough. Hotel on left as you approach Tonbridge.

Tring, Hertfordshire

Pendley Manor

★★★★ 🍴

Cow Lane, Tring, Hertfordshire, HP23 5QY
Tel: 01442 891891 Fax: 01442 890687
Email: info@pendley-manor.co.uk

Grade II Listed luxury country house hotel, 71 bedrooms, many with four-poster beds. Excellent conference facilities, all meeting rooms have natural light. Award-winning restaurant, leisure facilities.
SB £100 DB £120
CC: MC Vi Am DC Swi Delt

⚓ 🍳 ⛰ 🖥 🐎 ⊗ 🍳 🖥 ☎ 🦌 **P** 🚶 🦌 Ħ
🦢 ⅲ ⅲ 🧖 ⵣ 🦆 🔍 🗲

Old Forge

♦♦♦♦ 🦋

5 High Street, Ivinghoe, Leighton Buzzard, Berkshire, LU7 9EP
Tel: 01296 668122 Fax: 01296 668122
Children minimum age: 6
SB £48 DB £60
CC: MC Vi Am Swi Delt

🦌 ⊗ 🍳 🖥 **P** 🚶 🦌 🐎 Ħ 🦢

How to get there: Less than 30 minutes M1 J-8 or J-11. 5 minutes Tring rail station.

Tunbridge Wells, Kent

Royal Wells Inn

★★★

Mount Ephraim, Tunbridge Wells, Kent,
TN4 8BE
Tel: 01892 511188 Fax: 01892 511908

Spa Hotel

★★★ 🍴🍴

Mount Ephraim, Tunbridge Wells, Kent, TN4 8XJ
Tel: 01892 520331 Fax: 01892 510575
Email: info@spahotel.co.uk
Web: www.spahotel.co.uk
SB £92.50 DB £119.50 HBS £78 HBD £156
B £10.25 L £22 D £25.
CC: MC Vi Am DC Swi

⚓ 🦌 ⛰ 🖥 🍳 🖥 ☎ 🦌 **P**⊛ 🚶 🦌 🐎 Ħ 🦢
🦆 ⅲ ⅲ ⵣ 🔍 🗲 ⌂

How to get there: M25 J-5, A21. 4th exit for A26. Right onto A264. Hotel ½ mile on right.
See advert below

Russell Hotel

★★

80 London Road, Tunbridge Wells, Kent,
TN1 1DZ
Tel: 01892 544833 Fax: 01892 515846
Email: sales@russell-hotel.com
Web: www.russell-hotel.com
SB £70 DB £85 HBS £88 HBD £121
CC: MC Vi Am Swi Delt

🦌 ⊗ 🍳 🖥 ☎ **P** 🚶 🦌 🐎 Ħ 🦢 ⅲ ⅲ

How to get there: Centre Tunbridge Wells, opposite the common on main London Road.

Uckfield, East Sussex

Buxted Park
★★★★
Buxted, Uckfield, East Sussex, TN22 4AY
Tel: 01825 732711 Fax: 01825 732770

Hooke Hall
◆◆◆◆◆
250 High Street, Uckfield, East Sussex,
TN22 1EN
Tel: 01825 761578 Fax: 01825 768025
Email: a.percy@virgin.net
Children minimum age: 12. Closed Christmas
SB £50 DB £75 B £5.50 CC: MC Vi
How to get there: Hooke Hall at northern end of
High Street, set back from road.

Wallingford, Oxfordshire

George
★★★
High Street, Wallingford, Oxfordshire, OX10 0BS
Tel: 01491 836665 Fax: 01491 825359
Email: george_hotel@hotmail.com
Web: www.roundandabout.co.uk/
sites/george.htm
CC: MC Vi Am DC Swi Delt

Springs
★★★
Wallingford Road, North Stoke, Wallingford,
Oxfordshire, OX10 6BE
Tel: 01491 836687 Fax: 01491 836877

Beetle & Wedge
★★
Ferry Lane, Moulsford-on-Thames, Oxfordshire,
OX10 9JF
Tel: 01491 651381 Fax: 01491 651376
SB £95 DB £150 HBS £165 HBD £220 B £15
L £30 D £35. CC: MC Vi Am DC Swi Delt
How to get there: M4 J-12. A4 south. Second
roundabout head for Wallingford, through
Streatley to Moulsford. Right at Ferry Lane.

Waltham Abbey, Essex

Swallow Hotel Waltham Abbey
★★★★
Old Shire Lane, Waltham Abbey, Essex,
EN9 3LX
Tel: 01992 717170 Fax: 01992 711841

Web: www.swallowhotels.com
To become Marriott, Spring 2001.
SB £120 DB £145 HBS £145 HBD £185 B £9.75
L £15 D £21.50. CC: MC Vi Am DC Swi Delt
How to get there: At M25 J-26, 15 minutes
Central London.

Ware, Hertfordshire

Vintage Court
★★★
Puckeridge Corner, Puckeridge, Ware,
Hertfordshire, SG11 1SA
Tel: 01920 409955 Fax: 01920 468016
Email: countyware@msihotels.co.uk
CC: MC Vi Am DC
See advert on facing page top

Watford, Hertfordshire

The White House
★★★
Upton Road, Watford, Hertfordshire, WD18 0JF
Tel: 01923 237316 Fax: 01923 233109
Email: info@whitehousehotel.co.uk
Web: www.whitehousehotel.co.uk
SB £98.50 DB £123 HBS £117.45 HBD £160.90
B £9.50 L £17.95 D £17.95.
CC: MC Vi Am DC Swi Delt
How to get there: Signs to town centre ring
road. Take centre lane past lights at Market
Street. Upton Road is on left.
See advert on facing page bottom

Welwyn, Hertfordshire

Quality Hotel Welwyn
★★★
Welwyn, Hertfordshire, AL6 9XA
Tel: 01458 716911 Fax: 01458 714065
Email: admin@gb623.u-net.com
Web: www.choicehotels.com

SB £84.75 DB £99.75 HBS £99.25 HBD
£114.25 B £9.75 L £9.50 D £14.50.

CC: MC Vi Am DC Swi Delt

How to get there: Just off A1(M) J-6. Railway station at Welwyn Garden City.

Wembley, Middlesex

Adelphi

♦♦♦

4 Forty Lane, Wembley, HA9 9EB
Tel: 020 8904 5629 Fax: 020 8908 5314
Email: enquiry@adelphihotel.fsnet.co.uk
Web: www.hoteladelphi.co.uk
SB £38 DB £48
CC: MC Vi Am DC Swi Delt Solo

How to get there: M1 Junction North Circular Road.

Arena

♦♦♦

6 Forty Lane, Wembley, HA9 9EB
Tel: 020 8908 0670 Fax: 020 8908 2007
Email: enquiry@arenahotel.fsnet.co.uk
Web: www.arena-hotel.co.uk

All rooms are ensuite with satellite TV, tea and coffee-making facilities and direct dial telephone. Ideally situated with easy access to the Wembley Stadium complex only 1 mile away.
SB £49 DB £59
CC: MC Vi Am DC Swi Delt Solo

How to get there: Main road by Wembley Stadium.

Southeast

Elm Hotel

◆◆◆

Elm Road, Wembley, Middlesex, HA9 7JA
Tel: 020 8902 1764 Fax: 020 8903 8365
Email: info@elmhotel.co.uk
Web: www.elmhotel.co.uk
SB £48 DB £65 B £5
CC: MC Vi Swi Delt Visa Electron

How to get there: Wembley Central Station 150
yards (main line and Tube). From North Circular
(A406), turn west. Turn right at Woolwich
Building Society, Elm Road first left.

Westcliff-on-Sea, Essex

Rose House

◆◆◆

21–23 Manor Road, Westcliff-on-sea, Essex,
SS0 7SR
Tel: 01702 341959

Weybridge, Surrey

Oatlands Park

★★★★ ℛℛ
146 Oatlands Drive, Weybridge, Surrey,
KT13 9HB
Tel: 01932 847242 Fax: 01932 842252
Email: oatlandspark@btinternet.com
Web: www.oatlandsparkhotel.co.uk
B £12.50 L £21 D £28.
CC: MC Vi Am DC Swi Delt
How to get there: From Weybridge town centre,
up Monument Hill to mini-roundabout. Left into
Oatlands Drive. Hotel 500 yards on left.

Ship

★★★ ℛ
Monument Green, Weybridge, Surrey,
KT13 8BQ
Tel: 01932 848364 Fax: 01932 857153
Email: info@peelhotel.com
Web: www.peelhotel.com
SB £126.50 DB £158 HBS £146.25
HBD £197.50 B £11.50 L £13.75 D £19.75.
CC: MC Vi Am DC Swi Delt Solo
How to get there: M25 J-11, take A317 to
Weybridge. Straight over two roundabouts to
T-junction: left into High Street. Hotel approx
300 yards on left.

Winchester, Hampshire

Heritage Hotels – The Wessex

★★★★
Paternoster Row, Winchester, Hampshire,
SO23 9LQ
Tel: 0870 4008126 Fax: 01962 841503
Email: james.leeming@forte-hotels.com
Web: www.wessexhotel.co.uk
SB £127.55 DB £145.10 HBS £188 HBD £188
CC: MC Vi Am DC Swi Delt
How to get there: M3 J-9 towards Winnall.
Straight over main roundabout. Turn left, stay in
left lane. Right at King Alfred's statue round-
about. Left into Colebrook Street. Hotel on right.

Lainston House

★★★★ ℛℛℛ
Sparsholt, Winchester, Hampshire, SO21 2LT
Tel: 01962 863588 Fax: 01962 776672
Email: enquiries@lainstonhouse.com
Web: www.exclusivehotels.co.uk

An elegant William and Mary house with
breathtaking views over tranquil parkland and
only two and a half miles from the city of
Winchester and the Royal Winchester Golf Club.
The popular restaurant offers gourmet food and
superb service.
SB £115 DB £180 HBS £150 HBD £250
L £12.50 D £35.
CC: MC Vi Am DC Swi Delt JCB
How to get there: South on A34 take B3420
signs Winchester, right into Harestock Road for
1 mile for Stockbridge B3049, travel 1/2 mile,
sign on brow of hill 'Lainston next turning on
left'.

Shawlands

◆◆◆◆

46 Kilham Lane, Winchester, Hampshire,
SO22 5QD
Tel: 01962 861166 Fax: 01962 861166
Email: kathy@pollshaw.u-net.com
Children minimum age: 5

Attractive, modern house in quiet elevated
position overlooking countryside. 1¹/₂ miles from
city centre. Colour TV, hairdryers and welcome
tray in bedrooms. Breakfast includes
homemade bread and preserves with fruit from
garden.
SB £27.30 DB £40.40 CC: MC Vi Swi Delt
♿ 🐕 ⊗ 🖥 🖵 P 🛏 ⚙ 🐴 ♫ 🍴
How to get there: A3090 from Winchester.
Straight over roundabout, right at 2nd set of lights.

Wykeham Arms

◆◆◆◆

75 Kingsgate Street, Winchester, Hampshire,
SO23 9PE
Tel: 01962 853834 Fax: 01962 854411
Children minimum age: 14

An 18th-century coaching inn/hostelry with 13
ensuite bedrooms tucked away in the quiet
backstreets of historic Winchester.
SB £45 DB £79.50 L £5 D £12.95.
CC: MC Vi Am DC Swi Delt
🐕 ⊗ 🖥 🖵 ☎ 🅿 🛏 ⚙ 🐴 ♫ 🍴 ♨ ♨♨
How to get there: Immediately south of

cathedral by Kingsgate, junction of Canon
Street and Kingsgate Street.

Windsor, Berkshire

Heritage Hotels – The Castle Hotel

★★★ ♟

High Street, Windsor, Berkshire, SL4 1LJ
Tel: 01753 851011 Fax: 01753 621560
Email: heritagehotels_windsor.castle
@forte-hotels.com
Web: www.heritage-hotels.com
SB £166 DB £196 HBS £75 HBD £150
B £12.50 L £9.95 D £22.95.
CC: MC Vi Am DC Swi Delt JCB
🕹 ♨ 🐕 🐈 ⊗ 🖵 ☎ 📞 🅿 🛏 ⚙ 🐴 ♫ ♨♨ ♨♨♨
How to get there: M4 J-6. Signs for Windsor
Castle. Hotel on left at top of High Street.

Melrose House

◆◆◆

53 Frances Road, Windsor, Berkshire, Sl4 3AQ
Tel: 01753 865328 Fax: 01753 865328
Email: nina777melrose53@aol.com
SB £55 DB £65 CC: MC Vi Swi Delt
🐈 ⊗ 🖥 🖵 ☎ 🅿 🛏 ⚙ 🐴 🍴
How to get there: M4 J-6. Signs to Windsor.
Staines/Ascot at 3rd roundabout. Frances Rd left.

Netherton Hotel

◆◆◆

96–98 St Leonard's Road, Windsor, Berkshire,
SL4 3NU
Tel: 01753 855508 Fax: 01753 621267
Email: netherton@btconnect.com

The Netherton Hotel is situated in a quiet
residential area a few minutes walk from the
town centre, Windsor castle and the River

Thames. Eton, Ascot, Bray and Runnymead are almost on the doorstep. Legoland is just a mile away and children welcome. All rooms have ensuite bathrooms, televisions, telephone and tea & coffee making facilities. Car parking on-site.
SB £60 DB £65 CC: MC Vi Swi Delt

How to get there: M4 J-6. A355 to large roundabout. Second exit into Goslar Way, on over and first left immediately after traffic lights.

Park Farm

♦♦♦

St Leonards Road, Windsor, Berkshire, SL4 3EA
Tel: 01753 866823 Fax: 01753 850869
Email: park.farm@virgin.net
Web: www.parkfarm.com
SB £35 DB £45

How to get there: M4 J-6, towards Windsor. At roundabout with traffic lights, third exit. Right at T-junction. Park Farm is on left.

Clarence Hotel

♦♦

9 Clarence Road, Windsor, Berkshire, SL4 5AE
Tel: 01753 864436 Fax: 01753 857060

A comfortable hotel close to the town centre, Windsor Castle, Eton College and the Thames. Convenient for Heathrow Airport and Legoland.
SB £49 DB £61
CC: MC Vi Am DC Swi Delt JCB

How to get there: M4 J-4, follow dual carriageway for Windsor. Left at roundabout onto Clarence Road.

Woburn, Bedfordshire

Bedford Arms

★★★
George Street, Woburn, Milton Keynes, Bedfordshire, MK17 9PX

Tel: 01525 290441 Fax: 01525 290432
B £8 L £10.50 CC: MC Vi Am Swi Delt

How to get there: M1 J-13, signs to Woburn.

Woodstock, Oxfordshire

The Feathers

★★★ 🦅🦅🦅
Market Street, Woodstock, Oxfordshire, OX20 1SX
Tel: 01993 812291 Fax: 01933 813158

Heritage Hotels – The Bear

★★★ 🦅🦅
Park Street, Woodstock, Oxfordshire, OX20 1SZ
Tel: 0870 4008202 Fax: 01993 813380
Email: heritagehotels_woodstock.bear
        @forte-hotels.com
SB £85 DB £165 HBS £90 HBD £180 B £13.50
L £10.50 D £19.95. CC: MC Vi Am DC Swi Delt

How to get there: From London, M40 J-8 to Oxford. A40 to Oxford North. A44 to Woodstock and turn left into town centre.

Gorselands Hall

♦♦♦

Boddington Lane, North Leigh, Witney, Oxon, OX8 6PU
Tel: 01993 882292 Fax: 01993 883629
Email: hamilton@gorselandshall.com
Web: www.gorselandshall.com

Lovely old Cotswold stone farmhouse with oak beams and flagstone floors in delightful rural location. Large secluded garden. Ideal for Blenheim Palace, Oxford and Cotswolds.
SB £35 DB £45 CC: MC Vi Am DC Swi Delt JCB Solo Maestro

How to get there: 150yds from A4095 between North Leigh and Long Hanborough. 4 miles from Woodstock, 9 miles from Oxford.

Worthing, West Sussex

Beach Hotel

★★★ ℞

Marine Parade, Worthing, West Sussex,
BN11 3QJ
Tel: 01903 234001 Fax: 01903 234567
Email: thebeachhotel@btinternet.com
Web: www.thebeachhotel.co.uk
SB £59.45 DB £90 HBS £71.50 HBD £112.30
B £9.25 D £18.95. CC: MC Vi Am DC Swi Delt

Best Western Berkeley

★★★

86–95 Marine Parade, Worthing, West Sussex,
BN11 3QD
Tel: 01903 820000 Fax: 01903 821333
Email: berkeley@wakefordhotels.co.uk
Web: www.wakefordhotels.co.uk/berkeley
SB £69 DB £95 HBS £82 HBD £123
CC: MC Vi Am DC Swi

How to get there: Follow the signs to Worthing
seafront. Travel west from pier for ¹/₂ mile.

Chatsworth

★★★

Steyne, Worthing, West Sussex, BN11 3DU
Tel: 01903 236103 Fax: 01903 823726
Email: chatsworth@wakefordhotels.co.uk
Web: www.wakefordhotels.co.uk/
chatsworthworthing
SB £65 DB £84 HBS £45 HBD £45
B £7.50 L £12.95 D £15.95.
CC: MC Vi Am DC Swi Delt

How to get there: A24 South to seafront. Hotel
100 yards east of pier, overlooking Steyne
Gardens, adjacent to Promenade.

Windsor House Hotel

★★★

14–20 Windsor Road, Worthing, West Sussex,
BN11 2LX
Tel: 0800 136776 Fax: 01903 210763

Cavendish

★★

115–116 Marine Parade, Worthing, West
Sussex, BN11 3QG
Tel: 01903 236767 Fax: 01903 823840
Email: thecavendish@mistral.co.uk
Web: www3.mistral.co.uk/thecavendish
SB £45 DB £70 HBS £57.50 HBD £47.50
B £7.50 L £12.50 D £12.50.
CC: MC Vi Am Swi Delt

How to get there: From the A27 or A24, follow
signs to seafront. Hotel 600 yards from Pier
West.

Bonchurch House

♦♦♦

1 Winchester Road, Worthing, West Sussex,
BN11 4DJ
Tel: 01903 202492 Fax: 01903 202492
Web: www.smoothhound.co.uk/hotels/
bonchurch.html
Children minimum age: 3.
Closed January to early February
SB £24 DB £48 B £5
CC: MC Vi Swi Delt JCB Solo

How to get there: Enter Worthing, follow road
sign A259 to Littlehampton and tourist direction
signage 'Hotels West'. Hotel on junction
between Richmond and Wykeham Road.

Southeast

Southwest

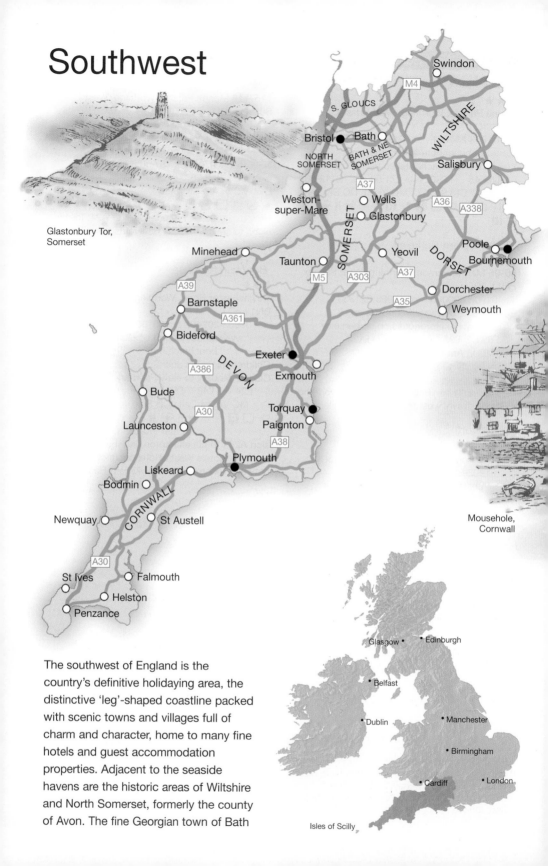

Glastonbury Tor,
Somerset

Swindon

S. GLOUCS

M4

WILTSHIRE

Bristol   Bath

NORTH
SOMERSET

BATH & NE
SOMERSET

Salisbury

A37

Weston-
super-Mare

Wells

A36

A338

Glastonbury

SOMERSET

Poole

Minehead

Yeovil

DORSET

Bournemouth

Taunton

M5   **A303**

A37

Dorchester

A39

A35

Weymouth

Barnstaple

A361

Bideford

Exeter

DEVON

A386

Exmouth

Bude

Torquay

A30

Paignton

Launceston

A38

Liskeard

Plymouth

Bodmin

CORNWALL

Newquay   St Austell

Mousehole,
Cornwall

A30

St Ives

Falmouth

Helston

Penzance

Glasgow •   • Edinburgh

• Belfast

• Dublin   • Manchester

• Birmingham

• Cardiff   • London

Isles of Scilly

The southwest of England is the
country's definitive holidaying area, the
distinctive 'leg'-shaped coastline packed
with scenic towns and villages full of
charm and character, home to many fine
hotels and guest accommodation
properties. Adjacent to the seaside
havens are the historic areas of Wiltshire
and North Somerset, formerly the county
of Avon. The fine Georgian town of Bath

still receives 250,000 gallons of hot, mineral-rich spring water daily. Here the Romans built the magnificent baths of Aquae Sulis, and their remains are an important attraction. Bath attracted the wealthy and the superlative buildings that were constructed as a result, such as Bath Abbey and Royal Crescent, now bring other visitors.

Technology has replaced engineering and shipping as the key industry in forward-thinking Bristol, but milestones remain in the form of the Clifton suspension bridge and SS Great Britain,

the first propeller-driven iron ship to cross the Atlantic, adjacent to the Maritime Heritage Centre.

Railway history is celebrated at the 'Steam' museum in Swindon, a key junction of the Great Western Railway and once the source of many engines and carriages. Further back in Wiltshire's history, Salisbury Cathedral is a stunning example of medieval architecture, and parts of Old Sarum fort remain, despite its Iron Age origin. Wiltshire's chalky plains have numerous examples of ancient monuments, from the stone circles of Avebury and Stonehenge to the site of Woodhenge and huge white horses cut into long, stretching hillsides.

Dorset's 'family resort' of Weymouth became popular thanks to King George III's belief that its waters were beneficial to health. Dorset's attractions include Thomas Hardy's birthplace near Dorchester, a primate sanctuary and the world's largest collection of armoured vehicles.

Fishing, weaving and mining blossomed in Devon, Cornwall and Somerset, but clement weather and beautiful scenery made them tourist hotspots many years ago. Much of Somerset's attractions are inland, such as the stunning cave formations at Cheddar Gorge and Wookey Hole in the Mendip Hills, and part of Exmoor National Park. Many believe Glastonbury has spiritual qualities, and few could deny the power of its abbey – the oldest Christian structure in England.

Sadly, little remains of the huge fort of Roman Exeter, but history lies around every corner, notably in its gothic cathedral, Rougemont Castle and underground passages cut to channel spring water. Plymouth has its maritime heritage and great entertainment facilities, and more restful times can be had in the picturesque villages of South Hams. Devon has the stirringly bleak landscape of Dartmoor and is the starting point of the 600-mile South West Coast Path, one of the many scenic walks of the Southwest.

Watersports are big in the region, typifyed by the surfing mecca of Newquay, Cornwall. Truro has the Royal Cornwall Museum and hosts the Three Spires International Arts Festival, named after its cathedral's architecture; the Tate Gallery, St Ives, contrasts with the town's legacy of shipping and fishing. Bodmin Moor is the setting for two of the county's many stone circles, and beyond St Michael's Mount and Cornwall's craggy coast, by ferry or helicopter, lie the outcrops that comprise the flower-garden Isles of Scilly.

Almondsbury, South Gloucestershire

Abbotts Way Guest House

◆◆◆◆

Gloucester Road, Almondsbury, Bristol,
BS32 4JB
Tel: 01454 613134 Fax: 01454 613131
SB £30 DB £50 CC: MC Vi Am DC Swi Delt

How to get there: From M4/M5 junction at
Lamondsbury, travel 2 miles north. Guest house
on left. From M5 north, leave at J-14. Follow
A38 for Bristol: guest house 7 miles on right.

Ashburton, Devon

Gages Mill

◆◆◆◆

Buckfastleigh Road, Ashburton, Devon,
TQ13 7JW
Tel: 01364 652391 Fax: 01364 652391
Email: moore@gagesmill.co.uk
Web: www.gagesmill.co.uk
Children minimum age: 12
Closed December to Februrary

14th-century former wool mill in over an acre of
gardens. On edge of Dartmoor, one mile from
Ashburton. Delightful rooms with country views.
Good food.
SB £29.50 DB £59 HBS £41 HBD £82 D £13.50.

How to get there: A38 towards Plymouth, 2nd
Ashburton turning (Peartree). Left at Shell
garage, direction Buckfastleigh and Totnes.
Gages Mill is 400m along the road on the left.

Axminster, Devon

Fairwater Head Hotel

★★★

Hawkchurch, Devon, EX13 5TX
Tel: 01297 678349 Fax: 01297 678459
Email: j.c.lowe@btinternet.com
Closed January
SB £84 DB £148 HBS £92 HBD £164

B £8 L £14 D £25. CC: MC Vi Am DC Swi Delt

How to get there: 2¹/₂ miles from A35 and 14
miles from Crewkerne on the B3165.
Signposted locally from B3165 to hotel near
village of Hawkchurch.

Barnstaple, Devon

The Imperial

★★★★

Taw Vale Parade, Barnstaple, Devon, EX32 8NB
Tel: 01271 345861 Fax: 01271 324448
Email: info@brend-imperial.co.uk
Web: www.brend-imperial.co.uk

With luxury refurbishment now completed,
The Imperial is Barnstaple's premier hotel and
the only 4-star. The hotel overlooks the
River Taw and Barnstaple.
SB £59 DB £78 HBS £79 HBD £118
B £9 L £13.50 D £21.
CC: MC Vi Am DC Swi Delt

How to get there: Exit M5 J-27, A361 to
Barnstaple. Follow signs to town centre,
passing Tesco. Straight over next two
roundabouts. River is on left, hotel on right.
See advert on facing page

Barnstaple Hotel

★★★

Braunton Road, Barnstaple, Devon, EX31 1LE
Tel: 01271 376221 Fax: 01271 324101
Email: info@barnstaplehotel.co.uk
Web: www.brend-hotels.co.uk
On the coastal side of Barnstaple, offering easy
access to North Devon's beaches and Exmoor.
The hotel has a superb health and leisure
complex.
SB £59 DB £84 HBS £77.50 HBD £121
B £10 L £11 D £18.
CC: MC Vi Am DC Swi Delt

🐟 ♿ 🐾 🍵 🖥 ☎ 📞 🅿 🐎 ⚒ 🐴 🎠 🍴 🏊 ♨ ⛺ 🛏
SPA ⛏ ℂ ⚖ 🗠 🗻 ⚘

How to get there: Take A361
Braunton/Ilfracombe road from Barnstaple.
Hotel is located on left approximately 1 mile
from town centre.

Park Hotel

★★★
New Road, Taw Vale, Barnstaple,
Devon, EX32 9AE
Tel: 01271 372166 Fax: 01271 323157
Email: info@parkhotel.co.uk
Web: www.brend-hotels.co.uk

With the whole of North Devon on your
doorstep The Park Hotel combines luxury with
excellent value. Overlooking park and the River
Taw and within easy walk of the town centre.
SB £56.50 DB £65 HBS £74 HBD £100 B £4.50
L £10 D £17.50. CC: MC Vi Am DC Swi Delt
🐟 ♿ 🐾 🍵 🖥 ☎ 📞 🅿 🐎 ℂ 🐴 🍴 🏊 ⛺ 🛏
How to get there: Exit M5 J-27, A361 to
Barnstaple. Follow signs to town centre,
passing Tesco. Straight ahead at next two
roundabouts. Rock Park is on left, the hotel
entrance on right.

Royal and Fortescue Hotel

★★★
Boutport Street, Barnstaple, Devon, EX31 3HG
Tel: 01271 342289
Email: info@royalfortescue.co.uk
Web: www.brend-hotels.co.uk

Recent refurbishment retains historic charm
while adding modern facilities. Lord Fortescue's
restaurant, beautiful bedrooms, and adjacent bar
and brasserie '62 Jut Bank' are at your disposal.
SB £56.50 DB £65 HBS £74 HBD £100 B £7.50
L £10 D £17.50. CC: MC Vi Am DC Swi Delt
♿ ⛛ 🍵 🖥 ☎ 📞 🅿 🐎 ℂ 🐴 🍴 🏊 ⛺ 🛏
How to get there: Located in the town centre at
the junction of High Street and Boutport Street.

Downrew House

★★ ♟

Bishops Tawton, Barnstaple, Devon, EX32 0DY
Tel: 01271 342497 Fax: 01271 323947
Email: downrew@globalnet.co.uk
Web: www.downrew.co.uk
SB £55 DB £80 HBS £70 HBD £110 B £7.50
L £14.95 D £22.50. CC: MC Vi Am DC Swi Delt

How to get there: Situated 3 miles south of
Barnstaple off A377. Signposted opposite
garage in Bishops Tawton. Hotel at top of lane.

Rising Sun Inn

★★ ♟

Umberleigh, Devon, EX37 9DU
Tel: 01769 560447 Fax: 01769 560764
Email: chas.heather@risingsuninn.com
Web: www.risingsuninn.com

Ideal for touring, 8 miles from busy Barnstaple,
this quiet 13th-century inn overlooks the
River Taw. Chas and Heather offer warm
hospitality, comfortable accommodation and
award winning food.
SB £40 DB £77 HBS £56 HBD £109 B £5.50
L £2.95 D £4.95. CC: MC Vi Swi Delt

How to get there: Junction of A377 and B3227.

Home Park

♦♦♦♦

Lower Blakewell, Muddiford, Barnstaple,
Devon, EX31 4ET
Tel: 01271 42955

Bath, Bath & NE Somerset

Heritage Hotels – The Bath Spa Hotel

★★★★★ ♟♟♟

Sydney Road, Bath, BA2 6JF
Tel: 0870 4008222 Fax: 01225 444006
Email: firestar@bathspa.u-net.com
Web: www.bathspahotel.com

B £14.75 L £17.50 D £35.
CC: MC Vi Am DC Swi Delt Solo JCB

How to get there: Exit M4 J-18, A46 to Bath, A4
for city centre. Left onto A36 at lights. Right at
mini-roundabout, next left into Sydney Place.
Hotel is 200 yards up hill on right.

Royal Crescent Hotel

★★★★★ ♟♟♟♟

16 Royal Crescent, Bath, Bath & NE Somerset,
BA1 2LS
UK freephone: 0800 980 0987
Tel: 01225 823333 Fax: 01225 339401
Email: reservations@royalcrescent.co.uk
Web: www.royalcrescent.co.uk
Situated in the centre of one of Europe's finest
architectural masterpieces with individually
designed bedrooms. Pimpernel's award-winning
restaurant and The Bath House spa.
SB £212.50 DB £230. HBS £255 HBD £320
B £14.50 L £15. D £42.
CC: MC Vi Am DC Swi Delt

How to get there: A4 London Road, right at
lights into Lansdown Road, second left into
Bennett Street, on to the Circus, second exit
into Brock Street, Royal Crescent ahead.
See advert on facing page

Combe Grove Manor

★★★★ ♟♟

Brassknocker Hill, Monkton Combe, BA2 7HS
Tel: 01225 834644 Fax: 01225 834961
Email: james.parker@combegrovemanor.com
Web: www.combegrovemanor.com
SB £99 DB £110 HBS £125 HBD £140 B £7.50
L £16.50 D £25.
CC: MC Vi Am DC Swi Delt JCB

How to get there: From Bath city centre follow
signs for the university. Go past the university
for 1½ miles; hotel entrance is on the left.

Lucknam Park Hotel

★★★★ ♟♟♟

Colerne, nr Bath, Wiltshire, SN14 8AZ
Tel: 01225 742777 Fax: 01225 743536
Email: reservations@lucknampark.co.uk
Web: www.lucknampark.co.uk
A magnificent 1720 Palladian Mansion set in
500 acres of parkland, six miles from Bath.
Beautifully decorated and sumptuously
furnished in period style, graced by antiques.
Extensive spa and equestrian facilities.

Southwest

SB £168 DB £226 HBS £190 HBD £270
B £18 L £25 D £40.
CC: MC Vi Am DC Swi Delt

⚓ ♿ 🖨 💻 ☎ 🅿 🧺 🕯 🎠 🍴 🦆 👓 ⚄ ⛷ 🧖
🍽 ⚲ 🛎 🐕

How to get there: Westbound, exit M4 J-17,
A350 to Chippenham, A420 to Ford, turn left to
Colerne, and right at crossroads to the hotel.

Ston Easton Park

★★★★ 🛏 🛏 🛏
Ston Easton, nr Bath, Bath & NE Somerset,
BA3 4DF
Tel: 01761 241631 Fax: 01761 241377

The Priory

★★★★ 🛏 🛏 🛏
Weston Road, Bath, BA1 2XT
Tel: 01225 331922 Fax: 01225 448276

Abbey Hotel

★★★
North Parade, Bath, BA1 1LF
Tel: 01225 461603 Fax: 01225 447758
Email: ahres@compasshotels.co.uk

SB £75 DB £115 HBS £85 HBD £130 B £7.50
L £14.50 D £21.50. CC: MC Vi Am DC Swi Delt

♿ ⛰ 🐾 ⊗ ⊖ 💻 ☎ 🧺 🕯 🍴 🦆 🛎 🚹

How to get there: In city centre, close to Bath
Abbey and railway station.

Dukes Hotel

★★★ 🐿

Great Pulteney Street, Bath, BA2 4DN
Tel: 01225 463512 Fax: 01225 483733

Heritage Hotels – The Francis

★★★

Queen Square, Bath, Bath & NE Somerset,
BA1 2HH
Tel: 0870 400 8223 Fax: 01225 319715
Email: heritagehotels-bath.francis@
        forte-hotels.com
Web: www.heritage-hotels.com
SB £137.50 DB £186 HBS £109 HBD £178
B £13.50 L £7.50 D £15.95.
CC: MC Vi Am DC Swi Delt JCB
♿ ♨ 🎿 🐕 🍃 💻 ☎ 🅿 ☕ 🕯 🎠 🎻 🦀 ♨♨♨ ⛲
How to get there: Exit M4 J-18, A46 to city
centre. Proceed to end of George Street, left
into Queen Square. The Francis is on the south
side of the square.

Lansdown Grove Hotel

★★★ 🐿🐿

Lansdown Road, Bath, Bath & NE Somerset,
BA1 5EH
Tel: 01225 483888 Fax: 01225 483838
Email: lansdown@marstonhotels.com
Web: www.marstonhotels.co.uk

```
MARSTON
HOTELS
```

SB £100 DB £128 HBD £135
B £11 L £10.95 D £20.
CC: MC Vi Am DC Swi Delt
🪂 ♿ ♨ 🎿 🌀 🍃 💻 ☎ 🔌 🅿 ☕ 🕯 🎠 🎻 🦀
♨♨♨ ⛲ ✗
How to get there: Exit M4 J-18, A46 to city
centre. Take Broad Street. Follow signs for
Lansdown and Bath Races.

Queensberry Hotel

★★★ 🐿🐿🐿

Russel Street, Bath, Bath & NE Somerset,
BA1 2QF
Tel: 01225 447928 Fax: 01225 446065
Email: queensberry@dial.pipex.com
Web: www.bathqueensberry.com
Closed Christmas
A luxury privately owned townhouse in Georgian
Bath, minutes from Royal Crescent, Roman
Baths and Pump Rooms. The Olive Tree
restaurant is nationally renowned for informal
contemporary British cooking.
SB £90 DB £120 B £9.50 L £14.50 D £24.
CC: MC Vi Swi Delt

♨ 🎿 💻 ☎ ☕ 🕯 🎠 🎻 🦀 ♨♨♨ ⛲
How to get there: Exit M4 J-18, A46 to city
centre. Right fork at mini-roundabout after 2nd
lights, right at next lights. Second left, first right.

George's Hotel

★★

2–3 South Parade, Bath, Bath & NE Somerset,
BA2 4AA
Tel: 01225 464923 Fax: 01225 425471
Email: info@georgeshotel.co.uk
Web: www.georgeshotel.co.uk

Grade I Listed building (1743) in city centre
between abbey and stations. Near to Roman
Baths and shopping areas and adjacent to
public car park. Fully licensed. Short breaks
available.
SB £58 DB £65 CC: MC Vi Am Swi Delt
♿ 🎿 🍃 💻 ☎ ☕ 🕯 🎠 🎻 🦀 ⛲

Limpley Stoke

★★

Lower Limpley Stoke, Bath,
Bath & NE Somerset, BA3 6HZ
Tel: 01225 723333 Fax: 01225 722400

Southwest

Old Mill

★★

Tollbridge Road, Batheaston, Bath, BA1 7DE
Tel: 01225 858476 Fax: 01225 852600
Email: oldmill@batheaston.freeserve.co.uk
Web: www.oldmillbath.co.uk

Riverside hotel with breathtaking views but only 1½ miles from centre of Bath. Unique waterwheel restaurant. All rooms recently refurbished. Free car parking. Private fishing.
SB £49 DB £65 HBS £55 HBD £45
B £5.95 D £14.75. CC: MC Vi Am Swi Delt

How to get there: Exit M4 J-18, A46 for 9 miles, left to Batheaston. Old Mill is located by the tollbridge, ½ mile from the A46.

Woolverton House

★★

Woolverton, Bath, BA3 6QS
Tel: 01373 830415 Fax: 01373 831243
Email: mail@bathhotel.com
Web: www.bathhotel.com
Children minimum age: 10

Close to Bath in lovely countryside setting. Warm welcome, good food and excellent wines. Delightful gardens, comfortable rooms to a high standard at affordable prices.
SB £49.50 DB £63.50 HBS £64.50 HBD £93.50
B £9.95 L £9.50 D £11.95. CC: MC Vi Delt

How to get there: Located on the A36, 8 miles south of Bath in direction of Warminster.

The Ayrlington

24/25 Pulteney Road, Bath BA2 4EZ
Tel: 01225 425495 Fax: 01225 469029
Email: mail@ayrlington.com Web: www.ayrlington.com
RAC, AA, ETC, ◆◆◆◆◆

A handsome listed Victorian house set in a splendid walled garden with exceptional views of the Abbey. Bath's centre and historic sites are just a five-minute level stroll away. The elegant interior is a graceful blend of English and Asian antiques, artwork and fine fabrics. All bedrooms have an individual theme and are beautifully furnished, some with 4-poster beds and spa baths. The Hotel has a residents' bar, private parking and is entirely non-smoking.
Closed 23rd December to 7th January

Windsor Hotel

69 Great Pulteney Street, Bath,
Bath & NE Somerset, BA2 4DL
Tel: 01225 422100 Fax: 01225 422550
Email: info@bathwindsorhotel.com
Web: www.bathwindsorhotel.com
Children minimum age: 12
SB £135 DB £165 D £32. CC: MC Vi Am DC
Swi Delt JCB

How to get there: Exit M5 J-18, A46 to city
centre. From south and west take A36 and
follow signs for London and M4.

Ayrlington Little Gem

24–25 Pulteney Road, Bath, Bath & NE
Somerset, BA2 4EZ
Tel: 01225 425495 Fax: 01225 469029
Email: mail@ayrlington.com
Web: www.ayrlington.com
Closed Christmas to New Year
DB £75 CC: MC Vi Am Swi Delt

How to get there: Exit M4 J-18, A46, A4 to city.
Left at lights (signed A36), right at end of road.
Over roundabout, hotel 100m on right.
See advert on previous page

Cheriton House

9 Upper Oldfield Park, Bath,
Bath & NE Somerset, BA2 3JX
Tel: 01225 429862 Fax: 01225 428403
Email: cheriton@which.net
Web: www.cheritonhouse.co.uk
Children minimum age: 12
SB £42 DB £62 CC: MC Vi Am DC Swi Delt

How to get there: South of city centre, just off
A367.

County Hotel Little Gem

18/19 Pulteney Road, Bath,
Bath & NE Somerset, BA2 4EZ
Tel: 01225 425003 Fax: 01225 466493
Email: reservations@county-hotel.co.uk
Web: www.county-hotel.co.uk
Children minimum age: 13. Closed Christmas
SB £60 DB £90 CC: MC Vi Am DC Swi Delt

How to get there: Follow A46. Before centre, left
at lights following signposts for Exeter on A36.
Right to Holborne Museum on left and proceed
over roundabout. Hotel 50m on right.

Dorian House

1 Upper Oldfield Park, Bath, BA2 3JX
Tel: 01225 426336 Fax: 01225 444699
Email: dorian.house@which.net
Web: www.smoothhound.co.uk/hotels/dorian.
html

Enter an atmosphere of period charm, c. 1880.
All en-suite bedrooms feature telephone, TV, tea
and coffee. Traditional solid oak four-poster
beds, panoramic views over Bath or our
beautiful garden. 10 minutes walk to the centre.
SB £42.59 DB £55.85
CC: MC Vi Am Swi Delt JCB Solo

How to get there: Exit M4 J-18, A46, A4 to
Bath. Follow A36 signposted Bristol. Left on
A367. First right is Upper Oldfield Park.

Oldfields

102 Wells Road, Bath, BA2 3AL
Tel: 01225 317984 Fax: 01225 444471
Email: info@oldfields.co.uk
Web: www.s-h-systems.co.uk/hotels/
oldfiel2.html
Closed December 20 to February
SB £48 DB £70 B £6 CC: MC Vi Am Swi Delt

How to get there: Exi M4 J-18, A46, A4 into city.
Take A36 Bristol road, then A367 (Wells Road).
Oldfields is 1/3 mile up hill on right.

White Smocks

Ashley, Box, Wiltshire, SN13 8AJ
Tel: 01225 742154 Fax: 01225 742212
Email: rachel.b@handbag.com
Web: www.whitesmocks.com
SB £35 DB £65 B £5 CC: MC Vi Swi

How to get there: A4 from Bath to Chippenham,
turn right to Ashley opposite Northy Arms pub.
Take right fork, White Smocks straight ahead.

Ashley Villa Hotel

◆◆◆◆

26 Newbridge Road, Bath, BA1 3JZ
Tel: 01225 421683 Fax: 01225 313604
Email: ashleyvilla@clearface.co.uk
SB £69 DB £79 CC: MC Vi Am Swi Delt

How to get there: From Bath on A4 to Bristol, take upper Bristol Road onto left fork. At 2nd lights into Newbridge Rd. Hotel 200m on right.
See advert on this page

Brompton House

◆◆◆◆

St John's Road, Bath, BA2 6PT
Tel: 01225 420972 Fax: 01225 420505
Email: bromptonhouse@btinternet.com
Web: www.bromptonhouse.co.uk
SB £48 DB £70 CC: MC Vi Am Swi Delt JCB

How to get there: M4 J-18, A46, A4 for city centre, A36. Turn into St Johns Road.
See advert on following page

Gainsborough

◆◆◆◆

Weston Lane, Bath, BA1 4AB
Tel: 01225 311380 Fax: 01225 447411
SB £42 DB £59 CC: MC Vi Am Swi

How to get there: A4 west from Queen's Square, 1 mile, right up Park Lane. Left at the top. Hotel 800 yards along, past Bell School.
See advert on this page

Haute Combe

◆◆◆◆

174–176 Newbridge Road, BA1 3LE
Tel: 01225 420061 Fax: 01225 446077
Email: enquiries@hautecombe.com
Web: www.hautecombe.com

Conveniently situated hotel with period character. Clean, non-smoking, well-equipped bedrooms with Sky TV. Bar and lounges (one smoking), à la carte evening menu. Large car park. Free golf locally.
SB £49 DB £59 D £12.
CC: MC Vi Am DC Swi Delt JCB

How to get there: Follow Upper Bristol Road from Queens Square. On second set of traffic lights keep left into Newbridge Road.

Highways House

◆◆◆◆

143 Wells Road, Bath, Bath & NE Somerset, BA2 3AL
Tel: 01225 421238 Fax: 01225 481169
Email: highways@toscar.clara.co.uk
Web: www.smoothhound.co.uk/hotels/
highways.htm
SB £40. DB £60. CC: MC Vi Swi

How to get there: Take A367 from city centre following signs to Exeter and Radstock. Highways House is 1/2 mile up Wells Rd, on left.

Brompton House

Charming Georgian house (former rectory 1777). Family owned and run. Car park and beautiful secluded gardens. 6 minutes level walk to main historic sights and restaurants. 16 tastefully furnished and fully equipped ensuite bedrooms. Delicious choice of breakfasts. No smoking.

St John's Road,
Bath BA2 6PT
Tel: 01225 420972
Fax: 01225 420505
Email: bromptonhouse@btinternet.com
Website: www.bromptonhouse.co.uk

RaC
♦♦♦♦

Laura Place Hotel
♦♦♦♦
3 Laura Place, Great Pulteney Street, BA2 4BH
Tel: 01225 463815 Fax: 01225 310222
Children minimum age: 8
Closed December 22 to March 1

Charming Georgian town house hotel in central location. Eight spacious bedrooms. Private car parking. No-smoking policy.
SB £60 DB £69.90 CC: MC Vi Am
🖨🚫🍵🖥☎🅿️🛏️🕯️🐴♨️
How to get there: From A4 via Bathwick Street, along Henrietta Street. Laura Place is a square with a central fountain.

Oakleigh House
♦♦♦♦
19 Upper Oldfield Park, Bath, BA2 3JX
Tel: 01225 315698 Fax: 01225 448223
Email: oakleigh@which.net
Web: www.oakleigh-house.co.uk
SB £45 DB £60 CC: MC Vi Am DC
🚫🍵🖥🅿️🛏️🕯️🐴♨️
How to get there: A367 from centre, first turning on right. Oakleigh is 100m on right.

Sydney Gardens
♦♦♦♦
Sydney Road, Bath, BA2 6NT
Tel: 01225 464818 Fax: 01225 484347
Email: pete@sydneygardens.co.uk
Web: www.sydneygardens.co.uk
Children minimum age: 10
Closed Christmas to January
SB £59 DB £75 CC: MC Vi Am Swi Delt
🚫🍵🖥☎🅿️🛏️🕯️🐴♨️
How to get there: Exit M4 J-18, A46, left at A36, cross river, right at Sydney Gardens, next left.

Tasburgh Hotel   Little Gem
♦♦♦♦ 🍴
Warminster Road, Bath, BA2 6SH
Tel: 01225 425096 Fax: 01225 463842
Email: reservations@bathtasburgh.co.uk
Web: www.bathtasburgh.co.uk

Charming Victorian mansion in seven acres of lovely gardens and meadowpark — along the Kennet and Avon Canal. Spectacular views and convenient for the city centre. Gourmet evening meals. Personal, caring service. Country house comforts in a city setting.
SB £52 DB £75 HBS £74.50 HBD £60
B £6.50 D £22.50. CC: MC Vi Am DC Swi Delt
🖨🚫🍵🖥☎🔦🅿️🛏️🕯️🐴♨️🎱🍴
How to get there: Follow A36 Warminster from centre. Hotel north side A36, 1/2 mile from Bathwick St roundabout and Sydney Gardens.

Southwest

Wentworth House

106 Bloomfield Road, Bath, BA2 2AP
Tel: 01225 339193 Fax: 01225 310460
Email: stay@wentworthhouse.co.uk
Web: www.wentworthhouse.co.uk
Children minimum age: 5
SB £50 DB £75 HBS £60 HBD £48
B £5.50 L £5 D £7. CC: MC Vi Am DC Swi Delt

How to get there: Take A367 south from city for
1 mile after rail station, right into Bloomfield Rd.
See advert on this page

Bonheur B & B

52 Box Road, Bathford, Bath, BA1 7QH
Tel: 01225 859537 Fax: 01225 859537
Email: bonheur@waitrose.com
Web: www.visitus.co.uk/bath/hotel/bonheur
SB £35 DB £55 CC: MC Vi Swi Delt

How to get there: From Bath A4 to Bathford.
Take Box/Chippenham road. Bonheur is 200m
past Dunsford Landrovers.

Edgar Private Hotel

64 Great Pulteney Street, Bath, BA2 4DN
Tel: 01225 420619 Fax: 01225 466916

Lamp Post Villa

3 Crescent Gardens, Bath, BA1 2NA
Tel: 01225 331221 Fax: 01225 426783
Closed Christmas
SB £35 DB £55 CC: MC Vi Am Swi Delt

How to get there: On A4 Bristol road, in western
side of city centre close to Victoria Park.

Wentworth House Hotel

An imposing Victorian mansion 15 minutes
walk from the city. Set in a peaceful location
with large gardens, sun terraces and superb
views. Heated swimming pool, licensed
restaurant, and cocktail bar. Golf and walks
nearby. Lovely rooms, some with four-poster
beds, and conservatories. Special offer short
breaks available.

106 Bloomfield Road, RAC
Bath BA2 2AP ♦♦♦♦
Tel: 01225 339193 Fax: 01225 310460
Email: stay@wentworthhouse.co.uk
Website: www.wentworthhouse.co.uk

Orchard Lodge

Warminster Road, Bathampton, BA2 6XG
Tel: 01225 466115 Fax: 01225 446050
Email: orchardlo@aol.com

A modern, comfortable 'lodge' style hotel, set in
a semi-rural village and yet only 1½ miles from
the centre of the magnificent city of Bath.
Well-equipped rooms.
SB £48 DB £69 CC: MC Vi Am DC Swi Delt

How to get there: On the main A36 Warminster
Road at Bathampton, 1½ miles from city centre.

Beaford, Devon

Beaford House

♦ ♦ ♦

Winkleigh, Beaford, Devon, EX19 8AB
Tel: 01805 603305

Bideford, Devon

Royal

★ ★ ★

Barnstaple Street, Bideford, Devon, EX39 4AE
Tel: 01237 472005 Fax: 01237 478957
Email: info@royalbideford.co.uk
Web: www.brend-hotels.co.uk

The Royal Hotel overlooks ancient Bideford
Bridge and the River Torridge and is a good
base for exploring the countryside and coastline
of North Devon.
SB £56.50 DB £65 HBS £74 HBD £100 B £7
L £10 D £17.50. CC: MC Vi Am DC Swi Delt
How to get there: At the eastern end of old
Bideford Bridge.

Hoops Inn

★ ★

Hoops, Horns Cross, Bideford, EX39 5DL
Tel: 01237 451222 Fax: 01237 451247

Riversford

★ ★

Limers Lane, Bideford, Devon, EX39 2RG
Tel: 01237 474239 Fax: 01237 421661

Pines at Eastleigh

♦ ♦ ♦ ♦

Eastleigh, Bideford, Devon, EX39 4PA
Tel: 01271 860561 Fax: 01271 861248/860561
Email: barry@thepinesateastleigh.co.uk
Web: www.thepinesateastleigh.co.uk
SB £45 DB £90 HBS £65 HBD £110
B £5 D £19. CC: MC Vi

How to get there: 2 miles east of Bideford. From
A39 take A386 South. After ³/₄ miles turn left to
Eastleigh. The Pines is 2 miles further.

Anchorage

♦ ♦ ♦

The Quay, Instow, nr Bideford, EX39 4HR
Tel: 01271 860655 Fax: 01271 860767

SB £32 DB £64 HBS £50 HBD £100 B £6 L £6.5
D £20. CC: MC Vi Swi Delt
How to get there: Exit M5 J-27, A361 Bideford
and Barnstaple. Instow turn-off before the new
Bideford Bridge. Turn left and hotel opposite
signal box.

Blandford Forum, Dorset

Crown

★ ★ ★

West Street, Blandford Forum, DT11 7AJ
Tel: 01258 456626 Fax: 01258 451084
SB £67 DB £80 B £7 L £14.95 D £14.95.
CC: MC Vi Am DC Swi

How to get there: Located in the centre of
Blandford Forum, by the River Stour.

Boscastle, Cornwall

Wellington

★ ★

The Harbour, Boscastle, Cornwall, PL35 0AQ
Tel: 01840 250202 Fax: 01840 250621

Bournemouth, Dorset

Norfolk Royale

★ ★ ★ ★

Richmond Hill, Bournemouth, BH2 6EN
Tel: 01202 551521
Fax: 01202 299729

Email: norfolkroyale@englishrosehotels.co.uk
Web: www.englishrosehotels.co.uk
A deluxe country house style located in the centre of town, with friendly, efficient staff. Bedrooms are beautifully appointed with all the amenities you would expect.
SB £105 DB £145 HBS £67.50 HBD £67.50 B £9.95 L £12.50 D £22.50.
CC: MC Vi Am DC Swi Delt
‖ ⌘ ⊘ ☺ ⬚ ☎ P ☂ ⁑ ⌘ ⛏ ⊼ ⬤ ♨ ⁞⁞⁞ ⁞⁞
SPA ♫
How to get there: M3 from London area then A27 via A33. Take A31 to Wessex Way and at A34 junction left into Richmond Hill.

Swallow Highcliff
★★★★
105 St Michael's Road, Bournemouth, Dorset, BH2 5DU
Tel: 01202 557702 Fax: 01202 292734
To become Marriott, Spring 2001.
DB £105 HBD £130 B £10.50 L £12 D £26.
CC: MC Vi Am DC Swi
♿ ⛦ ‖ ⛏ ⊘ ☺ ⬚ ☎ P ☂ ⁑ ⌘ ⊼ ⬤ ☞
⁞⁞⁞ ⁞⁞ SPA ⍑ ♨ ⍾ ♫ ⤻
How to get there: From M3, take M27, following signs for Bournemouth (A31). Turn left onto A338, 6 minutes Ashley Heath roundabout.

Bay View Court
★★★
35 East Overcliff Drive, East Cliff, Bournemouth, BH1 3AH
Tel: 01202 294449 Fax: 01202 292883
Email: enquiry@bayviewcourt.co.uk
Web: www.bayviewcourt.co.uk
SB £42 DB £84 HBS £50 HBD £100
B £12 D £18. CC: MC Vi Am Swi Delt
‖ ⛦ ⊘ ⬚ ☎ P ☂ ⁑ ⌘ ⊼ ⬤ ⁞⁞⁞ ⁞⁞ ⁞ SPA ⍑
♨ ⁄. ♫
How to get there: Turn off A338 at St Paul's roundabout. Head for clifftop.

Burley Court
★★★
Bath Road, Bournemouth, Dorset, BH1 2NP
Tel: 01202 552824 Fax: 01202 298514
Email: burleycourt@btclick.com
Web: www.smoothhound.co.uk/a02512.html
Closed early January
SB £31 DB £62 HBS £39 HBD £78 B £9 L £10 D £16. CC: MC Vi Swi Delt JCB Solo
‖ ⌘ ⛦ ⊘ ☺ ⬚ ☎ P ☂ ⁑ ⌘ ⊼ ♨ ⍾ ♨ ⤻
How to get there: Exit A338 at St Paul's roundabout, 3rd exit next two roundabouts. Burley Court is the first hotel after the crossing.

Chesterwood
★★★
East Overcliff Drive, Bournemouth, BH1 3AR
Tel: 01202 558057 Fax: 01202 556285
Email: enquiry@chesterwoodhotel.co.uk
SB £41.50 DB £79.50 HBS £49.50 HBD £89.50 B £4.95 L £7.95 D £11.95.
CC: MC Vi Am Swi Delt
‖ ⛦ ⊘ ⬚ ☎ P ☂ ⁑ ⌘ ⊼ ⬤ ⁞⁞⁞ ⁞⁞ ⍑ ⤻
How to get there: M3/M27, A338 to Wessex Way, signs for the East Cliff and the seafront.

Chine
★★★ ⌂
25 Boscombe Spa Road, Bournemouth, Dorset, BH5 1AX
Tel: 01202 396234 Fax: 01202 391737
Email: reservations@chinehotel.co.uk
Web: www.chinehotel.co.uk

An attractive Victorian hotel with award-winning cuisine, located in three acres of mature gardens with direct access to the beach. Indoor and outdoor pools.
B £9 L £15 D £19. CC: MC Vi Am DC Swi Delt
♿ ‖ ⌘ ⊘ ☺ ⬚ ☎ P ☂ ⁑ ⌘ ⊼ ⬤ ⁞⁞⁞ ⁞⁞
♫ ⤻
How to get there: First exit at St Paul's roundabout, then second exit, then first exit. Turn right into Boscome Spa Road.

Southwest

Cliffeside

★★★

East Overcliff Drive, Bournemouth, BH1 3AQ
Tel: 01202 555724 Fax: 01202 314534
Email: hotels@arthuryoung.co.uk
Web: www.arthuryoung.co.uk
B £4 L £3 D £17.95. CC: MC Vi Swi Delt

How to get there: Five minutes from A338.
Follow signs to the East Cliff.
See advert below

Cumberland

★★★

East Overcliff Drive, Bournemouth, BH1 3AF
Tel: 01202 290722 Fax: 01202 311394
Email: hotels@arthuryoung.co.uk
Web: www.arthuryoung.co.uk
Children minimum age: 6 months
SB £47 DB £94 HBS £56 HBD £112
B £6.95 L £8.95 D £18.95. CC: MC Vi Swi Delt

How to get there: A338 to Bournemouth, left at
first roundabout. At next, take 3rd exit, at next
take 2nd exit, at next take 2nd exit to T-junction.
Turn left. Hotel 200m on left.
See advert below

Durley Hall

★★★

Durley Chine Road, Bournemouth, BH2 5JS
Tel: 01202 751000 Fax: 01202 757535
Email: sales@durleyhall.co.uk
Web: www.durleyhall.co.uk
SB £50 DB £100 HBS £64 HBD £128
B £9.50 L £10.25 D £18.50.
CC: MC Vi Am DC Swi Delt

How to get there: Approaching on the A338
Wessex Way, follow signs to the West Cliff and
Bournemouth International Centre.

East Anglia Hotel

★★★

6 Poole Road, Bournemouth, Dorset, BH2 5QX
Tel: 01202 765163 Fax: 01202 752949
Email: info@eastangliahotel.com
Web: www.eastangliahotel.com
CC: MC Vi Am DC Swi Delt

How to get there: From A338 at Bournemouth
West roundabout, take exit signposted
Bournemouth International Centre & West Cliff.
Take 3rd exit at next roundabout into Poole
Road.

Elstead Hotel

★★★

Knyveton Road, Bournemouth, BH1 3QP
Tel: 01202 293071 Fax: 01202 293827
Email: info@the-elstead.co.uk
Web: www.the-elstead.co.uk
SB £52.50 DB £42.50 HBS £65 HBD £56
B £9.50 D £18.50. CC: MC Vi Am Swi Delt

How to get there: Exit M27 J-1, A31, A338 and
A35. Six miles from Bournemouth airport.

Grosvenor

★★★

1 Bath Road, Bournemouth, Dorset, BH1 2EX
Tel: 01202 558858 Fax: 01202 298332
Email: enquiries@grosvenor-bournemouth.co.uk
Web: www.grosvenor-bournemouth.co.uk
SB £32.50 DB £65 HBS £40 HBD £80
B £9.50 L £6.95 D £15.95.
CC: MC Vi Am Swi Delt

How to get there: From A338 turn left at the first
roundabout. Follow signs to seafront. The
Grosvenor is situated off St Peter's Roundabout.

Heathlands

★★★

12 Grove Road, East Cliff, Bournemouth,
Dorset, BH1 3AY
Tel: 01202 553336 Fax: 01202 555937
Email: info@heathlandshotel.com
Web: www.heathlandshotel.com
CC: MC Vi Swi Delt

How to get there: Follow signs to East Cliff. At
roundabout, turn into Gervis Road.

Hotel Courtlands

★★★

16 Boscombe Spa Road, Bournemouth,
Dorset, BH5 1BB
Tel: 01202 302442 Fax: 01202 309880
SB £39 DB £73 HBS £46 HBD £92
B £3.50 L £2.95 D £13.50. CC: MC Vi Swi Delt

How to get there: From London, the Midlands,
join M3/M27. Turn onto 31 and A338 (Wessex
Way). Follow the signs for Boscombe.

Hotel Miramar

★★★

East Overcliff Drive, Bournemouth,
Dorset, BH1 3AL
Tel: 01202 556581 Fax: 01202 291242

Situated atop the prestigious East Cliff.
Magnificent views overlooking landscaped
gardens and Bournemouth Bay. An elegant
hotel with traditional English interior.
SB £70 DB £130 HBS £85 HBD £160
B £8.50 L £10 D £20.95.
CC: MC Vi Am Swi Delt

How to get there: Turn into St Paul's Road off
the main Wessex Way roundabout. Turn right at
the next roundabout. Take third exit at the next
roundabout and second at the next. Hotel 50m
on right.

Hotel Piccadilly

★★★

Bath Road, Bournemouth, Dorset, BH1 2NN
Tel: 01202 552559 Fax: 01202 298235
SB £58 DB £96 HBS £68 HBD £116
B £6.50 L £5 D £18.95.
CC: MC Vi Am DC Swi Delt

How to get there: From A338, follow signs for
Lansdowne and take Bath Road off Lansdowne
roundabout.

Mayfair

★★★

27 Bath Road, Bournemouth, Dorset, BH1 2NW
Tel: 01202 551983 Fax: 01202 298459
Email: info@themayfair.com
Web: www.themayfair.com
SB £40 DB £80 HBS £49 HBD £98
B £6.95 D £14.75.
CC: MC Vi Am DC Swi Delt

How to get there: Take A338 southbound to first
roundabout. Take last exit off, and at next
roundabout 3rd exit off into Bath Road.

Southwest

Pavilion

★★★

Bath Road, Bournemouth, Dorset, BH1 2NS
Tel: 01202 291266 Fax: 01202 559264

Quality Hotel Bournemouth

★★★

8 Poole Road, Bournemouth, Dorset, BH2 5QU
Tel: 01202 763006 Fax: 01202 766168
Email: admin@gb641.u-net.com
Web: www.qualityinn.com/hotel/gb641

SB £49.50 DB £79.50 HBS £59.50 HBD £99.50
B £6.50 L £2.95 D £15.50.
CC: MC Vi Am DC Swi Delt

Lti 🐾🐕🚫🍵🖥☎📞🅿️🐎🗝♨
♨♨ ♟♟

How to get there: A338 into Bournemouth. Exit
at Town Centre West, right onto Poole Road.

Queens

★★★

Meyrick Road, Bournemouth, Dorset, BH1 3DL
Tel: 01202 554415 Fax: 01202 294810
Email: hotels@arthuryoung.co.uk
Web: www.arthuryoung.co.uk
SB £57.50 DB £97.50 HBS £67.50 HBD
£107.50 B £6.95 L £8.95 D £17.95.
CC: MC Vi Am DC Swi Delt

How to get there: From A338, signs into
Bournemouth and East Cliff. The Queens Hotel
is situated one road back from seafront.

See advert on previous page

Suncliff

★★★

East Overcliff Drive, Bournemouth, BH1 3AG
Tel: 01202 291711 Fax: 01202 293788

Located high on the East Cliff overlooking the
sea and noted for good food, friendly service
and entertainment. Rooms are tastefully
furnished and benefit from modern facilities.
Superb leisure facilities.
CC: MC Vi Am DC Swi Delt

Trouville

★★★

5 Priory Road, Westcliff, Bournemouth,
Dorset, BH2 5DH
Tel: 01202 552262 Fax: 01202 293324
Email: hotels@arthuryoung.co.uk
Web: www.arthuryoung.co.uk
SB £57.50 DB £115 HBS £70.50 HBD £141
B £8.95 D £18.95. CC: MC Vi Am DC Swi Delt

How to get there: M3, M27 to Bournemouth,
follow directions for Bournemouth International
Centre. At roundabout turn 2nd left. Hotel is on
right.

See advert on previous page

Winterbourne

★★★

4 Priory Road, Bournemouth, Dorset, BH2 5DJ
Tel: 01202 296366 Fax: 01202 780073
Email: reservations@winterbourne.co.uk
Web: www.winterbourne.co.uk

Enjoying a prime position on the West Cliff with
magnificent sea views. Adjacent to the
Bournemouth International Centre and within
400m of pier, beaches and town centre.
SB £35 DB £58 HBS £40 HBD £72
B £6 L £2.50 D £14.50.
CC: MC Vi Am Swi Delt

How to get there: Signs to BIC. Exit Wessex
Way to the BIC. As you approach the BIC,
Winterbourne is halfway down hill (Priory Road).

Southwest

Arlington

★★

Exeter Park Road, Lower Gardens,
Bournemouth, Dorset, BH2 5BD
Tel: 01202 552879 Fax: 01202 298317
Children minimum age: 2. Closed early January
SB £31.50 DB £63 HBS £38.50 HBD £77
B £6 D £12. CC: MC Vi Am Swi Delt
⑂ ⚊ ▣ ☎ ℙ ⚿ ⚘ ♘ ♯ ⚇ ♨ ♊ ♦
How to get there: Signs to Bournemouth
International Centre, Town Centre, Beach.
Exeter Park Rd runs behind Royal Exeter Hotel.

Bourne Hall

★★

14 Priory Road, Bournemouth, BH2 5DN
Tel: 01202 299715 Fax: 01202 552669
Email: info@bournehall.co.uk
Web: www.bournehall.co.uk
SB £40 DB £60 HBS £50 HBD £80 B £6 D £11.
CC: MC Vi Am DC Swi Delt
⚊ ⚘ ⚙ ▣ ☎ ℙ ⚿ ♘ ♯ ⚇ ♨ ♦ ⚐
How to get there: Signs for BIC onto West Cliff.
Hotel is just before BIC on right.

Chinehurst

★★

Studland Road, Bournemouth, Dorset, BH4 8JA
Tel: 01202 764583 Fax: 01202 762854
Children minimum age: 2
SB £35 DB £70 HBS £40 HBD £80
B £8.50 L £8.50 D £15. CC: MC Vi Swi Delt
⚿ ⚘ ⚊ ⚙ ▣ ☎ ℙ ⚿ ♘ ♯ ⚇ ♨ ♊ ♦
How to get there: From A338/A35, 3rd exit off
Frizzel roundabout into The Avenue. Left at
lights, right at roundabout into Alumhurst Road.
Take last turning left into Studland Road.

County

★★

Westover Road, Bournemouth, Dorset, BH1 2BT
Tel: 01202 552385 Fax: 01202 297255
SB £26 DB £52 HBS £34 HBD £68
B £5.50 D £12.50. CC: MC Vi Am DC Swi Delt
⚊ ⚙ ▣ ☎ ⚿ ♘ ♯ ⚇ ♨ ♊
How to get there: Entering by A338 from
Ringwood, turn left at Railway Station. Turn
right at next roundabout, straight over next two
roundabouts. Hotel on left at 3rd roundabout.

Croham Hurst

★★

9 Durley Road, West Cliff, Bournemouth,
Dorset, BH2 5JH
Tel: 01202 552353 Fax: 01202 311484

Fircroft

★★

Owls Road, Bournemouth, Dorset, BH5 1AE
Tel: 01202 309771 Fax: 01202 395644
Web: www.fircrofthotel.co.uk
SB £24 DB £48 HBS £35 HBD £70
CC: MC Vi Am DC Swi Delt
⚊ ♘ ⚙ ▣ ☎ ℙ ⚿ ♘ ♯ ⚇ ♨ ♊ ♦
♈ ⚐
How to get there: Off A338 over flyover. At next
exit follow signs for Boscombe Pier. The hotel is
situated on corner of St John's Road and Owls
Road.

Grange Hotel

★★

Overcliffe Drive, Southbourne,
Bournemouth, BH6 3NL
Tel: 01202 433093 Fax: 01202 424228
Web: www.bournemouthgrangehotel.co.uk
SB £29.50 DB £59 B £9.50 L £2.50 D £15.50.
CC: MC Vi Swi Delt
⚿ ⚊ ⚘ ♘ ⚙ ▣ ☎ ℙ ⚿ ♘ ♯ ⚇ ♨ ♦ ⚐
How to get there: Follow Overcliff Drive to
clifftop.

Hotel Riviera

★★

West Cliff Gardens, Bournemouth,
Dorset, BH2 5HL
Tel: 01202 552845 Fax: 01202 317717
Email: info@hotel-riviera.co.uk
Web: www.hotel-riviera.co.uk
Closed December to February
SB £25.34 DB £50.68 HBS £33.42 HBD £66.84
B £5.50 D £12.50. CC: MC Vi Am Swi Delt
⚊ ⚙ ▣ ☎ ℙ ⚿ ♘ ♯ ♦
How to get there: From the A338 Wessex Way,
at Bournemouth West roundabout take the first
exit. At St Michael's roundabout take the
second exit. At the next roundabout, take first
exit and immediate left.

Russell Court

★★

Bath Road, Bournemouth, Dorset, BH1 2EP
Tel: 01202 295819 Fax: 01202 293457
Email: russellcrt@aol.com
Web: www.enterprisehotel.co.uk
SB £63.50 DB £107 HBS £69.50 HBD £59.50
B £5.95 L £4 D £14.95.
CC: MC Vi Am DC Swi Delt
⚊ ♘ ⚙ ▣ ☎ ⚿ ♘ ♯ ⚇ ♨ ♦
How to get there: From M27, A31, left just past
Ringwood onto A338 for Bournemouth. Then
signs for Bournemouth International Centre.
Hotel on left on Bath Road.

St George

★★

West Cliff Gardens, Bournemouth, BH2 5HL
Tel: 01202 556075 Fax: 01202 557330

Sun Court

★★

West Hill Road, Bournemouth, Dorset, BH2 5PH
Tel: 01202 551343 Fax: 01202 316747
SB £30 DB £60 HBS £38 HBD £76
B £8.50 L £7.45 D £16. CC: MC Vi Am DC

How to get there: 4 miles from airport, 2 miles
from railway station, ½ mile from A338.

Taurus Park

★★

16 Knyveton Road, Bournemouth, BH1 3QN
Tel: 01202 557374

Tower House

★★

West Cliff Gardens, Bournemouth, BH2 5HP
Tel: 01202 290742

Ullswater

★★ ®

West Cliff Gardens, Bournemouth, BH2 5HW
Tel: 01202 555181 Fax: 01202 317896
Email: enq@ullswater.uk.com
Web: www.ullswater.uk.com

A family-run hotel, centrally situated close to all
amenities. Comfortable and tastefully furnished
with an emphasis on good food and personal
service.
SB £27 DB £54 HBS £32 HBD £64
B £4.50 L £7.50 D £11.50. CC: MC Vi Am Swi

How to get there: Follow signs for the West Cliff.
The Ullswater Hotel is situated in West Cliff
Gardens, just off the main West Cliff Road.

Whitehall

★★

Exeter Park Road, Bournemouth, BH2 5AX
Tel: 01202 554682 Fax: 01202 554682

Boltons

♦♦♦♦

9 Durley Chine Road South, Westcliff,
Bournemouth, Dorset, BH2 5JT
Tel: 01202 751517 Fax: 01202 751629

Tiffanys

♦♦♦♦

31 Chine Crescent, West Cliff, Bournemouth,
Dorset, BH2 5LB
Tel: 01202 551424 Fax: 01202 318559

Tudor Grange

♦♦♦♦

31 Gervis Road, Bournemouth, BH1 3EE
Tel: 01202 291472

Valberg

♦♦♦♦

1a Wollstonecraft Road, Boscombe,
Bournemouth, Dorset, BH5 1JQ
Tel: 01202 394644

Carisbrook

♦♦♦

42 Tregonwell Road, Bournemouth, BH2 5NT
Tel: 01202 290432 Fax: 01202 310499

Dorset Westbury

♦♦♦

62 Lansdowne Road North,
Bournemouth, BH1 1RS
Tel: 01202 551811 Fax: 01202 551811
SB £25 DB £48 HBS £30 B £4.50 D £6.
CC: MC Vi Swi Delt

Durley Court

♦♦♦

5 Durley Road, Bournemouth, Dorset, BH2 5JQ
Tel: 01202 556857 Fax: 01202 554455

Hotel Washington

♦♦♦

3 Durley Road, Bournemouth, Dorset, BH2 5JQ
Tel: 01202 557023

Ravenstone

♦♦♦

36 Burnaby Road, Alum Chine, Westbourne,
Bournemouth, Dorset, BH4 8JG
Tel: 01202 761047 Fax: 01202 761047

Email: holidays@ravenstone36.freeserve.co.uk
Web: www.ravenstone36.freeserve.co.uk
Closed November to March
SB £18 DB £36 HBS £25 HBD £50 D £7.
CC: MC Vi Swi Delt
🖭 💻 🅿 ⚡ ⚞ ⚘ 🎿 ⚓ 🍴 ⚐
How to get there: A338 to Westbourne, signs for
Alum Chine. From Alumhurst Road, left into
Beaulieu Rd. Then turn right into Burnaby Rd.

Bovey Tracey, Devon

Edgemoor

★★★ ☙☙

Lowerdown Cross, Haytor Road, Bovey Tracey,
Devon, TQ13 9LE
Tel: 01626 832466 Fax: 01626 834760
Email: edgemoor@btinternet.com
Web: www.edgemoor.co.uk
Closed New Year

Romantically styled creeper-clad country house
hotel on edge of Dartmoor National Park.
Log fires, beautiful riverside and moorland
walks, 14 miles from end of M5.
SB £57.50 DB £95 B £3.95 L £14.75 D £19.95.
CC: MC Vi Am DC Swi Delt JCB
♿ 🐎 🐕 🖭 💻 ☎ 🅿 ⚡ ⚞ ⚘ 🎿 ⚓ 🍴 ♨ 🍷 🍶
How to get there: From A38, A382 for Bovey
Tracey. B3387 for Haytor and Widecombe. Fork
left after 1/4 mile. Hotel is then 1/4 mile on right.

Coombe Cross

★★

Coombe Lane, Bovey Tracey, Devon, TQ13 9EY
Tel: 01626 832476 Fax: 01626 835298
Email: simontennant@btinternet.com
Web: www.coombecross.co.uk
Closed December
SB £45 DB £70 HBS £60 HBD £50 B £10.95 D
£22.95. CC: MC Vi Am Swi Delt
♿ 🐕 🖭 💻 ☎ 🅿 ⚡ ⚞ ⚘ 🎿 ⚓ 🍴 ♨ 🍷 🍶
How to get there: A38, A382 to Bovey Tracey, up
High Street past church — hotel 400m on left.

Riverside Inn

★★

Fore Street, Bovey Tracey, Devon, TQ13 9AF
Tel: 01626 832293 Fax: 01626 833880

Bradford-on-Avon, Wiltshire

Leigh Park Hotel

★★★

Leigh Road West, Bradford-on-Avon, BA15 2RA
Tel: 01225 864885 Fax: 01225 862315

Widbrook Grange Little Gem

◆◆◆◆◆ ☙ ⚘ ⚐

Trowbridge Road, Bradford-on-Avon, BA15 1UH
Tel: 01225 863173 Fax: 01225 862890

Burghope Manor

◆◆◆◆

Winsley, Bradford-on-Avon, Wiltshire, BA15 2LA
Tel: 01225 723557 Fax: 01225 723113

Brent Knoll, Somerset

Battleborough Grange

★★

Bristol Road, Brent Knoll, Highbridge,
Somerset, TA9 4HJ
Tel: 01278 760208 Fax: 01278 760208
Email: info@battleboroughgrangehotel.co.uk
Web: www.battleboroughgrangehotel.co.uk
SB £49 DB £65 HBS £64 HBD £95
B £5 L £4.95 D £15. CC: MC Vi Am DC Swi Delt
♿ 🐎 ☙ 🖭 💻 ☎ 📞 🅿 ⚡ ⚞ ⚘ 🎿 ⚓ ♨ ♨ 🍶
How to get there: Exit M5 J-22, A38 towards
Weston-Super-Mare for 1 mile. Hotel drive on
left, opposite Goat House Hotel.
See advert on following page

Bridgwater, Somerset

Walnut Tree

★★★ ☙

North Petherton, Bridgwater, Somerset,
TA6 6QA
Tel: 01278 662255 Fax: 01278 663946
Email: reservations@walnut-tree-hotel.co.uk
Web: www.walnut-tree-hotel.co.uk
SB £50 DB £60 HBS £63 HBD £86
B £6 L £6 D £13.
CC: MC Vi Am DC Swi Delt JCB
♿ 🐕 ☙ 🖭 💻 ☎ ✳ 🅿 ♨ 🍶
How to get there: The hotel is situated on A38,
one mile north of M5 J-25.

Southwest

Battleborough Grange Hotel

Surrounded by mellow Somerset countryside, the hotel is just one mile from M5, making it a convenient location for both business and leisure guests. Bedrooms are well equipped and some offer extensive views of the historic Iron Age fort of Brent Knoll. Public rooms include a convivial bar, conservatory restaurant and extensive function facilities.
Civil ceremonies also available.

Bristol Road, Highbridge, Somerset TA9 4HJ

Tel: 01278 760208   Fax: 01278 760208
Website: www.battleboroughgrange.com

When booking at an RAC Hotel or Guest Accommodation, please mention this Guide.

Bridport, Dorset

Haddon House
★★★
West Bay, Bridport, Dorset, DT6 4EL
Tel: 01308 423626 Fax: 01308 427348
DB £55 CC: MC Vi Am DC
♿⊗⑤▯☎☏▐P♞✽🐎▥♧♨▦▦
How to get there: Approaching Bridport, follow signs for West Bay. On entering West Bay, hotel is on right, opposite mini roundabout.

Roundham House
★★ ☕
Roundham Gardens, Bridport, Dorset, DT6 4BD
Tel: 01308 422753 Fax: 01308 421500
Email: cyprencom@compuserve.com
Closed January to March
SB £35 DB £60 HBS £50 HBD £88
B £10 D £17.95. CC: MC Vi Swi Delt
🎣⊗⑤▯☎P♞✽🐎▥♧♨▦▦
How to get there: From A35, as you enter Bridport, find the 'Crown Inn roundabout' and take signpost to West Bay. Take 2nd turning left into Roundham Gardens.

Betchworth House
♦♦♦♦   ✈☕
Main Street, Chideock, Dorset, DT6 6JW
Tel: 01297 489478 Fax: 01297 489932
Children minimum age: 10

17th-century Grade II listed guest house. Refurbished to a high standard retaining its country cottage character. Pretty cottage garden. $^3/_4$ mile from the sea.
SB £30 DB £50
CC: MC Vi Swi Delt JCB Solo Maestro
⊗⑤▯P♞✽🐎▥♧♨
How to get there: Located on A35, 2 miles from Bridport and 6 miles from Lyme Regis.

Bristol

Aztec
★★★★ ☕
Aztec West Business Park, Almondsbury, Bristol, BS12 4TS
Tel: 01282 414141 Fax: 01282 835586
Email: info@shireinns.co.uk
Web: www.shireinns.co.uk
SB £149 DB £169 CC: MC Vi Am DC Swi
⟁♿⊞♂🐾⊗⑤▯☎✽P♞✽🐎
♧🎣🍴▦▦ ⚹🍽
How to get there: Close to M4/M5 intersection. Exit M5 J-16. Follow signs for Aztec West.

Bristol Marriott Royal
★★★★ ☕☕
College Green, Bristol, BS1 5TA
Tel: 0117 9255100 Fax: 0117 9251515
Children minimum age: 14
SB £139 DB £149 HBS £159 HBD £189
B £10.50 L £15 D £20.
CC: MC Vi Am DC Swi Delt
⟁♿⊞♂🐾⊗⑤▯☎✽☏P♞✽🐎
🎣♧🍴▦▦▦ ⚹🍽
How to get there: Exit M4 J-19 onto M32 to Bristol. Follow signs for Bristol city centre. Hotel by cathedral.

Southwest

Avon Gorge

★★★
Sion Hill, Bristol, BS8 4LD
Tel: 0117 973 8955
Fax: 0117 923 8125
Email: info@avongorge-hotel-bristol.com
SB £99 DB £109 B £9.95 L £16.50 D £16.50.
CC: MC Vi Am DC Swi Delt

How to get there: Exit M5 J-19, signposted Clifton; cross suspension bridge, turn right. From M4, J-19, M32 to city; follow signs to Clifton and bridge.

Berkeley Square

★★★
Berkeley Square, Clifton, Bristol, BS8 1HB
Tel: 0117 925 4000 Fax: 0117 925 2970
Email: berkeley@cliftonhotels.com
Web: www.cliftonhotels.com

Bristol's most highly rated three-star hotel is situated in a magnificent Georgian Square in the heart of the city, and with just 41 bedrooms offers an exceptionally warm, friendly and personal service.
SB £86 DB £107 HBS £101 HBD £137
CC: MC Vi Am DC Swi Delt

Henbury Lodge

★★★ ®
Station Road, Henbury, Bristol, BS10 7QQ
Tel: 0117 9502615 Fax: 0117 9509532
Email: enquiries@henburylodge.com
Web: www.henburylodge.com
SB £50 DB £80 B £6.50 L £6.50 D £19.75.
CC: MC Vi Am DC Swi Delt Solo

How to get there: Exit M5 J-17, A4018 to 3rd roundabout. Turn right. At T-junction, turn right. Hotel is 200m up on corner.

Jurys Bristol

★★★
Prince Street, Bristol, BS1 4QF
Tel: 00353 1 6070055 Fax: 00353 1 6609625
Email: dorothy_cusack@jurysdoyle.com
Web: www.jurysdoyle.com
CC: MC Vi Am DC

Arno's Manor

★★
470 Bath Road, Bristol, BS4 3HQ
Tel: 0117 971 1461 Fax: 0117 971 5507

A wealth of history surrounds this 18th-century manor house with relaxed, friendly service and modern facilities. Situated two miles from central Bristol with parking for 300.
SB £68.50 DB £78.50 B £9.50 L £4.50 D £9.
CC: MC Vi Swi

How to get there: Exit M4 to M32 and leave at Junction 3. Follow A4320 to A4. Hotel situated on A4 opposite junction of A4320.

Best Western Glenroy

★★
Victoria Square, Clifton, Bristol, BS8 4EW
Tel: 01179 739058 Fax: 01179 739058
Email: admin@glenroyhotel.demon.co.uk
Web: www.glenroyhotel.demon.co.uk
Closed Christmas
SB £60 DB £82 HBS £72 HBD £106 D £10.
CC: MC Vi Am DC Swi Delt

How to get there: Exit M5 J-19, follow signs for Clifton. Proceed over bridge and turn right into Clifton Down, turn left into Merchants Road.

If you're looking for great dining when staying away, look for RAC Hotels and Guest Accommodation displaying the RAC Dining Award symbol in this Guide.

Clifton

★★

St Paul's Road, Clifton, Bristol, BS8 1LX
Tel: 0117 973 6882 Fax: 0117 974 1082
Email: clifton@cliftonhotels.com
Web: www.cliftonhotels.com

Recently refurbished to an extremely high standard, the Clifton is one of Bristol's most popular 2-star hotels, home also to Racks, a lively wine bar and restaurant.
SB £69 DB £79 HBS £84
CC: MC Vi Am DC Swi Delt

Rodney Hotel

★★

4 Rodney Place, Clifton, Bristol, BS8 4HY
Tel: 0117 973 5422 Fax: 0117 946 7092
Email: rodney@cliftonhotels.com

Web: www.cliftonhotels.com
Town house forming part of a Georgian Terrace. Sympathetically renovated and converted.
SB £64 DB £78 HBS £79 HBD £108
CC: MC Vi Am DC Swi Delt

Seeley's Hotel

★★

17–27 St Paul's Road, Clifton, Bristol, BS8 1LX
Tel: 0117 9738544 Fax: 0117 9732406
Email: admin@seeleys.demon.co.uk
Web: www.seeleys.demon.co.uk
Closed Christmas and New Year

SB £65 DB £80 HBS £77 HBD £104
B £5 D £12. CC: MC Vi Am DC Swi

How to get there: From city centre proceed up Park Street towards Clifton. Head towards BBC studios on Whiteladies Road and turn left opposite into St Pauls Road.
See advert on facing page

Downlands House

♦♦♦♦

33 Henleaze Gardens, Bristol, BS9 4HH
Tel: 0117 962 1639 Fax: 0117 962 1639
Email: mjdownlands@compuserve.com
Web: www.downlandshouse.com
SB £35 DB £48 CC: MC Vi Am Swi Delt

Westbury Park

♦♦♦♦

37 Westbury Road, Bristol, Avon, BS9 3AU
Tel: 0117 9629560 Fax: 0117 9628607
Closed Christmas
SB £88 DB £54 CC: MC Vi Am DC Swi Delt

How to get there: Situated on that section of the A4018 which runs from the M5 to the city centre known as Westbury Road.

Downs View Guest House

♦♦♦

38 Upper Belgrave Road, Clifton,
Bristol, BS8 2XN Tel: 0117 973 7046

Southwest

Firwood Guest House

Main Road, Easter Compton, Bristol, BS35 5RA
Tel: 01454 633394 Fax: 01454 633323
Email: cgriff572@aol.com
Web: www.travelcheck.co.uk/hotel/449.htm
SB £30 DB £50

How to get there: Exit M5 J-1, B4055 into
village of Easter Compton. Hotel is through
village at far end on left-hand side.

Oakfield

52–54 Oakfield Road, Bristol, BS8 2BG
Tel: 0117 973 5556 Fax: 0117 974 4141

Washington

St Paul's Road, Clifton, Bristol, BS8 1LX
Tel: 0117 9733980 Fax: 0117 9734740
Email: washington@cliftonhotels.com
Web: www.cliftonhotels.com

Tasteful conversion of Georgian buildings
situated close to shops and amenities.
SB £53 DB £67 CC: MC Vi Am DC Swi Delt

Westbourne

40-44 St Pauls Road, Clifton, Bristol, BS8 1LR
Tel: 0117 9734214

Brixham, Devon

The Smugglers Haunt Hotel

★

Church Hill, Brixham, Devon, TQ5 8HH
Tel: 01803 853050

Seeley's Hotel

Recently refurbished city centre hotel,
54 large ensuite rooms, satellite television,
tea maker, clothes press, lounge bar, excellent
restaurant, three conference suites, sauna,
gardens, car park.

17/27 St. Paul's Road, Clifton,
Bristol BS8 1LX
Tel: 0117 973 8544   Fax: 0117 973 2406
Email: admin@seeleys.demon.co.uk
Website: www.seeleys.demon.co.uk

Harbour View

65 King Street, Brixham, Devon, TQ5 9TH
Tel: 01803 853052
SB £25 DB £40 CC: MC Vi Delt

How to get there: A3022 Brixham road to town
centre/harbour, left at lights, right at T-junction.
Hotel is on right of inner harbour.

Bude, Cornwall

Hartland

★★★

Hartland Terrace, Bude, Cornwall, EX23 8JY
Tel: 01288 355661 Fax: 01288 355664
Closed December to February
SB £46 DB £70 HBS £64 HBD £106
B £8.50 D £20.

How to get there: Turn left into Hartland Terrace
from main street (opposite Boots). Hotel
signposted in main street.

Camelot

★★

Downs View, Bude, Cornwall, EX23 8RE
Tel: 01288 352361 Fax: 01288 355470
Email: stay@camelot-hotel.co.uk
Web: www.camelot-hotel.co.uk

Overlooking Bude Golf Course. A short walk from beaches and town centre. Elegantly refurbished to a high standard with first class, friendly sevice and superb freshly prepared food.
SB £34 DB £68 HBS £51 HBD £103 D £17.
CC: MC Vi Am Swi Delt

How to get there: Follow one-way system past post office. Stay in left lane; Camelot is at bottom of hill on left.

Cliff Hotel

♦♦♦♦

Maer Down Road, Bude, Cornwall, EX23 8NG
Tel: 01288 358110 Fax: 01288 353110
Web: www.cliffhotel.co.uk
Closed November to March
SB £29.50 DB £39.50 HBS £33.50 HBD £43.50
L £2.85 D £13.50.
CC: MC Vi Swi JCB Maestro Solo

How to get there: Through High Street, past post office on left. First right to crossroads. Straight across and bear left to end of road, hotel on right.

Coombe Barton Inn

♦♦♦

Crackington Haven, Cornwall, EX23 0JG
Tel: 01840 230345 Fax: 01840 230788
Fully licensed freehouse next to beach in beautiful Cornish bay serving fresh Cornish-landed fish, chargrilled steaks etc. Cornish real ales and a large selection of lagers and wines.
SB £30 DB £50 B £5 L £8 D £12.

CC: MC Vi Am Swi Delt

How to get there: Head south on A39 from Bude for 8 miles. Turn off right at Wainhouse Corner. Follow road down to the beach.

Budleigh Salterton, Devon

Long Range

♦♦♦♦

5 Vales Road, Budleigh Salterton,
Devon, EX9 6HS
Tel: 01395 443321 Fax: 01395 445220
Email: longrange@eclipse.co.uk
SB £30 DB £60 HBS £47.50 HBD £95
B £8 L £9.50 D £17.50. CC: MC Vi Swi Delt

How to get there: From Exeter approach Budleigh Salterton. Turn left at traffic lights. Continue to T-junction, turn left. Take first right and first right again. Hotel on left.

Castle Combe, Wiltshire

Manor House

★★★★

Castle Combe, Wiltshire, SN14 7HR
Tel: 01249 782206 Fax: 01249 782159

Chagford, Devon

Gidleigh Park

★★★

Chagford, Devon, TQ13 8HH
Tel: 01647 432367 Fax: 01647 432574
Email: gidleighpark@gidleigh.co.uk
Web: www.gidleigh.com
B £16 L £35 D £65. CC: MC Vi Swi Delt

How to get there: In Chagford Square, facing Webbers, turn right into Mill Street. Take first fork to right, go downhill to Factory Crossroads. Go straight over, follow lane 1½ miles to end.

Great Tree

★★★

Sandy Park, nr Chagford, Devon, TQ13 8JS
Tel: 01647 432491 Fax: 01647 432562
Email: nigel@greattree.co.uk
Web: www.greattree.co.uk

A delightfully quiet and secluded location in
25 acres of woods and gardens dedicated to
nature conservation. A lovely unpretentious and
homely atmosphere.
SB £55 DB £82 HBS £75 HBD £61
B £12.50 D £25. CC: MC Vi Am DC Swi Delt
🐎🛋💻☎️🅿️♨️🕯🎠🍸🍴🦮🍽♨️♨️♨️
How to get there: Take the A30 to Whiddon
Down roundabout. Drive south down A382 for
2¹/₂ miles.

Three Crowns

★★

High Street, Chagford, Devon, TQ13 8AJ
Tel: 01647 433444 Fax: 01647 433441/117
Email: threecrowns@msn.com
Web: www.chagford-accom.co.uk

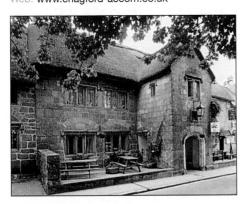

A warm and friendly 13th-century inn situated in
a picturesque village within Dartmoor. Oak
beams, four poster beds. Noted for good food
and ale.
SB £42.50 DB £65 HBS £60 HBD £99
B £5.50 L £4.95 D £17.50. CC: MC Vi Swi Delt
🛏🐎💍🛋💻☎️🅿️♨️🕯🎠🍸🍴🦮♨️♨️♨️🍷

Queens Arms

★★ 🍴

The Street, Charmouth, Dorset, DT6 6QF
Tel: 01297 560339

Chideock, Dorset

Chimneys

♦♦♦♦ 🍷

Main Street, Chideock, Bridport, Dorset,
DT6 6JH
Tel: 01297 489368
SB £25 DB £44
🛏🐎💍🛋💻🅿️♨️🕯🎠🍸🍴🦮
How to get there: On the A35 near Bridport.

Chippenham, Wiltshire

Oxford

♦♦♦

32–36 Langley Road, Chippenham,
Wiltshire, SN15 1BX
Tel: 01249 652542

Christchurch, Dorset

Heritage Hotels – The Avonmouth

★★★

95 Mudeford, Christchurch, Dorset, BH23 3NT
Tel: 0870 400 8120 Fax: 01202 479004

Waterford Lodge

★★★ 🍴🍴🍴

87 Bure Lane, Friars Cliff, Christchurch, Dorset,
BH23 4DN
Tel: 01425 278801 Fax: 01425 279130
Email: waterford@bestwestern.co.uk
Web: www.waterfordlodge.com
SB £79 DB £108 HBS £97 HBD £144
B £10.50 L £14.50 D £25.50.
CC: MC Vi Am DC Swi Delt
🛏🐎💍🛋☎️🅿️♨️🕯🎠🍸🍴🦮♨️♨️♨️
How to get there: 2 miles east of Christchurch
on A337, turn south towards Mudeford and
hotel is ¹/₂ mile on left.

Clevedon, North Somerset

Walton Park

★★★ 🍴

1 Wellington Terrace, Clevedon, BS21 7BL
Tel: 01275 874253 Fax: 01275 343577

Combe Martin, Devon

Blair Lodge

♦♦♦

Moory Meadow, Seaside, Combe Martin, Devon, EX34 0DG
Tel: 01291 882294
Children minimum age: 10
SB £21 DB £23

How to get there: Exit M5 J-27, A361 towards Barnstaple. On roundabout near South Molton join A399 to Combe Martin.

Corsham, Wiltshire

Methuen Arms

★★
High Street, Corsham, Wiltshire, SN13 0HB
Tel: 01249 714867 Fax: 01249 712004

Countisbury, Devon

Exmoor Sandpiper

★★
Lynton, Countisbury, Devon, EX35 6NE
Tel: 01598 741263 Fax: 01598 741358

Crediton, Devon

Lower Burrow Coombe

♦♦♦
Cheriton Fitzpaine, Crediton, Devon, EX17 4JS
Tel: 01363 866220
Closed December to February
SB £22 DB £34

Cricklade, Wiltshire

White Hart

♣
High Street, Cricklade, Swindon, SN6 6AA
Tel: 01793 750206 Fax: 01793 750650
Web: www.the-whitehart-hotel.co.uk
SB £33 DB £65 B £5 L £5 D £5.
CC: MC Vi DC Swi Delt

How to get there: Exit M5 J-15, A419 to Cirencester. Approximately 9 miles.

Looking for great dining? Look for RAC Hotels and Guest Accommodation displaying the RAC Dining Award symbol in this Guide.

Croyde, Devon

Kittiwell House

★★
St Marys Road, Croyde, Devon, EX33 1PG
Tel: 01271 890247 Fax: 01271 890469
Children minimum age: 4

Kittiwell House is a thatched 16th-century hotel with 12 en-suite bedrooms and an award-winning restaurant. Situated in the seaside village of Croyde. Ideal for golfers, walkers and surfers.
SB £49 DB £78 HBS £69 HBD £114
B £7.50 D £21.50. CC: MC Vi Swi Delt

How to get there: Exit M5 J-27, A361 to Barnstaple. Continue on A361 to Braunton. Turn left at traffic lights in Braunton. In centre of Croyde, turn right into St Mary's road for 500m. Kittiwell House is behind Manor House pub.

Croyde Bay House Little Gem

♦♦♦♦♦
Moor Lane, Croyde, Devon, EX33 1PA
Tel: 01271 890270
Closed December to February
SB £35 DB £70 HBS £47 HBD £94
CC: MC Vi Am Swi Delt

How to get there: Exit M5 J-27, A361 to Barnstaple, then signs for Braunton. Left in Braunton to Croyde village. Left in centre of Croyde, then left again into Moor Lane. Follow road into slipway ³/₄ mile.

Denham Farm & Country House

♦♦♦♦
North Buckland, Braunton, Devon, EX33 1HY
Tel: 01271 890297 Fax: 01271 890297
Email: jean@denhamfarm.co.uk
Web: www.denhamfarm.co.uk
Closed November to January
DB £50 CC: MC Vi

A place for all seasons, this lovely farmhouse is

situated amidst rolling Devon hills only two miles from the glorious coastline of Croyde and Woolacombe.
SB £35 DB £50 CC: MC Vi

How to get there: Off A361 Braunton to Ilfracombe Road. After Knowle village turn left at first crossroads, signposted North Buckland. 1 mile, in centre of hamlet.

Cullompton, Devon

Manor House

★★
2/4 Fore Street, Cullompton, Devon, EX15 1JL
Tel: 01884 32281
SB £46.50 DB £59.50
CC: MC Vi Am DC Swi Delt

Dartmouth, Devon

Heritage Hotels – The Dart Marina

★★★
Sandquay, Dartmouth, Devon, TQ6 9PH
Tel: 01803 832580 Fax: 01803 835040
Email: heritagehotels_dartmouth.dart_marina@forte-hotels.com
Web: www.heritage-hotels.com
SB £45 DB £90 HBS £60 HBD £120
B £12 L £7.50 D £18.50.
CC: MC Vi Am DC Swi Delt Electron Solo

How to get there: A3122 from Totnes and follow signs for Dart Marina. Hotel is overlooking the marina itself, beside the Higher Ferry.

Royal Castle

★★★
11 The Quay, Dartmouth, Devon, TQ6 9PS
Tel: 01803 833033 Fax: 01803 835445
Email: enquiry@royalcastle.co.uk
Web: www.royalcastle.co.uk
Two bars serving choice bar meals, ales and

wines. Adam room restaurant specialising in local seafood. 25 luxuriously appointed en-suite bedrooms to choose from.
SB £53.45 DB £109.90 HBS £66.45
HBD £139.90 B £6.50 L £7.50 D £15.50.
CC: MC Vi Am Swi Delt

How to get there: Exit M5, A38 to Totnes. In Totnes, right towards Dartmouth at first lights. The hotel is in the town centre.

Stoke Lodge

★★★
Stoke Fleming, Dartmouth, Devon, TQ6 0RA
Tel: 01803 770523 Fax: 01803 770851
Email: mail@stokelodge.co.uk
Web: www.stokelodge.co.uk
SB £47 DB £78 HBS £60 HBD £103
B £5.95 L £11.95 D £16.95. CC: MC Vi Swi Delt

Dawlish, Devon

Langstone Cliff

★★★
Dawlish, Devon, EX7 0NA
Tel: 01626 868000 Fax: 01626 868006
Email: rac@langstone-hotel.co.uk
Web: www.langstone-hotel.co.uk
SB £55 DB £94 HBS £69 HBD £122
B £7.50 L £9 D £16.
CC: MC Vi Am DC Swi Delt JCB Solo

How to get there: Exit M5 J-30, A379 for Dawlish. Turn left at Harbour. Hotel is approx $1^1/_2$ miles past beach up hill on left.
See advert on following page

Guests should check in advance whether properties displaying the 'no-smoking rooms available' symbol allow smoking in any rooms.

West Hatch Private Hotel

◆◆◆◆

34 West Cliff, Dawlish, Devon, EX7 9DN
Tel: 01626 864211 Fax: 01626 864211

Devizes, Wiltshire

Bear Hotel

★★★

Market Place, Devizes, Wiltshire, SN10 1HS
Tel: 01380 722444 Fax: 01380 722450
Closed Christmas
SB £65 DB £94 CC: MC Vi Am Swi Delt

How to get there: Exit M4 J-15 at Chippenham, signs to Devizes. Hotel is in the town centre.

Dorchester, Dorset

The Wessex Royale

★★★

High West Street, Dorchester, Dorset, DT1 1UP
Tel: 01305 262660 Fax: 01305 251941

Yellowham Farmhouse

◆◆◆◆

Yellowham Wood, Dorchester, Dorset, DT2 8RW
Tel: 01305 262892 Fax: 01305 257707
Email: b+b@yellowham.freeserve.co.uk
Web: www.yellowham.freeserve.co.uk
Children minimum age: 6

Accommodation is on the ground floor to the rear of main house in cloister-type setting. Peaceful and secluded in 120 acres. 1½ miles east of Dorchester.
SB £30 DB £50 HBS £45 HBD £40 D £15.

How to get there: Off A35 on the edge of Yellowham Wood.

Dulverton, Devon

Jubilee House

◆◆◆◆

Highaton Farm, West Anstey, South Molton, Devon, EX36 3PJ
Tel: 01398 341312 Fax: 01398 341323
Email: denton@exmoorholiday.co.uk
Web: www.exmoorholiday.co.uk
SB £19.50 DB £39 D £12.

How to get there: Off B3227 between South Molton/Bampton, turn to West Anstey/Yeo Mill at side of the Jubilee Inn. Jubilee House is 400m along lane on right.

Dunster, Somerset

Heritage Hotels — The Luttrell Arms

★★★

32-36 High Street, Dunster, TA24 6SG
Tel: 0870 400 8110 Fax: 01643 821567

Evercreech, Somerset

Pecking Mill Inn

◆ ◆ ◆

A371, Evercreech, Somerset, BA4 6PG
Tel: 01749 830336 Fax: 01749 831316

Evershot, Dorset

Summer Lodge

★★★ ☂ ☂ ☂ ☂
Evershot, Dorset, DT2 0JR
Tel: 01935 83424 Fax: 01935 83005

Exeter, Devon

Heritage Hotels – The Southgate

★★★★ ☂
Southernway East, Exeter, Devon, EX1 1QF
Tel: 0870 400 8333 Fax: 01392 413549
Email: tony.aspen@fortehotels.com
Web: www.heritage-hotels.com
SB £120.75 DB £131.50 HBS £103 HBD £140
CC: MC Vi Am DC Swi Delt

Manor House Hotel & Golf Course

★★★★ ☂ ☂
Moretonhampstead, Devon, TQ13 8RE
Tel: 01647 440355 Fax: 01647 440355
Email: reception@principalhotels.co.uk
Web: www.principalhotels.co.uk
SB £85 DB £120 HBS £89 HBD £79
B £11.50 L £12.50 D £23.
CC: MC Vi Am DC Swi

Woodbury Park Hotel Golf & Country Club

★★★★
Woodbury Castle, Woodbury, Exeter, EX5 1JJ
Tel: 01395 233382 Fax: 01395 234701

Barton Cross Hotel

★★★ ☂
Huxham, Stoke Canon, Exeter, Devon, EX5 4EJ
Tel: 01392 841245 Fax: 01392 841942

Devon Hotel

★★★
Exeter Bypass, Matford, Exeter, Devon,
EX2 8XU
Tel: 01392 259268 Fax: 01392 413142
Email: info@devonhotel.co.uk
Web: www.brend-hotels.co.uk

Luxurious standards of comfort, personal
service and fine wine in the hotel's bar and
brasserie 'Carriages'. The Devon Hotel is
conveniently located within easy reach of the
M25 and Exeter city centre.
SB £59 DB £82 HBS £74 HBD £112 B £6.50
L £11 D £15. CC: MC Vi Am DC Swi Delt
How to get there: Exit M5 J-30. Take 3rd exit,
signposted Torquay. On old Exeter bypass at
Matford.

Queen's Court

★★★ ☂
6–8 Bystock Terrace, Exeter, Devon, EX4 4HY
Tel: 01392 272709 Fax: 01392 491390

Fingle Glen Hotel Golf & Country Club

★★
Old Tedburn Road, Tedburn St Mary,
Exeter, Devon, EX6 6AF
Tel: 01647 61817

Great Western

★★
St David's Station Approach, Exeter, EX4 4NU
Tel: 01392 274039 Fax: 01392 425529
Email: reception@greatwesternhotel.co.uk
Web: www.greatwesternhotel.co.uk
SB £42 DB £66 HBS £52 HBD £86 B £5.50
L £11 D £12. CC: MC Vi Am DC Swi Delt

Red House

★★
2 Whipton Village Road, Whipton, Exeter,
Devon, EX4 8AR
Tel: 01392 256104 Fax: 01392 666145
Email: red.house.hotel@eclipse.co.uk
SB £42 DB £56 HBS £52 HBD £76 B £6 L £4.95
D £12.95. CC: MC Vi Am DC Swi Delt
How to get there: The hotel is on the B3212
Pinhoe to Exeter road.

Southwest

St Andrews

★★

28 Alphington Road, Exeter, Devon, EX2 8HN
Tel: 01392 276784 Fax: 01392 250249
Closed Christmas to New Year

St Andrews is a long-established, family-run hotel offering a high standard of comfort and service in a friendly relaxing atmosphere. Excellent home cooking.
SB £45 DB £60 B £7.50 D £9.
CC: MC Vi Am DC Swi Delt Solo

How to get there: Exit M5 J-31 for Exeter, signs to city centre and Marsh Barton along Alphington Road (A377). St Andrews is on left.

Hotel Gledhills

♦♦♦

32 Alphington Road, Exeter, Devon, EX2 8HN
Tel: 01392 430469 Fax: 01392 430469
Email: hotelgledhills@netscapeonline.co.uk
Web: www.uk-explorer.co.uk/gledhills
Closed Christmas
SB £24 DB £42 CC: MC Vi Swi Delt

How to get there: Exit M5 J-3 to city centre, road becomes Alphington Rd. Gledhills on left.

Reservations ГЭС

RAC Hotel Reservations is your one-stop booking service for over 3,000 RAC Hotels & Guest Accommodation. So if the hotel or B&B of your choice doesn't have availability, we'll be able to source the next best alternative for you free of charge. Call 0870 603 9109 to make a booking at any of the properties featured in this Guide.

For your complete reassurance, only RAC Hotels and Guest Accommodation have been assessed on your behalf by our team of independent inspectors for quality, facilities and service.

Park View

♦♦♦

8 Howell Road, Exeter, Devon, EX4 4LG
Tel: 01392 271772
Email: philbatho@parkviewhotel.freeserve.co.uk
Web: www.parkviewhotel.freeserve.co.uk

Charming, family-owned hotel in a peaceful setting overlooking park, close to city centre. All rooms equipped with modern facilities, dining room overlooks well-maintained garden.
SB £32 DB £47 CC: MC Vi Am Swi Delt

How to get there: Follow B3183 to city centre, until clocktower. Take fourth exit (Elm Grove Road). At end, turn left into Howell Road. Park View 100m on right.

Telstar

♦♦♦

75–77 St David's Hill, Exeter, Devon, EX4 4DW
Tel: 01392 272466 Fax: 01392 272466
Email: reception@telstar-hotel.co.uk
Web: www.telstar-hotel.co.uk
SB £22 DB £45 CC: MC Vi Swi Delt

How to get there: Drive through city centre from A30 or J-30 of M5. Hotel is between city centre and St Davids station.

Braeside

♦♦

21 New North Road, Exeter, Devon, EX4 4HF
Tel: 01392 256875 Fax: 01392 256875
SB £21 DB £36 HBS £29 HBD £52
CC: MC Vi Swi Delt
How to get there: Exit M5 J-31 for Exeter, signs to city centre. Hotel in centre between the clock tower and the prison.

Exford, Somerset

Crown

★★★

Exford, Somerset, TA24 7QP
Tel: 01643 831554 Fax: 01643 831665
Email: bradleyhotelsexmoor@easynet.co.uk
Web: www.gratton.co.uk/crown
SB £47.50 DB £80 HBD £69
B £9.50 L £18 D £21.
CC: MC Vi Am DC Swi Delt Solo Eurocard
🐴🖥☎🅿♨🕯🐴🎠🐎♻♨♨ ♨♨♨
How to get there: Exit M5 J-25, A38. Turn left
onto B3224. Follow for 20 miles to Exford. Hotel
at bottom of hill on right.

Exmouth, Devon

Royal Beacon

★★★ ℞

The Beacon, Exmouth, Devon, EX8 2AF
Tel: 01395 264886 Fax: 01395 268890
Email: reception@royalbeaconhotel.co.uk
Web: www.royalbeaconhotel.co.uk

Former Georgian posting house overlooking the
sea, with 25 guest rooms, spacious lounge and
bar and a charming restaurant featuring
superbly prepared fresh local cuisine.
SB £45 DB £85 HBS £57 HBD £110
B £6 L £9 D £13. CC: MC Vi Am DC Swi Delt
🐴👶🖥☎🐎🎠🐎♻☎🅿♨🕯🐴🎠🐎♻♨♨♨

Manor Hotel

★★

The Beacon, Exmouth, Devon, EX8 2AG
Tel: 01395 272549 Fax: 01395 225519

Falmouth, Cornwall

Budock Vean – The Hotel On The River

★★★★ ℞℞

Mawnan Smith, nr Falmouth, TR11 5LG

Tel: 01326 250288 Fax: 01326 250892
Email: relax@budockvean.co.uk
Web: www.budockvean.co.uk
Children minimum age: 7

Friendly, peaceful, family-run 4-star hotel in 65
acres with subtropical gardens, golf course,
large indoor pool, boat, jetty, health spa and
award-winning restaurant.
SB £49 DB £98 HBS £59 HBD £118
B £12 L £10 D £24.50. CC: MC Vi DC Swi
🐴👶〽🐎🎠🐎♻☎🅿♨🕯🐴🎠🐎♻
🐎♨♨♨♨♨ SPA ⚲🔍ℹ🗂🛥
How to get there: From A39 Truro to Falmouth
road, tourist signs to Trebah Garden. Continue
for ½ mile past Trebah to the hotel.

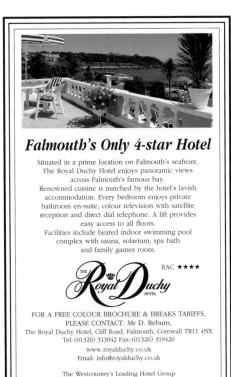

Royal Duchy

★★★★ ☆☆

Cliff Road, Falmouth, Cornwall, TR11 4NX
Tel: 01326 313042 Fax: 01326 319420
Email: info@royalduchy.co.uk
Web: www.brend-hotels.co.uk

On the seafront, Falmouth's only 4-star hotel is renowned for award-winning cuisine, warm attentive service and luxurious accommodation.
SB £60 DB £112 HBS £72 HBD £136 B £6.75 L £10 D £16.95. CC: MC Vi Am DC Swi Delt

How to get there: Castle end of seafront on left.
See advert on previous page

The Greenbank Hotel is Falmouth's oldest, and the only hotel on the water's edge of one of the world's largest and deepest natural harbours.

Dating from the mid-seventeenth century and with its own private quay.

Spring 2000 saw completion, by the new owners, of a million-pound refurbishment programme

HARBOURSIDE FALMOUTH
CORNWALL TR11 2SR

TELEPHONE 01326 312440
FAX 01326 211362

Falmouth Hotel

★★★

Castle Beach, Falmouth, Cornwall, TR11 4NZ
Tel: 01326 312671 Fax: 01326 319533

Green Lawns

★★★

Western Terrace, Falmouth, Cornwall,
TR11 4QJ
Tel: 01326 312734 Fax: 01326 211427
Email: info@greenlawnshotel.com
Web: www.greenlawnshotel.com
SB £50 DB £100 HBS £70 HBD £140
B £8 L £5 D £12. CC: MC Vi Am DC Swi Delt

The Greenbank

★★★

Harbourside, Falmouth, Cornwall, TR11 2SR
Tel: 01326 312440 Fax: 01326 211362
Email: sales@greenbank-hotel.co.uk
Web: www.greenbank-hotel.com
SB £57 DB £87 HBS £69 HBD £54 L £8 D £15.
CC: MC Vi Am DC Swi Delt

How to get there: Approach Falmouth from Penryn. Take left turn along north parade and follow the Greenbank sign. Hotel is 1 mile further on left.
See advert on the left

Gyllyngdune Manor

★★★

Melvill Road, Falmouth, Cornwall, TR11 4AR
Tel: 01326 312978 Fax: 01326 211881
SB £50 DB £100 HBS £66 HBD £132 CC: MC Vi Am DC Swi Delt

How to get there: A39 to Falmouth. Follow signs for hotels, beaches and docks. Join Melvill Road at Western Terrace. Hotel approx 1/2 mile on right.

Bosanneth

♦♦♦♦

Gyllyngvase Hill, Falmouth, Cornwall,
TR11 4DW
Tel: 01326 314649 Fax: 01326 314649
Email: bosanneth.falmouth@tinyworld.co.uk
Children minimum age: 5
SB £25 DB £50 HBS £31 HBD £62

How to get there: Enter Falmouth on A39, follow signs for beaches. Take Dracaena Avenue, Western Terrace, Melvill Road. Turn right after rail bridge into Gyllyngvase Hill.

Chellowdene

♦♦♦♦

Gyllyngvase Hill, Falmouth, Cornwall, TR11 4DN
Tel: 01326 314950
Closed May to October
DB £20 HBD £30

How to get there: A39 into Falmouth. Follow road signed Beaches, Gyllyngvase Beach. Chellowdene 60m from main beach.

Ivanhoe Guest House

♦♦♦♦

7 Melvill Road, Falmouth, Cornwall, TR11 4AS
Tel: 01326 319083

Tudor Court Hotel

♦♦♦♦

55 Melvill Road, Falmouth, Cornwall, TR11 4DF
Tel: 01326 312807 Fax: 01326 312807
Email: peterb@tudor-court-hotel.freeserve.co.uk
Web: www.cornwall-online.co.uk/tudor-court-hotel
Children minimum age: 6
SB £22.50 DB £44 CC: MC Vi Am DC

How to get there: From Truro, continue on main road for docks. Hotel on right of Melvill Road.

Gyllyngvase House Hotel

♦♦♦

Gyllyngvase Road, Falmouth, TR11 4DJ
Tel: 01326 312956 Fax: 01326 316166
Email: gyllyngvase@btinternet.com
Web: www.smoothhound.co.uk/hotels/
gyllyngv.html
SB £27.50 DB £55 HBS £39 HBD £78
CC: MC Vi Am DC Swi Delt

How to get there: From A30, follow signs to Truro, then from Truro to Falmouth. Follow sign to beaches and dock on corner of Gyllyngvase and Melvill roads.

Rathgowry Hotel

♦♦♦

Gyllyngvase Hill, Falmouth, Cornwall,
TR11 4DN
Tel: 01326 313482
Email: a.ranford@virgin.net
Closed October to March
SB £21 DB £42 HBS £30 HBD £60 D £9.

How to get there: Follow signs for docks and beaches along Dracaena Avenue, Western Terrace and Melville Road. Then turn right into Gyllyngvase Hill.

Trevaylor

♦♦♦

8 Pennance Road, Falmouth, Cornwall,
TR11 4EA
Tel: 01326 313041 Fax: 01326 316899
Email: stay@trevaylor.co.uk
SB £19.50 DB £39 HBS £29 HBD £58
B £3 D £9.50. CC: MC Vi Swi Delt

How to get there: Take signs for the beaches. Go along Western Terrace, Green Lawns Hotel on right, turn right at mini roundabout.

Fowey, Cornwall

Fowey Hotel

★★★ ♟♟
The Esplanade, Fowey, Cornwall, PL23 1HX
Tel: 01726 832551 Fax: 01726 832125
Email: fowey@richardsonhotels.co.uk
B £8.50 L £5 D £26.95. CC: MC Vi Am Swi

How to get there: Continue along A390. Just past Lostwithiel, take left turn for Fowey. Follow signage from roundabout.

Cormorant On The River

★★ ♟
Golant by Fowey, Cornwall, PL23 1LL
Tel: 01726 833426 Fax: 01726 833574
Email: relax@cormoranthotels.co.uk
Web: www.cormoranthotels.co.uk
Children minimum age: 12

Small luxury hotel in idyllic picturesque setting. Breathtaking views of the river, creeks and wooded slopes below from all bedrooms, lounge, terraced gardens and restaurant.
SB £51 DB £76 HBS £66 HBD £53
B £7 L £4.50 D £20. CC: MC Vi

How to get there: From B3259 Fowey road, turn left into Golant. Drive along water's edge. The Cormorant is the last drive on right.

Old Quay House

Fore Street, Fowey, Cornwall, PL23 1AQ
Tel: 01726 833302

Frome, Somerset

The Sun Inn

6 Catherine Street, Frome, Somerset, BA11 1DA
Tel: 01373 471913

Mendip Lodge

Bath Road, Frome, Somerset, BA11 2HP
Tel: 01373 463223 Fax: 01373 463990

Gillingham, Dorset

Stock Hill House

★★★★
Stock Hill, Gillingham, Dorset, SP8 5NR
Tel: 01747 823626 Fax: 01747 825628
Email: reception@stockhill.net
Web: www.stockhill.net
Children minimum age: 7
HBS £165 HBD £290 B £15 L £22 D £35.
CC: MC Vi Swi

How to get there: 3 miles off the A303, situated
on the B3081. 1 mile from Gillingham station.

Glastonbury, Somerset

Cradlebridge Farm

♦♦♦♦
Glastonbury, Somerset, BA16 9SD
Tel: 01458 831827
Children minimum age: 3. Closed Christmas
SB £35 DB £45

How to get there: Exit M5 J-23, A39. After 12
miles take first left after Street Bypass. Farm
sign on left after 1 mile.

Southtown House

♦♦♦
West Pennard, Glastonbury, Somerset,
BA6 8NS
Tel: 01458 834552

When booking at an RAC Hotel or Guest
Accommodation, please mention this Guide.

Helston, Cornwall

Nansloe Manor

★★
Meneage Road, Helston, Cornwall, TR13 0SB
Tel: 01326 574691 Fax: 01326 564680
Email: info@nansloe-manor.co.uk
Web: www.nansloe-manor.co.uk
Children minimum age: 10
SB £59 DB £110 HBS £83 HBD £158
B £10 L £13 D £24. CC: MC Vi Swi Delt JCB

How to get there: 300m on the left from
Helston/Lizard roundabout A394/A3083.

Holford, Somerset

Alfoxton Park

★★
Holford, Somerset, TA5 1SG
Tel: 01278 741211

Honiton, Devon

Combe House Hotel at Gittisham

★★★
Honiton, Devon, EX14 3AD
Tel: 01404 540400 Fax: 01404 46004

The Deer Park Country Hotel

★★★
Buckerell Village, Honiton, Devon, EX14 0PG
Tel: 01404 41266 Fax: 01404 46598

Hope Cove, Devon

Hope Cove

♦♦♦
Kingsbridge, Hope Cove, Devon, TQ7 3HH
Tel: 01548 561233 Fax: 01548 561233

Ilfracombe, Devon

Arlington

★★
Sommers Crescent, Ilfracombe,
Devon, EX34 9DT
Tel: 01271 862002 Fax: 01271 862803
Email: bookings@devoniahotels.co.uk
Web: www.devoniahotels.co.uk
Family-run seaside hotel offering good value for
money breaks. Located in a central position
close to all amenities. Close to the sea. Try one
of our champagne weekends.

SB £26 DB £52 HBS £33 HBD £66
CC: MC Vi Am Swi Delt
⊔⊥ 🐾☕🖥☎🅿🛁 ⋇🐴ℏ🦪🛏🕯🛋
How to get there: Exit M5 J-27. A361 to
Barnstaple, then to Ilfracombe. Straight across
two sets of lights, then left fork and first left.

Elmfield Hotel
★★
Torrs Park, Ilfracombe, Devon, EX34 8AZ
Tel: 01271 863377 Fax: 01271 866828
Web: www.northdevon.co.uk/elmfieldhotel
Closed November to March
SB £40 DB £80 HBS £45 HBD £90 B £8 D £16.
CC: MC Vi Swi Delt
🚗☕🖥🅿🛁⋇🅲🐴ℏ🦪🛏🕯 ⵙℂ🗒
How to get there: A361 from Barnstaple to
Ilfracombe, left at first lights, left at 2nd lights,
10m left again, hotel at top of hill on the left.
See advert on the right

Ilfracombe Carlton
★★
Runnacleave Road, Ilfracombe, EX34 8AR
Tel: 01271 862446 Fax: 01271 865379
Closed January to February

Lovely (refurbished for 2000) Victorian style
hotel. Central location adjacent to coastal
walks, beach, gardens and theatre. We aim to
please — somewhere special for you!
SB £27.50 DB £50 HBS £35 HBD £70

Elmfield Hotel

Stands in an acre of gardens, with a heated
indoor swimming pool, jacuzzi, sauna,
solarium, and car park. For that special
occasion two rooms have four-poster beds.
The Hotel has an excellent reputation for its
English and Continental cuisine and has
received a Dining Award from the RAC.

**Torrs Park, Ilfracombe, North Devon
EX34 8AZ**
Tel: 01271 863377 Fax: 01271 866828
Website: www.northdevon.co.uk/
elmfieldhotel

B £12.50 D £12.50. CC: MC Vi Am Swi Delt
⊔⊥☕🖥☎🅿🛁⋇🐴ℏ🦪🛏
How to get there: M5 J-27, A361 to Barnstaple,
A361 to Ilfracombe. Left at seafront, left again.

St Helier
★★
Hillsborough Road, Ilfracombe, EX34 9QQ
Tel: 01271 864906 Fax: 01271 864906
Email: st_helier_hotel@yahoo.com
Closed October to April
SB £29 DB £52 HBS £36 HBD £68
B £3.50 D £11. CC: MC Vi Delt
🐾☕🖥🅿🛁⋇🅲🐴ℏ🦪🛏
How to get there: Exit M5 J-27, A361 towards
Barnstaple to Ilfracombe. Through high street
towards Combe Martin, hotel is on the left.

Tracy House
★★
Belmont Road, Ilfracombe, Devon, EX34 8DR
Tel: 01271 863933
SB £23 DB £46 HBS £31 HBD £60
CC: MC Vi
🐾☕🖥☎🅿🛁⋇🅲🐴ℏ🦪🛏🕯
How to get there: Approx 200m from end of
High Street. Ascend Chuch Hill from A361. Turn
left into Belmont Road, property is fourth on left.

Cairn House

★

43 St Brannocks Road, Ilfracombe EX34 8EH
Tel: 01271 863911 Fax: 01271 863911

A comfortable small hotel set in its own grounds with superb views of the sea and surrounding hills.
SB £18 DB £36 HBS £36 HBD £36 D £10.
CC: MC Vi

How to get there: M5 J-27, A361 to Barnstaple, and on to Ilfracombe. Go straight across Mullacott Cross roundabout: hotel 1¼ miles.

Torrs

★

Torrs Park, Ilfracombe, Devon, EX34 8AY
Tel: 01271 862334
Children minimum age: 5
Closed mid-November to mid-February
SB £20 DB £40 HBS £30 HBD £60 D £10.
CC: MC Vi Swi Delt JCB Solo

How to get there: From Barnstaple (A361), left at first set of lights in Ilfracombe. At 2nd set turn left, then left again.

Westwell Hall

★

Torrs Park, Ilfracombe, Devon, EX34 8AZ
Tel: 01271 862792 Fax: 01271 862792
Email: westwellhall@btconnect.com
Children minimum age: 8. Closed Dec to March
SB £22 DB £44 HBS £34 HBD £68
CC: MC Vi Swi Delt

How to get there: Take A361 from Barnstaple. Turn left at both first and second traffic lights, then immediately left. Take second on right into Upper Torrs.

Book an RAC inspected Hotel or Guest Accommodation, visit www.rac.co.uk/hotels

Avalon Hotel

♦♦♦♦

6 Capstone Crescent, Ilfracombe, EX34 9BT
Tel: 01271 863325 Fax: 01271 866543
Email: christine@avalon-hotel.co.uk
Web: www.avalon-hotel.co.uk
Closed December to January
SB £30 DB £45 HBS £40 HBD £64 D £10.
CC: MC Vi Am Swi Delt

How to get there: Along seafront to harbour edge and Sandpiper pub. Left into Capstone.

Seven Hills Hotel

♦♦♦♦

Torrs Park, Ilfracombe, North Devon, EX34 8AY
Tel: 01271 862207
Email: seven.hills@hydrocomputers.force9.co.uk
Children minimum age: 1
SB £20 DB £40 HBS £30 HBD £50 D £10.
CC: MC Vi Am Swi Delt

How to get there: Left at lights entering Ilfracombe from Barnstaple. Next left, then immediate right, hotel is immediately in front.

Southcliffe

♦♦♦♦

Torrs Park, Ilfracombe, Devon, EX34 8AZ
Tel: 01271 862958
Children minimum age: 16
Closed November to March
SB £40 DB £50 HBS £51 HBD £72 D £11.
CC: MC Vi Swi Delt

How to get there: From Barnstaple on A361, left at first lights, left at next. Hotel on the left.

Strathmore

♦♦♦♦

57 St Brannocks Road, Ilfracombe, EX34 8EQ
Tel: 01271 862248 Fax: 01271 862243
SB £25 DB £50 HBS £37.95 HBD £75.90
CC: MC Vi Swi Delt

Capstone Hotel & Restaurant

♦♦♦

15–16 St James Place, Ilfracombe, EX34 9BJ
Tel: 01271 863540 Fax: 01271 862277
Closed November to Easter
SB £18.50 DB £37 HBS £28.50 HBD £57
B £5 L £4 D £5. CC: MC Vi Am Swi Delt

How to get there: Left at lights to seafront, past Landmark Theatre, to St James' Place. Look for bow-windowed restaurant on left.

Greyven House

♦♦♦

4 St James Place, Ilfracombe, EX34 9BH
Tel: 01271 862505 Fax: 01271 863928
Closed November to February
SB £18 DB £36 HBS £26.50 HBD £53
B £4 L £5 D £6.50.
CC: MC Vi Am DC Swi Delt Solo Maestro

How to get there: Seafront into Ilfracombe, then
150m past the Pavilion on the left-hand side.

St Brannocks House

♦♦♦

61 St Brannocks Road, Ilfracombe, EX34 8EQ
Tel: 01271 863873 Fax: 01271 863873
Email: stbrannocks@aol.com
SB £23 DB £46 HBS £33 HBD £66
CC: MC Vi Am

How to get there: M5 J-27, A361 to Ilfracombe.
Hotel is on A361 on left as you approach town.

Instow, Devon

Commodore

★★★

Marine Parade, Instow, Devon, EX39 4JN
Tel: 01271 860347 Fax: 01271 861233
Email: admin@the-commodore.freeserve.co.uk
Web: www.commodore-instow.co.uk
SB £52 DB £100 HBS £62.5 HBD £130 B £8.5 L
£13.5 D £21. CC: MC Vi Am Swi Delt

How to get there: M5 J-27, North Devon Link
Road. Instow turn-off signposted before the
Torridge Bridge. Follow the signs for Instow and
these will bring you to Marine Parade.

Isles of Scilly

Island

★★★

Tresco, Isles of Scilly, TR24 0PU
Tel: 01720 422883 Fax: 01720 423008
Email: islandhotel@tresco.co.uk
Closed November to February
SB £90 DB £220 HBS £90 HBD £250
B £9 L £12 D £33. CC: MC Vi Swi Delt

How to get there: Departure from Penzance
recommended via British International
Helicopters. Direct to Tresco Heliport for
collection. Departure St Mary's via boat to
Tresco for collection.

St Martins on the Isle

★★★

St Martin's, Isles of Scilly, Cornwall, TR25 0QW
Tel: 01720 422092 Fax: 01720 422298
Email: stay@stmartinshotel.co.uk
Web: www.stmartinshotel.co.uk
SB £85 DB £170 HBS £95 HBD £190
B £12 L £10 D £30.
CC: MC Vi Am DC Swi Delt

How to get there: Departure from Penzance
recommended via British International
Helicopters,direct to Tresco Heliport. Departure
St Mary's via boat to Tresco, 20 minutes.

Hotel Godolphin

★★

St Marys, Isles of Scilly, Cornwall, TR21 0JR
Tel: 01720 422316 Fax: 01720 422252
Closed November to March
SB £50 DB £110 HBS £60 HBD £130
B £8 D £20. CC: MC Vi Swi Delt

Tregarthen's Hotel

★★

Hughtown, St Mary's, Isles of Scilly, TR21 0PP
Tel: 01720 422540 Fax: 01720 422089
Email: reception@tregarthens-hotel.co.uk
Web: www.tregarthens-hotel.co.uk
Children minimum age: 5
Closed October to March
CC: MC Vi Am DC Swi Delt

Seaview Moorings

♦♦♦♦♦

The Strand, St Mary's, Isles of Scilly, TR21 0PT
Tel: 01720 422327 Fax: 01720 422211
Children minimum age: 14
SB £36 DB £72

How to get there: Hotel is situated directly
opposite St Mary's harbour quay.

Carnwethers Country House

♦♦♦♦

Pelistry Bay, St Mary's, Isles of Scilly, TR21 0NX
Tel: 01720 422415 Fax: 01720 422415
Children minimum age: 12
Closed October to April
HBS £58 HBD £96

How to get there: 2½ miles from Hughtown, 1½
miles from St Mary's Heliport. Guests are met
by taxi or minibus.

Ivybridge, Devon

Sportsmans Inn

★★

Exeter Road, Ivybridge, Devon,
Tel: 01752 892280 Fax: 01752 690714
SB £40 DB £50 HBS £50 HBD £70
B £8 L £4 D £6. CC: MC Vi Am Swi Delt
♿ 🖥 ⊗ ☎ 📺 🖥 📞 **P** ⛱ ♨ ⚑ ⚒
How to get there: Just off A38, 10 miles from
Plymouth, centre of Ivybridge town.

Keynsham, Bristol

Grasmere Court

♦♦♦♦ 🚲 ✈

22 Bath Road, Keynsham, Bristol, BS31 1SN
Tel: 01179 862662 Fax: 01179 862762

Superior family-run hotel conveniently situated
between Bristol and Bath. The hotel has been
recently refurbished to a high standard. All
rooms are well appointed with private facilities.
Free parking for all.
SB £48 DB £64 B Inclusive D £15.
CC: MC Vi Am Swi Delt
⚓ 🖥 ⊗ 🖥 ☎ **P** ⛱ ♨ 🐴 ♨ ⚑ ⚒
How to get there: Situated on main A4 road,
midway between the cities of Bristol and Bath.

Kingsbridge, Devon

Cottage Hotel

★★ 🚲

Hope Cove, Kingsbridge, Devon, TQ7 3HJ
Tel: 01548 561555 Fax: 01548 561455
Email: info@hopecove.com
Web: www.hopecove.com
Closed January
SB £22 DB £44 HBS £38 HBD £76 B £8.95
L £9.35 D £18.55. CC: Swi Delt Solo Electron
♿ 🐴 ⊗ **P** ✿ ⛱ ♨ 🐴 ♨ ⚑ ⚒ ⚒
How to get there: A381 for Salcombe; Hope
Cove signposted. Continue towards Hope Cove,
left for Inner Hope. Hotel is on right.

Crabshell Lodge

Travel Accommodation
Embankment Road, Kingsbridge, Devon,
TQ7 1JZ
Tel: 01548 853301 Fax: 01548 856283

Launceston, Cornwall

Hurdon Farm

♦♦♦♦ ✈

Launceston, Cornwall, PL15 9LS
Tel: 01566 772955
Closed November to April
SB £20 DB £40 HBS £32 HBD £64
⊗ 🖥 🖥 **P** ⛱ ♨ 🐴 ♨ ♨
How to get there: Leave A30 at first Launceston
exit. From Bodmin right off roundabout. From
Exeter left exit off roundabout, then second
right signed Trebullet. Hurdon first right.
See advert on facing page

Lifton, Devon

Arundell Arms

★★★ 🚲🚲🚲

Lifton, Devon, PL16 0AA
Tel: 01566 784666 Fax: 01566 784494
Email: arundellarms@btinternet.com
Closed Christmas
SB £74 DB £113 HBS £90 HBD £160
B £10 L £17 D £29.50.
CC: MC Vi Am DC Swi
🐴 ⊗ 🖥 ☎ **P** ✿ ⛱ ♨ 🐴 ♨ ⚑ ⚒ ⚒ ♨
How to get there: Exit M5 J-31, A30 towards
Launceston. Hotel is 2 miles east of Launceston
in Lifton village.

Liskeard, Cornwall

The London Inn

♦♦♦♦ ✈

St Neot, Liskeard, Cornwall, PL14 6NG
Tel: 01579 320263

Manor House Inn

♦♦♦ ✈

Rilla Mill, Nr Callington, Liskeard, PL17 7NT
Tel: 01579 362354 Fax: 01579 363305

Lizard, Cornwall

Housel Bay Hotel

★★★ ♜

Housel Cove, Lizard, Cornwall, TR12 7PL
Tel: 01326 290 417/917 Fax: 01326 290 359
Email: info@houselbay.com
Web: www.houselbay.com
B £7.50 L £6.95 D £15.50.
CC: MC Vi Am Swi Delt

 ♿ ⑪ ⬚ ⊗ ☎ ☐ ☎ ☎ P ⚡ ⌖ ♞ ♬ ✪ iii

How to get there: At the Lizard signpost, take the left fork. Follow hotel signs.
See advert below

Parc Brawse House

♦♦♦♦

Penmenner Road, Lizard, Cornwall, TR12 7NR
Tel: 01326 290466 Fax: 01326 290466
SB £17 DB £32 HBS £30 HBD £58
B £4.95 D £13. CC: MC Vi

♞ ⊗ ☎ ☐ P ⚡ ⌖ ♞ ♬ ✪ ⅲ i

How to get there: From Helston, take A3083 to Lizard village. Turn right after phone boxes into Penmenner Road. Hotel at end on right.

Southwest

Looe, Cornwall

Talland Bay Hotel

★★★ ®

Talland Bay, Looe, Cornwall, PL13 2JB
Tel: 01503 272667 Fax: 01503 272940
Email: tallandbay@aol.com
Closed January to mid-February
SB £47 DB £94 HBS £67 HBD £134
L £9.50 D £22. CC: MC Vi Am DC Swi Delt

🛋🐾🛎🖥📞☎🅿️♿️🎠🎵🛏️🐾♨️🍴 ⛷️🛗

How to get there: A38 Liskeard to Looe, then
Polperro road. Left at small crossroads. Follow
lane down towards the sea. Hotel on left.

Klymiarven

★★ ®

Barbican Hill, Looe, Cornwall, PL13 1BH
Tel: 01503 262333 Fax: 01503 262333
Email: klymiarven@cwcom.net
Web: www.klymiarven.co.uk
Closed January
DB £56 HBD £78 B £ L £5 D £15.
CC: MC Vi Swi

🛋🐾🐕🛎🖥📞☎🅿️♿️🎠🛏️🐾♨️🍴 ⛷️

How to get there: M5, A38, A374, B3253. Left
after Looe Garden Centre onto Barbican. Take
tourist bed sign Barbican Hill to Klymiarven.

Coombe Farm
Country House   Cornwall

Relax in a lovely country house in a wonderful
setting with superb views down a wooded
valley to the sea. Enjoy delicious food,
candlelit dining, log fires, heated outdoor pool
and warm, friendly hospitality.

Nearby golf, horse-riding, glorious walks,
beaches, National Trust houses, gardens
and the Eden Project.

Widegates, Nʳ Looe PL13 1QN
Tel: 01503 240223   Fax: 01503 240895
Email: coombe_farm@hotmail.com

 RaC
♦♦♦♦

The Commonwood

♦♦♦♦   ✍

St Martin's Road, Looe, Cornwall, PL13 1LP
Tel: 01503 262929 Fax: 01503 262632
Email: commonwood@compuserve.com
Web: www.commonwood.co.uk
Children minimum age: 9
Closed January to March

Victorian Villa in six acre grounds with
spectacular river and countryside views. Only
five minutes walk to Looe harbour and town.
New restaurant opening March 2001.
SB £45 DB £90 B £7 D £25.
CC: MC Vi Am Swi Delt JCB

🐾🛎🖥☎🅿️♿️🎠🛏️🐾♨️🍴 ⛷️

How to get there: On B3253 entering Looe.

Coombe Farm

♦♦♦♦   ✍ ®

Widegates, Looe, Cornwall, PL13 1QN
Tel: 01503 240223 Fax: 01503 240895
Email: coombe_farm@hotmail.com
Closed November to February
SB £40 DB £60 HBS £57 HBD £77 D £17.50.
CC: MC Vi Am Swi Delt

♿🐾🐕🛎🖥📞☎🅿️♿️🎠🛏️🐾♨️🍴 ⛷️🛗

How to get there: A38 for Liskgard, A387 to
Looe at Trerulefoot roundabout. Continue on
A387 to Hessenford, hotel 1 mile beyond on left.
See advert on the left

Panorama

♦♦♦♦   ✍

Hannafore Road, Looe, Cornwall, PL13 2DE
Tel: 01503 262123 Fax: 01503 265654
Email: alan@looe.co.uk
Web: www.looe.co.uk
Children minimum age: 5
SB £25 DB £47 HBS £39 HBD £37 D £14.
CC: MC Vi Swi Delt

🛋🛎🖥🅿️♿️🎠🛏️🐾♨️🍴

How to get there: Hotel is in west Looe
overlooking pier and beach.

Southwest

Deganwy

Station Road, Looe, Cornwall, PL13 1HL
Tel: 01503 262984
Closed November to December
SB £22 DB £17

How to get there: Situated in East Looe, 100m from East/West Looe Bridge, on the A387, opposite doctors' surgery.

Lostwithiel, Cornwall

Lostwithiel Hotel Golf & Country Club

★★★
Lower Polscoe, Lostwithiel, Cornwall,
PL22 0HQ
Tel: 01208 873550 Fax: 01208 873479
Email: reception@golf-hotel.co.uk
Web: www.golf-hotel.co.uk
SB £40 DB £80 HBS £39 HBD £78
B £5 L £3 D £14.95.
CC: MC Vi Am DC Swi Delt

How to get there: Signed off A390 on eastern outskirts of Lostwithiel.
See advert on this page

Royal Oak Inn

★★
Duke Street, Lostwithiel, Cornwall, PL22 0AH
Tel: 01208 872552 Fax: 01208 872552
Email: mghine@aol.com
SB £37.50 DB £63 B £4 L £4 D £7.50.
CC: MC Vi Am DC Swi Delt Solo

How to get there: The hotel is located on A390 from Plymouth.

Lydford, Devon

Moor View House   Little Gem

♦♦♦♦♦
Vale Down, Lydford, Okehampton,
Devon, EX20 4BB
Tel: 01822 820220 Fax: 01822 820220
Children minimum age: 12
SB £45 DB £65 HBS £60 HBD £95 D £20.

How to get there: From M5 at Exeter, take A30 to Sourton Cross, and then turn onto A386 towards Tavistock: Moor View Drive is 4 miles on right, 8 miles before Tavistock.
See advert on the right

LOSTWITHIEL Hotel RAC ★★★
GOLF & COUNTRY CLUB

Ideally located for all of Cornwall, this Country Club Hotel offers everything for leisure and relaxation. 18 ensuite bedrooms, games room, indoor swimming pool, gymnasium, tennis courts, golf course, fishing. Conference facilities for up to 150 persons.

Lower Polscoe, Lostwithiel, Cornwall
PL22 0HQ
Tel: 01208 873550   Fax: 01208 873479
Email: reception@golf-hotel.co.uk
Website: www.golf-hotel.co.uk

Moor View House

Always putting their guests' comfort first, David and Wendy Sharples have created a friendly hotel with a genuinely relaxing ambience. Reception rooms are warmed by the glow of traditional open fires and a Victorian theme characterises the well-appointed bedrooms. Spectacular views across Devon and Cornwall to the rear and Dartmoor to the front, once inspired Victorian writer Eden Phillpots to write the play 'Widdicombe Fair'. A daily four-course dinner menu offers traditional country-style recipes made from the finest local produce.

Vale Down, Lydford, Devon EX20 4BB
Tel/Fax: 01822 820220

    Little Gem

Lyme Regis, Dorset

Alexandra

★★★

Pound Street, Lyme Regis, Dorset, DT7 3HZ
Tel: 01297 442010 Fax: 01297 443229
Email: enquiries@hotelalexandra.co.uk
Web: www.hotelalexandra.co.uk
Closed January
SB £50 DB £110 HBS £65 HBD £140
B £8 L £13 D £22.50. CC: MC Vi Am Swi

How to get there: Exit M5 J-25, A358 to
Axminster. Take B3261 to B3165 Lyme Regis.
From M3, take A303 to reach A358.

Dower House

★★★ 🐎🐎

Rousdon, Lyme Regis, Dorset, DT7 3RB
Tel: 01297 21047 Fax: 01297 24748
Email: mdowerhouse@aol.com
Closed December to January

Tranquil country charm by the sea. Relax in our
award winning gardens, swim in our heated
indoor pool. Voted best hotel in Dorset 2001
and recommended by Which Hotel Guide 2001.
SB £55 DB £90 HBS £74 HBD £130
B £8 L £14 D £20. CC: MC Vi Am Swi Delt

How to get there: Dower House is 3 miles
outside of Lyme Regis on the A3052 between
Lyme Regis and Seaton.

Kersbrook

♦♦♦♦

Pound Road, Lyme Regis, Dorset, DT7 3HX
Tel: 01297 442596 Fax: 01297 442596
Web: www.lymeregis.com/kersbrook-hotel
Closed November to March
SB £35 DB £60 CC: MC Vi Am Swi Delt
How to get there: The road that leads to the
harbour is Cobb Road. Pound Road is at the
top of Cobb Road crossroads.

Devon

♦♦♦

Uplyme, Lyme Regis, Dorset, DT7 3TQ
Tel: 01297 443231 Fax: 01297 445836
Email: thedevon.hotel@virgin.net
Web: www.lymeregis.com/devon-hotel
SB £35 DB £70 HBS £45 HBD £90
CC: MC Vi Swi Delt

How to get there: From A35, into Lyme Road by
Hunters Lodge pub. Hotel is on left after 1 mile.

Tudor House Hotel

♦♦♦

Church Street, Lyme Regis, Dorset, DT7 3BU
Tel: 01297 442472

Lympsham, Somerset

Batch Country Hotel

★★

Batch Lane, Lympsham, Somerset, BS24 0EX
Tel: 01934 750371

Lynmouth, Devon

Tors

★★★

Lynmouth, Devon, EX35 6NA
Tel: 01598 753236 Fax: 01598 752544
Email: torshotel@torslynmouth.co.uk
Web: www.torslynmouth.co.uk
Closed January to February
SB £40 DB £70 HBS £55 HBD £100
B £6.95 L £16 D £24.
CC: MC Vi Am DC Swi Delt Solo Electron

How to get there: Exit M5 J-23, A39 for
Bridgwater, west for 40 miles through Minehead
and Porlock. Down Countisbury Hill, the hotel is
on left as you enter Lynmouth.

Bath Hotel

★★

Seafront, Lynmouth, Devon, EX35 6EL
Tel: 01598 752238 Fax: 01598 752544
Email: bathhotel@torslynmouth.co.uk
Web: www.torslynmouth.co.uk
Closed December to January
SB £35 DB £58 HBS £44 HBD £76
B £6 L £6 D £17. CC: MC Vi Am DC Swi Delt
How to get there: On A39 from Minehead, on
entering Lynmouth turn right towards the sea.
Hotel on left by harbour.

Southwest

Lynton, Devon

Lynton Cottage

★★★ ℞

North Walk Hill, Lynton, Devon, EX35 6ED
Tel: 01598 752342 Fax: 01598 752597
Email: enquiries@lynton-cottage.co.uk
Web: www.lynton-cottage.co.uk
Children minimum age: 14
Closed December to January
SB £29 DB £58 HBS £48 HBD £96
B £9 L £6 D £15. CC: MC Vi Am Swi Delt
♿ 🛏 🕯 🍃 💻 ☎ 🅿 ✂ ⌚ 🐎 🎠 🍴 ♨ ♨♨ ♨♨♨
How to get there: Turn down North Walk Hill
next to church. Hotel entrance 50m on right.

Sandrock

★★

Longmead, Lynton, Devon, EX35 6DH
Tel: 01598 753307 Fax: 01598 752665
Closed November to January

Family-run hotel with modern comforts. Ideal for
relaxing and exploring Exmoor's coastal beauty.
SB £26 DB £27 HBS £41 HBD £84
B £4.50 D £15. CC: MC Vi Am Swi Delt
🛏 🍃 💻 ☎ 🅿 ✂ ⌚ 🐎 🎠 🍴 ♨♨♨ ℂ
How to get there: Follow the signs in Lynton to
The Valley of Rocks.

Seawood

★ ℞

North Walk, Lynton, Devon, EX35 6HJ
Tel: 01598 752272 Fax: 01598 752272
Children minimum age: 12

Closed November to April
Seawood was originally built in 1848 as a retreat
for wealthy Victorian families. Situated in its own
grounds on wooded cliffs overlooking Lynmouth
Bay, it provides a tranquil setting from which to
explore Exmoor.
SB £29 DB £58 HBS £44.50 HBD £89 D £15.50.
🛏 🍃 🍃 💻 🅿 ✂ ⌚ 🐎 🍴 ♨ 🍴 🍴
How to get there: Turn right at St Mary's church
in Lynton High Street into the North Walk and
Seawood is second property on left.

Mayfair

◆◆◆

The Lynway, Lynton, Devon, EX35 6AY
Tel: 01598 753227

Malmesbury, Wiltshire

Knoll House

★★★ ℞℞

Swindon Road, Malmesbury, Wiltshire,
SN16 9LU
Tel: 01666 823114 Fax: 01666 823897
Email: knollhouse@malmesbury64.freeserve.
   co.uk
Web: www.knoll-house.com
SB £67.50 DB £90 HBS £85 HBD £130
B £5 L £5 D £10.
CC: MC Vi Am Swi Delt
♿ 🛏 🍃 🍃 💻 ☎ 🅿 ✂ ⌚ 🐎 🍴 ♨ ♨♨ ♨♨♨ 🎣
How to get there: Exit M4 J-17, A429 towards
Cirencester. At first roundabout after 5 miles
take third exit (B4042). Hotel 500 yards on right.

Old Bell

★★★ ℞℞

Abbey Row, Malmesbury, Wiltshire, SN16 0AG
Tel: 01666 822344 Fax: 01666 825145
Email: info@oldbellhotel.com
Web: www.oldbellhotel.com
SB £70 DB £100 CC: MC Vi Am DC Swi Delt
🔔 🛏 🍃 🍃 💻 ☎ 🅿 ✂ ⌚ 🐎 🍴 ♨ ♨♨ ♨♨♨

Mayfield House

★★ ℞

Crudwell, Malmesbury, Wiltshire, SN16 9EW
Tel: 01666 577409 Fax: 01666 577977
Email: mayfield@callnetuk.com
SB £56 DB £78 B £4.95 L £5 D £17.95.
CC: MC Vi Am DC Swi Delt
🛏 🍃 💻 ☎ 🖊 🅿 ✂ ⌚ 🐎 🍴 ♨ ♨♨ 🍴 🍴
How to get there: Situated on the A429 between
Malmesbury and Cirencester. 7 miles north of
J-17 on the M4.

Marazion, Cornwall

Chymorvah Private Hotel

♦♦♦

Marazion, Cornwall, TR17 0DQ
Tel: 01736 710497 Fax: 01736 710508
Web: www.smoothhound.co.uk/hotels/
chymorvah.html
Closed Christmas and New Year
SB £26 DB £52 HBS £38 HBD £76
B £2.25 L £2.50 D £12. CC: MC Vi Swi Delt
♿ 🏨 🐕 ⊗ ⍟ 🖥 ☎ 🅿 ⚒ ⌨ 🐎 🍴 🍽

How to get there: A30 at Marazion/St Michael's
Mount roundabout towards Helston on A390
and turn right after Fire Engine Inn.

Marlborough, Wiltshire

Ivy House

★★★ ⍟⍟

Marlborough, Wiltshire, SN8 1HJ
Tel: 01672 515333 Fax: 01672 515338
Email: ivyhouse@btconnect.com

Overlooking Marlborough's famous High Street,
this hotel combines the luxuries of 3-star
accommodation, first-class food and friendly,
efficient service with the character of a listed
Georgian building.
SB £79 DB £98 B £6.50 L £9.50 D £19.50.
CC: MC Vi Am Swi Delt
♿ ⊗ ⍟ 🖥 ☎ 🅿 ⚒ ⌨ 🐎 🍴 🍽 ♨ 👪

How to get there: Exit M4 J-15, A346 to
Marlborough. Ivy House is on A4 (High Street).

The Vines

♦♦♦♦ ⍟

High Street, Marlborough, Wiltshire, SN4 1HJG
Tel: 01672 515333 Fax: 01672 515338
SB £47.50 DB £65 L £9.50 D £19.50.
CC: MC Vi Am Swi Delt
⊗ ⍟ 🖥 ☎ 🅿 ⚒ ⌨ 🐎 🍴 🍽 ♨ 👪

How to get there: Exit M4 J-15, A346 to
Marlborough. Ivy House is on A4 opposite The
Vines. Come to Ivy House Hotel to check in.

Merlin

♦♦♦

High Street, Marlborough, Wiltshire, SN8 1LW
Tel: 01672 512151 Fax: 01672 515310
SB £40 DB £60 CC: MC Vi Swi Delt
🐎 ⊗ ⍟ 🖥 🅿

How to get there: The Merlin Hotel is in the
middle of this historic High Street.

Melksham, Wiltshire

Beechfield House

★★★ ⍟⍟

Beanacre, Melksham, Wiltshire, SN12 7PU
Tel: 01225 703700

Conigre Farm

★★ ⍟

Semington Road, Melksham, Wiltshire,
SN12 6BZ
Tel: 01225 702229 Fax: 01225 707392

Shaw Country Hotel

★★ ⍟

Bath Road, Shaw, Melksham, Wiltshire,
SN12 8EF
Tel: 01225 702836 Fax: 01225 790275

Mevagissey, Cornwall

Fountain Inn

♦♦♦

Mevagissey, Cornwall, PL26 6QH
Tel: 01726 842320

Ship Inn

♦♦♦

Fore Street, Mevagissey, Cornwall, PL26 6UQ
Tel: 01726 843324 Fax: 01726 843324
SB £30 DB £50 L £4.50 D £4.95.
CC: MC Vi Swi Delt
⍟ 🖥 🍴 ⌨ 🐎 🍴 🍽 ♨ 👪

How to get there: Follow A30 south to
St Austell. Follow signs to Mevagissey.
The Ship Inn is in centre of village.

Midsomer Norton, Somerset

Centurion Hotel

★★★

Charlton Lane, Midsomer Norton,
Somerset, BA3 4BD
Tel: 01761 417711 Fax: 01761 418357

Minehead, Somerset

Benares

★★★

Northfield Road, Minehead, Somerset,
TA24 5PT
Tel: 01643 704911 Fax: 01643 706375
Email: pmas213508@aol.com
Children minimum age: 6 months
Closed November to mid-March
SB £53 DB £96 HBS £63 HBD £120
B £9.50 L £12 D £23.
CC: MC Vi Am DC Swi Delt JCB

How to get there: Follow seafront towards
harbour. Turn left into Blenheim Road. After 40
yards turn right into Northfield Road.

Beaconwood

★★

Church Road, North Hill, Minehead, Somerset,
TA24 5SB
Tel: 01643 702032 Fax: 01643 702032
Email: beaconwood@madasafish.com
Web: www.beaconwoodhotel.co.uk

Edwardian country house hotel set in two acres
of gardens with panoramic views of Exmoor
National Park and sea, with swimming pool and
tennis court.
SB £45 DB £70 HBS £60 HBD £100 D £15.
CC: MC Vi Swi Delt

How to get there: From the Avenue, turn into
Martlet Road. Bear right at St Michael's Church.
Hotel 300 yards on right.

Rectory House Hotel

★★

Northfield Road, Minehead, Somerset,
TA24 5QH
Tel: 01643 702611
SB £30 DB £60 HBD £41 D £21. CC: MC Vi

How to get there: Located two streets away
from Minehead High Street.

Gascony

◆◆◆◆

50 The Avenue, Minehead, Somerset, TA24 5BB
Tel: 01643 705939 Fax: 01643 709926
Closed November to February
SB £28.50 DB £50 HBS £39.50 HBD £74
CC: MC Vi Swi Delt

How to get there: On main road between town
centre and seafront.

Mayfair

◆◆◆◆

25 The Avenue, Minehead, Somerset, TA24 5AY
Tel: 01643 702719 Fax: 01643 702719
Closed October to March
SB £25 DB £50 HBS £37 HBD £74 B £5 D £12.
CC: MC Vi Delt

How to get there: Towards seafront. After
hospital and church. Mayfair is only hotel on left.

Rest and Be Thankful Inn

◆◆◆◆

Wheddon Cross, Exmoor, Somerset, TA24 7DR
Tel: 01643 841222 Fax: 01643 841813
Email: enquiries@restandbethankful.co.uk
Web: www.restandbethankful.co.uk
Children minimum age: 11
SB £30 DB £60 HBS £39.50 HBD £39.50
B £6.25 L £3 D £5.
CC: MC Vi Am DC Swi Delt JCB Electron

How to get there: On A396/B3224 crossroads,
9 miles south of Minehead.

Beverleigh

◆◆◆

Beacon Road, Minehead, Somerset, TA24 5SE
Tel: 01643 708450
Email: beverleigh@talk21.com
SB £25 DB £40

How to get there: Off main shopping street, into
Blenheim Rd, first left Martlet Rd into Burgundy
Road and Beacon Rd. Park at North Hill Road.

Stockleigh Lodge

◆◆◆

Exford, Exmoor, Somerset, TA24 7PZ
Tel: 01643 831500 Fax: 01643 831595
SB £25 DB £50 HBS £40 HBD £80 D £15.

How to get there: Exit M5 J-25, A358 signs to
Minehead. At Bishops Lydeard left onto B3224
for Exford, Simons Bath road out of Exford.
Lodge on right.

Southwest

Montagute, Somerset

Slipper Cottage

♦♦♦

41 Bishopston, Montagute, TA15 6UX
Tel: 01935 823073
Email: sue.weir@totalise.co.uk
SB £26 DB £38

♿ 🛏 ⊗ 🕒 ▯ ◻ ▯ 🅿 ⚡ ☼ 🎠 ♬ ✂

How to get there: From A303, take B3088 to
Yeovil. Montacute first right, then first left.
Cottage is on left in village, just before church.

Mortehoe, Devon

Cleeve House

♦♦♦♦   ⚑ ☼ 🍴

Mortehoe, Woolacombe, Devon, EX34 7ED
Tel: 01271 870719 Fax: 01271 870719
Email: info@cleevehouse.co.uk
Web: www.cleevehouse.co.uk
Children minimum age: 12
Closed November to March

A warm welcome awaits guests at this homely
hotel. The bedrooms are comfortable and well
equipped with many thoughtful extras. The
ground floor bedroom has wheelchair access.
DB £58 HBD £88 B £6 D £15.
CC: MC Vi Swi Delt Solo JCB

♿ ⊗ ◻ ◻ 🅿 ⚡ ☼ ♬ ✂ ♟ ♙

Newquay, Cornwall

Barrowfield Hotel

★★★

Hilgrove Road, Newquay, Cornwall, TR7 2QY
Tel: 01637 878878 Fax: 01637 879490
Email: booking@barrowfield.prestel.co.uk
SB £30 DB £60 HBS £30 HBD £60
CC: MC Vi Am Swi Delt

◬ ♿ ⊪ 🛏 ☼ ⊗ ◻ ☎ 🅿 ⚡ ☼ ♬ ✂ ☀

♨ ♙♙ 🚩 ☂ ☕ ⚐ ⚑ ♟

How to get there: Enter Newquay via seafront.
Left onto Hilgrove Road. Situated on right.

Hotel Bristol

★★★

Narrowcliff , Newquay, Cornwall, TR7 2PQ
Tel: 01637 875181 Fax: 01637 879347
Email: info@hotelbristol.co.uk
Web: www.hotelbristol.co.uk
SB £57.77 DB £94.11 HBS £72.92
HBD £122.42 B £9.50 L £12.50 D £19.50.
CC: MC Vi Am DC Swi Delt JCB

⊪ ☼ ⊗ ◻ ☎ 🅿 ⚡ ☼ 🎠 ♬ ✂ ☀ ♨ ♙♙ 🚩

⚐ ⚑

How to get there: Turn off A30 onto A392, then
onto A3058. Hotel is located 2½ miles on left.
See advert on facing page

Hotel Riviera

★★★

Lusty Glaze Road, Newquay, Cornwall, TR7 3AA
Tel: 01637 874251 Fax: 01637 850823
SB £45 DB £90 HBS £550 HBD £110
B £7.50 L £10 D £15. CC: MC Vi Am Swi Delt

◬ ♿ ⊪ 🛏 ⊗ ◻ ☎ 🅿 ⚡ ☼ 🎠 ♬ ✂ ☀ ♨

♙♙ ⚐ ⚑

See advert on facing page (below)

Kilbirnie

★★★

Narrowcliffe, Newquay, Cornwall, TR7 2RS
Tel: 01637 875155 Fax: 01637 850769
Email: enquirykilbirnie@aol.com
Web: www.kilbirniehotel.com

Centrally situated for town and beaches.
Excellent accommodation, cuisine and service.
Heated swimming pools, sauna, solarium, spa
bath. Snooker room. Lift to all floors.
SB £32 DB £64 HBS £40 HBD £80
B £5.50 D £14. CC: MC Vi Am DC Swi Delt

◬ ♿ ⊪ ⊗ ◻ ☎ 🅿 ⚡ ☼ ♬ ✂ ☀ ♨ ♙♙ 🆂🅿🅰 ⚐

⚐ ♟ ♙

How to get there: Entering Quintrell Downs,
right on seafront road for approximately 3 miles.
Hotel is on left overlooking seafront.
See advert on facing page (above)

Southwest

Trebarwith Hotel
"Probably the best views in Newquay"

There's more too! Gardens, sun terraces, private beach entrance, large indoor pool. All complemented by relaxing, comfortable, friendly atmosphere, high standards of housekeeping, excellent food and caring hospitality. Extensive indoor leisure facilities, entertainment, secure parking. Quiet, central location, an oasis in the heart of Newquay!

Newquay, Cornwall TR7 1BZ
Tel: 01637 872288   Fax: 01637 875431
Email: enquiry@trebarwith-hotel.co.uk
Website: www.trebarwith-hotel.co.uk

Trebarwith Hotel
★★★
Trebarwith Crescent, Newquay, TR7 1BZ
Tel: 01637 872288 Fax: 01637 875431
Email: enquiry@trebarwith-hotel.co.uk
Web: www.trebarwith-hotel.co.uk
SB £30 DB £60 HBS £35 HBD £70
B £7 L £3 D £14.
CC: MC Vi Am Swi Delt
How to get there: From town centre turn left just before bus station into Trebarwith Crescent. Hotel is located at end of crescent.
See advert above

Beachcroft
★★
Cliff Road, Newquay, Cornwall, TR7 1SW
Tel: 01637 873022 Fax: 01637 873022
Closed November to March
SB £25 DB £50
CC: MC Vi Am Swi Delt
How to get there: 10 miles from A30, via RAF airfield. On main road into Newquay, opposite rail station.

Great Western
★★
Cliff Road, Newquay, Cornwall, TR7 2PT
Tel: 01637 872010 Fax: 01637 874435
Web: www.chycor.co.uk/greatwestern
B £8 L £10 D £14. CC: MC Vi Am DC Swi Delt
How to get there: A30 to Quintrell Downs roundabout. Turn right, over level crossing, to seafront in Newquay. Hotel is on right.

Philema
★★
Esplanade Road, Pentire, Newquay, TR7 1PY
Tel: 01637 872571 Fax: 01637 873188
Email: info@philema.demon.co.uk
Web: www.smoothhound.co.uk/hotels/philema.
html
Closed November to February
SB £25 DB £50 HBS £30 HBD £60
B £5 D £7.50. CC: MC Vi Swi Delt
How to get there: At the end of A392, turn left at roundabout. Continue until road splits: Philema is on corner.

Pendeen
◆◆◆◆
7 Alexandra Road, Porth, Newquay, Cornwall, TR7 3ND
Tel: 01637 873521 Fax: 01637 873521
Email: pendeen@cornwall.net
Web: www.cornwall.net/pendeen
Children minimum age: 5
Closed November to January

Superb location on coastal path. Very close to beach. A welcoming peaceful atmosphere — efficient, friendly service assured. Excellent food. Licensed, car park.
SB £29 DB £45 HBS £39 HBD £65
B £4.75 D £10. CC: MC Vi Am Swi
How to get there: A30, A392, A3058. After 2 miles take B3276. Pendeen is ¼ mile further.

Porth Enodoc

◆◆◆◆

4 Esplanade Road, Pentire, Newquay, TR7 1PY
Tel: 01637 872372 Fax: 01637 878219
Email: info@porthenodoc.co.uk
Web: www.porthenodoc.co.uk
Closed November to February
DB £41 HBD £51.50

Priory Lodge

◆◆◆◆

30 Mount Wise, Newquay, Cornwall, TR7 2BH
Tel: 01637 874111 Fax: 01637 851803
Closed January to February
SB £25 DB £50 HBS £35 HBD £70
B £4 L £2 D £5. CC: MC Vi Swi Delt

How to get there: Mount Wise Rd, hotel 500m
on right, black and white phone box in grounds.

Windward Hotel

◆◆◆◆

Alexandra Road, Porth, Newquay, TR7 3NB
Tel: 01637 873185 Fax: 01637 852436
Email: caswind@aol.com
Closed November to January
SB £26 DB £38 HBS £34 HBD £54
L £10 D £12. CC: MC Vi Am Swi Delt

How to get there: Join the A392 at Indian
Queens. At Quintell Downs, take A3058 to
Newquay, then B3276 to Padstow at double
roundabout. Hotel is on right after 1 mile.

Carlton

◆◆◆

Towan Headland, 6 Dane Road, Newquay,
Cornwall, TR7 1HL
Tel: 01637 872658
Closed November to Easter

The hotel occupies one of the finest positions in
Newquay. Standing on Towan Headland, we are
within minutes' walk of beach, harbour, and golf
course.

SB £20 DB £40

How to get there: Newquay on A30 onto A392,
down Higher Tower Road. Left at Red Lion. The
Carlton Hotel is at top of Dane Road.

Copper Beech

◆◆◆

70 Edgcumbe Avenue, Newquay, TR7 2NN
Tel: 01637 873376

Rolling Waves Hotel

◆◆◆

Alexandra Road, Porth, Newquay, TR7 3NB
Tel: 01637 873236 Fax: 01637 873236
Email: rollingwaves@barclays.net
SB £20 DB £40 HBS £27 HBD £54
CC: MC Vi Swi Delt

How to get there: From A30 turn into A3059
Newquay Road. On entering Newquay at first
roundabout turn right into B3276 to Padstow.
Hotel is on right past Porth beach.

Newton Abbot, Devon

Ilsington Country Hotel

★★★

Ilsington Village, Newton Abbot, TQ13 9RR
Tel: 01364 661452 Fax: 01364 661307
Email: hotel@ilsington.co.uk
Web: www.ilsington.co.uk
Set in a stunning setting within Dartmoor
National Park. Indoor swimming pool and
award-winning food make this family-owned
hotel an ideal destination.
SB £69 DB £100 HBS £78 HBD £130 B £8.50
L £13.50 D £24.50. CC: MC Vi Am Swi Delt

How to get there: A38 to Bovey Tracey exit,
then 3rd exit from roundabout, right to Ilsington.
Hotel 5 miles on, on right.

Passage House

★★★

Hackney Lane, Kingsteignton, Newton Abbot,
Devon, TQ12 3QH
Tel: 01626 355515 Fax: 01626 363336
Email: mail@passagehousehotel.co.uk
Web: www.passagehousehotel.co.uk
SB £67.50 DB £80 B £7.50
L £10.95 D £18.95. CC: MC Vi Am DC Swi Delt

How to get there: Exit M5 J-31 for A380. Leave
at A381 exit and follow racecourse signs.

Southwest

PERCY'S
COUNTRY HOTEL & RESTAURANT

Percy's award winning Country Hotel and Restaurant extend a warm welcome to you. We guarantee you will enjoy your stay here as you experience the beauty of the 130-acre estate, designated as one of only three areas in England to offer complete tranquility. Experience contemporary cuisine and a well deserved rest in our comfortable, spacious rooms.

On arrival at Percy's you will immediately get away from it all. The air is fresh and clean. The pace of life is completely relaxed. All you have to do now is unwind. Maybe take a woodland stroll before dining to work up a well deserved appetite.

Percy's Country Hotel
& Restaurant
Coombeshead Estate
Virginstow, Devon EX21 5EA
Tel: 01409 211236
Fax: 01409 211275
Email: info@percys.co.uk
Website: www.percys.co.uk

June Cottage

◆◆◆◆

Dornafield Road, Ipplepen, Newton Abbot,
Devon, TQ12 5SH
Tel: 01803 813081
Children minimum age: 7

SB £18.50 DB £37 HBS £31 HBD £62 D £12.50.
⊛ ⌇ **P** 🐾 ⁙ 🐴 ⼌ ⚓
How to get there: A381 from Newton Abbot, 3¹/₂
miles to Ipplepen, 2nd right, then 100m on left.

Okehampton, Devon

Percy's Country Hotel & Restaurant

★★ ☕ ☕
Coombeshead Estate, Virginstow, EX21 5EA
Tel: 01409 211236 Fax: 01409 211275
Email: info@percys.co.uk
Web: www.percys.co.uk
SB £79.50 DB £99.50 HBS £107 HBD £78
B £8 L £12 D £28.50. CC: MC Vi Am Swi Delt
⟐ ⛄ ⁘ ⊛ ⌇ ▢ ☎ 🔋 **P** 🐾 ⁙ 🐴 ⼌ ⚓ ⁙ ⁙⁙
See advert on facing page

Ottery St Mary, Devon

Tumbling Weir

★★ ☕ ☕
Ottery St Mary, Devon, EX11 1AQ
Tel: 01404 812752 Fax: 01404 812752
Email: bpyoung2@cs.com

A beautifully thatched 17th-century cottage
hotel standing in a parkland setting, between
the River Otter and its millstream, complete with
a very fine restaurant.
⁙ ⁘ ▢ ☎ **P** ⁙⁙

Pitt Farm

◆◆◆◆ ⁙ ⁙
Fairmile, Ottery St Mary, Devon, EX11 1NL
Tel: 01404 812439 Fax: 01404 812439

This 16th-century thatched farmhouse nestles in
the picturesque Otter Valley. Ideal centre for
touring. Devon/Exeter 10 miles, Honiton 6 miles.
SB £20 DB £40 CC: MC Vi Swi
⊛ ⌇ ▢ **P** 🐾 ⁙ 🐴 ⼌ ⚓
How to get there: Signs for Fairmile on A30. In
Fairmile turn into B3176 towards Cadhay
House. After ¹/₂ mile, Pitt Farm is on left. From
Ottery St Mary, take Fairmile Road. Farm 1 mile.

Padstow, Cornwall

Heritage Hotels – The Metropole

★★★ ☕
Station Road, Padstow, Cornwall, PL28 8DB
Tel: 01841 532486 Fax: 01841 532867
Email: heritagehotels-padstow.metropole@
forte-hotels.com
Web: www.heritage-hotels.com
HBS £74 HBD £148 B £12.95 D £23.
CC: MC Vi Am DC Swi Delt
⛄ ⁙ ⁘ ⁙ ⊛ ⌇ ▢ ☎ **P** 🐾 ⁙ 🐴 ⼌ ⚓
⁙⁙ ⁙
How to get there: Follow A30 from Bodmin to
Wadebridge. Locate B3890 to Padstow. Take
2nd on right (School Hill). The Metropole is on
the left.

Old Customs House Inn

★★★ ☕
South Quay, Padstow, Cornwall, PL28 8BY
Tel: 01841 532359

Green Waves Private Hotel

★★ ⍼

Trevone Bay, Padstow, Cornwall, PL28 8RD
Tel: 01841 520114 Fax: 01841 520568
Children minimum age: 4
Closed October to March
CC: MC Vi

🍵 ⬜ 🅿 ⛱ 🕯 🐎 ♁ 🛏 ⛵ 🍴

Bedruthan House

◆◆◆

Bedruthan Steps, St Eval, Cornwall, PL27 7UW
Tel: 01637 860346 Fax: 01637 860763
Email: bedruthanhouse@excite.co.uk
Web: www.chycor.co.uk/hotels/bedruthan
Children minimum age: 3
SB £20 DB £40 HBS £28 HBD £56 L £7 D £8.
CC: MC Vi Swi Delt JCB Solo Eurocard

🌐 🍵 🅿 ⛱ 🕯 🐎 🛏 ⛵ 🍴 👤👤

How to get there: On B3276 Coast Road
halfway between Newquay and Padstow.

Woodlands Country House

◆◆◆   ✍

Treator, Padstow, Cornwall, PL28 8RU
Tel: 01841 532426 Fax: 01841 532426
Closed November to March
SB £25 DB £50

Torbay Holiday Motel
Paignton

Purpose-built motel on the A385
Totnes/Paignton road,
2 miles from Paignton.

Totnes Road, Paignton TQ4 7PP

Tel: 01803 558226   Fax: 01803 663375
Email: enquiries@thm.co.uk
Website: www.thm.co.uk

🐎 🌐 🍵 ⬜ 🅿 ⛱ 🕯 🐎 🛏 ⛵ 🍴

How to get there: Hotel is on B3276 between
Padstow and Trevone, 1/2 mile from Padstow.

Paignton, Devon

Redcliffe

★★★

Marine Drive, Paignton, Devon, TQ3 2NL
Tel: 01803 526397 Fax: 01803 528030
Email: redcliffe@aol.com
Web: www.redcliffehotel.co.uk
SB £50 DB £100 HBS £60 HBD £120
B £8 L £11 D £17. CC: MC Vi Am DC Swi Delt

⚓ ♿ ⛰ 🍵 ⬜ 📞 🅿 ⛱ 🕯 🐎 🛏 ⛵ 🎱 👤👤 SPA 🍴 💺 🧗

How to get there: Head for Paignton seafront.
Hotel is at the Torquay end of seafront, on the
sea side of the road.

Dainton

★★

95 Dartmouth Road, Three Beaches
Goodrington, Paignton, Devon, TQ4 6NA
Tel: 01803 550067 Fax: 01803 666339

Preston Sands

★★

Marine Parade, Sea Front, Paignton, TQ3 2NU
Tel: 01803 558718 Fax: 01803 527345

Sea Verge Hotel

★★

Marine Drive, Preston, Paignton, TQ3 2NJ
Tel: 01803 557795
Children minimum age: 9
Closed November to March
DB £18 HBD £36 D £9.

🍵 ⬜ 🅿 ⛱ 🕯 🐎 🛏 ⛵ 🍴

How to get there: On seafront overlooking
Preston beach and Green.

Torbay Holiday Motel

★★

Totnes Road, Paignton, Devon, TQ4 7PP
Tel: 01803 558226 Fax: 01803 663375
Email: enquiries@thm.co.uk
Web: www.thm.co.uk
SB £35.50 DB £57 HBS £42.50 HBD £71
CC: MC Vi Swi Solo

♿ ⛰ 🐎 🍵 ⬜ 📞 🅿 ⛱ 🕯 🐎 🛏 ⛵ 👤👤 🍴 💺 🧗

How to get there: We are situated 2 1/2 miles
from Paignton town centre, on main road A385
towards Totnes.
See advert on the left

Roundham Lodge

♦♦♦♦♦

16 Roundham Road, Paignton, Devon,
TQ4 6DN
Tel: 01803 558485 Fax: 01803 553090
Email: vivien@vega68.freeserve.co.uk
Web: www.adnet.co.uk/roundham
SB £20 DB £40

How to get there: Take A380 to Torquay
seafront. Turn right to Paignton. Follow road to
Marine Drive. At end of Marine Drive, turn into
Roundham Road at mini roundabout. Take 2nd
right. 2nd house on left.

Redcliffe Lodge

♦♦♦

1 Marine Drive, Paignton, Devon, TQ3 2NJ
Tel: 01803 551394
Children minimum age: 16

The family-run hotel that offers a great friendly
atmosphere with an excellent cuisine and
breathtaking sea views. If it is a fun-packed
holiday you want, or just to unwind and relax,
Paignton's the place to be.
SB £30 DB £48 HBS £25 HBD £56
CC: MC Vi Swi Delt

How to get there: At northern end of Paignton
seafront, opposite Paignton Green and close to
the beach.

Sealawn

♦♦♦

20 Esplanade Road, Paignton, Devon, TQ4 6BE
Tel: 01803 559031
Closed Christmas to New Year
SB £24 DB £48 HBS £32 HBD £64
B £4 D £8. CC: MC Vi Delt

How to get there: The Sealawn Hotel is situated
between the pier and the multiplex cinema on
Paignton seafront.

Par, Cornwall

Elmswood House Hotel

♦♦♦♦

73 Tehidy Road, Tywardreath, Par,
Cornwall, PL24 2QD
Tel: 01726 814221 Fax: 01726 814399
SB £27 DB £47 HBS £37 HBD £67 D £10.

How to get there: Turn off A390 at junction for
Fowey. Follow road for 3 miles B3269 turn left
at junction for Tywardreath & Par. Hotel opposite
St Andrew's Church.

Parkham, Devon

Penhaven Country House

★★★ ♥♥

Rectory Lane, Parkham, Devon, EX39 5PL
Tel: 01237 451711 Fax: 01237 451878
Email: reservations@penhaven.co.uk
Web: www.penhaven.co.uk
Children minimum age: 10
SB £65 DB £130 HBS £80 HBD £150
B £8 L £12 D £16.50. CC: MC Vi DC Swi

How to get there: Turn left opposite Coach &
Horses at Horns Cross on A39. Follow signs to
Parkham, continue up hill to church then take
second left.

Penzance, Cornwall

Mount Prospect Hotel

★★★

Britons Hill, Penzance, Cornwall, TR18 3AE
Tel: 01736 363117 Fax: 01736 350970
Email: mtpros2000@aol.com
Web: www.cornwall-online.co.uk/mount-
prospect
SB £54 DB £80 HBS £65 HBD £55
B £7.50 D £14.50.
CC: MC Vi Am Swi Delt JCB

How to get there: Past Heliport on A30. At
roundabout head for town centre. Turn right at
Pirates Hotel. Mount Prospect is 70m on right.

Guide dogs

If a Hotel or Guest Accommodation
does not display this 'dogs welcome'
symbol in its listing, the hotelier may
still be happy to welcome guests with guide
dogs; please contact the property first.

Southwest

Queens

★★★

Promenade, Penzance, Cornwall, TR18 4HG
Tel: 01736 362371 Fax: 01736 350033
Email: enquiries@queens-hotel.com
Web: www.queens-hotel.com

An elegant Victorian hotel enjoying pride of
place on the seafront promenade of Penzance
with majestic views which sweep across
Mount's Bay from St Michael's Mount to the
Lizard Peninsula.
SB £40 DB £76 HBS £45 HBD £90 B £7.50
L £5.50 D £13.50. CC: MC Vi Am DC Swi Delt

How to get there: Follow signs for harbour and
Promenade. Follow to Promenade on seafront.
See advert on facing page

Tarbert Hotel & Restaurant

★★

11 Clarence Street, Penzance, Cornwall,
TR18 2NU
Tel: 01736 363758 Fax: 01736 331336
Email: reception@tarbert-hotel.co.uk
Web: www.tarbert-hotel.co.uk
Closed January

A superb example of a Georgian period hotel
where personal attention and high standards
of service are guaranteed. A warm welcome
awaits you.

SB £30 DB £60 HBS £53.50 HBD £48.50
B £7.50 D £20. CC: MC Vi Am Swi Delt JCB

How to get there: Take ring after heliport for
Land's End. Left at 3rd roundabout, then right.

Estoril

★

46 Morrab Road, Penzance, TR18 4EX
Tel: 01736 362468 Fax: 01736 367471
Email: estorilhotel@aol.com
Web: www.estorilhotel.co.uk
SB £28.50 DB £57 CC: MC Vi Swi

Carlton

♦♦♦

Promenade, Penzance, Cornwall, TR18 4NW
Tel: 01736 362081
SB £19 DB £23

How to get there: Follow signs for seafront and
harbour. Carlton is one mile on the right.

Keigwin

♦♦♦

Alexandra Road, Penzance, Cornwall, TR18 4LZ
Tel: 01736 363930 Fax: 0870 1673499
Email: info@keigwinhotel.co.uk
Web: www.keigwinhotel.co.uk
SB £15 DB £30 HBS £25.50 HBD £51
D £10.50. CC: MC Vi

How to get there: Along seafront to roundabout,
right into Alexandra Rd, hotel halfway on right.

Kimberley House

♦♦♦

10 Morrab Road, Penzance, TR18 4EZ
Tel: 01736 362727 Fax: 01736 362727
Email: kimberley.house@faxvia.net
Children minimum age: 5
SB £18 DB £36

How to get there: On promenade at Queens
Hotel turn right, we are two-thirds up on right.

Lynwood Guest House

♦♦♦

41 Morrab Road, Penzance, TR18 4EX
Tel: 01736 365871 Fax: 01736 365871
Email: lynwoodpz@aol.com
Web: www.penzance.co.uk/lynwood-
                           guesthouse
SB £17.50 DB £39 CC: MC Vi Am DC Swi Delt

How to get there: On promenade at Queens
Hotel turn right, we are 200m up on left.

Mount Royal

♦♦♦

Chyandour Cliff, Penzance, Cornwall, TR18 3LQ
Tel: 01736 362233 Fax: 01736 362233
Email: mountroyal@talk21.com
Web: www.s-h-systems.co.uk/hotels/
         mountroyal.html
Closed November to February
SB £30 DB £21

⊚⊜⊒**P**🐎🐈🐕⛺⚓🚲📶

How to get there: On old A30 at start Penzance.

Penmorvah

♦♦♦

Alexandra Road, Penzance, Cornwall, TR18 4LZ
Tel: 01736 363711 Fax: 01736 363711
SB £18 DB £36 HBS £32 HBD £64
CC: MC Vi Am Swi Delt

🐎🍴⊜⊒🐈🐕⛺🚲⚓🍴

How to get there: Off promenade, right up
Alexandra Road at mini-roundabout, hotel on
right near top.

Woodstock

♦♦♦

29 Morrab Road, Penzance, TR18 4EZ
Tel: 01736 369049 Fax: 01736 369049
Email: woodstocp@aol.com
Web: www.cruising-america.com/woodstock
Children minimum age: 5
SB £15 DB £30 CC: MC Vi Am DC Swi Delt
JCB

🍴🐎⊚⊜⊒🐈🐕⛺🚲⚓

How to get there: Off promenade, right after The
Lugger Inn. Woodstock 200m on right.

Carnson House

♦

East Terrace, Penzance, Cornwall, TR18 2TD
Tel: 01736 65589

Pewsey, Wiltshire

The Woodbridge Inn

♦♦♦

North Newton (A345), Pewsey, SN9 6JZ
Tel: 01980 630266 Fax: 01980 630266

Plymouth, Devon

Copthorne Hotel

★★★★

Armada Way, Plymouth, Devon, PL1 1AR
Tel: 01752 224161 Fax: 01752 670688
Email: sales.plymouth@mill-cop.com

The Queens Hotel

Penzance ★★★

Elegant Victorian Hotel enjoying pride of
place on the sea front promenade of
Penzance with majestic views which sweep
across Mounts Bay to St. Michael's Mount
and Lizard Peninsula. Excellent restaurant
with local seafood. Lands End, Minack
Theatre, Tate Gallery within a short drive.

The Promenade, Penzance TR18 4HG
Tel: 01736 362371 Fax: 01736 350033
Email: enquiries@queens-hotel.com
Website: www.queens-hotel.com

CC: MC Vi Am DC Swi Delt

♿🛗⊚⊜⊒☎📞**P**🐈🐕⛺🚲⚓♨♨♨
🍴📶

How to get there: From M5 follow signs for A38
Plymouth. On arrival at Plymouth, take the left-
hand lane signposted 'City Centre'. Follow Ferry
Port signs over 3 roundabouts; on 4th
roundabout hotel is 1st left.

Boringdon Hall Hotel

★★★

Colebrook, Plympton, Plymouth, Devon,
PL7 4DP
Tel: 01752 344455 Fax: 01752 346578

New Continental Hotel

★★★

Mill Bay Road, Plymouth, Devon, PL1 3LD
Tel: 01752 220782 Fax: 01752 227013
Email: newconti@aol.com
Web: www.newcontinental.co.uk
Closed December 24 to January 4
CC: MC Vi Am Swi Delt

♿🛗🍴🐎⊚⊜⊒☎📞**P**🐈🐕⛺🚲⚓
🍷♨♨♨🍴📶

How to get there: From A38, follow signs for city
centre, Pavilions Conference Centre and
Continental Ferryport. Hotel is adjacent to
Pavilions Conference Centre in Millbay Road.

Novotel

★★★

Marsh Mills Roundabout, 270 Plymouth Road,
Plymouth, Devon, PL6 8NH
Tel: 01752 221422 Fax: 01752 223922
Email: h0508sb@accor-hotels.com
Web: www.accor-hotels.com
SB £73.95 DB £87.90 HBS £89.90 HBD £59.90
B £8.95 L £11 D £15.95.
CC: MC Vi Am DC Swi Delt

How to get there: At the gateway to Plymouth,
exit A38 at Marsh Mills (opposite Sainsbury's).

Strathmore

★★★

Elliot Street, The Hoe, Plymouth, PL1 2PR
Tel: 01752 662101 Fax: 01752 223690
SB £42 DB £54 HBS £54 HBD £69
B £6 L £8 D £12.5. CC: MC Vi Am Swi Delt

How to get there: City centre then Hoe and
Barbican. Left into Athenaeum St onto Elliot St.

Camelot

★★

5 Elliott Street, Plymouth, Devon, PL1 2PP
Tel: 01752 221255 Fax: 01752 603660
Email: camelotuk@supanet.com
SB £39 DB £50 HBS £51 HBD £37 B £7.50
L £5.95 D £5.95. CC: MC Vi Am DC Swi Delt

How to get there: City centre then Hoe and
Barbican. Left into Athenaeum St onto Elliot St.

Invicta

★★

11–12 Osborne Place, Lockyer Street, The Hoe,
Plymouth, Devon, PL1 2PU
Tel: 01752 664997 Fax: 01752 664994
Email: info@invictahotel.co.uk
Web: www.invictahotel.co.uk
Closed Christmas to New Year

Invicta is an elegant Victorian building with 23
well-appointed bedrooms, all en-suite. Close to
the city centre, Barbican and Brittany Ferries.
Fresh food, licensed. Lock-up car park. Friendly
atmosphere.
SB £52 DB £62 HBS £62.50 HBD £82.50
B £6 D £10.50. CC: MC Vi Am Swi Delt

How to get there: To city centre. Left at sign for
The Hoe, 2nd left after Barclays Bank, Lockyer
Street. Hotel opposite bowling green.

Langdon Court

★★

Down Thomas, Wembury, Plymouth, PL9 0DY
Tel: 01752 862358 Fax: 01752 863428
Email: enquiries@langdoncourt.co.uk
Web: www.langdoncourt.co.uk

Charming Tudor Manor, with unique
17th-century walled garden, glorious South
Hams countryside, award-winning cuisine, 6
miles from Plymouth city centre and one mile
from Wembury Beach. Civil Wedding Licence.
SB £39.50 DB £68 B £7.50
CC: MC Vi Am DC Swi Delt

How to get there: Leave A38 at Plymouth, signs
to A379 Kingsbridge. Right at 4th roundabout,
follow HMS Cambridge/Langdon Court signs.
After 1/2 mile left at lights, next right, next left.
Hotel is 1 3/4 miles, 200 yards past tight right bend.

Drake

★

1 Windsor Villas, Lockyer Street, Plymouth,
PL1 2QD
Tel: 01752 229730 Fax: 01752 255092
Closed Christmas to New Year
SB £42 DB £52 HBS £54 HBD £76 B £5 D £12.
CC: MC Vi Am DC Swi Delt

How to get there: Follow signs to city centre.
Turn left at Theatre Royal. Take last left and
first right.

Imperial

★

Lockyer Street, The Hoe, Plymouth, PL1 2QD
Tel: 01752 227311 Fax: 01752 674986
Closed December 24 to January 1
SB £35 DB £49 HBS £47 HBD £73 B £5 D £12.
CC: MC Vi Am DC Swi Delt Electron
🌀 🖵 ☎ 🅿 ⚒ 🕯 🐎 ♨ ♨ ⅲ ⅰ
How to get there: City centre, at Theatre Royal
left up hill, left at lights, then first right.

Victoria Court

★

64 North Road East, Plymouth, Devon, PL4 6AL
Tel: 01752 668133 Fax: 01752 668133
Email: victoria.court@btinternet.com
SB £42 DB £55 B £5.50 D £14.50.
CC: MC Vi Am DC Swi Delt

🌀 🖵 ☎ 🕿 🅿 ⚒ 🕯 🐎 ♨ ⅲ

Aaron Guest House

◆◆◆

Hoe Villa, 11 Sussex Street, Plymouth, PL1 2HR
Tel: 01752 600022

Ashgrove

◆◆◆

218 Citadel Road, The Hoe, Plymouth, PL1 3BB
Tel: 01752 664046 Fax: 01752 252112
Email: ashgroveho@aol.com
Closed Christmas and New Year
SB £25 DB £ 40 CC: MC Vi Am Swi Delt
⊗ 🌀 🖵 ⚒ 🕯 🐎 ♨
How to get there: City centre, left at Theatre
Royal, right at lights, left at next lights (Walrus
pub). Up Athenaeum St, right, Ashgrove on left.

Georgian House

◆◆◆

51 Citadel Road, The Hoe, Plymouth, PL1 3AU
Tel: 01752 663237 Fax: 01752 253953

Headland

◆◆◆

1a Radford Road, West Hoe, Plymouth,
Devon, PL1 3BY
Tel: 01752 660866 Fax: 01752 313339
Email: info@headlandhotelplymouth.co.uk
Web: www.headlandhotelplymouth.co.uk
Children minimum age: 3
SB £20 DB £30 HBS £25 HBD £40
B £2.50 D £3. CC: MC Vi Am Swi
♿ ⅲ ⊗ 🌀 🖵 ⚒ 🕯 🐎 ♨ ♨ ⅲ ⅰ ⅲ
How to get there: From city centre, follow brown
sign 'Pavilions'. At mini-roundabout follow sign
for West Hoe and Seafront. The hotel is directly
in front.

Plympton, Devon

Elfordleigh

★★★

Colebrook, Shaugh Prior Road, Plympton,
Devon, PL7 5EB
Tel: 01752 336428 Fax: 01752 344581
Email: elfordleigh@cs.com
Web: www.elfordleigh.co.uk
SB £64.50 DB £74.50 HBS £79.50 HBD £110
£7.50 D £15.95. CC: MC Vi Am Swi Delt
🌀 ♿ ⅲ ⚒ 🏹 🌀 🖵 ☎ 🅿 ⚒ 🕯 🐎 ♨ 👁
ⅲ ⅲ 🧖 🍴 🎱 🔍 🛡
How to get there: A38 to Plymouth. At Marsh
Mill roundabout, A374 to Plympton, left at
Texaco garage, signs for Elfordleigh Hotel.

Polperro, Cornwall

Claremont

◆◆◆

The Coombes, Fore Street, Polperro, PL13 2RG
Tel: 01503 272241 Fax: 01503 272241

Poole, Dorset

Haven

★★★★ ⍟ ⍟

Sandbanks, Poole, Dorset, BH13 7QL
Tel: 01202 707333 Fax: 01202 708796
Email: lynn.chissell@havenhotel.co.uk
Web: www.havenhotel.co.uk

An exclusive hotel located on the tip of
Sandbanks peninsula. The Haven offers
splendid sea views, award-winning cuisine, first-
class service and leisure facilities.
SB £82 DB £164 HBS £92 HBD £148
B £10 L £16 D £25. CC: MC Vi Am DC Swi Delt
🌀 ♿ ⅲ 🌀 🖵 ☎ 🅿 ⚒ 🕯 🐎 ♨ 👁 ⅲ ⅲ
🧖 🍴 🎱 🔍 🛡 🏃
How to get there: A31 for Bournemouth, A338
Wessex Way, onto B3065. Left at Sandbanks
Bay peninsula's end, hotel on left by Ferry Point.

Southwest

Harbour Heights
★★★
73 Haven Road, Poole, Dorset, BH13 7LW
Tel: 01202 707272 Fax: 01202 708594

Salterns
★★★
38 Salterns Way, Lilliput, Poole, BH14 8JR
Tel: 01202 707321 Fax: 01202 707488
SB £86 DB £126 HBS £106 HBD £80 B £10
L £20 D £25. CC: MC Vi Am DC Swi Delt
How to get there: From Poole, signs for Sandbanks, at Lilliput right by Barclays Bank into Saltern Way.
See advert on facing page

Sandbanks
★★★
Banks Road, Poole, Dorset, BH13 7PS
Tel: 01202 707377 Fax: 01202 708885
Email: john@sandbankshotel.co.uk
Web: www.sandbankshotel.co.uk

On Blue Flag Award golden sands, the Sandbanks is perfect for holidays and short breaks. Special children's restaurant and play facilities, waterside brasserie and leisure centre.
SB £70 DB £140 HBS £75 HBD £150 B £8.50
L £15.50 D £19.50. CC: MC Vi Am DC Swi Delt
How to get there: Take A31 towards Bournemouth. Turn onto A338. At Liverpool Victoria roundabout keep far left and take B3065 to Sandbanks Beach. At T-junction, turn left. Hotel 500m on left.

Norfolk Lodge
★★
1 Flaghead Road, Canford Cliffs, Poole, Dorset, BH13 7JL
Tel: 01202 708614 Fax: 01202 708614

41 Sandhurst Close
♦♦♦
Poole, Dorset, BH17 9JS
Tel: 01202 690218

Porlock, Somerset

Anchor & Ship
★★★
Porlock Weir, Somerset, TA24 8PB
Tel: 01643 862753 Fax: 01643 862843

Oaks
★★
Porlock, Somerset, TA24 8ES
Tel: 01643 862265 Fax: 01643 863131
Email: oakshotel@aol.com
Children minimum age: 8
Closed November to March
SB £60 DB £100 HBS £80 HBD £140 D £25.
CC: MC Vi Swi Delt

Ship Inn
★
High Street, Porlock, Somerset, TA24 8QD
Tel: 01643 862507 Fax: 01643 863244

Andrews on the Weir
♦♦♦♦
Porlock Weir, Porlock, Somerset, TA24 8PB
Tel: 01643 863300 Fax: 01643 863311

Port Isaac, Cornwall

Cornish Arms at Pendoggett
★★
Pendoggett, nr Port Isaac, Cornwall, PL30 3HH
Tel: 01208 880263 Fax: 01208 880335
Email: cornisharm@aol.com
SB £39 DB £59 HBS £42.95 HBD £37.95
B £6.50 L £4 D £13. CC: MC Vi Am Swi Delt
How to get there: A30, A395, A39 for 2 miles, right on B3314 through Delabole. Cornish Arms is 4 miles on right.

Portland, Dorset

Alessandria
♦♦♦
71 Wakeham, Easton, Portland, Dorset, DT5 1HW
Tel: 01305 822270 Fax: 01305 820561

Redruth, Cornwall

Lyndhurst Guest House

◆◆◆

80 Agar Road, Illogan Highway, Redruth, Cornwall, TR15 3NB
Tel: 01209 215146 Fax: 01209 313625
Email: sales@lyndhurst-guesthouse.net
Web: www.lyndhurst-guesthouse.net
SB £19 DB £38 HBS £25 HBD £50
CC: MC Vi Swi Delt
🌀🖳🅿️♨️🌍🐴🎵♿
How to get there: On the A3047, Redruth–Camborne road, about halfway between the two centres close to Pool Industrial Estate.

Rock, Cornwall

The Mariners

★★

Slipway, Rock, Cornwall, PL27 6LD
Tel: 01208 862312 Fax: 01208 863827
Email: amiller767@aol.com
Web: www.marinershotel.com
Closed November to March
SB £35 DB £60 B £7 D £8.
CC: MC Vi Am Swi Delt
🏨🌀🖳🅿️♨️🌍🐴🎵♿🎱
How to get there: From B3314, Rock is signposted. As you near the estuary, hotel is on right.

St Agnes, Cornwall

Rose-in-Vale Country House

★★★ ⓡ
Mithian, St Agnes, Cornwall, TR5 0QD
Tel: 01872 552202 Fax: 01872 552700

Rosemundy House

★★

8 Rosemundy, St Agnes, Cornwall, TR5 0UF
Tel: 01872 552101 Fax: 01872 554000
Email: info@rosemundy.co.uk
Web: www.rosemundy.co.uk
SB £25 DB £50 HBS £30 HBD £60
B £5 D £14. CC: MC Vi Swi Delt
♿🏨🌀🖳♨️🌍🐴🎵♿🎱⚱️♨️
How to get there: Follow the brown signs.

If you're looking for great dining when staying away, look for RAC Hotels and Guest Accommodation displaying the RAC Dining Award symbol in this Guide.

Salterns ★★★

In a glorious location on the edge of Poole Harbour, Salterns ranks as one of the top three-star hotels in the country. 20 themed bedrooms offer high standards of comfort with all the extras to enhance your stay. Dinner in the candlelit restaurant is a romantic affair and with food that has earned two AA Rosettes for 7 years, or go less formal at Shellies Bistro.

38 Salterns Way, Poole, Dorset BH14 8JR
Tel: 01202 707321   Fax: 01202 707488

Penkerris

◆◆
Penwinnick Road, St Agnes, Cornwall, TR5 0PA
Tel: 01872 552262 Fax: 01872 552262

Enchanting Edwardian residence with garden in unspoilt Cornish village. Beautiful rooms, usual facilities, log fires, piano, TV, video. Superb home cooking using fresh local produce. Dramatic cliff walks and beaches nearby.
SB £17.50 DB £30.50 HBS £27.50 HBD £50
D £10. CC: MC Vi Am Delt
🏨🌀🖳🅿️♨️🌍🐴🎵♿🎱⚱️
How to get there: From roundabout at Chiverton Cross on A30, take B3277 to St Agnes itself. Penkerris is first on right inside 30mph limit.

Southwest

St Austell, Cornwall

Carlyon Bay Hotel

★★★★ 🏨🏨

Sea Road, Carlyon Bay, St Austell, PL25 3RD
Tel: 01726 812304 Fax: 01726 814938
Email: info@carlyonbay.co.uk
Web: www.brend-hotels.co.uk

A superb hotel in a cliff-top location offering spectacular views. The hotel's 18-hole golf course runs along the clifftop next to the hotel.
SB £72 DB £146 HBS £84 HBD £170 B £7.50
L £12 D £24. CC: MC Vi Am DC Swi Delt

See advert below

Cliff Head

★★★ 🏨

Sea Road, Carlyon Bay, St Austell, PL25 3RB
Tel: 01726 812345 Fax: 01726 815511
Email: cliffheadhotel@btconnect.com
Web: www.cornishriviera.co.uk/cliffhead
SB £45 DB £75 HBS £62 HBD £105
B £7.50 L £7.95 D £12.95.
CC: MC Vi Am DC Swi Delt

How to get there: Just before entering St Austell, follow signs to Carlyon Bay.

Boscundle Manor

★★ 🏨🏨

Tregrehan, St Austell, Cornwall, PL25 3RL
Tel: 01726 813557 Fax: 01726 814997
Email: stay@boscundlemanor.co.uk
Web: www.boscundlemanor.co.uk
Closed November to March
SB £65 DB £110 HBS £87.50 HBD £150
D £22.50. CC: MC Vi Am Swi Delt

How to get there: 2 miles east of St Austell, off A390 on road signposted 'Tregrehan'.

St Ives, Cornwall

Porthminster

★★★

The Terrace, St Ives, Cornwall, TR26 2BN
Tel: 01736 795221 Fax: 01736 797043
Email: reception@porthminster-hotel.co.uk
Web: www.porthminster-hotel.co.uk
Closed early January
SB £44 DB £88 HBS £59 HBD £118
B £9 L £8 D £16. CC: MC Vi Am DC Swi Delt

How to get there: On A3074.

Chy-an-albany

★★

Albany Terrace, St Ives, Cornwall, TR26 2BS
Tel: 01736 796759 Fax: 01736 795584

Chy-An-Dour

★★

Trelyon Avenue, St Ives, Cornwall, TR26 2AD
Tel: 01736 796436 Fax: 01736 795772
Email: chyndour@aol.com
Web: www.connexions.co.uk/chyandourhotel
SB £61 DB £70 HBS £77 HBD £102
B £6 D £16. CC: MC Vi Swi Delt

How to get there: From A30, A3074 for St Ives.
Hotel is on right 50m past Jet filling station.

Dean Court

◆◆◆◆

Trelyon Avenue, St Ives, Cornwall, TR26 2AD
Tel: 01736 796023 Fax: 01736 796233

Longships

◆◆◆◆

Talland Road, St Ives, Cornwall, TR26 2DF
Tel: 01736 798180 Fax: 01736 798180
SB £30 DB £60 HBS £36 HBD £72 D £10.
CC: MC Vi Swi Delt

How to get there: Left fork at Portminster Hotel.
Follow Talland Area Accomm sign. Hotel is first
in Talland Road.

Regent

◆◆◆◆

Fern Lea Terrace, St Ives, Cornwall, TR26 2BH
Tel: 01736 796195 Fax: 01736 794641

Trewinnard

◆◆◆◆

4 Parc Avenue, St Ives, Cornwall, TR26 2DN
Tel: 01736 794168 Fax: 01736 798161
Email: trewinnard@cwcom.net
Web: www.connexions.co.uk/trewinnard
Children minimum age: 6
Closed November to March
SB £23 DB £22 CC: MC Vi Swi Delt JCB Solo

How to get there: A3074 to St Ives, left at
Natwest Bank. Left at mini-roundabout, go past
car park, and house is 150m on right.

Hollies

◆◆◆

Talland Road, St Ives, Cornwall, TR26 2DF
Tel: 01736 796605 Fax: 01736 796605
Email: john@hollieshotel.freeserve.co.uk
Web: www.hollieshotel.freeserve.co.uk
Closed December to February except for
Christmas and New Year
SB £19 DB £32

How to get there: Through Carbis Bay into
St Ives, fork left at Porminster Hotel. Take 1st
left. After 50m turn left again. 3rd hotel on right.

St Mawes, Cornwall

Idle Rocks

★★★

Harbourside, St Mawes, Cornwall, TR2 5AN
Tel: 01326 270771 Fax: 01326 270062
Email: idlerocks@richardsonhotels.co.uk
Web: www.richardsonhotels.co.uk
SB £48 DB £96 HBS £60 HBD £120
B £9.75 L £3.50 D £27.95.
CC: MC Vi Am Swi Delt

How to get there: M5 onto A30, then onto A39,
A390 and A3078. Hotel first on left in village.

See advert on following page

Rosevine

★★★

Rosevine, Porthscatho, St Mawes, Truro,
Cornwall, TR2 5EW
Tel: 01872 580206 Fax: 01872 580230
Email: info@makepeacehotels.co.uk
Web: www.makepeacehotels.co.uk
Closed November to January

Cornwall's newest luxury hotel with award
winning cuisine. Overlooking sub-tropical
gardens with glorious sea views. Deluxe
bedrooms with many thoughtful extras and a
heated indoor swimming pool are to be enjoyed.
SB £105 DB £140 HBS £135 HBD £190
B £8 L £8 D £28.
CC: MC Vi Am Swi Delt

How to get there: When approaching St Mawes
on A3078, turn right at sign for Rosevine Hotel
and Porthcurnic beach.

Southwest

The Idle Rocks Hotel

Situated on the harbourside in the tranquil village of St. Mawes, The Idle Rocks Hotel blends a relaxing Cornish atmosphere with a high level of comfort, service and superb, cuisine, which has won two RAC Dining Awards. Rooms are individually furnished and many have sea views. "1203 Terrace" is ideal for light lunches and to watch the world go by.

Harbourside, St. Mawes TR2 5AN
Tel: FREEPHONE 0800 243 202
Fax: 01326 270062
Email: idlerocks@richardsonhotels.co.uk
Website: www.richardsonhotels.co.uk

RaC
★★★

Salcombe, Devon

Thurlestone
★★★★ ♔
Thurlestone, Devon, TQ7 3NN
Tel: 01548 560382 Fax: 01548 561069
Email: enquiries@thurlestone.co.uk
Web: www.thurlestone.co.uk
SB £50 DB £100 HBS £50 HBD £100
B £4 L £3.50 D £28. CC: MC Vi Am Swi

How to get there: A38, A384, A381 to Kingsbridge. A379 to Churchston. At second roundabout turn left into B3197, then right into lane to Thurlestone.

Bolt Head
★★★ ♔
South Sands, Salcombe, Devon, TQ8 8LL
Tel: 01548 843751
Email: info@bolthead-salcombe.co.uk
Web: www.bolthead-salcombe.co.uk
Closed November to February
B £9.50 L £16.50 D £27.
CC: MC Vi Am DC Swi Delt

How to get there: A38, A384, A381 for Totnes. Signs for South Sands and Salcombe.

Heron House
★★★
Thurlstone Sands, Kingsbridge, nr Salcombe, Devon, TQ7 3JY
Tel: 01548 561308 Fax: 01548 560180
CC: MC Vi Swi Delt

How to get there: A38, A381 to Totnes and Kingsbridge. Take Salcombe road (ignore Thurlstone), 2 miles, right to S. Milton. In village, left to Thurlstone Rock. After 1 mile, hotel is 300 yards down beach road.

Soar Mill Cove
★★★ ♔♔♔
Soar Mill Cove, Salcombe, Devon, TQ7 3DS
Tel: 01548 561566 Fax: 01548 561223
Email: info@makepeacehotels.co.uk
Web: www.makepeacehotels.co.uk
Closed January

Dramatically situated luxury hotel with award-winning cuisine. Completely within National Trust coastline, overlooking a glorious sandy beach. Deluxe bedrooms with many thoughtful extras and heated indoor swimming pool are to be enjoyed.
SB £72 DB £144 HBS £98 HBD £98
B £15 L £15 D £20. CC: MC Vi Am Swi Delt

How to get there: A38, A384, A381 into Kingsbridge. Right for Salcombe, 4 miles at Malborough, right to Soar. After church, left.

Tides Reach
★★★ ♔♔
South Sands, Salcombe, Devon, TQ8 8LJ
Tel: 01548 843466 Fax: 01548 843954
Email: enquire@tidesreach.com
Web: www.tidesreach.com
Children minimum age: 8
SB £75 DB £130 HBS £90 HBD £80
B £9 L £15 D £29. CC: MC Vi Am DC Swi Delt

Devon Tor

Devon Road, Salcombe, Devon, TQ8 8HJ
Tel: 01548 843106

Torre View

Devon Road, Salcombe, Devon, TQ8 8HJ
Tel: 01548 842633 Fax: 01548 842633
Email: torreview@eurobell.co.uk
Children minimum age: 4
Closed November to February
SB £30 DB £56 HBS £42 HBD £78
CC: MC Vi Delt

How to get there: A381 (Main Rd), Devon Rd off
left; 1/2 mile down Devon Rd on left side.

Penn Torr

Herbert Road, Salcombe, Devon, TQ8 8HN
Tel: 01548 842234

Terrapins Hotel & Restaurant

Buckley Street, Salcombe, Devon, TQ8 8DD
Tel: 01548 842861 Fax: 01548 842265

Salisbury, Wiltshire

Heritage Hotels – The White Hart

★★★
St John Street, Salisbury, Wiltshire, SP1 2SD
Tel: 0870 4008125 Fax: 01722 412761
SB £91 DB £128 HBS £70 HBD £140
B £11 L £8 D £14.50. CC: MC Vi Am DC Swi

How to get there: To city centre cathedral, into
Exeter St, and St John St. Hotel at end on right.

Please mention the RAC Inspected Guide
when you make your booking at an RAC
Hotel or Guest Accommodation.

Reservations RaC

RAC Hotel Reservations is your one-stop
booking service for over 3,000 RAC Hotels &
Guest Accommodation. So if the hotel or B&B
of your choice doesn't have availability, we'll
be able to source the next best alternative for
you free of charge. Call 0870 603 9109 to
make a booking at any of the properties
featured in this Guide.

Red Lion

★★★
Milford Street, Salisbury, Wiltshire, SP1 2AN
Tel: 01722 323334 Fax: 01722 325756
Email: reception@the-redlion.co.uk
Web: www.the-redlion.co.uk

Traditional 13th-century coaching inn. Famous
for its creeper-clad courtyard, charm and
antique-filled rooms. An ideal touring base for a
wealth of nearby attractions.
B £5.50 L £11.95 D £19.
CC: MC Vi Am DC Swi Delt

The Lamb at Hindon

★★
High Street, Hindon, Wiltshire, SP3 6DP
Tel: 01747 820573 Fax: 01747 820605
Email: cora@the-lamb.demon.co.uk
Web: www.the-lamb.demon.co.uk

A traditional freehold country inn with a relaxed
and friendly atmosphere, fresh well-cooked food
is offered both in the bar and restaurant.
SB £45 DB £70 B £8.50 L £9.50 D £19.95.
CC: MC Vi Am Swi Delt

How to get there: The Lamb at Hindon is in the
centre of the village.

The Red House

★★

Parkhouse Cross, Cholderton, Salisbury,
Wiltshire, SP4 0EG
Tel: 01980 629542 Fax: 01980 629481

Old Sub Deanery

♦♦♦♦♦

18 The Close, Salisbury, Wiltshire, SP1 2EB
Tel: 01722 336331
DB £68

How to get there: In the Cathedral Close.

Cricket Field House

♦♦♦♦

Wilton Road, Salisbury, Wiltshire, SP2 9NS
Tel: 01722 322595 Fax: 01722 322595
Email: cricketfieldhousehotel@btinternet.com
Web: www.cricketfieldhousehotel.com
Children minimum age: 14
SB £40 DB £55 L £5.50 D £12.95.
CC: MC Vi Swi Delt

How to get there: A36 east from Salisbury; over
railway bridge, 2nd left. Hotel on right.

Holly House

♦♦♦♦

Hurdcott Lane, Winterbourne Earls, Salisbury,
Wiltshire, SP4 6HL
Tel: 01980 610813 Fax: 01980 610813

Pembroke Arms

♦♦♦♦

Wilton Road, Wilton, Salisbury, SP2 0BN
Tel: 01722 743328 Fax: 01722 744886

Stratford Lodge

♦♦♦♦

4 Park Lane, Salisbury, Wiltshire, SP1 3NP
Tel: 01722 325177 Fax: 01722 325177
Email: enquiries@stratfordlodge.co.uk
Web: www.stratfordlodge.co.uk
Children minimum age: 5

Stratford Lodge is tucked away in a quiet lane
overlooking Victoria Park and has all the charm
of the Victorian era.
SB £40 DB £60 HBS £55 HBD £86.50 D £15.
CC: MC Vi Am Swi Delt

How to get there: A345 for Salisbury. Right after
Alldays shop. Park Lane is on right.

Websters

♦♦♦♦

11 Hartington Road, Salisbury, SP2 7LG
Tel: 01722 339779 Fax: 01722 339779
Email: websters.salis@eclipse.co.uk
Web: www.smoothhound.co.uk
Children minimum age: 12

Set on the end of a colourful Victorian terrace,
with off-street parking and scrumptious choices
for breakfast. 15 minutes walk from city centre.
SB £34 DB £42 HBS £46 HBD £66
D £12. CC: MC Vi Swi Delt

How to get there: From city, west for Wilton,
A360 (Devizes). Hartington Rd is 400m on left.

Byways House

♦♦♦

31 Fowler's Road, City Centre, Salisbury,
Wiltshire, SP1 2QP
Tel: 01722 328364 Fax: 01722 322146
Email: byways@bed-breakfast-salisbury.co.uk
Web: www.bed-breakfast-salisbury.co.uk
Closed Christmas and New Year

Southwest

Attractive family-run Victorian house close to cathedral in quiet area of city centre. Large car park. Traditional English or vegetarian breakfasts. Ideal for Stonehenge and Wilton House.
SB £30 DB £45 CC: MC Vi Swi Delt JCB

How to get there: Take A36 Southampton, left at sign for city centre (service traffic only), right at junction, left at lights. Fowlers Road is 1st right.

Cornmarket Inn

◆◆◆

29–32 Cheesemarket, Salisbury, P1 1TL
Tel: 01722 412925 Fax: 01722 412927
SB £45 DB £55 L £3
CC: MC Vi Am DC Swi Delt

How to get there: In centre, on west side of market square, next to public library.

Hayburn Wyke Guest House

◆◆◆

72 Castle Road, Salisbury, Wiltshire, SP1 3RL
Tel: 01722 412627 Fax: 01722 412627
Email: hayburn.wyke@tinyonline.co.uk
Web: www.hotels.uk.com/hayburnwyke.htm
SB £29 DB £40 CC: MC Vi Am Swi Delt

How to get there: On A345 ¹/₂ mile north of centre at junction with Stratford Road.

Saunton, Devon

Saunton Sands Hotel

★★★★

Saunton, Devon, EX33 1LQ
Tel: 01271 890212 Fax: 01271 890145
Email: info@sauntonsands.co.uk
Web: www.brend-hotels.co.uk

North Devon's premier four-star hotel commands spectacular views, and provides a wealth of facilities.
SB £68 DB £132 HBS £80 HBD £156 B £6.50 L £10.50 D £22.50. CC: MC Vi Am DC Swi Delt

How to get there: From Barnstaple town centre take A361 Braunton road. From Braunton follow the Saunton sign.
See advert on this page

Seaton, Devon

Mariners

◆◆◆◆

The Esplanade, Seaton, Devon, EX12 2NP
Tel: 01297 20560
SB £30 DB £45 HBS £41 HBD £70 D £11.50.
CC: MC Vi

How to get there: Situated on the seafront in the middle.

Sennen, Cornwall

Old Success Inn

★★

Sennen Cove, Cornwall, TR19 7DG
Tel: 01736 871232 Fax: 01736 788354

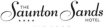

Homefields

♦♦♦

Mayon, Sennen, Cornwall, TR19 7AD
Tel: 01736 871418 Fax: 01736 871666
Email: homefields1bandb@aol.com
Closed Christmas

A warm welcome awaits you at our small and
friendly guest house overlooking Cornwall.
Close to beaches, with sea views. Good food,
and pets are welcome.
SB £18 DB £36

How to get there: 8 miles from Penzance (A30)
to Sennen. Homefields is opposite Post Office.

Shaftesbury, Dorset

Royal Chase

★★★ 🍴🍴

Salisbury Road, Shaftesbury, Dorset, SP7 8DB
Tel: 01747 853355 Fax: 01747 851969
Email: royalchasehotel@btinternet.com
B £8.50 L £5.95 D £21.
CC: MC Vi Am DC Swi Delt

How to get there: On roundabout of A30/A350.

Grove Arms Inn

♦♦♦♦

Ludwell, nr Shaftesbury, Dorset, SP7 9ND
Tel: 01747 828328 Fax: 01747 828960
Email: info@dorsetaccommodation.com
Web: www.dorsetaccommodation.com

Grade II listed thatched property, refurbished in
1999 to high standard. Surrounded by beautiful
countryside for walks and picturesque scenery.
Good food and friendly welcome.
SB £40 DB £50 L £4.25 D £5. CC: MC Vi Swi

How to get there: On main A30.

Grove House Hotel & Guest House

♦♦♦♦ 🍴

Ludwell, Shaftesbury, Dorset, SP7 9ND
Tel: 01747 828365 Fax: 01747 828365

Friendly family-run guest house in village
location two miles east of Shaftesbury.
Large beautiful garden in peaceful countryside.
All rooms en-suite.
SB £31.50 DB £63 CC: MC Vi

How to get there: On A30 towards Salisbury.

Shepton Mallet, Somerset

Shrubbery

★★ 🍴🍴

17 Commercial Road, Shepton Mallet, BA4 5BU
Tel: 01749 346671 Fax: 01749 346581
SB £52.50 DB £75 B £6.95 L £9.95 D £14.95.
CC: MC Vi Am DC Swi Delt

How to get there: Town centre, next to police stn.

Belfield House

♦♦♦

34 Charlton Road, Shepton Mallet, BA4 5PA
Tel: 01749 344353 Fax: 01749 344353
Email: andrea@belfield-house.co.uk
SB £18 DB £40

How to get there: Opposite Leisure Centre on
main A361, 200m from main A37 junction.

43 Maesdown Road

Evercreech, Shepton Mallet, Somerset, BA4 6LE
Tel: 01749 830721

Southwest

Sherborne, Dorset

Eastbury
★★★ ♟♟
Long Street, Sherborne, Dorset, DT9 3BY
Tel: 01935 813131 Fax: 01935 817296

Heritage Hotels – The Sherborne
★★★
Horsecastles Lane, Sherborne, Dorset, DT9 6BB
Tel: 01935 813191 Fax: 01935 816493
Web: www.forte-heritage.com
SB £60 DB £45 HBS £70 HBD £110 B £9.50
L £10.50 D £15.50. CC: MC Vi Am DC Swi Delt

Old Vicarage
♦♦♦♦♦
Sherborne Road, Milborne Port, Sherborne,
Dorset, DT9 5AT
Tel: 01963 251117 Fax: 01963 251515
Web: www.milborneport.freeserve.co.uk
Children minimum age: 5. Closed January
SB £27 DB £53 HBS £43 HBD £86 D £17.
CC: MC Vi Am Swi Delt

How to get there: On the A30 at the western
end of Milborne Port, 2 miles to the west of
Sherborne.

Shipham, Somerset

Daneswood House
★★★
Cuck Hill, Shipham, Somerset, BS25 1RD
Tel: 01934 843145 Fax: 01934 843824
Email: reception@daneswoodhotel.co.uk
Web: www.daneswoodhotel.co.uk
SB £79.50 DB £95 CC: MC Vi Am DC Swi

How to get there: One mile inland off A38
Bridgwater-Bristol road, at far side of village on
left.

Sidmouth, Devon

Belmont
★★★★
The Esplanade, Sidmouth, Devon, EX10 8RX
Tel: 01395 512555 Fax: 01395 579101
Email: info@belmont-hotel.co.uk
Web: www.brend-hotels.co.uk

Located on Sidmouth's famous esplanade, the
Belmont offers all the amenities you would
expect from a four-star hotel, while retaining the
charm and character of its origin.
SB £59 DB £108 HBS £74 HBD £138 B £12.50
L £14 D £24. CC: MC Vi Am DC Swi Delt

How to get there: On Sidmouth seafront.
See advert on following page

Hotel Riviera
★★★★ ♟♟♟
The Esplanade, Sidmouth, Devon, EX10 8AY
Tel: 01395 515201 Fax: 01395 577775
Email: enquiries@hotelriviera.co.uk
Web: www.hotelriviera.co.uk

A majestic Regency hotel, situated on the
Esplanade with panoramic sea views and a
splendid terrace overlooking Lyme Bay.
SB £77 DB £67 HBS £87 HBD £77 B £9.50
L £17 D £27. CC: MC Vi Am DC

How to get there: In centre of the Esplanade.
See advert on following page

Victoria

★★★★

The Esplanade, Sidmouth, Devon, EX10 8RY
Tel: 01395 512651 Fax: 01395 579154
Email: info@victoriahotel.co.uk
Web: www.brend-hotels.co.uk

Overlooking the esplanade and the sea,
magnificent rooms, renowned cuisine and
superb leisure facilities make the Victoria one of
England's finest hotels.
SB £71 DB £130 HBS £86 HBD £160 B £12.50
L £15 D £25. CC: MC Vi Am DC Swi Delt

How to get there: On Sidmouth seafront.
See advert below

Bedford

★★★

The Esplanade, Sidmouth, Devon, EX10 8NR
Tel: 01395 513047 Fax: 01395 578563
Closed February
SB £60 DB £120 HBS £64 HBD £128
B £9.95 L £12.50 D £19.95. CC: MC Vi Swi Delt

See advert on second page following

Royal Glen

★★★

Glen Road, Sidmouth, Devon, EX10 8RW
Tel: 01395 513221 Fax: 01395 514922
Email: sidmouthroyalglen.hotel@virgin.net

In a secluded position close to the seafront, this one-time Royal residence will appeal to those seeking old world charm, comfort, good catering and personal service.
B £7 D £16. CC: MC Vi Am Swi Delt

How to get there: Follow signs to seafront. Turn right onto Esplanade. Turn right into your road at the end of the Promenade.

Salcombe Hill House
★★★
Beatlands Road, Sidmouth, Devon, EX10 8JQ
Tel: 01395 514697 Fax: 01395 578310

Westcliff
★★★
Manor Road, Sidmouth, Devon, EX10 8RU
Tel: 01395 513252 Fax: 01395 578203
Email: stay@westcliffhotel.co.uk
Web: www.westcliffhotel.co.uk
Children minimum age: 6
Closed November to March
Westcliff occupies the prime position in the most delightful resort in the west country. Offering real quality hospitality, comfort, service and cuisine, we are neatly poised to meet your exacting expectations for total fulfilment.
SB £61 DB £108 HBS £73 HBD £132

B £11 L £4 D £24. CC: MC Vi Delt

How to get there: On Sidmouth seafront.

Brownlands Country House
★★ 🍴
Brownlands Road, Sidmouth, Devon, EX10 9AG
Tel: 01395 513053 Fax: 01395 513053
Email: brownlands.hotel@virgin.net
Web: freespace.virgin.net/brownlands.hotel/
Children minimum age: 8
Closed November to mid-March
SB £54 DB £108 HBS £68 HBD £136
L £3 D £21.50.

How to get there: A3052 through Sidford, right after Blue Ball Inn (left from Lyme Regis).

Southwest

The Bedford Hotel

Owned and run by the Pyne family, the Bedford Hotel on the famous Esplanade evokes the charm of the Regency period, with the accent being on excellent cuisine and gracious hospitality.

Bedrooms are ensuite, accessible by lift and individually furnished.

We look forward to welcoming you to the Bedford Hotel

Esplanade, Sidmouth, Devon EX10 8NR
Tel: 01395 513047   Fax: 01395 578563

Byes
★★
Sid Road, Sidmouth, Devon, EX10 9AA
Tel: 01395 513129 Fax: 01395 513311

Royal York & Faulkner Hotel
★★
Esplanade, Sidmouth, Devon, EX10 8AZ
Tel: 0800 220714 Fax: 01395 577472
Email: yorkhotel@eclipse.co.uk
Web: www.royal-york-hotel.co.uk
Closed January
SB £28.50 DB £57 HBS £36.50 HBD £73
B £7 L £4.95 D £15. CC: MC Vi Swi Delt
How to get there: Hotel is situated in the centre of Sidmouth's Esplanade.

Westbourne
★★
Manor Road, Sidmouth, Devon, EX10 8RR
Tel: 01395 513774 Fax: 01395 512231
Email: jan@westbournehotelsidmouth.co.uk
Web: www.westbournehotelsidmouth.co.uk
Closed November to February
SB £25 DB £50 HBS £37.50 HBD £75
B £6.50 L £2.50 D £13.50.

Groveside
◆ ◆ ◆
Vicarage Road, Sidmouth, Devon, EX10 8UQ
Tel: 01395 513406
Email: groveside.sidmouth@virgin.net
Web: www.eastdevon.net/groveside
SB £22 DB £44
How to get there: From M5 or A303 follow signs to Honiton, then to Sidmouth. Hotel is just on the edge of town, to left on the main road.

Somerton, Somerset

Lower Farm
◆ ◆ ◆ ◆
Kingweston, Somerton, Somerset, TA11 6BA
Tel: 01458 223237 Fax: 01458 223276
Email: lowerfarm@kingweston.demon.co.uk
Web: www.lowerfarm.net
SB £25 DB £50 CC: MC Vi Swi Delt JCB Solo
How to get there: A37 north for Shepton Mallet. Left at lights in Lydford-on-Fosse onto B3153 to Kingweston. Lower Farm is on right.

South Molton, Devon

High Bullen Hotel
★★★
Chittlehamholt, Devon, EX37 9HD
Tel: 01769 540561 Fax: 01769 540492
Email: info@highbullen.co.uk
Web: www.highbullen.co.uk
SB £57.50 DB £47.50 HBS £75 HBD £70
B £2.50 L £5.50 D £25. CC: MC Vi Swi Delt
How to get there: Exit M5 J-27, A361, B3226. After 5 miles turn right up hill to Chittlehamholt. High Bullen is ½ mile beyond village, on left.

Northcote Manor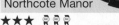
★★★
Burrington, nr South Molton, EX39 9LZ
Tel: 01769 560501 Fax: 01769 560770
Email: rest@northcotemanor.co.uk
Web: www.northcotemanor.co.uk
Children minimum age: 10
SB £124 DB £164 HBS £150 HBD £234
B £15 L £20 D £35. CC: MC Vi Am DC Swi Delt
How to get there: Avoid Burrington; entrance off A377, opposite Portsmouth Arms Station.
See advert on facing page

Southwest

Stoke Gabriel, Devon

Gabriel Court

★★★ ®

Stoke Hill, Stoke Gabriel, nr Totnes, TQ9 6SF
Tel: 01803 782206 Fax: 01803 782333
Email: obeacom@aol.com
SB £59 DB £80 HBS £85 HBD £66
B £10 L £13 D £27. CC: MC Vi Am DC Swi Delt

How to get there: Exit A385 (Totnes/Paignton) at
Parkers Arms pub. Head for Stoke Gabriel. On
entering village, stay left to reach hotel.

Street, Somerset

Wessex

★★★

High Street, Street, Somerset, BA16 0EF
Tel: 01458 443383 Fax: 01458 446589
Email: wessex@hotel-street.freeserve.co.uk
Web: www.travel-uk.net/wessexhotel
SB £56.50 DB £73 HBS £66.50 HBD £83
B £6.50 CC: MC Vi Am DC Swi

How to get there: Exit M5 J-23 to Bridgewater,
from A303, B3151 to Somerton and Street.

The Birches

◆◆◆◆

13 Housman Road, Street, Somerset, BA16 0SD
Tel: 01458 442902
Email: askins@ukonline.co.uk
Closed November to February
SB £28 DB £46

How to get there: From A37, B3151 to Millfield
lights, 2nd right, then first right (Housman Rd).

Reservations ⓡⓐⓒ

RAC Hotel Reservations is your one-stop
booking service for over 3,000 RAC Hotels &
Guest Accommodation. So if the hotel or B&B
of your choice doesn't have availability, we'll
be able to source the next best alternative for
you free of charge. Call 0870 603 9109 to
make a booking at any of the properties
featured in this Guide.

For your complete reassurance, only RAC
Hotels and Guest Accommodation have been
assessed on your behalf by our team of
independent inspectors for quality, facilities
and service.

Northcote Manor Hotel

Stay a while in timeless tranquility. We pride
ourselves on luxury quality with professional
service. Member of Pride of Britain &
Johansens. RAC Dining Award Level 3 for fine
cuisine — see us in the Good Food Guide.
Northcote Manor is one of the highest rated
RAC Blue Ribbon hotels in Devon. For further
information, visit our website.

**Burrington, South Molton,
Devon EX39 9LZ**
Tel: 01769 560501   Fax: 01769 560770
Email: rest@northcotemanor.co.uk
Website: www.northcotemanor.co.uk

Swanage, Dorset

Pines

★★★ ®

Burlington Road, Swanage, Dorset, BH19 1LT
Tel: 01929 425211 Fax: 01929 422075
Email: reservations@pineshotel.co.uk
Web: www.pineshotel.co.uk

Situated at the secluded end of Swanage Bay
with marvellous panoramic sea views and steps
down to beach. Long-established reputation for
service and cuisine.
SB £45 DB £90 HBS £57 HBD £114
B £7.50 L £13 D £20. CC: MC Vi Swi

How to get there: At seafront, left then 2nd right
to end of road.

Purbeck House

★★★

91 High Street, Swanage, Dorset, BH19 2LZ
Tel: 01929 422872 Fax: 01929 421194
Email: purbeckhouse@easynet.co.uk
Web: www.purbeckhousehotel.co.uk
Children minimum age: 2

A family run hotel, set in extensive grounds
close to sandy beaches and town centre. Large
private car park.
SB £45 DB £80 HBS £57 HBD £104
B £7.95 L £4 D £18.95.
CC: MC Vi Am DC Swi Delt

How to get there: Arrive in Swanage by ferry.
Head for town centre. Turn right at White Swan
public house. Hotel on left.

Havenhurst

★★

3 Cranborne Road, Swanage, BH19 1 EA
Tel: 01929 424224 Fax: 01929 422173
SB £23 DB £46 HBS £42 HBD £84
B £5 L £9 D £16. CC: MC Vi Swi Delt

How to get there: A351 to Swanage along
Victoria Avenue. Turn right at traffic lights. First
right into Cranborne Road.

Chines

♦♦♦

9 Burlington Road, Swanage, Dorset, BH19 1LR
Tel: 01929 422457

Sandringham

♦♦♦

20 Durlston Road, Swanage, Dorset, BH19 2HX
Tel: 01929 423076 Fax: 01929 423076
Email: silk@sandhot.fsnet.co.uk
SB £27 DB £54 HBS £38 HBD £76 B £6 D £11.
CC: MC Vi Swi Delt

How to get there: On entering Swanage, follow
signs to Durlston Country Park.

Blunsdon House

★★★★

The Ridge, Blunsdon, Swindon,
Wiltshire, SN26 7AS
Tel: 01793 720623 Fax: 01793 720625
Email: philip.dodds@blunsdonhouse.co.uk
Web: www.blunsdonhouse.co.uk
SB £94 DB £122 HBS £67.50 HBD £135
B £10 L £11.50 D £20.
CC: MC Vi Am DC Swi Delt

How to get there: Exit M4 J-15, A419 to
Cirencester. After 7 miles you reach Broad
Blunsdon. 200 yards past traffic lights turn right
into village.

Chiseldon House

★★★

New Road, Chiseldon, Swindon,
Wiltshire, SN4 0NE
Tel: 01793 741010 Fax: 01793 741059
CC: MC Vi Am DC Swi Delt Solo

Marsh Farm

★★★

Coped Hall, Wootton, Swindon, Wiltshire,
SN4 8ER
Tel: 01793 848044 Fax: 01793 851528

This beautiful and prestigious Grade II listed
Victorian farmhouse has been tastefully
restored. Standing in three acres of garden and
surrounded by open countryside, the hotel
offers an oasis of tranquility to business and
leisure travellers.
SB £100 DB £120 B £9.50 L £14.50 D £22.50.
CC: MC Vi Am DC Swi Delt Electron Solo

How to get there: 1½ miles from M4 J-16, and
2 miles west of Swindon.

Southwest

Pear Tree at Purton

★★★ ♔♔♔

Church End, Purton, Swindon, Wiltshire,
SN5 4ED
Tel: 01793 772100 Fax: 01793 772369
Email: stay@peartreepurton.co.uk
Web: www.peartreepurton.co.uk
SB £110 DB £110 HBS £145 HBD £180
B £10.50 L £14 D £33.
CC: MC Vi Am DC Swi Delt

How to get there: Exit M4 J-16. Follow signs to
Purton. At Spar grocers turn right. Hotel is ¹/₂
mile on left.

Stanton House Hotel

★★★ ♔

The Avenue, Stanton, Fitzwarren, Swindon,
Wiltshire, SN6 7SD
Tel: 01793 861777 Fax: 01793 861857
SB £69 DB £109 B £10 L £12 D £12.
CC: MC Vi Am DC Swi Delt

How to get there: Exit M4 J-15 northbound
A419, at Handa turnoff to Highworth. After 3rd
roundabout, take left turning to Stanton
Fitzwarren.
See advert on right

Villiers Inn

★★★

Moormead Road, Wroughton, Swindon,
Wiltshire, SN4 9BY
Tel: 01793 814744 Fax: 01793 814119
Email: hotels@villiersinn.co.uk
Web: www.villiersinn.co.uk
SB £77 DB £88 B £4.50 L £3 D £20.
CC: MC Vi Am DC Swi Delt

How to get there: Exit M4 J-15, A346 for
Chiseldon, B4005 for Wroughton, A4361 to
Swindon. Hotel 100m on right.

Fir Tree Lodge

♦♦♦

17 Highworth Road, Stratton St Margaret,
Swindon, Wiltshire, SN3 4QL
Tel: 01793 822372 Fax: 01793 822372
SB £30 DB £48

How to get there: A419 to A361 Highworth-
Burford turn. Opposite Rat Trap public house.
See advert on previous page

Taunton, Somerset

Bindon Country House

★★★ ♊♊♊

Langford Budville, Wellington, TA21 0RU
Tel: 01823 4000 70 Fax: 01823 4000 71
Email: bindonhouse@msn.com

Nestled among seven acres of stunning formal
and woodland gardens there is at once a sense
of calm... 'Je trouve bien' ('I find well') is the
motto of the house.
SB £85 DB £95 HBD £70 B £10
L £12.95 D £29.50. CC: MC Vi Am DC Swi Delt

How to get there: Exit M5 J-26, A38 to
Wellington. B3187 to Langford Budville, then
follow hotel signs.

Castle

★★★ ♊♊♊♊

Castle Green, Taunton, Somerset, TA1 1NF
Tel: 01823 287004 Fax: 01823 336066
Email: spodro@the-castle-hotel.com
Web: www.the-castle-hotel.com
SB £95 DB £150 B £12.50
L £20 D £20. CC: MC Vi Am DC Swi Delt

How to get there: Exit M5 J-25, signs to town
centre, then brown signs to Castle Hotel.

Forte Posthouse Taunton

★★★

Deane Gate Avenue, Taunton, TA1 2UA
Tel: 01823 332222 Fax: 01823 332266

Meryan House Hotel

♦♦♦♦   ♊♊

Bishops Hull, Taunton, Somerset, TA1 5EG
Tel: 01823 337445 Fax: 01823 322355
Email: meryanhouse@mywebpage.net
Web: www.mywebpage.net/meryanhouse
SB £30 DB £50 HBS £46 HBD £86 B £7 D £16.
CC: MC Vi Swi Delt JCB

How to get there: A38 from Taunton towards
Wellington. After 1¼ miles, crematorium on left,
right into Bishops Hull Rd. Hotel 600 yards.
See advert on facing page

Northam Mill   Little Gem

♦♦♦♦   ♊

Water Lane, Stogumber, Taunton, West
Somerset, TA4 3TT
Tel: 01984 656916 Fax: 01984 656144
Email: bmsspicer@aol.com
Web: www.northam-mill.co.uk

SB £35.50 DB £51 HBS £54 HBD £69.50
B £9.50 D £18.50. CC: MC Vi Am Swi Delt

How to get there: A358 12 miles from Taunton,
left to Bee World/Stogumber, then take 2nd left,
1st right into Water Lane, car park at bottom.

Southwest

Stilegate

◆◆◆◆

Staple Close, West Quantoxhead, Taunton,
Somerset, TA4 4DN
Tel: 01984 639119 Fax: 01984 639119
Email: stilegate@aol.com
SB £28 DB £48

How to get there: Take A39 from Bridgwater to
Minehead. Take first left past Windmill Public
House, through West Quantoxhead. Take
second right into Staple Lane, first right into
Staple Close.

Salisbury House

❖

14 Billetfield, Taunton, Somerset, TA1 3NN
Tel: 01823 272083 Fax: 01823 272083

Whether en-route or visiting Taunton, this is the
place to stay. Central town location near Vivary
Park. Own car park. Elegant spacious rooms
recently refurbished.
SB £38 DB £48 B £6

How to get there: Follow signs to Taunton town
centre. From east reach, bear left and go past
Sainsburys and BP garage. Hotel is on right-
hand side, past church.

Tavistock, Devon

Bedford

★★★

1 Plymouth Road, Tavistock, Devon, PL19 8BB
Tel: 01822 613221 Fax: 01822 618034
Email: jane@bedford-hotel.co.uk
Web: www.warm-welcome-hotels.co.uk
SB £47.50 DB £75 HBS £67.50 HBD £57.50
B £6.50 L £7.95 D £19.95.
CC: MC Vi Am DC Swi Delt

How to get there: In the centre of Tavistock,
opposite the parish church.
See advert on the right

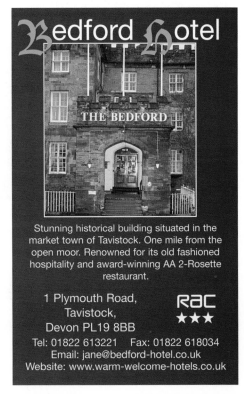

Port William Inn
Trebarwith Strand

Probably the best located inn in Cornwall, romatically situated 50 yards from the sea, overlooking the sea, beach and cliffs at Trebarwith Strand.
The Inn is known for its food, offering homecooked dishes, local fish and seafood, and a good range of vegetarian fare, all at 'bar menu' prices. All rooms are newly refurbished, ensuite and have views across the bay.
We welcome well behaved children and dogs.

Trebarwith Strand, Tintagel, Cornwall
Tel: 01840 770230
Fax: 01840 770936
Email: william@eurobell.co.uk

Browns
★★★ ®

80 West Street, Tavistock, Devon, PL19 8AQ
Tel: 01822 618686 Fax: 01822 618646
See advert below

Tintagel, Cornwall

Port William Inn
♦♦♦♦

Trebarwith Strand, Tintagel, Cornwall, PL34 0HB
Tel: 01840 770230 Fax: 01840 770936
Email: william@eurobell.co.uk
SB £55 DB £75 B £8.50 L £5 D £7.
CC: MC Vi Am Swi Delt
See advert on the left

Tiverton, Devon

Bridge Guest House
♦♦♦

23 Angel Hill, Tiverton, Devon, EX16 6PE
Tel: 01884 252804 Fax: 01884 252804
Web: www.smoothhound.co.uk/hotels/bridgegh.html

Browns Hotel

Warm and intimate, Browns offers luxurious accommodation, complemented by lively menus and superb standards of service. Situated in the centre of the ancient stannary town of Tavistock, Browns is well placed for touring the beautiful landscapes of Dartmoor and villlages of Devon. The Hotel incorporates a brasserie, Wine Bar, conservatory, courtyard garden and function room. The combination of stylish environment and professional hospitality ensure a memorable visit. Specialist breaks including fly fishing and Dartmoor painting are also available.

80 West Street, Tavistock, Devon PL19 8AQ
Tel: 01822 618686   Fax: 01822 618646
Email: enquiries@brownsdevon.co.uk
Website: www.brownsdevon.co.uk

RAC
★★★

SB £24 DB £48 HBS £36 HBD £72 B £4 D £12.

How to get there: Exit M5 J-27, A361. Bridge Guest House situated in centre of town, by river.

Lodge Hill Farm Guest House

♦♦♦

Ashley, Tiverton, Devon, EX16 5PA
Tel: 01884 252907 Fax: 01884 242090

Torcross, Devon

Greyhomes

★

Torcross, Devon, TQ7 2TH
Tel: 01548 580220 Fax: 01548 580832
Email: howard@greyhomeshotel.co.uk
Web: www.greyhomeshotel.co.uk
Children minimum age: 5
Closed November to March
SB £34 DB £56 B £6.80 D £16. CC: MC Vi Euro

How to get there: Leave A379 between Kingsbridge-Dartmouth to village square. Pass shops, up hill. Hotel 2nd turning on left.

Tormarton, South Gloucestershire

Compass Inn

★★

Badminton, Tormarton, South Gloucestershire, GL9 1JB
Tel: 01454 218242 Fax: 01454 218417

Torpoint, Cornwall

Whitsand Bay

★★

Portwrinkle, Crafthole, Torpoint, PL11 3BU
Tel: 01503 230276 Fax: 01503 230329
Web: www.cornish-golf-hotels.co.uk
SB £42 DB £33 HBS £53 HBD £44 B £9.50
L £5 D £19.50. CC: MC Vi Am DC Swi Delt

How to get there: Leave A38 at Trerulefoot roundabout, and take A374 towards Torpoint.

Torquay, Devon

The Imperial

★★★★★

Paramount Hotels, Park Hill Road, Torquay, Devon, TQ1 2DG

Tel: 01803 294301 Fax: 01803 298293
Email: imperialtorquay@paramount-hotels.co.uk
Web: www.paramount-hotels.co.uk
HBS £105 HBD £220 B £7.50 L £10 D £25.
CC: MC Vi Am DC Swi Delt

How to get there: Exit M5 J-31, A38, A380 to Torquay, sea front east, hotel on right.

The Grand

★★★★

Seafront, Torquay, Devon, TQ2 6NT
Tel: 01803 296677 Fax: 01803 213462
Email: grandhotel@netsite.co.uk
Web: www.grandtorquay.co.uk

Set in its own grounds with panoramic views over Torbay. Award winning cuisine, sumptuous surroundings, indoor and outdoor swimming pools and friendly, attentive staff.
SB £69 DB £100 HBS £93.50 HBD £168
L £7.50 D £24.50.
CC: MC Vi Am DC Swi Delt JCB

How to get there: M5, A380 to seafront, right. The Grand is the first on right.

Palace

★★★★

Babbacombe Road, Torquay, Devon, TQ1 3TG
Tel: 01803 200200 Fax: 01803 299899
Email: info@palacetorquay.co.uk
Web: www.palacetorquay.co.uk
Fine independent hotel beautifully set in 25 acres of magnificent grounds, leading to Anstey's Cove. Excellent leisure facilities include golf, swimming pools and tennis courts.
SB £71 DB £142 HBS £81 HBD £162 B £9.50
L £14.50 D £22.50. CC: MC Vi Am DC Swi Delt

How to get there: Exit M5 J-30, A380 to Newton Abbot, then signs to Torquay and Babbacombe.
See advert on following page

Southwest

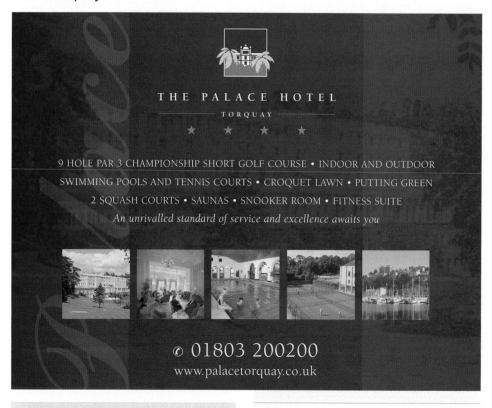

Corbyn Head Hotel

Situated in an unrivalled location, The Corbyn Head Hotel enjoys panoramic views over Torbay. Renowned for its hospitality and service. We offer a discerning clientele a taste of luxury in our main hotel restaurant, The Harbour View. Also superb, award-winning cuisine is available in the Orchid Restaurant prepared by Executive Chef Wayne Pearson, one of only 80 'Master Chefs of Great Britain'.

Orchid Restaurant RaC ♟♟♟
Harbour View Restaurant RaC ♟

Seafront, Torquay, Devon TQ2 6RH
Tel: 01803 213611   Fax: 01803 296152
Email: info@corbynhead.com
Website: www.corbynhead.com

Belgrave

★★★
Sea Front, Torquay, Devon, TQ2 5HE
Tel: 01803 296666 Fax: 01803 211308
Email: info@belgrave-hotel.co.uk
Web: www.belgrave-hotel.co.uk
SB £40 DB £80 HBS £46 HBD £92
B £5 L £2.35 D £16. CC: MC Vi Am DC Swi Delt
Ⅱ ⚘ ⊗ ⎃ ⌨ ☎ P ✂ ⚲ ♘ ♄ ⚓ ♨ ♨ ⚓
How to get there: Follow signs to Torquay seafront. Turn left and go along seafront. The hotel is situated after the gardens on your right.

Corbyn Head

★★★ ♟ ♟ ♟
Seafront, Torquay, TQ2 6RH
Tel: 01803 213611 Fax: 01803 296152
Email: info@corbynhead.com
Web: www.corbynhead.com
Children minimum age: 10
CC: MC Vi Am DC Swi
♿ ⚘ ⊗ ⎃ ⌨ ☎ ✂ ⚲ ♘ ♄ ⚓ ♨ ♨ ⚓
See advert on the left

Hotel Gleneagles

★★★
Asheldon Road, Wellswood, Torquay, Devon, TQ1 2QS

Southwest

Tel: 01803 293637 Fax: 01803 295106
Email: hotelgleneagles@lineone.net
Web: www.hotel-gleneagles.com
Children minimum age: 14

Under ³/₄ mile from the harbour in a tree-lined avenue, overlooking Anstey's Cove, with path to the beach. All rooms are en-suite with balconies, TVs and telephones. Poolside restaurant.
SB £35 DB £70 HBS £41 HBD £81
B £7 L £5 D £15. CC: MC Vi Am Swi Delt

How to get there: Babbacombe Road to St Mathias Church. Hollies Hotel on right. Right into Asheldon Road and hotel is on right.

Livermead Cliff
★★★
Seafront, Torquay, Devon, TQ2 6RQ
Tel: 01803 299666 Fax: 01803 294496
Email: enquiries@livermeadcliff.co.uk
Web: www.livermeadcliff.co.uk
SB £39.50 DB £77.50 HBS £47.50 HBD £89.50
B £8 L £9.50 D £16.75.
CC: MC Vi Am DC Swi Delt JCB

How to get there: From M5, take A379 to Torquay. Follow A3022 through town to seafront. Turn right, sign to Paignton. Hotel 600 yards seaward side.

Livermead House
★★★
Seafront, Torquay, Devon, TQ2 6QJ
Tel: 01803 294361 Fax: 01803 200758
Email: rewhotels@aol.com
Web: www.hotellink.co.uk/livermead.html
SB £38 DB £76 HBS £47 HBD £94
CC: MC Vi Am DC Swi Delt

How to get there: From Exeter, take A380 to Torquay then follow the signs for seafront.
See advert on the right

Osborne Hotel
★★★ ℛℛ
Hesketh Crescent, Meadfoot, Torquay, Devon, TQ1 2LL
Tel: 01803 213311 Fax: 01803 296788
Email: id@osborne-torquay.co.uk
Web: www.osborne-torquay.co.uk
CC: MC Vi Am DC Swi

Toorak Hotel
★★★
Chestnut Avenue, Torquay, Devon, TQ2 5JS
Tel: 01803 400400 Fax: 01803 400140
Email: rheale@tlh.co.uk
Web: www.tlh.co.uk
SB £42 DB £84 HBS £52 HBD £104
B £8.75 D £19.50. CC: MC Vi Am Swi Delt

How to get there: Immediately opposite the Riviera Centre, which is clearly signed from all major routes into the town.

Livermead
House Hotel

RAC
★★★
Torquay

This elegant Seafront Three Star hotel provides the comforts and service synonymous with a luxurious family owned country house. Set in three acres of its own grounds, it possesses both an unrivalled location and excellent facilities. The menu offers a superb choice of fine cuisine which is complemented by an extensive wine list.

Sea Front, Torquay, Devon TQ2 6QJ
Tel: 01803 294361   Fax: 01803 200758
Reservations: 0800 146947
Email: rewhotels@aol.com
Website: www.hotellink.co.uk/livermead.html

Abbey Court

★★

Falkland Road, Torquay, Devon, TQ2 5JR
Tel: 01803 297316 Fax: 01803 297316

Ansteys Lea

★★

Babbacombe Road, Torquay, Devon, TQ1 2QJ
Tel: 01803 294843 Fax: 01803 214333
Email: stay@ansteys-lea.co.uk
Web: www.ansteys-lea.co.uk
SB £25 DB £50 HBS £35
CC: MC Vi Swi Delt Access

Apsley

★★

Torwood Gardens Road, Torquay,
Devon, TQ1 1EG
Tel: 01803 292058 Fax: 01803 215105

Barn Hayes Country

★★

Brim Hill, Maidencombe, Torquay,
Devon, TQ1 4TR
Tel: 01803 327980 Fax: 01803 327980
Email: barnhayes@barnhayes.junglelink.co.uk
Web: www.smoothhound.co.uk/hotels/
                barnhaye.html
Closed December to February

Warm, friendly family run non-smoking hotel in
an Area of Outstanding Natural Beauty.
Excellent home cooking, with a prestigious RAC
Dining Award.
SB £32 DB £64 HBS £47 HBD £94 D £15.
CC: MC Vi Swi Delt Electron Solo JCB

How to get there: Maidencombe is midway
between Torquay and Teignmouth on the A379.
Brim Hill is almost opposite a car sales
forecourt.

Burlington

★★

Babbacombe Road, Torquay, Devon, TQ1 1HN
Tel: 01803 294374 Fax: 01803 200189
Email: burlingtonhotel@virgin.net
Web: www.torquayhotels.co.uk
SB £37 DB £60 HBS £47 HBD £80
L £3 D £10. CC: MC Vi Swi Delt Solo

How to get there: M5 to Exeter, signs to
Torquay. Left at Torquay seafront, left at clock
tower. Hotel ½ mile on right.

Bute Court

★★

Belgrave Road, Torquay, Devon, TQ2 5HQ
Tel: 01803 293771 Fax: 01803 213429
Email: bute-court-hotel@talk21.com
Web: www.bute-court-hotel.co.uk
CC: MC Vi Swi Delt

How to get there: In Torquay take 2nd sign to
seafront. Hotel situated 200m on the right.

Cavendish

★★

Belgrave Road, Torquay, Devon, TQ2 5HN
Tel: 01803 293682 Fax: 01803 292802

Coppice

★★

Barrington Quay, Torquay, Devon, TQ1 2QJ
Tel: 01803 297786 Fax: 01803 211085
Closed November to January
SB £27.50 DB £55 HBS £37.50 HBD £75
B £7.50 D £13.50.

How to get there: Signs to seafront, hotel on
left, 1 mile from harbour.

Crofton House

★★

Croft Road, Torquay, Devon, TQ2 5TZ
Tel: 01803 293461 Fax: 01803 211790
Email: enquiries@croftonhouse.freeserve.co.uk
Web: www.crofton-house-hotel.co.uk
Closed January
SB £33 DB £66 HBS £38 HBD £76 D £3.95.
CC: MC Vi Swi Delt

How to get there: Follow signs for town centre
into Belgrave Road, turn left into Lucius Street
at lights, and take first right into Croft Road.

Southwest

Gresham Court

★★

Babbacombe Road, Torquay, Devon, TQ1 1HG
Tel: 01803 293007 Fax: 01803 215951
Email: greshamcourthotel@hotmail.com
Web: www.gresham-court-hotel.co.uk
Closed January
SB £26 DB £52 HBS £32 HBD £64 B £6 D £12.
CC: MC Vi Am Swi Delt JCB

How to get there: From harbourside, left at clocktower to Babbacombe. Hotel on left side near Torquay Musuem, approx ¼ mile.

Homers

★★ ℞℞

Warren Road, Torquay, Devon, TQ2 5TN
Tel: 01803 213456 Fax: 01803 213458
Email: homers@tinyonline.co.uk
Web: www.homers-hotel.co.uk
SB £25 DB £70 L £16 D £25.
CC: MC Vi Am Swi Delt Solo

How to get there: At seafront, left. Take hill in front of Belgrave Hotel, then first turn on right.

Hotel Sydore

★★

Meadfoot Road, Torquay, Devon, TQ1 2JP
Tel: 01803 294758 Fax: 01803 294489
Email: john@sydore.co.uk
Web: www.sydore.co.uk

A charming Georgian villa set in award-winning secluded gardens surrounded by mature trees. Close to harbour, shops and nightlife. Traditional cuisine. Licensed bar and restaurant.
SB £30 DB £60 HBS £35 HBD £70
CC: MC Vi Am Swi Delt

Howden Court

★★

23 Croft Road, Torquay, Devon, TQ2 5UD
Tel: 01803 294844 Fax: 01803 211350

Meadfoot Bay

★★

Meadfoot Sea Road, Torquay, Devon, TQ1 2LQ
Tel: 01803 294722 Fax: 01803 214473
Email: stay@meadfoot.com
Web: www.meadfoot.com
Closed November to February
SB £26 DB £52 HBS £38 HBD £76 D £17.
CC: MC Vi Swi Delt

How to get there: From Torquay Marina, take left exit from clocktower roundabout. Turn right at traffic lights. Hotel is ½ mile on right.

Norcliffe

★★

Seafront, Babbacombe Downs Road,
Torquay, TQ1 3LF
Tel: 01803 328456 Fax: 01803 328023
SB £18 DB £36 HBS £28 HBD £56
B £5 L £7.50 D £10.50. CC: MC Vi

How to get there: Join A380 Exeter-Newton Abbot. Continue along Newton Road. Left at lights. Follow signs to TUFC. Turn left at Manor Road lights, right at crossroads. Turn left.

Roseland

★★

Warren Road, Torquay, Devon, TQ2 5TT
Tel: 01803 213829 Fax: 01803 291266

Shedden Hall

★★

Shedden Hill, Torquay, Devon, TQ2 5TY
Tel: 01803 292964 Fax: 01803 295306
Email: sheddenhtl@aol.com
Web: www.sheddenhallhotel.co.uk
Children minimum age: 4
Closed January
SB £35 DB £70 HBS £40 HBD £80
CC: MC Vi Am DC Swi Delt JCB Electron Solo

How to get there: From M5, take A380 and follow signs to Torquay seafront. Turn left at seafront traffic lights. At next set join Belgrave Road, and proceed up hill. Shedden Hall is 2nd hotel.

Ashley Rise

★

18 Babbacombe Road, Torquay, TQ1 3SJ
Tel: 01803 327282

Colindale

◆◆◆◆

20 Rathmore Road, Torquay, Devon, TQ2 6NZ
Tel: 01803 293947
Children minimum age: 6
Closed Christmas to New Year
SB £22 DB £44 HBS £33.50 HBD £67 D £11.50.
CC: MC Vi Delt

How to get there: From seafront head for
Torquay station, Colindale Hotel is approx 300m
past station, on left.

Kingston House

◆◆◆◆

75 Avenue Road, Torquay, TQ2 5LL
Tel: 01803 212760
Children minimum age: 8
SB £22.50 DB £35 HBD £115 CC: MC Vi DC

Lindens

◆◆◆◆

31 Bampfylde Road, Torquay, Devon, TQ2 5AX
Tel: 01803 212281
Closed November to December
SB £18 DB £36 HBS £26 HBD £52

How to get there: Fork right at rail station,
across lights, Lindens is in first road on left.

Seaway

◆◆◆◆

Chelston Road, Torquay, Devon, TQ2 6PU
Tel: 01803 605320 Fax: 01803 605320
SB £25 DB £50 HBS £33.50 HBD £67
CC: MC Vi Am Delt

How to get there: Leave seafront on Seaway
Lane, then 2nd right, first property on left.

Briarfields

◆◆◆

84–86 Avenue Road, Torquay, Devon, TQ2 5LF
Tel: 01803 297844 Fax: 01803 297844
Email: denns@msn.com
Closed December
SB £30 DB £36 CC: MC Vi

How to get there: From Newton Abbot, right at
the junction of Torre station and Halfords. Hotel
is situated halfway down on right.

Devon Court

◆◆◆

Croft Road, Torquay, Devon, TQ2 5UE
Tel: 01803 293603 Fax: 01803 213660

Elmdene

◆◆◆

Rathmore Road, Torquay, Devon, TQ2 6NZ
Tel: 01803 294940 Fax: 01803 294940
Email: elmdenehotel@torquay5563.
    freeserve.co.uk
Web: www.s-h-systems.co.uk/hotels/elmdene.
    html
SB £20 DB £40 HBS £30 HBD £50 D £10.
CC: MC Vi

How to get there: Right fork at Torre station, to
2nd lights. Right into Walnut Road. Take first
right into Rathmore Road. Hotel is on corner.

Glenwood

◆◆◆

Rowdens Road, Torquay, Devon, TQ2 5AZ
Tel: 01803 296318 Fax: 01803 296318
Email: enquiries@glenwood-hotel.co.uk
Web: www.glenwood-hotel.co.uk
SB £25 DB £52 HBS £37.50 HBD £69
B £5 D £10. CC: MC Vi

How to get there: Right by traffic lights at rail
station. After next set of lights in Avenue Road,
turn left into Bampfylde Road. Take first left.

Haldon Priors

◆◆◆

Meadfoot Sea Road, Torquay, Devon, TQ1 2LQ
Tel: 01803 213365 Fax: 01803 215577
Closed November to February
SB £28 DB £56

How to get there: Pass Torquay Harbour on
right. Turn left at the clocktower. Turn right at
lights. Hotel on left, just before the beach.

Morley Hotel

◆◆◆

16 Bridge Road, Torquay, Devon, TQ2 5BA
Tel: 01803 292955 Fax: 01803 290111
Email: morleyhotel@aol.com
Web: www.hotelstorquay.com
SB £15 DB £30 HBS £23 HBD £46
CC: MC Vi Swi Delt

How to get there: Approaching Torquay, turn
right into Avenue Road. Proceed past traffic
lights. Take first left into Bampfylde Road.
Bridge Road is second left.

Richwood

20 Newton Road, Torquay, Devon, TQ2 5BZ
Tel: 01803 293729 Fax: 01803 213632

Totnes, Devon

Royal Seven Stars

★★

The Plains, Totnes, Devon, TQ9 5DD
Tel: 01803 862125 Fax: 01803 867925
SB £59 DB £69 B £7 L £9 D £18. CC: MC Vi Am
DC Swi Delt Maestro Electron JCB

How to get there: Follow signs for Totnes from
A38 for 6 miles, then signs for town centre.

Trowbridge, Wiltshire

Hilbury Court

★★

Hilperton Road, Trowbridge, BA14 7JW
Tel: 01225 752949 Fax: 01225 777990

Truro, Cornwall

Nare Hotel

★★★★ ℞ ℞

Carne Beach, Veryan, Truro, Cornwall, TR2 5PF
Tel: 01872 501111 Fax: 01872 501856
Email: office@narehotel.co.uk
Web: www.narehotel.co.uk
SB £76 DB £76 HBS £86 HBD £86
B £15 L £13 D £33. CC: MC Vi Swi

How to get there: M5, A30, B3275, A3078, over
Veryan bridge and turn left after 1½ miles for
Veryan. The hotel is one mile beyond the village.

Alverton Manor

★★★ ℞

Tregolls Road, Truro, Cornwall, TR1 1ZQ
Tel: 01872 276633 Fax: 01872 222989
Email: alverton@connexions.co.uk
SB £67 DB £99 HBS £79 HBD £123
B £9.75 L £3.70 D £21.50.
CC: MC Vi Am DC Swi Delt JCB Solo

How to get there: Route from Exeter passes
through Cornwall on A30. Then take A39,
turning left at Carnon Downs service station.
See advert on this page

Alverton Manor

- Banqueting & Conference facilities up to 200
- 34 Luxury bedrooms all ensuite
- Cornwall's most popular venue for wedding ceremonies
- Ideal for wedding receptions and special occasions
- Award-winning Terrace Restaurant, à la carte & table d'hote menus
- Own 18-hole golf course within the historic Killiow Estate five minutes away by car
- Cornwall's centre of business

Tregolls Road, Truro TR1 1ZQ
Tel: 01872 276633   Fax: 01872 222989
Email: alverton@connexions.co.uk

Carlton

★★

Falmouth Road, Truro, Cornwall, TR1 2HL
Tel: 01872 272450 Fax: 01872 223928
SB £39.50 DB £47.50 HBS £49 HBD £33.25
B £5 L £5.50 D £9.75.
CC: MC Vi Am DC Swi Delt

How to get there: A39 to Truro. Cross two
roundabouts onto bypass. At top of hill, right
into Falmouth Road. Hotel is 100m on right.

Marcorrie

♦♦♦♦

20 Falmouth Road, Truro, Cornwall, TR1 2HX
Tel: 01872 277374 Fax: 01872 241666
Email: marcorrie@aol.com
Web: www.hotelstruro.com
SB £38.50 DB £48.50
CC: MC Vi Am Swi Delt

How to get there: Hotel is 400 yards down
Falmouth Road from A39/A390 Junction of Arch
Hill roundabout.
See advert on following page

Southwest

Trevispian Vean

◆◆◆◆

St Erme, Truro, Cornwall, TR4 9BL
Tel: 01872 279514 Fax: 01872 263730
Closed November to February
SB £24 DB £21 HBS £34 HBD £31

How to get there: A30, A39, 2 miles to Trispen. In village, 2nd left, 1/2 mile, sharp left, 100 yards.

Wadebridge, Cornwall

Roskarnon House

◆◆◆

Rock, nr Wadebridge, Cornwall, PL27 6LD
Tel: 01208 862785
Closed October to March
SB £30 DB £55 HBS £40 HBD £75 CC: Am

How to get there: From Wadebridge, Rock, Trebetherick, Polzeath to golf course.

Wareham, Dorset

Priory

★★★

Church Green, Wareham, Dorset, BH20 4ND
Tel: 01929 551666 Fax: 01929 556485
Email: reception@theprioryhotel.co.uk
Web: www.theprioryhotel.co.uk
Children minimum age: 8
SB £80 DB £250 B £10.50 L £14.50 D £27.50.
CC: MC Vi Am DC Swi Delt

How to get there: At southern end of town between church and river.

Springfield Country Hotel

★★★

Grange Road, Stoborough, Dorset, BH20 5AL
Tel: 01929 552177 Fax: 01929 551862
SB £70 DB £110 HBS £89.50 HBD £149
B £9.50 L £10 D £19.50.
CC: MC Vi Am DC Swi Delt

How to get there: A35 for Wareham, A351 to roundabout, 2nd exit. Straight over next roundabout. After 3/4 mile turn right. Hotel 300 yards on left.

Cromwell House

★★

Lulworth Cove, Wareham, Dorset, BH20 5RJ
Tel: 01929 400253 Fax: 01929 400566

Worgret Manor

★★

Worgret, Wareham, Dorset, BH20 6AB
Tel: 01929 552957 Fax: 01929 554804

Wells, Somerset

Swan Hotel

★★★

Sadler Street, Wells, Somerset, BA5 2RX
Tel: 01749 678877 Fax: 01749 677647
Email: swan@bhere.co.uk
Web: www.bhere.co.uk
Closed January

15th-century coaching hotel, with original four-poster beds and cheerful log fires, facing west front of Wells cathedral. Traditional English food and an ideal location for touring.
SB £75 DB £85 HBS £62.50 HBD £52.50
B £9 L £4 D £19.50. CC: MC Vi Am Swi Delt
⚓ 🏌 🎿 🍵 ☐ ☎ 🅿 🛁 ㊎ 🐴 🎠 ♨ 🛎 ♨♨
How to get there: Hotel faces the west front of Wells Cathedral in city centre.

White Hart

★★ ☕

Sadler Street, Wells, Somerset, BA5 2RR
Tel: 01749 672056 Fax: 01749 672056
Email: whitehart@wells.demon.co.uk
Web: www.wells.demon.co.uk
SB £57.50 DB £80 HBS £72 HBD £57.50
B £5 L £8 D £12.50. CC: MC Vi Am Swi Delt
🎿 ㊎ 🍵 ☐ ☎ 🔌 🅿 🛁 ㊎ 🐴 🎠 ♨ 🛎 ♨♨
See advert on facing page

Bekynton House

♦♦♦♦ ✂

7 St Thomas Street, Wells, Somerset, BA5 2UU
Tel: 01749 672222 Fax: 01749 672222
Email: reservations@bekynton.freeserve.co.uk
Children minimum age: 5
SB £38 DB £52 CC: MC Vi
㊎ 🍵 ☐ 🅿 🛁 ㊎ 🐴 🎠 ♨

Double Gate Farm

♦♦♦♦ ✂

Godney, Wells, Somerset, BA5 1RZ
Tel: 01458 832217 Fax: 01458 835612
Email: hilary@doublegate.demon.co.uk
Web: www.doublegatefarm.com
Closed Christmas to New Year

Award-winning farmhouse accommodation — outdoor, sunshine breakfasts in summertime. Ideally situated for sightseeing, walking and cycling. Two golden retrievers and two mischievous moggies!
SB £30 DB £45 CC: MC Vi Swi Delt
♿ ㊎ 🍵 ☐ 🅿 🛁 ㊎ 🐴 🎠 ♨ ㋐ ⛳
How to get there: From Wells take A39 south. At Polsham turn right. Continue approx 3 miles. Farmhouse on left.

Weston-super-Mare, North Somerset

Beachlands

★★★

17 Uphill Road North, Weston-super-Mare,
North Somerset, BS23 4NG
Tel: 01934 621401 Fax: 01934 621966
Email: info@beachlands.com
Web: www.beachlands.com

Charming family-run hotel overlooking golf
course. Fine food and large Malt Whiskey
collection are complemented by indoor pool and
sauna, secluded gardens and ample parking.
SB £47.50 DB £82.50 HBS £65 HBD £117.50
B £8.50 L £11.95 D £17.50.
CC: MC Vi Am Swi Delt
How to get there: Exit M5 J-21, follow tourist
signs for Tropicana. Hotel is 6¹/₂ miles from M5,
overlooking golf course 200yds before seafront.

Commodore

★★★

Beach Road, Sand Bay, Kewstoke,
Weston-super-Mare, BS22 9UZ
Tel: 01934 415778 Fax: 01934 636483

Arosfa

★★

Lower Church Road, Weston-super-Mare,
North Somerset, BS23 2AG
Tel: 01934 419523 Fax: 01934 636084
Email: reception@arosfahotel.co.uk
Web: www.arosfahotel.co.uk
SB £45 DB £60 HBS £50 HBD £45
B £6.50 L £5 D £16. CC: MC Vi Am DC Swi Delt
How to get there: Follow seafront signs, then
north, with the sea on your left. Take first right
past Winter Gardens. Arosfa is 100m on left.

Bay Hotel

★★

60 Knightstone Road, Weston-super-Mare,
North Somerset, BS23 2BE
Tel: 01934 624137 Fax: 01934 626969

Dauncey's

★★

Claremont Crescent, Weston-super-Mare,
North Somerset, BS23 2EE
Tel: 01934 410180 Fax: 01934 410181
Email: david@daunceyshotel.fsnet.co.uk

Dauncey's has been run by the Hunt family for
40 years. Superb views across Weston Bay.
Well-appointed sea view rooms. Open to
non-residents.
SB £33 DB £66 HBS £45 HBD £90
B £6.25 L £4.50 D £12. CC: MC Vi Swi Delt
How to get there: Situated at the north end of
the promenade, in a Victorian crescent.

Queenswood

★★

Victoria Park, Weston-super-Mare,
North Somerset, BS23 2HZ
Tel: 01934 416141 Fax: 01934 621759
Email: queenswood.hotel@btinternet.com
Web: www.s-h-systems.co.uk/hotels/
queensw.html
SB £48 DB £70 HBS £63.50 HBD £45.50
CC: MC Vi Am DC Swi Delt
How to get there: The Queenswood is centrally
situated in a quite cul-de-sac just off the
seafront, in a slightly elevated position.

Wychwood

◆◆◆◆

148 Milton Road, Weston-super-Mare,
North Somerset, BS23 2UZ
Tel: 01934 627793
Closed Christmas
SB £29 DB £47 HBS £41 HBD £36 D £12.
CC: MC Vi Delt
How to get there: Exit M5 J-21, follow signs for
town centre. Take third exit at 5th roundabout
and at 2nd lights turn right into Milton Road —
hotel is 400 yards on right.

Baymead

♦♦♦

19–23 Longton Grove Road,
Weston-super-Mare, North Somerset, BS23 1LS
Tel: 01934 622951 Fax: 01934 620640
SB £26 DB £46 HBS £34.50 HBD £63
B £5 D £8.50.

How to get there: Exit M5 J-21. At seafront
right, then right again into Knightstone Road.
Turn left into West Street. At T-junction, left.
Keep right, hotel on right.

Blakeney Guest House

♦♦♦

52 Locking Road, Weston-super-Mare,
BS23 3DN
Tel: 01934 624772
SB £16 DB £14 HBS £23 HBD £21
CC: MC Vi Am DC Swi Delt

How to get there: Exit M5 J-21, follow local
council road signs for local accommodation.

L'Arrivee Guest House

♦♦♦

75 Locking Road, Weston-super-Mare,
Somerset, BS23 3DW
Tel: 01934 625328 Fax: 01934 625328
Email: carolinetr@bun.co.uk
SB £20 DB £40 HBS £28.5 HBD £57 D £9.
CC: MC Vi Am DC Swi Delt

How to get there: Exit M5 J-21, B3440 Locking
Road signs. L'Arrivee is about 4 miles from
J-21, into Weston-super-Mare and is on right.

Oakover Guest House

♦♦♦

25 Clevedon Road, Weston-super-Mare,
Somerset, BS23 1DA
Tel: 01934 620125
SB £18 DB £36 CC: MC Vi Swi Delt

How to get there: Exit M5 J-21, follow signs to
Tropicana/seafront. Left into Cleveden Road.
Hotel is on left, just before traffic lights.

Weymouth, Dorset

Hotel Rembrandt

★★★

12-18 Dorchester Road, Weymouth, DT4 7JU
Tel: 01305 764000 Fax: 01305 764022
Email: reception@hotelrembrandt.co.uk
Web: www.hotelrembrandt.co.uk

SB £74 DB £96 HBS £84 HBD £54
B £6.95 L £4.95 D £12.95.
CC: MC Vi Am DC Swi Delt

How to get there: From Dorchester, along A354,
straight on at Manor roundabout (by Safeway).
Hotel ¾ mile on left, 800 yards seafront.

Hotel Rex

★★★

29 The Esplanade, Weymouth, Dorset, DT4 8DN
Tel: 01305 760400 Fax: 01305 760500
Email: rex@kingshotels.f9.co.uk
SB £47 DB £78 HBS £58 HBD £100
B £7 D £12.25. CC: MC Vi Am DC Swi Delt

How to get there: On the seafront, adjacent to
the harbour opposite the beach.

Central

★★

15 Maiden Street, Weymouth, Dorset, DT4 8BB
Tel: 01305 760700 Fax: 01305 760300
Email: central@kingshotels.f9.co.uk
SB £34 DB £62 HBS £40 HBD £74
CC: MC Vi Am Swi

How to get there: A354 from Dorchester. Head
for seafront. At Marks & Spencer, take small
road called New Street to rear of hotel.

Crown

★★

51–52 St Thomas Street, Weymouth, DT4 8EQ
Tel: 01305 760800 Fax: 01305 760300
Email: crown@kingshotels.f9.co.uk
SB £35 DB £64 HBS £43 HBD £59 L £6
CC: MC Vi Am Swi

How to get there: From Dorchester, take the
A354 to Weymouth. Follow signs to town
centre. Take the second bridge over the water.
Crown Hotel is on left.

Fairhaven

★★

37 The Esplanade, Weymouth, Dorset, DT4 8DH
Tel: 01305 760200
Email: fairhaven@kingshotels.f9.co.uk
Closed November to March
SB £35 DB £64 HBS £41 HBD £76
CC: MC Vi Am Swi

How to get there: Take A354 to Weymouth.
Head towards seafront. Follow signs towards
Ferry. Fairhaven Hotel is 200 yards before Ferry
Terminal.

Hotel Prince Regent

★★

139 The Esplanade, Weymouth, Dorset,
DT4 7NR
Tel: 01305 771313 Fax: 01305 778100
Email: hprwey@aol.com

Seafront location with magnificent views of the
bay and coastline. A short level stroll to town
centre and attractions. A good base to explore
Dorset.
SB £48 DB £65 HBS £58 HBD £85
B £6.50 D £13.75. CC: MC Vi Am DC Swi
How to get there: In Weymouth centre, left at
clock tower and proceed along Esplanade.

Kenora Private Hotel

♦♦♦♦

5 Stavordale Road, Westham, Dorset, DT4 0AD
Tel: 01305 771215
Email: kenora.hotel@wdi.co.uk
Closed October to Easter
SB £36.50 DB £60 HBS £47.50 HBD £82
D £11. CC: MC Vi Delt
How to get there: In town centre, 3rd exit at
Westham roundabout, left at Betterment, right
into Stavordale Road.

Birchfields

♦♦♦

22 Abbotsbury Road, Weymouth, DT4 0AE
Tel: 01305 773255 Fax: 01305 773255
Closed November to February
SB £18 DB £36
How to get there: From Jubilee Clock on
Esplanade, go down King Street, 2nd exit at
Kings roundabout, over Swannery Bridge, 2nd
exit Westham roundabout onto Abbotsbury
Road. Birchfields 100m on right.

Concorde

♦♦♦

131 The Esplanade, Weymouth, DT4 7EY
Tel: 01305 776900 Fax: 01305 776900
SB £26 DB £52 HBS £34 HBD £68 D £8.
How to get there: Hotel is situated on The
Esplanade.

Greenhill Hotel

♦♦♦

8 Greenhill, Weymouth, Dorset, DT4 7SQ
Tel: 01305 786026
Closed December to January
SB £35 DB £55 HBS £43 HBD £70 B £5 D £8.
CC: MC Vi Swi Delt
How to get there: Situated on Weymouth
promenade at Junction of A353 and A354.

Sunningdale

♦♦♦

52 Preston Road, Weymouth, Dorset, DT3 6QD
Tel: 01305 832179 Fax: 01305 832179

Trelawney Hotel

♦♦♦

1 Old Castle Road, Weymouth, DT4 8QB
Tel: 01305 783188 Fax: 01305 783181
Email: trelawney@freeuk.com
Web: www.trelawneyhotel.com
SB £35 DB £60 CC: Vi
How to get there: Town centre 1 mile. A354 for
Portland. Hotel 800y from Harbour roundabout.

Westwey Hotel

♦♦♦

62 Abbotsbury Road, Weymouth, DT4 0BJ
Tel: 01305 784564
Children minimum age: 3
Closed December to Christmas
SB £22 DB £44
How to get there: From Esplanade clock tower,
right into King Street, 2nd exit at roundabout,
2nd at next roundabout into Abbotsbury Road.

Williton, Somerset

White House

★★

Long Street, Williton, Somerset, TA4 4QW
Tel: 01984 632306
Closed November to May
SB £55 DB £90 HBS £88 HBD £155

B £11 D £33.

& 🐕 ⛄ 🖥 ☎ P 🏸 ℃ 🐴 � 🍽 ‖

How to get there: On A39 in centre of village.

Fairfield House

◆ ◆ ◆

51 Long Street, Williton, Somerset, TA4 4RY
Tel: 01984 632636 Fax: 01984 632636

Wimborne Minster, Dorset

Beechleas

★ ★ 🍴

17 Poole Road, Wimborne Minster, BH21 1QA
Tel: 01202 841684 Fax: 01202 849344
Email: beechleas@hotmail.com
Web: www.beechleas.com

A beautifully restored Grade II listed Georgian
house, delightfully furnished, award-winning
restaurant, log fires, stunning conservatory,
walled garden. Ideal for New Forest, Thomas
Hardy country, Bournemouth, Poole.
SB £69 DB £79 B £8.95 L £15.75 D £15.75.
CC: MC Vi Am DC Swi Delt

& 🐕 ⛄ 🖥 ☎ P 🏸 ℃ 🐴 ⊓ 🍽 ♨ ‖

How to get there: Short distance from town on
A349 Poole road, on the right.

Winsford, Somerset

Royal Oak Inn

★ ★ ★ 🍴

Exmoor National Park, Winsford, TA24 7FE
Tel: 01643 851455 Fax: 01643 851009
Email: enquiries@royaloak-somerset.co.uk
Web: www.royaloak-somerset.co.uk
SB £70 DB £89 B £12.50 L £16.50
CC: MC Vi Am DC Swi Delt

🍴 🐕 ⛄ 🖥 ☎ ☎ P 🏸 ℃ 🐴 ⊓ 🍽 ‖ ◀🐾

How to get there: M5 south, exit at J-27. At
Tiverton roundabout take A396 north for 20
miles through Exbridge and Bridgetown. Next
turning left to Winsford.
See advert on the right

Woolacombe, Devon

Watersmeet Hotel

★ ★ ★ 🍴 🍴

Mortehoe, Woolacombe, Devon, EX34 7EB
Tel: 01271 870333 Fax: 01271 870890
Email: watersmeethotel@compuserve.com
Web: www.watersmeethotel.co.uk
Closed January

Watersmeet enjoys panoramic sea views across
Woolacombe Bay to Lundy Island. Award-
winning cuisine and fine wines. Indoor and
outdoor pools. Steps to private beach.
SB £83 DB £150 HBS £98 HBD £166 B £16.50
L £2.40 D £16.50. CC: MC Vi Am Swi Delt

🏸 ⛄ 🖥 ☎ P 🏸 ℃ 🐴 🍽 ♨ ‖ ⤢ 🔍 📷 🐾

How to get there: Hotel left on Esplanade.

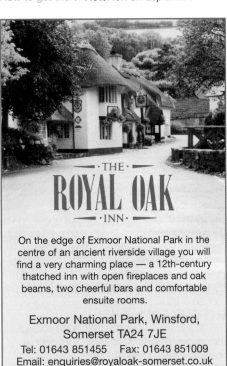

Southwest

Woolacombe Bay

★★★ ☕

Woolacombe, Devon, EX34 7BN
Tel: 01271 870388 Fax: 01271 870613
Email: woolacombe.bayhotel@btinternet.com
Web: www.woolacombe-bay-hotel.co.uk
Closed January to mid-February
SB £35 DB £70 HBS £50 HBD £100
CC: MC Vi Am DC Swi Delt JCB

How to get there: Exit M5 J-27, A361 to
Mullacott Cross, B3343 to Woolacombe. Hotel
in centre of village.

Headlands

★★

Beach Road, Woolacombe, Devon, EX34 7BT
Tel: 01271 870320 Fax: 01271 870320
Email: headhotel@lineone.net
Children minimum age: 4
SB £30 DB £60 HBS £42 HBD £84
CC: MC Vi Swi Delt

How to get there: A361 from Barnstaple to
Millacott Cross. Turn left. Follow road into
Woolacombe. The Headlands is situated on
right, just before seafront.

Lundy House

★★

Mortehoe, Woolacombe, Devon, EX34 7DZ
Tel: 01271 870372 Fax: 01271 871001
Web: www.lundyhousehotel.co.uk
Closed January
SB £34 DB £48 HBS £43.95 HBD £67.90
B £4.95 D £9.95. CC: MC Vi Swi Delt

How to get there: In Woolacombe, proceed to
the end of the Esplanade, and Lundy House is
the 3rd property on the seaside.

Crossways

★ ☕

The Seafront, Woolacombe, Devon, EX34 7DJ
Tel: 01271 870395 Fax: 01271 870395
Web: www.s-h-systems.co.uk/hotels/
crossway.html
Closed November to February
SB £24 DB £48 HBS £29 HBD £58
L £1.50 D £5.

How to get there: Exit M5 J-27, A361 through
Barnstaple towards Ilfracombe. Turn right at
seafront. Hotel ½ mile on right.

Sunnycliffe

♦♦♦♦

Chapel Hill, Mortehoe, Woolacombe, North
Devon, EX34 7EB
Tel: 01271 870597 Fax: 01271 870597
SB £26 DB £52 HBS £41 HBD £82 D £15.
CC: MC Vi Swi Delt

How to get there: At Woolacombe turn right
along Esplanade. Sunnycliffe is on the right as
you proceed up the hill to Mortehoe.

Caertref

♦♦♦

Beach Road, Woolacombe, Devon, EX34 7BT
Tel: 01271 870361
Closed December to March
DB £40 HBD £58 D £9.

How to get there: Caertref can be easily found
at the bottom of the main approach road into
Woolacombe, on the left.

Yelverton, Devon

Two Bridges Hotel

★★ ☕☕

Two Bridges, Yelverton, Devon, PL20 6SW
Tel: 01822 890581 Fax: 01822 890575
Email: tb@warm-welcome-hotels.co.uk
Web: www.warm-welcome-hotels.co.uk

Historic 18th-century hotel with a beautiful
riverside location at the heart of Dartmoor.
Award-winning restaurant, cosy bars and
comfortable lounges. Warmest welcome
guaranteed.
SB £37.50 DB £75 HBS £57.50 HBD £57.50
B £6.50 L £7.95 D £21.50.
CC: MC Vi Am DC Swi Delt

How to get there: At junction of B3357 and
B3212 roads.

Harrabeer Country House Hotel

♦♦♦♦ ✕

Harrowbeer Lane, Yelverton, Devon, PL20 6EA
Tel: 01822 853302

Lydgate House

❖

Postbridge, Yelverton, Devon, PL20 6TJ
Tel: 01822 880209 Fax: 01822 880202
Children minimum age: 12
SB £32 DB £64 HBS £50 HBD £80 D £12.
CC: MC Vi Swi Delt

How to get there: Between Moreton Hampstead
and Princetown on B3212. Turn south just by
bridge over East Dart. 500m down single track.
See advert on this page

Yeovil, Somerset

Yeovil Court Hotel

★★★ ℞℞

West Coker Road, Yeovil, Somerset, BA20 2HE
Tel: 01935 863746 Fax: 01935 863990
Email: verne@yeovilcourt.freeserve.co.uk
Web: www.yeovilcourt.freeserve.co.uk
SB £66.5 DB £75 HBS £71.50 HBD £99
B £5.95 L £5 D £10. CC: MC Vi Am DC Swi Delt

How to get there: Situated 2¹/₂ miles west of
Yeovil town centre on main A30. Easy access
from A303.

Little Barwick House

★ ℞℞℞

Barwick Village, nr Yeovil, Somerset, BA22 9TD
Tel: 01935 423902 Fax: 01935 420908

A listed Georgian Dower House with a delightful
garden offers exceptional comfort and charm.
The restaurant, locally popular and nationally
renowned, serves superb food and interesting
wines at affordable prices — worth a detour!
SB £58.50 DB £93 HBS £78 HBD £132
B £7 L £10.50 D £25.95. CC: MC Vi Am Swi

How to get there: On A37 south from Yeovil, left
at first roundabout (by Red House pub) through
village. House signed left after 200 yards.

Southwest

East Anglia

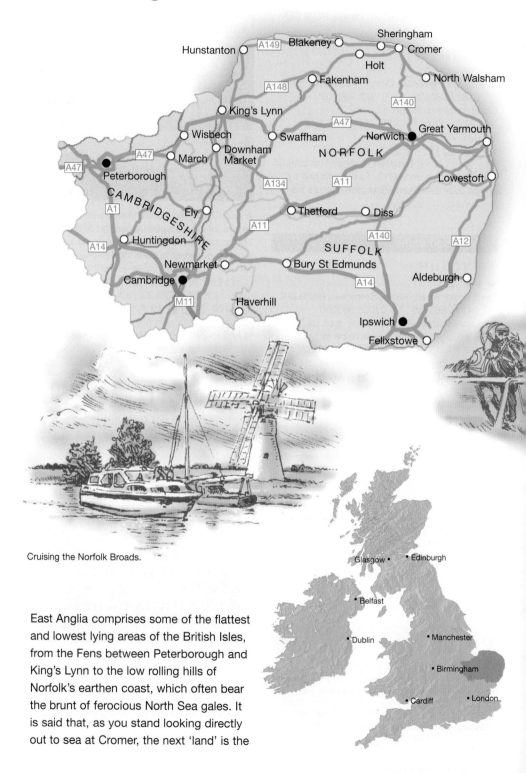

Cruising the Norfolk Broads.

East Anglia comprises some of the flattest and lowest lying areas of the British Isles, from the Fens between Peterborough and King's Lynn to the low rolling hills of Norfolk's earthen coast, which often bear the brunt of ferocious North Sea gales. It is said that, as you stand looking directly out to sea at Cromer, the next 'land' is the

North Pole – a fitting setting for the two fine links golf courses at Cromer and neighbouring Sheringham.

Yet East Anglia is a hospitable and fascinating region, full of diversity and rich in history. Here, near the site of modern Colchester, Queen Boudicca battled the conquering Romans, and later, along the estuaries, landed the Saxon pirates, ravaging the remnants of Roman civilisation. Today, the Saxon heritage is in evidence everywhere, from the accents of the people to the earliest Christian churches in England. Oliver Cromwell held land in Cambridgeshire and returned after

Racehorses on the gallops at Newmarket.

the end of the Civil War to take stock and prepare to give England its first truly democratic parliament. The beginnings of modern agricultural practices were founded in East Anglia; in Cambridgeshire the most ambitious civil engineering programme of the time drained the Fens, which lie below sea level, to provide thousands of hectares of agricultural land.

Along the northern Norfolk coast, visit the many galleries where contemporary artists keep alive the tradition of water-colourist John Sell Cotman, their imagery inspired by the beautifully bleak bird

sanctuary at Blakeney. In fact, the coast from Hunstanton in the west to Blakeney and Cley-next-the-sea in the east is a birdwatcher's paradise. Protected from the sea by a pebble bank, the salty marshes are alive with land and sea fowl. Norfolk's county town of Norwich boasts a fine cathedral and castle, and was the home of 'English' mustard.

Bury St Edmunds and Ely also have glorious cathedrals, while at nearby Newmarket the famous thoroughbred racing horses are reared and trained, providing stunning sights as, in long strings, they are put through their paces alongside the roads. Cambridge is not complete without a stroll along the 'backs', the lush meadows running beside the River Cam, with the backdrop of the famous and ancient University buildings on the opposite bank.

The Suffolk coast is lined with old fishing villages and towns, such as Great Yarmouth, Lowestoft, and Dunwich. Dunwich has lost 12 churches to the seas, the last in 1919, a victim of relentless erosion that has reduced Suffolk's largest port city to a humble village. Just inland from Great Yarmouth is one of Britain's best-loved pleasure waterways formed from the marshes and banks of the River Yare – the Norfolk Broads.

Whatever your interests, you can be sure of finding many excellent hotels throughout East Anglia, as well as a bountiful supply of first-rate Guest Accommodation to suit your chosen location.

Blakeney, Norfolk

Blakeney Hotel

★★★ ♟

Quayside, Blakeney, Norfolk, NR25 7NE
Tel: 01263 740797 Fax: 01263 740795
Email: reception@blakeney-hotel.co.uk
Web: www.blakeney-hotel.co.uk
SB £58 DB £116 HBS £60 HBD £120
B £8.50 L £12.90 D £19. CC: MC Vi Am DC Swi

How to get there: The hotel is situated on the Quay at Blakeney and is signposted from the A149 coast road midway between Sheringham and Wells.

Manor

★★ ♟

Holt, Blakeney, Norfolk, NR25 7ND
Tel: 01263 740376 Fax: 01263 741116
Children minimum age: 14. Closed January.

This privately owned 16th-century manor house, with flint-faced barn conversions, has period charm and character matched only by its excellent cuisine.
SB £33 DB £66 HBS £38 HBD £76
B £7.50 L £6.95 D £16. CC: MC Vi Swi Delt

Bury St Edmunds, Suffolk

Butterfly

★★★

Symonds Road, Moreton Hall Estate,
Bury St Edmunds, Suffolk, IP32 7BW
Tel: 01284 705800 Fax: 01284 702545
Web: www.butterflyhotels.co.uk
SB £75.45 DB £83.40 HBS £90.45
HBD £105.45 B £6.50 L £15 D £15.
CC: MC Vi Am DC Swi Delt

How to get there: Take A14 towards Bury St Edmunds (Bury East exit).

Cambridge, Cambridgeshire

Huntingdon Marriott

★★★★

Kingfisher Way, Huntingdon, PE29 6FL
Tel: 01480 446000 Fax: 01480 451111
CC: MC Vi Am DC Swi Delt

How to get there: On edge of Huntingdon, next to A14, connections to A1, M11, M1 and M6.

Gonville

★★★ ♟

Gonville Place, Cambridge, CB1 1LY
Tel: 01223 221101 Fax: 01223 315470
Email: info@gonvillehotel.co.uk
Web: www.gonvillehotel.co.uk
SB £99 DB £131 HBS £118.50 HBD £170
B £9.50 L £5 D £11.50.
CC: MC Vi Am DC Swi Delt

How to get there: Exit M11 J-11 to city centre. Right at 2nd mini-roundabout, straight on at main junction. Hotel 20yds on right.

Royal Cambridge

★★★

Trumpington Street, Cambridge, CB2 1PY
Tel: 01223 351631 Fax: 01223 352972

Arundel House

★★ ♟♟

Chesterton Road, Cambridge, CB4 3AN
Tel: 01223 367701 Fax: 01223 367721
Email: info@arundelhousehotels.co.uk
Web: www.arundelhousehotels.co.uk

Beautifully located overlooking the River Cam and open parkland, this elegant terrace hotel offers some of the best food in the area. Close to city centre.
SB £53 DB £69 B £4.95 L £15.95 D £15.95.
CC: MC Vi Am DC Swi Delt

How to get there: Exit M11 J-13, for centre, left at mini-roundabout, cross lights, 400yds on left.

Centennial

★★

63–71 Hills Road, Cambridge, CB2 1PG
Tel: 01223 314652 Fax: 01223 315443
Closed Christmas to New Year
SB £77 DB £93 HBS £92 HBD £118
CC: MC Vi Am DC

&⊗♨⎕☎P♨℈☾ 艸⚡️𝄞 ♨👪👤

How to get there: Opposite botanical gardens,
near railway station and city centre.
See advert on this page

Aylesbury Lodge

♦♦♦♦

5 Mowbray Road, Cambridge, CB1 4SR
Tel: 01223 240089 Fax: 01223 528678
SB £30 DB £45 CC: MC Vi Am Swi Delt

🛏⊗♨⎕☎❉P♨℈☾♘⚡️♨👤

How to get there: Exit M11 J-11. At 2nd lights,
right to A1134. Left at first roundabout and hotel
is 50yds on right.

Cambridge Lodge `Little Gem`

♦♦♦♦ ☞☞☜

139 Huntingdon Road, Cambridge, CB3 0DQ
Tel: 01223 352833 Fax: 01223 355166

Lensfield

♦♦♦♦

53 Lensfield Road, Cambridge, CB2 1EN
Tel: 01223 355017 Fax: 01223 312022
Email: enquiries@lensfieldhotel.co.uk
Web: www.lensfieldhotel.co.uk
Closed Christmas
SB £55 DB £80 HBS £63 HBD £98
B £5 L £ D £8. CC: MC Vi Am DC Swi Delt

⊗♨⎕☎📞P♨℈☾♘⚡️♨👤

How to get there: From city ring road, approach
via Silver Street or Trumpington Street, turning
into Lensfield Road.

Suffolk House

♦♦♦♦

69 Milton Road, Cambridge, CB4 1XA
Tel: 01223 352016 Fax: 01223 566816
Children minimum age: 15

Friendly, non-smoking, family run establishment,
within easy walking distance of city centre and
colleges. All rooms ensuite with direct dial
telephone. Pleasant secluded garden. Private
car park.
SB £58 DB £65 CC: MC Vi Am Swi Delt

⊗♨⎕☎P♨℈☾♘⚡️♨

How to get there: 1¼ miles from
A10/A14/A1309 junction.

East Anglia

Ashtrees Guest House

♦♦♦

128 Perne Road, Cambridge, Cambridgeshire, CB1 3RR

Tel: 01223 411233 Fax: 01223 411233
Email: mandy@mhill22.fsnet.co.uk
Closed January
SB £21 DB £39 HBS £31 HBD £59
CC: MC Vi JCB

How to get there: On city ring road between Trumpington and Newmarket Road. From M11 leave at Junction 11. From A14 westbound use A1303, eastbound B1047.

Assisi Guest House

♦♦♦

913 Cherry Hinton Road, Cambridge, Cambridgeshire, CB1 4BX

Tel: 01223 246648 Fax: 01223 412900
Closed Christmas to New Year

Fine detached Victorian house ideally situated for the university and Addenbrookes Hospital. Family run offering personal service, with spacious rooms all ensuite with colour TV, telephone and tea/coffee-making facilities. Large car park.
SB £34 DB £48 CC: MC Vi Am Swi Delt

How to get there: From the centre of Cambridge, take the Hills Road toward Addenbrook Hills. Cherry Hinton Road is the first left after the railway station turning.

Brooklands

♦♦♦

95 Cherry Hinton Road, Cambridge, Cambridgeshire, CB1 7BS

Tel: 01223 242035 Fax: 01223 242035
SB £30 DB £50 CC: MC Vi Am DC Swi Delt

Chatteris, Cambridgeshire

Cross Keys

★ 🏆🏆

12–16 Market Hill, Chatteris, Cambridgeshire, PE16 6BA

Tel: 01354 693036 Fax: 01354 694454
Email: thefens@crosskeyshotel.fsnet.co.uk

This delightful 16th-century inn offers old world charm, traditional hospitality and friendly service in the heart of the Fens.
SB £21.50 DB £32.50 HBD £44
B £5.50 L £9.50 D £12.50. CC: MC Vi Swi Delt

How to get there: On A141 and A142 in town centre, opposite church of St Peter & St Paul.

Cromer, Norfolk

Anglia Court

★ 🏆

Seafront, Runton Road, Cromer, NR27 9AR

Tel: 01263 512443 Fax: 01263 573104
Email: cward31567@aol.com
Web: www.smoothhound.co.uk/hotels/angliaco.html
SB £27.50 DB £53 HBS £48.50 HBD £97
CC: MC Vi Am DC Swi Delt

How to get there: From King's Lynn (A148) or Norwich (A140), enter Cromer, then follow A149 to Sheringham.

Westgate Lodge

♦♦♦♦

Macdonald Road, Cromer, Norfolk, NR27 9AP

Tel: 01263 512840
Children minimum age: 3
DB £57 HBD £75 D £12.
CC: MC Vi Swi Delt Solo

How to get there: Just off the main seafront opposite the Putting Green.

Cliff Cottage Bed & Breakfast

◆◆◆

18 High Street, Overstrand, Norfolk, NR27 0AB
Tel: 01263 578179
Email: roymin@nationwideisp.net
DB £36

How to get there: From Cromer B1159 for
Mundesley, left into Overstrand village. Left
before Sea Marge. Cottage at end of lane.

Grachelle Lodge

◆◆◆

25 MacDonald Road, Cromer, NR27 9AP
Tel: 01263 515932
SB £16 DB £36 HBS £25 HBD £54
CC: MC Vi Swi Delt JCB Solo

How to get there: Head for seafront. Hotel near
the Sandcliff hotel on the left-hand side.

Wellington

◆◆◆

Garden Street, Cromer, Norfolk, NR27 9HN
Tel: 01263 511075 Fax: 01263 513750
Closed Christmas
SB £30 DB £40 L £5 CC: MC Vi Swi Delt

How to get there: Above the pier and beaches.

Dereham, Norfolk

Yaxham Mill

◆◆◆

Norwich Road, Yaxham, Dereham, NR19 1RP
Tel: 01362 693144 Fax: 01362 699801
Web: www.yaxham-mill.co.uk
SB £25 DB £39.50
B £2.99 L £2.99 D £5.95. CC: MC Vi Swi Delt

How to get there: A47, turn for Dereham, signs
for Lynmondham 2 miles. At Yaxham, follow
sign for Norwich ½ mile.

Downham Market, Norfolk

Castle Hotel

★★

High Street, Downham Market, Norfolk,
PE38 9HF
Tel: 01366 384311 Fax: 01366 384311

Duxford, Cambridgeshire

Duxford Lodge

★★★ ♚♚♚

Duxford, Cambridgeshire, CB2 4RU
Tel: 01223 836444 Fax: 01223 832271
Email: duxford@btclick.com
Web: www.touristnetuk.com/em/duxford

Twelve miles south of Cambridge. Set in its own
grounds offering award winning restaurant and
15 ensuite bedrooms. Ideal for business and
leisure.
SB £50 DB £89 HBS £50 HBD £89 B £3.50
L £16.50 D £22.50. CC: MC Vi Am DC Swi Delt

How to get there: Exit M11 J-10, A505
eastbound, first right turn. Hotel half a mile.

Ely, Cambridgeshire

Nyton

★

7 Barton Road, Ely, Cambridgeshire, CB7 4HZ
Tel: 01353 662459 Fax: 01353 666217

Email: nytonhotel@yahoo.co.uk
Comfortable family hotel with ensuite rooms,
secluded from main roads. Attractive grounds,
adjoining golf course. Ample car parking. 10
mins walk to cathedral and city centre.
SB £40 DB £65 HBS £55 HBD £47.50

East Anglia

CC: MC Vi Am DC

♿ 🐕 🏠 💻 ☎ 🔌 **P** 🍴 ⚜ 🐎 🎻 ♻ ⛲ 🛏 🛏

How to get there: From A10, pass golf centre on right. Take first turning on right, signposted 'Cathedral Car Park'. Hotel is on right hand side, 200 yards into turning.

Eye, Suffolk

Cornwallis Country Hotel & Restaurant

★★★ 🥄🥄

Brome, Eye, Suffolk, IP23 8AJ
Tel: 01379 870326 Fax: 01379 870051

Delightful 16th-century dower house in 20 acres of gardens with topiary and ducks! Great restaurant & Tudor bar complete with well.
SB £72.50 DB £90 HBS £92.50 HBD £65
B £9.50 L £6 D £8.50. CC: MC Vi Swi Delt

🦢 ♿ 🐟 🐕 🏠 💻 ☎ **P** 🍴 ⚜ 🐎 🎻 ♻ ⛲ 🛏 🛏

How to get there: A140 Norwich to Ipswich, take B1077 to Eye. After 20yds turn left into hotel.

Fakenham, Norfolk

Wensum Lodge

★★ 🥄

Bridge Street, Fakenham, Norfolk, NR21 9AY
Tel: 01328 862100 Fax: 01328 863365
SB £50 DB £65 HBS £65 HBD £47.50 B £7.95
L £6.50 D £15. CC: MC Vi Swi Delt Solo

🦢 🐟 🏠 💻 ☎ **P** 🍴 ⚜ 🐎 🎻 ♻ ⛲ 🛏 🛏 🛶

How to get there: Situated a few yards away from town centre.

Felixstowe, Suffolk

Orwell

★★★ 🥄

Hamilton Road, Felixstowe, Suffolk, IP11 7DX
Tel: 01394 285511 Fax: 01394 670687
B £9.50 L £15.50 D £18.
CC: MC Vi Am DC Swi Delt

🏨 🏠 💻 ☎ **P** 🍴 ⚜ 🐎 🎻 ♻ ⛲ 🛏 🛏

How to get there: A12 to Ipswich then A14 to Felixstowe. At Dock roundabout, keep straight, Felixstowe & Walton to second roundabout, straight to third. Take third exit, Beatrice Avenue, hotel at end.

Dolphin Hotel

♦♦

41 Beach Station Road, Felixstowe, IP11 8EY
Tel: 01394 282261 Fax: 01394 278319
B £5 L £2.50 D £2.50. CC: MC Vi Am Swi Delt

🏠 💻 **P** ⚜ 🐎 🎻 ♻ ⛲ 🛏

How to get there: Off A14 to Dock roundabout, turn to Dockgate number 1, over roundabout, over railway and hotel is on right.

Gorleston-on-sea, Norfolk

The Pier

★★

Harbour Mouth, Gorleston-on-sea, NR31 6PL
Tel: 01493 662631 Fax: 01493 440263

Avalon Private Hotel

♦♦♦

54 Clarence Road, Gorleston-on-Sea, N31 6DR
Tel: 01493 662114 Fax: 01493 661521
SB £21 DB £42 HBS £28 HBD £56 B £3.50
L £4.50 D £4.50. CC: MC Vi Am DC Swi Delt

🐕 🏠 💻 ⚜ 🐎 🎻 ♻ ⛲ ♻

How to get there: From Yarmouth, A12 for Lowestoft; at 3rd roundabout to Gorleston. Left at T-junction, first right is Clarence Road.

Great Yarmouth, Norfolk

Hotel Elizabeth

✤

1 Marine Parade, Great Yarmouth, NR30 3AG
Tel: 01493 855551

Marina Guest House

✤

12 Trafalgar Road, Great Yarmouth, NR30 2LD
Tel: 01493 844119

Seamore Guest House

✤

116 Wellesley Road, Great Yarmouth, NR30 2AR
Tel: 01493 857389

Windy Shore Hotel

✤

29 North Drive, Great Yarmouth, NR30 4EW
Tel: 01493 844145

Cliff

★★★

Cliff Hill, Gorleston-on-Sea, Norfolk, NR31 6DH
Tel: 01493 662179 Fax: 01493 653617
Email: cliffhotel@aol.com
SB £69 DB £97 HBS £58 HBD £116 B £7.50
L £16.50 D £16.50. CC: MC Vi Am DC Swi Delt

How to get there: Hotel is at north end of Gorleston's Upper Marine Parade.

Imperial

★★★

North Drive, Great Yarmouth, Norfolk, NR30 1EQ
Tel: 01493 851113 Fax: 01493 852229
Email: imperial@scs-datacom.co.uk
Web: www.imperialhotel.co.uk
SB £68 DB £84 HBS £88 HBD £64 B £8.50
L £12.50 D £19.50. CC: MC Vi Am DC Swi

How to get there: At seafront, left into North Drive. Hotel is 1/2 mile north of Britannia Pier.

The Regency Dolphin

★★★

14-16 Albert Square, Great Yarmouth, Norfolk, NR30 3JH
Tel: 01493 855070 Fax: 01493 853798
Email: regency@meridianleisure.com
Web: www.meridianleisure.com
SB £65 DB £75 HBS £77.50 HBD £100
L £8.95 D £16.95.
CC: MC Vi Am DC Swi Delt Solo

How to get there: Follow signs to pleasure beach along north drive. Turn right at the Sea Life Centre. Follow road into Albert Square.
See advert on this page

Star

★★★

Hall Quay, Great Yarmouth, Norfolk, NR30 1HG
Tel: 01493 842294 Fax: 01493 330215

Burlington Palm Court

★★

North Drive, Great Yarmouth, Norfolk, NR30 1EG
Tel: 01493 844568 Fax: 01493 331848
Closed December to January
This family-run hotel has views of the sea and recreation grounds. There is ample car parking and an indoor swimming pool.
SB £50 DB £70 HBS £35 HBD £45 CC: MC Vi Am DC Swi Delt Solo Electron

Regency Dolphin Hotel

RaC
★★★

- Great Yarmouth's Premier and unique venue
- Ideally located within walking distance of central beach
- 49 luxurious ensuite bedrooms with satellite channels and all modern amenities
- Weddings, Conferences & Special Occasion Dining successfully catered for
- Licensed to perform Registry Marriages
- Heated Swimming Pool, Landscaped garden & complementary parking

Albert Square, Great Yarmouth, Norfolk NR30 3JH
Tel: 01493 855070   Fax: 01493 853798
Email: regency@meridianleisure.com
Website: www.meridianleisure.com

How to get there: Follow signs for seafront. Hotel is 600 yards from Britannia Pier, at the quieter end of town.

Sandringham

★★

74-75 Marine Parade, Great Yarmouth, Norfolk, NR30 2BU
Tel: 01493 852427 Fax: 01493 852336
SB £29.50 DB £56.50 HBS £37.50 HBD £70
B £5.50 L £6.50 D £9.50. CC: MC Vi

How to get there: From seafront, turn inland opposite Britannia Pier.

Two Bears

★★

Southtown Road, Great Yarmouth, NR31 0HU
Tel: 01493 603198 Fax: 01493 440486

Admiral House

♦♦♦♦

12a Nelson Road South, Great Yarmouth,
Norfolk, NR30 3JL
Tel: 01493 343712 Fax: 01493 843712

All Seasons Lodge

♦♦♦♦

55–56 Clarence Road, Gorleston, NR31 6DR
Tel: 01493 651111

Corner House

♦♦♦♦

Albert Square, Great Yarmouth, NR30 3JH
Tel: 01493 842773
Closed October to March
SB £25 DB £50 HBS £32 HBD £64 B £5 D £9.

How to get there: From A12/A47, south along
seafront; opposite Pier and Winter Gardens.

The Grange Hotel & Freehouse

♦♦♦♦

Ormesby St Margaret, Great Yarmouth, Norfolk,
NR29 3QG
Tel: 01493 731877 Fax: 01493 731877

Alclive

♦♦♦

33–35 North Denes Road, Great Yarmouth,
Norfolk, NR30 4LU
Tel: 01493 844741   Closed October to April
SB £26 DB £46 HBS £30 HBD £54 CC: MC Vi

How to get there: In Great Yarmouth, left onto
A149, right at lights, first left into Salisbury
Road. Turn left at North Denes Road.

Anglia House

♦♦♦

56 Wellesley Road, Great Yarmouth, NR30 1EX
Tel: 01493 844395
Children minimum age: 2
Closed November to March
SB £20 DB £38 HBS £27 HBD £52 D £7.

Arch House

♦♦♦

14 Wellington Road, Great Yarmouth,
Norfolk, NR30 3AQ
Tel: 01493 854258

Armani

♦♦♦

14-15 Sandown Road, Great Yarmouth, Norfolk,
NR30 1EY
Tel: 01493 843870 Fax: 01493 843870
Web: www.smoothhound.co.uk/hotels/armanih.
html
Children minimum age: 3
SB £20 DB £20 HBS £28 HBD £28 D £8.

How to get there: Left on seafront, 2nd left
opposite entrance to Waterways Garden.

Arrandale

♦♦♦

58 Wellesley Road, Great Yarmouth, NR30 1EX
Tel: 01493 855046 Fax: 01493 855041
Closed November to January

Beaumont House

♦♦♦

52 Wellesley Road, Great Yarmouth, NR30 1EX
Tel: 01493 843957 Fax: 01493 301241
Email: hotelbeaumont@virgin.net
SB £16 DB £32 HBS £23 HBD £46 D £7.
CC: MC Vi Swi Delt

How to get there: One street away from beach,
overlooking Wellesley Park recreation ground.

Belvedere

♦♦♦

90 North Denes Road, Great Yarmouth, Norfolk,
NR30 4LN
Tel: 01493 844200

Open all year. Car parking. Ensuite rooms
available with central heating, colour TVs, tea
and coffee-making facilities. Own keys: access
at all times. Varied menu.

How to get there: At seafront, north to
Waterways Garden, left into Beaconsfield Road.
right at mini-roundabout. Hotel fifth on right.

East Anglia

Bonheur

◆◆◆

3 Norfolk Square, Great Yarmouth, NR30 1EE
Tel: 01493 843042 Fax: 01493 745235
Email: pw@bonheur-hotel.co.uk
Web: www.bonheur-hotel.co.uk
SB £15.25 DB £35.45 HBS £22.32 HBD £50.60
D £7.50. CC: MC Vi Am Swi

How to get there: 200yds north of Britannia Pier,
left into Albemarle Road (opposite bowling
greens). Hotel 50yds on left.

Bramalea Balmoral

◆◆◆

114-115 Wellesley Road, Great Yarmouth,
Norfolk, NR30 2AR
Tel: 01493 844722

Chateau

◆◆◆

1 North Drive, Great Yarmouth, Norfolk,
NR30 1ED
Tel: 01493 859052
Closed October to March
SB £27.50 DB £45 CC: MC Vi Delt

How to get there: Opposite bowling greens on
seafront, just north of Britannia Pier.

Chequers

◆◆◆

27 Nelson Road South, Great Yarmouth,
Norfolk, NR30 3JA
Tel: 01493 853091
Email: david@chequershotel.freeserve.co.uk
SB £18 DB £36 HBS £24 HBD £48

How to get there: Turn inland opposite
Wellington Pier for 200yds down Albert Square
to T-junction. Chequers is ahead on corner.

Collingwood

◆◆◆

25/26 Princes Road, Great Yarmouth, Norfolk,
NR30 2DG
Tel: 01493 844398 Fax: 01493 844398
Web: www.smoothhound.co.uk/hotels/
collingwood.html
Children minimum age: 6
Closed December and January
SB £18 DB £19 CC: MC Vi Am Swi Delt

How to get there: Follow signs to the seafront.
Turn right. Princes Road is opposite the
Britannia Pier. Collingwood is the second hotel
on the left.

Concorde

◆◆◆

84 North Denes Road, Great Yarmouth,
Norfolk, NR30 4LW
Tel: 01493 843709
Email: concordeyarmouth@hotmail.com
SB £17.50 DB £35.60 HBS £25 HBD £50
CC: MC Vi

How to get there: 300yds from coach park,
between Beaconsfield and Salisbury Road.

Dene

◆◆◆

89 North Denes Road, Great Yarmouth,
Norfolk, NR30 4LW
Tel: 01493 844181 Fax: 01493 302359
Email: pulham@denehouse.fsbusiness.co.uk
SB £10 DB £20 HBS £17 HBD £34
CC: MC Vi Swi Delt Electron JCB Solo

How to get there: At seafront, turn north to
Salisbury Road, left into Denes Road. Hotel
100yds on left.

Fairholme

◆◆◆

23–24 Princes Road, Great Yarmouth,
Norfolk, NR30 2DG
Tel: 01493 843447

Gai-Sejour

◆◆◆

21 Princes Road, Great Yarmouth,
Norfolk, NR30 2DG
Tel: 01493 843371
SB £14 DB £30 HBS £19 HBD £40 D £5.

How to get there: Off Marine Parade, just
opposite Brittania Pier.

Hamilton

◆◆◆

23/24 North Drive, Great Yarmouth,
Norfolk, NR30 4EU
Tel: 01493 844662

Hotel Victoria

◆◆◆

2 Kings Road, Great Yarmouth, Norfolk,
NR30 3JW
Tel: 01493 843872 Fax: 01493 843872
SB £15 DB £30 HBS £23 HBD £46

How to get there: Second building in from
seafront, Kings Road is opposite the model
village, close to Wellington Pier.

Kilbrannan Guest House

♦♦♦

14 Trafalgar Road, Great Yarmouth, NR30 2LD
Tel: 01493 850383
SB £20 DB £36

How to get there: Left at seafront. Before the
Marina Centre, right up Trafalgar Road.

Kingsley House

♦♦♦

68 King Street, Great Yarmouth, NR30 2PP
Tel: 01493 850948 Fax: 01493 850948
SB £18 DB £36 HBS £23 HBD £46

How to get there: Southern end of King Street.

Lea-Hurst

♦♦♦

117 Wellesley Road, Great Yarmouth, NR30 2AP
Tel: 01493 843063

How to get there: Right at Brittania Pier onto
Regent Road, first left, Lea-Hurst 30yds on right.

Little Emily

♦♦♦

18 Princes Road, Great Yarmouth, NR30 2DG
Tel: 01493 842515
SB £15 DB £30 HBS £21 HBD £42

How to get there: Princes Road is left
immediately before Britannia Pier.

Maryland

♦♦♦

53 Wellesley Road, Great Yarmouth, NR30 1EX
Tel: 01493 844409
Children minimum age: 2
SB £18 DB £17 HBS £28 HBD £27
CC: Vi

How to get there: Follow seafront signs, left at
lights into St Nicholas Road. Go straight over
traffic lights, turn left. 400yds on left.

Raynscourt

♦♦♦

83 Marine Parade, Great Yarmouth, Norfolk,
NR30 2DJ
Tel: 01493 856554

Rhonadean

♦♦♦

110-111 Wellesley Road, Great Yarmouth,
Norfolk, NR30 2AR
Tel: 01493 842004

Richmond House

♦♦♦

113 Wellesley Road, Great Yarmouth, NR30 2AR
Tel: 01493 853995

Russell Private Hotel

♦♦♦

26 Nelson Road South, Great Yarmouth,
Norfolk, NR30 3JL
Tel: 01493 843788
Email: russellhotel@yarmouth18.freeserve.co.uk
Closed October to April
SB £20 DB £40 HBS £26 HBD £50
CC: MC Vi Delt

How to get there: Right past Wellington Pier, onto
Kings Road, next right. Hotel 150yds on left.

Sandholme

♦♦♦

12-13 Sandown Road, Great Yarmouth, Norfolk,
NR30 1EY
Tel: 01493 300001 Fax: 01493 842161
Email: sandholme@lineone.net
Web: www.sandholme-hotel.co.uk
Children minimum age: 3
SB £20 DB £35 HBS £29 HBD £47
CC: MC Vi Am Swi Delt

How to get there: Left on seafront to Imperial
Hotel & Waterways, left. Hotel 50yds on left.

Sedley House

♦♦♦

5 St Georges Road, Great Yarmouth, NR30 2JR
Tel: 01493 855409
Children minimum age: 10
SB £13 DB £26

How to get there: From A12, take bypass to
A47. Enter town via A47. Continue over
roundabout. Cross four sets of lights, left after
park. Sedley House is 50yds on left.

Senglea Lodge

♦♦♦

7 Euston Road, Great Yarmouth, NR30 1DX
Tel: 01493 859632
Email: juliaformosa@aol.com
SB £15 DB £30 HBS £20 HBD £40
CC: MC Vi Swi

How to get there: On entering Great Yarmouth
on the A47 or A12, go straight over 1st and 2nd
roundabouts. Take a left turn to seafront. Go
straight through traffic lights. Lodge on right
hand side.

Shemara Guest House

♦♦♦

11 Wellesley Road, Great Yarmouth, NR30 2AR
Tel: 01493 844054
Closed December

How to get there: Follow signs for seafront.
Take fourth turning right. Wellesley Road is
halfway down on right.

Sienna Lodge

♦♦♦

17–18 Camperdown, Great Yarmouth, Norfolk,
NR30 3JB
Tel: 01493 843361
Closed November
SB £22 DB £44 HBS £28 HBD £56

How to get there: Turn off seafront opposite Sea
Life Centre into Camperdown. Sienna Lodge is
on the corner of Nelson Road South.

Siesta Lodge

♦♦♦

53–54 York Road, Great Yarmouth, NR30 2NE
Tel: 01493 843207 Fax: 01493 842440
Email: siesta-lodge@ic24.net
Web: stop.at/siestalodge
SB £15 DB £30 HBS £20 HBD £40 D
£5.
How to get there: Along the seafront, locate
York Road and hotel is 50yds on right.

Southern Hotel

♦♦♦

46 Queens Road, Great Yarmouth, NR30 3JR
Tel: 01493 843313 Fax: 01493 853047
Email: southern.hotel@anyonline.co.uk
Web: www.southernhotel.co.uk
Closed March and October
SB £22 DB £40 HBS £27 HBD £50
How to get there: Southern Hotel is situated
close to Wellington Pier and Model Village on
Great Yarmouth's Golden Mile.

Sunshine Lodge

♦♦♦

73 Marine Parade, Great Yarmouth, NR30 2DQ
Tel: 01493 842250 Fax: 01493 857521
Email: john@sunshinelodge.freeserve.co.uk
Web: www.sunshinelodge.freeserve.co.uk
DB £30 CC: MC Vi Swi Delt
How to get there: Head towards seafront and
Britannia Pier. Hotel is opposite Britannia Pier
and the Hollywood cinema.

The Merivon Private Hotel

♦♦♦

6 Trafalgar Road, Great Yarmouth, NR30 2LD
Tel: 01493 844419

Thelton House

♦♦♦

60 Wellesley Road, Great Yarmouth, NR30 1EX
Tel: 01493 843288

Trevi Guest House

♦♦♦

57 Wellesley Road, Great Yarmouth, Norfolk,
NR30 1EX
Tel: 01493 842821
SB £15 DB £30 HBS £21 HBD £42

How to get there: Follow signs to seafront,
through lights past Sainsbury's, first left. Trevi
Guest House is opposite the recreation ground.

Woods End

♦♦♦

49 Wellesley Road, Great Yarmouth, Norfolk,
NR30 1EX
Tel: 01493 842229
Closed Christmas and New Year
SB £15 DB £15 HBS £21 HBD £14

How to get there: Overlooking Wellesley Park.

Charron Guest House

♦♦

151 Nelson Road Central, Great Yarmouth,
Norfolk, NR30 2HZ
Tel: 01493 843177

Chatsworth

♦♦

32 Wellesley Road, Great Yarmouth, NR30 1EU
Tel: 01493 842890

Gable End

♦♦

30 North Drive, Great Yarmouth, NR30 4EW
Tel: 01493 842112

Kentville Guest House

♦♦

5 Kent Square, Great Yarmouth, Norfolk,
NR30 2EX
Tel: 01493 844783
SB £15 DB £34 HBS £20 HBD £44

How to get there: Kent Square is just off the
seafront. Take Standard Road (opposite Marina
Leisure Centre). Hotel is in corner.

East Anglia

Marine Lodge

♦♦

19-20 Euston Road, Great Yarmouth, NR30 1DY
Tel: 01493 331210 Fax: 01493 332040
Closed November to March
B £3 CC: MC Vi Am DC Swi Delt

How to get there: 300yds north of the Britannia Pier on Great Yarmouth seafront.

Windmill Lodge

♦♦

81 North Denes Road, Great Yarmouth, Norfolk, NR30 4LW
Tel: 01493 843864

Gladon

❖

59 Clarence Road, Gorleston, Great Yarmouth, Norfolk, NR31 6DR
Tel: 01493 661067
SB £16 DB £32

How to get there: Yarmouth 3 miles, off A12.

Lyndhurst

♦

22 Princes Road, Great Yarmouth, NR30 2DG
Tel: 01493 332393

Holt, Norfolk

Daubeney Hall Farm

♦♦♦♦

Lower Hall Lane, Sharrington, NR24 2PQ
Tel: 01263 861412
Email: ninaogier@hotmail.com
SB £23 DB £40

How to get there: Fakenham, A148, 9 miles, right for Sharrington, first left past church.

Lawns

♦♦♦♦

26 Station Road, Holt, Norfolk, NR25 6BS
Tel: 01263 713390

Horning, Norfolk

Petersfield House

★★★

Lower Street, Horning, Norfolk, NR12 8PF
Tel: 01692 630741 Fax: 01692 630745
Email: reception@petersfieldhotel.co.uk
Web: www.petersfieldhotel.co.uk

SB £58 DB £75 HBS £64.50 HBD £49.50
B £7.50 L £13.95 D £16.95. CC: MC Vi Am DC

How to get there: A1151 from Norwich for Wroxham, right at Hoveton, A1062 to Horning. The hotel is in the centre of the village.

Hunstanton, Norfolk

Caley Hall Motel

★★

Old Hunstanton, Hunstanton, PE36 6HH
Tel: 01485 533486 Fax: 01485 533348

Lodge Hotel & Restaurant

★★

Old Hunstanton Road, Hunstanton, PE36 6HX
Tel: 01485 532896 Fax: 01485 535007
Email: reception@thelodge-hotel.co.uk
Web: www.thelodge-hotel.co.uk
SB £49 DB £94 HBS £69 HBD £134
B £7.50 L £10 D £20. CC: MC Vi Am Swi Delt

How to get there: A149 from King's Lynn to Old Hunstanton. Hotel is on main road, on right.

Huntingdon, Cambridgeshire

Lion Hotel

★★

High Street, Buckden, Huntingdon, Cambridgeshire, PE18 9XA
Tel: 01480 810313 Fax: 01480 811070

Ipswich, Suffolk

Hintlesham Hall

★★★★ 🐾🐾🐾🐾

Hintlesham, nr Ipswich, Suffolk, IP8 3NS
Tel: 01473 652334 Fax: 01473 652463
Email: reservations@hintlesham-hall.co.uk
Web: www.hintleshamhall.com
SB £94 DB £120 L £21 D £27.
CC: MC Vi Am DC Swi

How to get there: 5 miles west of Ipswich on the A1071.

Novotel

★★★

Greyfriars Road, Ipswich, Suffolk, IP1 1UP
Tel: 01473 232400 Fax: 01473 232414
Web: www.novotel.com

SB £88 DB £98 HBS £103 HBD £128
B £10 L £12 D £14. CC: MC Vi Am DC Swi

♿ ♨ 🛏 ⊘ ⚒ 🖥 ☎ ❄ 📞 🅿 🐴 🕯 🐎 🎠 🏇 🐕
♨♨♨ 👥👥 ⚗

How to get there: A137 for Ipswich and Docks for 2 miles. Novotel on a double roundabout.

Swallow Belstead Brook

★★★ 🏵🏵

Belstead Road, Ipswich, Suffolk,
Tel: 01473 68241 Fax: 01473 681249
Email: ipswich.swallow@whitbread.com
Web: www.belsteadbrookhotel.com

This 16th-century former hunting lodge, found in the suburbs, offers superb grounds, original features and fine food, recognised by our RAC Dining Award level 2.

SB £99 DB £108.75 HBS £119.50 HBD £140
CC: MC Vi Am DC Swi Delt

♨ ♿ ♨ 🛏 ⊘ ⚒ 🖥 ☎ 🅿 🐴 🕯 🐎 🎠 🐕 ♨
🕆 📷

How to get there: Just south of Ipswich within easy reach of the A12 and A14.

Highview House

♦♦♦

56 Belstead Road, Ipswich, Suffolk, IP2 8BE
Tel: 01473 601620 Fax: 01473 688659
Closed Christmas to New Year

Comfortable converted Victorian rectory – nine generously proportioned well-equipped modern

en-suite rooms. Garden, residential licence, professional snooker table. 5 mins to station, 10 mins town centre by foot. Ample car parking.

SB £42 DB £56 CC: MC Vi Delt JCB

🛏 ⊘ ⚒ 🖥 ☎ 🅿 🐴 🕯 🐎 🎠 🐕 ⚗ ⚗

How to get there: Pass rail station on right, take first turning on right into Willoughby Road, up hill to T-junction, turn right: hotel 500yds on right.

Anglesea

♦♦

Oban Street, Ipswich, Suffolk, IP1 3PH
Tel: 01473 255630 Fax: 01473 255630

King's Lynn, Norfolk

Butterfly

★★★

Beveridge Way, Hardwick Narrows Estate, King's Lynn, Norfolk, PE30 4NB
Tel: 01284 705800 Fax: 01284 702545
Email: reception@butterflyhotels.co.uk
Web: www.butterflyhotels.co.uk

SB £75.45 DB £83.40 HBS £90.45 HBD £48.95
B £6.50 L £15 D £15. CC: MC Vi Am DC Swi

🛏 ⊘ ⚒ 🖥 ☎ 📞 🅿 🐴 🕯 🐎 🎠 🐕 ♨ 👥👥

How to get there: A10/A147 roundabout.

Congham Hall

★★★ 🏵🏵🏵🏵

Grimston, Kings Lynn, Norfolk, PE32 1AH
Tel: 01485 600250 Fax: 01485 601191

Kismet Bed & Breakfast

♦♦♦♦ 🥄 🏵

Main Road, Terrington St John, King's Lynn, Norfolk, PE14 7RR
Tel: 01945 881364 Fax: 01945 881364
Children minimum age: 8

DB £45

⊘ ⚒ 🖥 🅿 🐴 🕯 🐎 🎠 🐕 ♨

How to get there: From King's Lynn take A47 to Wisbech. Take 1st slip road off A47. Turn left, and after 150yds left again. Hotel is white property 500yds on left.

Beeches Guest House

♦♦

2 Guanock Terrace, King's Lynn, Norfolk, PE30 5QT
Tel: 01553 766577 Fax: 01553 776664
Closed Christmas

SB £25 DB £38 HBS £30 HBD £53
CC: MC Vi Am Delt

🛏 ⊘ ⚒ 🖥 ☎ 🅿 🐴 🕯 🐎 🎠 🐕 ♨ 👥 ⚗

East Anglia

Guanock

South Gates, King's Lynn, Norfolk, PE30 5JG
Tel: 01553 772959 Fax: 01553 772959
SB £21.24 DB £36.33 D £5.
CC: MC Vi Am DC Swi Delt

How to get there: From A47 to town centre, on right after passing through the south gates.

Twinson Lee

♦

109 Tennyson Road, Kings Lynn, PE30 5PA
Tel: 01553 762900

Lavenham, Suffolk

Heritage Hotels – The Swan

★★★★
High Street, Lavenham, Suffolk, CO10 9QA
Tel: 0870 4008116 Fax: 01787 248286
Email: heritagehotels_lavenham.swan
@forte-hotels.com
Web: www.heritage-hotels.com
SB £100 DB £145 HBS £89 HBD £104 B £14.95
L £13.95 D £26.95. CC: MC Vi Am DC Swi Delt

How to get there: On the main High Street.

Leiston, Suffolk

White Horse Hotel

★
Station Road, Leiston, Suffolk, IP16 4HD
Tel: 01728 830694 Fax: 01728 833105
Email: whitehorse@globalnet.co.uk
Web: www.whitehorsehotel.co.uk
SB £35 DB £55 B £5.50 L £7.50 D £11.50.
CC: MC Vi Am DC Swi Delt

Lowestoft, Suffolk

Albany Hotel

♦♦♦♦
400 London Road South, Lowestoft, Suffolk,
NR33 0BQ
Tel: 01502 574394 Fax: 01502 581198
Email: geoffrey.ward@btclick.com
Web: www.albanyhotel-lowestoft.co.uk
SB £26.50 DB £42 D £6.95. CC: MC Vi Swi Delt
How to get there: On A12 northbound, 350yds on right at start of one-way system.

Hotel Katherine

♦♦♦
49 Kirkley Cliff Road, Lowestoft, NR33 0DF
Tel: 01502 567858 Fax: 01502 581341
Web: www.gazetteer.interdart.co.uk/east/hotel/
kath.htm
Children minimum age: 3

Attractive hotel with ten comfortable ensuite rooms, all with private facilities, lounge, and a popular Thai restaurant serving lunch and dinner to both guests and non-residents.
SB £37 DB £52 HBS £49.95 HBD £77.90
B £5 L £9.95 D £12.95. CC: MC Vi Am Swi Delt

How to get there: From rail station heading toward Ipswich on A12, hotel situated on the seafront at south beach, opposite Kensington Gardens.

Hazeldene

♣
21 Marine Parade, Lowestoft, Suffolk,
NR33 0QL
Tel: 01502 517 907
SB £20 DB £34
How to get there: Seafront location. Five minute walk from town centre and railway station.

March, Cambridgeshire

Olde Griffin Inn

★★
High Street, March, Cambridgeshire, PE15 9EJ
Tel: 01354 652517 Fax: 01354 650086
SB £45 DB £59.50 B £5.45 L £5.45 D £6.95.
CC: MC Vi Am DC Swi Delt
How to get there: Entering March from any direction, the hotel is the biggest white building in the middle of the High Street.

Mildenhall, Suffolk

Smoke House

★★★

Beck Row, Mildenhall, Suffolk, IP28 8DH
Tel: 01638 713223 Fax: 01638 712202
Email: enquiries@smoke-house.co.uk
Web: www.smoke-house.co.uk

Oak beams, log fires and a warm welcome
await you at the Smoke House. Facilities
include modern bedrooms, two bars, two
lounges and a restaurant. 96 bedrooms, all
ensuite.
SB £90 DB £110 HBS £90 HBD £110 B £9.50
L £14.95 D £14.95. CC: MC Vi Am DC Swi Delt

Cobbles Restaurant Little Gem

◆◆◆◆

38 Market Place, Mildenhall, Suffolk, IP28 7EF
Tel: 01638 717022 Fax: 01638 717022
Email: gordon@thecobbles.netlineuk.net
Web: www.cobblesrestaurant.co.uk
Children minimum age: 3
SB £50 DB £55 HBS £65 HBD £79 B £7.95
L £5.45 D £13.50. CC: MC Vi Am Swi Delt

How to get there: Exit A11 at Barton Mills,
A1101 to Mildenhall. At second mini-roundabout
left, next left to Market Place.

Newmarket, Suffolk

Bedford Lodge

★★★

Bury Road, Newmarket, Suffolk, CB8 7BX
Tel: 01638 663175 Fax: 01638 667391

Rutland Arms

★★★

High Street, Newmarket, Suffolk, CB8 8NB
Tel: 01206 210001 Fax: 01206 212167
Email: sales@patenhotels.co.uk

Web: www.virtualhotels.com/rutland-arms
SB £77.45 DB £96.40 HBD £55 B £8.95
L £11.50 D £16.50. CC: MC Vi Am DC Swi Delt

How to get there: Exit M11 J-9, take A11 to
Newmarket town centre. The Rutland Arms is
on the High Street.

Swynford Paddocks

★★★

Six Mile Bottom, Newmarket, Suffolk, CB8 0UE
Tel: 01638 570234 Fax: 01638 570283
Email: sales@swynfordpaddocks.com

Web: www.swynfordpaddocks.com
An elegant 18th-century country house hotel
nestling in idyllic countryside with racehorses
grazing its pastures. Conveniently situated for
both Newmarket and Cambridge, the hotel
offers delightful accommodation and a first
class restaurant.
SB £110 DB £135 B £12.50 L £24.50 D £28.50.
CC: MC Vi Am DC Swi Delt

How to get there: From A14 take A1303
signposted Newmarket. After ¾ mile, turn right
after Prince Albert pub. Continue for 5 miles to
crossroads at Six Mile Bottom. Turn left.
See advert on following page

Norwich, Norfolk

De Vere Dunston Hall

★★★★

Ipswich Road, Norwich, Norfolk, NR14 8PQ
Tel: 01508 473803 Fax: 01508 470689
Email: benita.millward@devere-hotels.com
SB £105 DB £150 HBS £121 HBD £182 B £13 L
£7 D £16. CC: MC Vi Am DC Swi Delt

How to get there: On the A140 Ipswich Road, 3
miles south of Norwich centre, just off the A47.

East Anglia

Swynford Paddocks Hotel

★★★

Swynford Paddocks Hotel is an elegant 18th-century country house nestling in idyllic countryside with racehorses grazing its pastures. It's the ideal base for exploring both Newmarket and Cambridge. Individually decorated bedrooms, all with Sky TV and mini bar. Award winning restaurant, spacious lounge and bar area.

Six Mile Bottom, Suffolk CB8 0UE
Tel: 01638 570234   Fax: 01638 570283
Email: sales@swynfordpaddocks.com
Website: www.swynfordpaddocks.com

Marriott Sprowston Manor Hotel
★★★★
Wroxham Road, Norwich, Norfolk, NR7 8RP
Tel: 01603 410871 Fax: 01603 423911

Barnham Broom
★★★
Honingham Road, Barnham Broom, NR9 4DD
Tel: 01603 759393 Fax: 01603 758224
Email: enquiry@barnhambroomhotel.co.uk
Web: www.barnham-broom.co.uk

Set in 250 acres, Barnham Broom has 52 ensuite bedrooms (fully refurbished April 2000), two 18-hole golf courses, leisure complex with indoor pool and full conference facilities.
SB £75 DB £99 HBS £92.95 HBD £134.90
B £8.50 L £10.95 D £18.25.
CC: MC Vi Am DC Swi Delt
How to get there: 10 miles southwest of Norwich, off A47/A11 trunk routes.

Oaklands
★★★
89 Yarmouth Road, Thorpe St Andrews, Norfolk, NR7 0HH
Tel: 01603 434471 Fax: 01603 700318
SB £60 DB £70 HBS £47.50 HBD £45 B £7.50
L £7.50 D £16.95. CC: MC Vi Am Swi Delt
How to get there: A47, A1042, A1242 towards Norwich. The Oaklands is on the right.

Quality Hotel Norwich
★★★
2 Barnard Road, Bowthorpe, Norwich, Norfolk, NR5 9JB
Tel: 01603 741161 Fax: 01603 741500
Email: admin@gb619.u-net.com
Web: www.choicehotelseurope.com

SB £90 DB £120 HBS £100 HBD £140 B £10
L £10 D £15. CC: MC Vi Am DC Swi Delt JCB
How to get there: On A1074 Norwich–Cromer road. At double roundabout go straight over. Hotel next roundabout on right.

Swallow Nelson
★★★
Prince of Wales Road, Norwich, NR1 1DX
Tel: 01603 760260 Fax: 01603 620008
SB £98 DB £115 B £7.75 L £10 D £16.50.
CC: MC Vi Am DC Swi Delt
How to get there: Opposite the railway station.

Annesley House
★★
6 Newmarket Road, Norwich, Norfolk, NR2 2LA
Tel: 01603 624553 Fax: 01603 621577
SB £67.50 DB £80 B £3.95 L £4.95 D £9.95.
CC: MC Vi Am DC Swi Delt
How to get there: On A11, ½ mile from city.

Hotel Wroxham

★★

The Bridge, Wroxham, Norwich, NR12 8AJ
Tel: 01603 782061 Fax: 01603 784279

Gables Guest House

♦♦♦♦

527 Earlham Road, Norwich, Norfolk, NR4 7HN
Tel: 01603 456666 Fax: 01603 250320
Closed December 20 to January 2

Friendly, family-run non-smoking guest house
with secluded gardens, high quality illuminated
car park at rear. Snooker table. Close to city,
walking distance to university.
SB £40 DB £58.50 CC: MC Vi Swi Delt JCB,
Eurocard, Electron
How to get there: From southern bypass, take
B1108 Watton Road and follow signs for
University/City Centre. After Fiveways
roundabout, Gables 300yds on left.

Kings Head Inn

♦♦♦

The Street, Acle, Norwich, Norfolk, NR13 3DY
Tel: 01493 750204 Fax: 01493 750713
SB £33 DB £59.95 B £3.75 L £3.95 D £5.95.
CC: MC Vi Swi Delt
How to get there: From A11 or A140, join A47 to
Yarmouth. Continue to Acle, turn off into Acle,
Kings Head in centre.

Wedgewood House

♦♦♦

42 St Stephens Road, Norwich, Norfolk,
NR1 3RE
Tel: 01603 625730 Fax: 01603 615035
Email: mail@wedgewoodhouse.co.uk
SB £28 DB £48 CC: MC Vi Am DC Swi Delt
How to get there: Follow A1/Newmarket Road
towards city centre. Wedgewood House is on
right, opposite Hospital.

Swallow Hotel

★★★★

Alwalton Village, Lynch Wood, Peterborough,
Cambridgeshire, PE2 6GB
Tel: 01733 375511 Fax: 01733 238077
To become Marriott, Spring 2001.
SB £95 DB £105 HBS £110 HBD £130 L £15.50
D £18.50. CC: MC Vi Am Swi Delt
How to get there: Exit A1 at Alwalton. Left at T-
junction. Hotel on next roundabout on your left.

Bull

★★★

Westgate, Peterborough,
PE1 1RB
Tel: 01733 561364
Fax: 01733 557304

PEEL HOTELS PLC

Email: info@bull-hotel-peterborough.com
SB £95.50 DB £116 B £10.50 L £17.95
D £17.95. CC: MC Vi Am DC Swi Delt
How to get there: From A1 to city centre.
Boures Blvd, St John's Rd. First left at
roundabout, New Rd, right, hotel on left.

Butterfly

★★★

Thorpe Meadows, Peterborough, PE3 6GA
Tel: 01284 705800 Fax: 01284 702545
Email: reception@butterflyhotels.co.uk
Web: www.butterflyhotels.co.uk
SB £77.45 DB £85.40 HBS £92.45 HBD £48.25
B £6.50 L £15 D £15. CC: MC Vi Am DC Swi

Thorpe Lodge

♦♦♦

83 Thorpe Road, Peterborough, PE3 6JQ
Tel: 01733 348759 Fax: 01733 891598

Dolphin

★★★

London Road, St Ives, Huntingdon, PE27 5EP
Tel: 01480 466966 Fax: 01480 495597
SB £75 DB £95 B £6 L £5.50 D £14.50.
CC: MC Vi Am DC Swi Delt
How to get there: A14, A1096 for St Ives. Left at
first roundabout, right. Dolphin is 800yds further.

East Anglia

Olivers Lodge

★★★

Needingworth Road, St Ives, PE17 4JP
Tel: 01480 463252 Fax: 01480 461150
Email: reception@oliverslodge.co.uk
Web: www.oliverslodge.co.uk
SB £61.75 DB £70.85 HBD £49.50
B £7 L £12 D £14. CC: MC Vi Am Swi Delt JCB
How to get there: From M11/A1, A14, A1096 to St Ives. Across first roundabout, left at next and first right. Hotel 500yds on right.

Slepe Hall

★★★

Ramsey Road, St Ives, PE17 4RB
Tel: 01480 463122 Fax: 01480 300706
Email: mail@slepehall.co.uk
Web: www.slepehall.co.uk
SB £80 DB £95 B £7.50 L £12.50 D £15.50.
CC: MC Vi Am DC Swi Delt
How to get there: Exit A14, A1096. At Manchester Arms, A1123 for Huntingdon. Left at lights by Toyota garage, then 1/3 mile on left.

Sheringham, Norfolk

Fairlawns

♦♦♦♦

26 Hooks Hill Road, Sheringham, NR26 8NL
Tel: 01263 824717 Fax: 01263 824717

Southwold, Suffolk

Anchor House

19 North Road, Southwold, Suffolk, IP18 6BG
Tel: 01502 725055 Fax: 01502 725055
SB £35 DB £50
How to get there: Take main road into Southwold over 'Mights Bridge'. Take first left into North Road. Anchor House is 10th property on right.

Stalham, Norfolk

Kingfisher

★★

High Street, Stalham, Norfolk, NR12 9AN
Tel: 01692 581974 Fax: 01692 582544

Sudbury, Suffolk

The Mill

★★★

Walnut Tree Lane, Sudbury, Suffolk, CO10 6BD
Tel: 01787 375544 Fax: 01787 373027
SB £69.50 DB £99 B £.50 L £15 D £25.
CC: MC Vi Am DC Swi

How to get there: From A12 Colchester, A134 to Sudbury. Follow signs for A131. Pass main square, 3rd on right.

Old Bull & Trivets Guesthouse

♦♦♦

Church Street, Sudbury, Suffolk, CO10 6BL
Tel: 01787 374120 Fax: 01787 379044

Swaffham, Norfolk

Lydney House

★★

Norwich Road, Swaffham, Norfolk, PE37 7QS
Tel: 01760 723355 Fax: 01760 721410
Email: rooms@lydney-house.demon.co.uk
Web: www.lydney-house.demon.co.uk
SB £58 DB £77 HBS £73 HBD £107
B £6.50 L £6.50 D £8. CC: MC Vi Am Swi JCB

How to get there: On Norwich Road, 1/4 mile from centre of town.

Horse & Groom

♦♦♦

40 Lynn Street, Swaffham, Norfolk, PE37 7AX
Tel: 01760 721567

Thetford, Norfolk

Lynford Hall

★★★

Lynford Hall, Mundford, nr Thetford, Norfolk, IP26 5HW
Tel: 01842 878351 Fax: 01842 878252
SB £79 DB £99 B £11 L £16 D £25.
CC: MC Vi Am Swi Delt
How to get there: From A134 Mundford roundabout, A1065 to Swaffham. Take first right.
See advert on facing page

East Anglia

Comfort Inn Thetford

★★

Thetford Road, Northwold, nr Thetford, Norfolk,
IP26 5LQ
Tel: 01366 728888 Fax: 01366 727121
Email: admin@gb632.u-net.com
Web: www.choicehotels.com
Children minimum age: 14

SB £50.75 DB £54.80 HBS £56.25 HBD £37
B £7.75 L £5 D £10.75.
CC: MC Vi Am DC Swi Delt JCB
How to get there: From Thetford roundabout
(A11/A134 north) follow A134 north for 12 miles
over a roundabout and past Northwold. Hotel
then on left.

Tivetshall St Mary, Norfolk

Old Ram Coaching Inn

★★

Ipswich Road, Tivetshall St Mary, Norfolk,
NR15 2DE
Tel: 01379 676794 Fax: 01379 608399
Email: theoldram@btinternet.com
Web: www.theoldram.com

Listed 17th-century hotel, restaurant and free
house. Award winning food. Big on fish. Over
sixties' and children's menus. Superb
accommodation, meeting space. Ample car
parking.
SB £57.95 DB £70 HBS £55 HBD £85
B £6.95 L £9.95 D £11.95.
CC: MC Vi Swi Delt Connect
How to get there: On the A140, 15 minutes
south of Norwich and the A47 bypass. Five
miles from the market town of Diss.

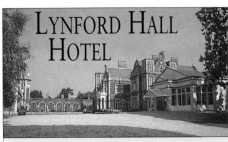

Walshingham, Norfolk

Old Rectory

♦♦♦

Waterden, Walshingham, Norfolk, NR22 6AT
Tel: 01328 823298
DB £42
How to get there: Take the B1355 Fakenham to
Burnham market road, turn right at Waterden
sign before the village centre of South Creake.
One mile up lane on left hand side.

Wells-next-the-Sea, Norfolk

Kilcoroon

♦♦♦

Chancery Lane, Wells-next-the-Sea, Norfolk,
NR23 1ER
Tel: 01328 710270
Children minimum age: 10
DB £38
How to get there: At Wells town sign, turn
towards town centre. Third turning right onto
Buttlands, Kilcoroon situated left of Crown
Hotel.

Oyster Cottage Bed & Breakfast

Oyster Cottage, 20 High Street,
Wells-next-the-Sea, Norfolk, NR23 1EP
Tel: 01328 711997 Fax: 01328 711910
Email: bb@oyster-cottage.co.uk
Web: www.oyster-cottage.co.uk
SB £20 DB £35

How to get there: From town sign take Mill
Road to town centre, at junction by Barclays
Bank – High St is on the right.

Wisbech, Cambridgeshire

Crown Lodge

★★

Downham Road, Outwell, Wisbech,
Cambridgeshire, PE14 8SE
Tel: 01945 773391 Fax: 01945 772668
Email: crownlodgehotel@hotmail.com

Situated on the banks of Well Creek, in the
village of Outwell, this family-run hotel offers a
warm, friendly atmosphere with excellent
standards of accommodation and cuisine.
SB £50 DB £65 B £4.50 L £6.50 D £10.50.
CC: MC Vi Am DC Swi Delt Solo Electron

How to get there: Situated on the A1122/A1101
Downham Market to Wisbech road.
Approximately 5 miles to Wisbech and 7 miles
to Downham Market.

Rose & Crown

★★

Market Place, Wisbech, Cambridgeshire,
PE13 1DG
Tel: 01945 589800 Fax: 01945 474610
SB £60 DB £65 HBS £70 HBD £80
CC: MC Vi Am DC Swi Delt

How to get there: From London, leave A1 at J-
10 and follow A47 to Wisbech. From Suffolk,
take A1101 and then A47 from King's Lynn. The
hotel is in the centre of Wisbech.

Woodbridge, Suffolk

Seckford Hall

★★★

Great Bealings, Woodbridge, Suffolk, IP13 6NU
Tel: 01394 385678 Fax: 01394 380610
Email: reception@seckford.co.uk
Web: www.seckford.co.uk
SB £79 DB £110 HBS £105 HBD £165 B £8.50
L £14 D £27. CC: MC Vi Am DC Swi Delt

How to get there: From A12/A14, travel east
over Orwell Bridge. Bear left on A12 to
Lowestoft. Do not turn off into Woodbridge
town centre. Seckford Hall Hotel on left.

Ufford Park

★★★

Yarmouth Road, Ufford, Woodbridge, Suffolk,
IP12 1QW
Tel: 01394 383555 Fax: 01394 383582
Email: uffordpark@btinternet.com
Web: www.uffordpark.co.uk
SB £79 DB £99 HBS £95.95 HBD £132.90
B £7.95 L £4.95 D £16.95.
CC: MC Vi Am DC Swi Solo

Commission-free
foreign currency

Your journey can get off to a flying start, thanks to a commission free service RAC has organised with currency experts, Travelex.

Forget standing in long queues, just order your commission free currency and travellers cheques from the comfort of your home and your order will be delivered to your door.

Call RAC Travel Sales
0800 55 00 55
quoting GUI1

A to B - we RAC to it

RaC

East Midlands

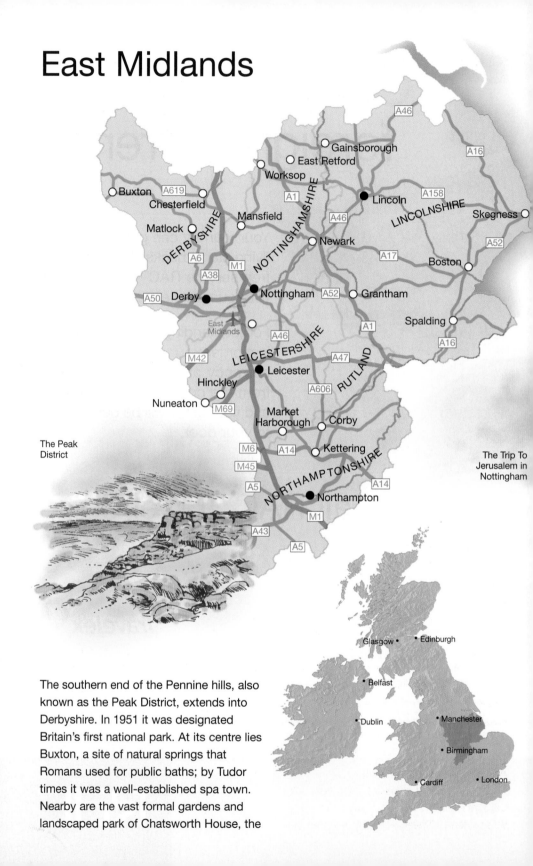

The Peak District

The Trip To Jerusalem in Nottingham

The southern end of the Pennine hills, also known as the Peak District, extends into Derbyshire. In 1951 it was designated Britain's first national park. At its centre lies Buxton, a site of natural springs that Romans used for public baths; by Tudor times it was a well-established spa town. Nearby are the vast formal gardens and landscaped park of Chatsworth House, the

17th-century home of the Dukes of Devonshire.

A famous resident of Nottinghamshire was DH Lawrence, whose humble first home in Eastwood is now an intimate museum dedicated to the author's life. Today, although Clumber Park is a better choice for a woodland walk than Robin Hood's famous but depleted Sherwood Forest, Nottingham's distant past is still alive. At the foot of Castle Rock you can

find Trip To Jerusalem, Britain's oldest public house, and the Goose Fair is still held in October, over a thousand years since it began.

Melton Mowbray in Leicestershire has an abundance of historical attractions. The earliest date from its beginnings as a junction of several Roman roads, including the Fosse Way, or visitors can see as many as 28 monuments of the Civil War, when Roundheads garrisoned the town. In fact, for those with the time, there are over 700 buildings of Special Historical and Architectural Interest to visit.

Stone Age and Roman settlements have been discovered at Market Bosworth, where Henry VII slew Richard III in the Battle of Bosworth (1485), and the first post-Reformation Catholic abbey in England can be visited at Coalville. Although the smallest county in England, Rutland (which merged with Leicestershire between 1974–97) has the second largest artificial lake in England, with a 20-mile circumference, created by damming the River Gwash in 1976.

At Donington Park, site of the first British Grand Prix, you can visit the world's largest collection of Grand Prix cars, or take advantage of the region's other racing circuits at Mallory Park and also at Silverstone in Northamptonshire. The county boasts England's longest tunnel at Stoke Bruerne on the Grand Union Canal, and the shoe-making museum in Northampton is an amusing reminder of the county's industrial past. Althorp Park, Great Brington, is the resting place of Diana, Princess of Wales, where an exhibition celebrates her life in photographs and fashion.

Scenic Stamford in Lincolnshire, England's first conservation area (1968), appeared as the scenic backdrop to BBC Television's mini-series interpretation of George Eliot's Middlemarch; Walter Scott believed Stamford to be the finest sight on the road from London to Edinburgh. Lincolnshire was known as Bomber County, because of the many Second World War airfields scattered among its wolds, and an aviation heritage centre in East Kirkby is based around a 1940s bomber airfield.

Near to the traditional seaside fare of Skegness and its 20 miles of sands and dunes, past life can be visited at the Church Farm Museum and wild animals observed at Gibraltar Point Nature Reserve.

Alkmonton, Derbyshire

Dairy House Farm

◆◆◆◆

Alkmonton, Longford, Derbyshire, DE6 3DG
Tel: 01335 330359 Fax: 01335 330359
Email: andy@dairyhousefarm.force9.co.uk
Web: www.digitalpaces.co.uk/dairyhousefarm

Red brick farmhouse with oak-beamed dining
room and lounge. Large inglenook fireplace.
Tranquil location, good home cooking and
colourful garden.
SB £25 DB £50 HBS £40 HBD £80
B £5 L £8 D £15.

How to get there: Off A515 at Cubley: take road
to Alkmonton. Dairy House Farm is 1½ miles
south.

Ashbourne, Derbyshire

Callow Hall Hotel

★★★

Mappleton, Ashbourne, Derbyshire, DE6 2AA
Tel: 01335 300900 Fax: 01335 300512
Email: reservations@callowhall.co.uk
Web: www.callowhall.co.uk
Closed Christmas Day and Boxing Day
SB £85 DB £130 HBS £123 HBD £206
CC: MC Vi Am DC Swi

How to get there: A515 through Ashbourne,
after Market Square turn left past Bowling
Green pub. First right for Mappleton, entrance
on right after bridge.
See advert on facing page

Get your personalised route to the Hotel or
Guest Accommodation of your choice with
RAC's free on-line Route Planner facility —
visit www.rac.co.uk

Hanover International Ashbourne

★★★

Derby Road, Ashbourne, Derbyshire, DE6 1XH
Tel: 01335 346666 Fax: 01335 346549
Web: www.hanover-international.com

HANOVER INTERNATIONAL

Attractively purpose-built hotel and leisure club
at the 'Gateway to Dovedale' with the highest
standards of traditional comfort and warm
friendly service.
SB £45 DB £90 HBS £54.50 HBD £109
B £6.50 L £5 D £19.95.
CC: MC Vi Am DC Swi Delt Solo

How to get there: M1 J-24. A50 Stoke-on-Trent,
A515 Ashbourne. Right at first roundabout, at
next turn left. Hotel ½ mile on left. M6 J-15/
J-16, A50 towards Derby before A515.

Heritage Hotels – The Peveril of the Peak

★★★

Thorpe, Dovedale, Derbyshire, DE6 2AW
Tel: 0870 4008109 Fax: 01335 350507
SB £105 DB £115 HBS £65 HBD £55
B £10.50 L £10 D £22.
CC: MC Vi Am DC Swi Delt

How to get there: A515 Ashbourne towards
Buxton. 1 mile out turn left, sign Thorpe/Ilam.
Along this road and hotel in Thorpe.

Dog and Partridge Country Inn

★★

Swinscoe, Ashbourne, Derbyshire, DE6 2HS
Tel: 01335 343183 Fax: 01335 342742
Email: dogpart@fsbdial.co.uk
Web: www.dogandpartridge.co.uk
17th-century family-run inn with rooms in the
grounds. Children and pets welcome. Good food
and real ales. Alton Towers only five miles away.

B £10 L £5 D £15.
CC: MC Vi Am DC Swi Delt Solo

How to get there: A52 Ashbourne towards Leek. On left, 3 miles from Ashbourne.

Courtyard

♦♦♦♦

Dairy House Farm, Alkmonton, Longford, Derbyshire, DE6 3DG
Tel: 01336 330187 Fax: 01336 330187
Email: andy@dairyhousefarm.force9.co.uk
Web: www.digitalpages.co.uk/courtyard
Closed December

The Courtyard is situated in a tranquil location and has been converted from early Victorian cowsheds into tastefully well appointed bedrooms, all rooms ensuite.
SB £30 DB £46 CC: MC Vi DC Swi Delt

How to get there: A50 for Church Broughton. A515 for Alkmonton. A52 for Longford.

Lichfield House

♦♦♦♦

Bridgeview, Mayfield, Ashbourne, Derbyshire, DE6 2HN
Tel: 01335 344422 Fax: 01335 344422
Email: brionybull@ukonline.co.uk
Closed Christmas
Elegant Georgian residence offering easy access to Dovedale, Peak District, Chatsworth, Alton Towers etc. Pleasing, well-appointed

bedrooms. Hearty breakfast from our extensive menu.
DB £45

How to get there: A53 Ashbourne to Leek. Left onto B5032. Lichfield House first house on left.

Ashby-de-la-Zouch, Leicestershire

Fallen Knight

★★★ ♖♖

Kilwardby Street, Ashby-de-la-Zouch, Leicestershire, LE65 2FQ
Tel: 01530 412230 Fax: 01530 417596

East Midlands

Ashford-in-the-Water, Derbyshire

Rowdale

♦♦♦ ✿ ✧

Ashford-in-the-Water, Bakewell, Derbyshire, DE45 1NX
Tel: 01629 640260
Web: www.rowdale.co.uk
SB £25 DB £50

🛏🐾🌂🍵 P ✧ ❀ 🎠 ♒

How to get there: Off A6 at Ashford (2 miles north of Bakewell), follow A6020, farm on left after 1¹/₂ miles, entry 100 yards past buildings.

Ashover, Derbyshire

Old School Farm

♦♦♦♦ ✿

Uppertown, Ashover, Derbyshire, S45 0JF
Tel: 01246 590813
Closed November to March
SB £22 DB £44 HBS £30 HBD £60

🌂🍵🖥 P ✧ ❀ 🎠 ♒

How to get there: A362 Chesterfield to Matlock. Into B5057 Darley Dale road. Left to Uppertown.

Bakewell, Derbyshire

The Old Bakery

✤

Church Street, Youlgrave, Bakewell, Derbyshire, DE45 1UR
Tel: 01629 636887

Barton-upon-Humber, Lincolnshire

Reeds Hotel

★★★ 🍷🍷

Far-ings Road, Barton-upon-Humber, Lincolnshire, DN18 5RG
Tel: 01652 632313 Fax: 01652 636361
Email: sally@reedshotel.co.uk
Web: www.reedshotel.co.uk
SB £66 DB £78 B £6.95 L £5.25 D £5.25.
CC: MC Vi Am DC Swi Delt

⚓🌂🌂🍵🖥🕿 P 🏸 🎽

Baslow, Derbyshire

Cavendish Hotel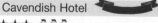

★★★ 🍷🍷🍷

Baslow, Derbyshire, DE45 1SP
Tel: 01246 582311 Fax: 01246 582312
Email: info@cavendish-hotel.net

Web: www.cavendish-hotel.net
SB £104 DB £146 HBS £142 HBD £220
B £5 L £26 D £26. CC: MC Vi Am DC Swi Delt

🌂⊗🌂🖥🕿 P ✧ ❀ 🎠 ♒ 🍴 🐟

Belper, Derbyshire

Shottle Hall Guest House

♦♦♦♦

Shottle, Belper, Derbyshire, DE56 2EB
Tel: 01773 550276/550203
Closed Christmas to New Year
SB £36 DB £68 B £6 D £15.

♿🐾🌂 P ✧ ❀ 🎠 ♒ 🏸🍴

How to get there: Off B5023, 200m north of crossroads with A517 Belper–Ashbourne road.

Boston, Lincolnshire

Comfort Inn Boston

★★

Bicker Bar roundabout, A17/A52 Junction, Boston, Lincolnshire, PE20 3AN
Tel: 01205 820118 Fax: 01205 820228
Email: admin@gb607.u/net.com

Web: www.choicehotels.com
SB £51 DB £29 HBS £60.50 HBD £39 B £7.75
L £2.95 D £10.75. CC: MC Vi Am DC Swi Delt

⚓♿🌂🐾⊗🍵🖥🕿 P ✧ ❀ 🎠 ♒ 🏸
🍴 🏹

Bourne, Lincolnshire

Angel

♦♦♦

Market Place, Bourne, Lincolnshire, PE10 9AE
Tel: 01778 422346 Fax: 01778 393990

Buxton, Derbyshire

Lee Wood

★★★★ 🍷

Manchester Road, Buxton, SK17 6TQ
Tel: 01298 23002 Fax: 01298 23228
Email: leewoodhotel@btinternet.com
SB £84 DB £105 HBD £61 B £9 L £12 D £24.
CC: MC Vi Am DC Swi Delt Solo

⚓🍴🐾⊗🌂🖥🕿🍷 P ✧ ❀ 🎠 ♒
🏸🍴 🏹

How to get there: From north, M1 J-29, Chester-field-Baslow-Buxton. From south, M1 J-23A/J-24, A50 for approx 19 miles, A515 to Buxton.

Palace

★★★★

Palace Road, Buxton, Derbyshire, SK17 6AG
Tel: 01298 22001 Fax: 01298 72131
Email: palace@paramount-hotels.co.uk
Web: www.paramount-hotels.co.uk
SB £105 DB £120 HSB £124 HDB £138
B £9 D £18 CC: MC Vi Am Swi Delt

How to get there: From north M6 J-20, south M6 J-15, north and south M1 J-29. Detailed directions from hotel.

Buckingham Hotel

★★★

1–2 Burlington Road, Buxton, Derbyshire, SK17 9AS
Tel: 01298 70481 Fax: 01298 72186
Email: frontdesk@buckinghamhotel.co.uk
Web: www.buckinghamhotel.co.uk
SB £51 DB £70 HBS £65 HBD £105
B £7.50 D £15. CC: MC Vi Am DC Swi Delt

How to get there: On A53 to Leek, opposite signposted Pavilion Gardens car park.

Grove

★★

Grove Parade, Buxton, Derbyshire, SK17 6AJ
Tel: 01298 23804 Fax: 01298 77906
SB £32.50 DB £70 HBS £42.50 HBD £90
B £3.50 L £5.95 D £10.50. CC: MC Vi Swi

How to get there: In centre, opposite Spa Baths.

Hartington

★★

18 Broad Walk, Buxton, Derbyshire, SK17 6JR
Tel: 01298 22638 Fax: 01298 22638
Email: harthot@globalnet.co.uk
Closed Christmas to New Year
SB £55 DB £65 HBS £67.50 HBD £90
B £6.50 D £12.50. CC: MC Vi Am

How to get there: Motor access from Hartington Road at back of hotel.

Looking for great dining? Look for RAC Hotels and Guest Accommodation displaying the RAC Dining Award symbol in this Guide.

Netherdale Guest House

♦♦♦♦

16 Green Lane, Buxton, Derbyshire, SK17 9DP
Tel: 01298 23896 Fax: 01298 23896
Closed November to January
SB £24 DB £48

How to get there: From London Rd traffic lights, hotel 250m up Green Lane to Pooles Cavern.

Hawthorn Farm Guest House

♦♦♦

Fairfield Road, Buxton, Derbyshire, SK17 7ED
Tel: 01298 23230
Closed November to March
SB £23 DB £52

How to get there: On A6 towards Manchester.

Roseleigh

♦♦♦

19 Broad Walk, Buxton, Derbyshire, SK17 6JR
Tel: 01298 24904 Fax: 01298 24904
Email: enquiries@roseleighhotel.co.uk
Web: www.roseleighhotel.co.uk
SB £22 DB £48 B £5 CC: MC Vi Swi Delt

Westminster

♦♦♦

21 Broad Walk, Buxton, Derbyshire, SK17 6JR
Tel: 01298 23929 Fax: 01298 71121
Email: cecelia@westminsterhotel.demon.co.uk
Web: www.westminsterhotel.demon.co.uk
SB £30 DB £50 CC: MC Vi Swi Delt

How to get there: From A6 Macclesfield signs over lights to crossroads. Right to Bath Road, second left to Hartington Road.

Castle Donington, Leicestershire

Donington Park Farmhouse

♦♦♦

Melbourne Road, Isley Walton, nr Derby, Leicestershire, DE74 2RN
Tel: 01332 862400 Fax: 01332 862364
Email: info@parkfarmhouse.co.uk
Web: www.parkfarmhouse.co.uk
Closed Christmas
SB £50.70 DB £72.90 D £19.
CC: MC Vi Am DC Swi Delt JCB

How to get there: M1 J-23A or J-24, past East Midlands airport to Isley Walton. Turn right, hotel is ¹/₂ mile on right.

Cleethorpes, Lincolnshire

Holmhirst

♦♦♦

3 Alexandra Road, Cleethorpes, Lincolnshire,
DN35 8LQ
Tel: 01472 692656 Fax: 01472 692656
Email: holmhirst@aol.com
Children minimum age: 3
SB £25 DB £42 L £4
CC: MC Vi

How to get there: From M1: M18, M180, A180.
Signs to Cleethorpes. Hotel on seafront near
pier gardens.

Mallow View

♦♦

9/11 Albert Road, Cleethorpes, Lincolnshire,
Tel: 01472 691297 Fax: 01472 691297
SB £15 DB £30

How to get there: Just off sea front, centre.

Coalville, Leicestershire

Hermitage Park

★★★

Whitwick Road, Coalville, Leicestershire,
LE67 3FA
Tel: 01530 814814 Fax: 01530 814202
Email: hotel@hermitagepark.com
Web: www.hermitagepark.com

SB £45 DB £90 HBS £59.50 HBD £74.50
B £6.50 L £6.95 D £12.95.
CC: MC Vi Am Swi Delt JCB

How to get there: Exit A42 J-13 or M1 J-22.
A511 to Coalville, then follow tourism signs to
Hermitage Park Hotel.
See advert below left

Charnwood Arms

★★

Beveridge Lane, Bardon Hill, Coalville,
Leicestershire, LE67 1TB
Tel: 01530 813644 Fax: 01530 815425
SB £44.45 DB £49.40 B £3.50 L £4.50 D £5.90.
CC: MC Vi Am DC Swi Delt

How to get there: M1 J-22. A511 towards
Coalville. Stay to left on second roundabout:
take B585 towards Ibstock.

Collingham

The Laurels

✜

34 High Street, Collingham, Newark, NG23 7LA
Tel: 01636 893618
Email: thelaurels@talk21.com
SB £20 DB £30

How to get there: Take A46 towards Lincoln.
Turn left onto A1133. The house is in
Collingham, on right before traffic lights.

Corby, Northamptonshire

Thatches-On-The-Green

♦♦♦♦

9 School Lane, Weldon, Corby,
Northamptonshire, NN17 3JN
Tel: 01536 266681 Fax: 01536 266659

Daventry, Northamptonshire

Hanover International Daventry

★★★★

Sedgemoor Way, Ashby Road, Daventry,
Northamptonshire, NN11 5SG
Tel: 01327 301777 Fax: 01327 702730
Web: www.hanover-international.com

HANOVER INTERNATIONAL

Stylish and elegant, located in the Nene Valley
close to Silverstone, with a superb fully
equipped leisure club. The Waterside Restaurant
overlooks beautiful Drayton Water.
B £10.50 D £19.45. CC: MC Vi Am DC Swi Delt

How to get there: M1 J-18. A361 to Daventry,
5 miles from motorway on edge of town.

Derby, Derbyshire

Best Western Midland

★★★
Midland Road, Derby, Derbyshire, DE1 2SQ
Tel: 01332 345894 Fax: 01332 293522
Email: sales@midland-derby.co.uk
Web: www.midland-derby.co.uk
SB £91 DB £109 B £8.50 L £12.95 D £19.85.
CC: MC Vi Am DC Swi Delt

How to get there: M1 J-24, A50 then A6, or
from J-25, take A52. Hotel is situated off inner
ring road, opposite Derby railway station.

Hotel La Gondola

★★★ ℝ
220 Osmaston Road, Derby, Derbyshire,
DE23 8JX
Tel: 01332 332895 Fax: 01332 384512
SB £53 DB £59 HBS £64.50 HBD £82
B £6.50 L £7.20 D £12.
CC: MC Vi Am DC Swi Delt

How to get there: M1 J-25. A514 for Melbourne.
Hotel 5 minutes city centre, 10 minutes Derby
station.

The International

★★★
Burton Road, Derby, Derbyshire, DE23 6AD
Tel: 01332 369321 Fax: 01332 294430

European Inn

Travel Accommodation
Midland Road, Derby, Derbyshire, DE1 2SL
Tel: 01332 292000 Fax: 01332 293940
Email: admin@euro-derby.co.uk
Web: www.euro-derby.co.uk
SB £53 DB £59.50 B £6.50
CC: MC Vi Am DC Swi Delt Solo

How to get there: M1 J-25. A52 to Derby. Signs
to railway station – hotel opposite station.

Rangemoor Park

♦♦♦

67 Macklin Street, Derby, Derbyshire, DE1 1LF
Tel: 01332 347252 Fax: 01332 369319

Rose & Thistle

♦♦♦

21 Charnwood Street, Derby, Derbyshire,
DE1 2GG
Tel: 01332 344103 Fax: 01332 291006
Email: rosethistle@gpanet.co.uk
SB £21.50 DB £40
CC: MC Vi Swi Delt Solo

How to get there: M1 J-24. A6 to Derby. Inner
ring road to Charnwood Street.

East Midlands

Non smoking policy RAC

Properties displaying this symbol in
the Guide have non smoking rooms
available for guests. However, smokers
should check in advance whether the Hotel or
Guest Accommodation displaying this symbol
actually allows smoking in any room.

Dovedale, Derbyshire

Izaak Walton

★★★

Dovedale, Derbyshire, DE6 2AY
Tel: 01335 350555 Fax: 01335 350539
Email: reception@izaakwalton-hotel.com
Web: www.izaakwalton-hotel.com
SB £84 DB £110 B £9 L £15.25 D £24.
CC: MC Vi Am DC Swi Delt

How to get there: Hotel 5 miles NW Ashbourne. A515 towards Buxton. After 2 miles left on B5054 to Thorpe, Dovedale and Ilam. Hotel after 4 miles.

Finedon, Northamptonshire

Tudor Gate

★★ ♖ ♖

35 High Street, Finedon, Northamptonshire, NN9 5JN
Tel: 01933 680408 Fax: 01933 680745

Glossop, Derbyshire

Wind in the Willows

★★ ♖ ♖

Derbyshire Level, off Sheffield Road, Glossop, Derbyshire, SK13 7PT
Tel: 01457 868001 Fax: 01457 853354
Email: info@windinthewillows.co.uk
Web: www.windinthewillows.co.uk
Children minimum age: 8
SB £74 DB £99 B £8 D £24.
CC: MC Vi Am DC Swi Delt

How to get there: On A57 1 mile east of Glossop centre. Turn right opposite Royal Oak pub. Hotel 400 yards on right.

George

♦ ♦

34 Norfolk Street, Glossop, SK13 9QU
Tel: 01457 855449 Fax: 01457 857033
SB £25 DB £40 L £4 D £10.
CC: MC Vi Swi Delt

How to get there: George Hotel is in town centre location, opposite railway station.

Kings Clough Head Farm

off Monks Road, Glossop, Derbyshire, SK13 6ED
Tel: 01457 862668
SB £18 DB £36

How to get there: By A624 Glossop-Hayfield road.

Grantham, Lincolnshire

Swallow Hotel

★★★

Swingbridge Road, Grantham, Lincolnshire, NG31 7XT
Tel: 01476 593000 Fax: 01476 592592
To become Courtyard by Marriott, Spring 2001.
SB £89 DB £99 B £6.50 L £10 D £15.
CC: MC Vi Am DC Swi Delt

How to get there: A1 north, A607 Melton Mowbray. Hotel at end of slip road. A1 south, A607 then first right, first left, hotel straight ahead.

Grindleford, Derbyshire

Maynard Arms

★★★ ♖ ♖

Main Road, Grindleford, Derbyshire, S32 2HE
Tel: 01433 630321 Fax: 01433 630445
SB £69 DB £79 HBD £49.50 B £6.50 L £21.50 D £21.50. CC: MC Vi Am Swi Delt

How to get there: M1 J-29, J-33. On B6521, Grindleford.

Hassop, Derbyshire

Hassop Hall

★★★ ♖ ♖

Hassop, Bakewell, Derbyshire, DE45 1NS
Tel: 01629 640488
Fax: 01629 640577
Email: hassophallhotel@btinternet.com
Closed Christmas
The ancient seat of the Eyre family, in a tranquil setting at the heart of the Peak District National Park.
SB £87 DB £95 HBS £115 HBD £151 B £7.95 L £16.90 D £27.75.
CC: MC Vi Am DC Swi Delt

How to get there: M1 J-29, signs to Chesterfield town centre, then A619 to Baslow and A623 to Calver. Left at traffic lights onto B6001. Hassop is 1 mile.

Hathersage, Derbyshire

George
★★★ ♙♙
Main Street, Hathersage, Derbyshire, S30 1BB
Tel: 01433 650436 Fax: 01433 650099
Email: info@george-hotel.net
Web: www.george-hotel.net
SB £69.50 DB £99.50 HBS £89.50
HBD £139.50 B £5.50 L £10 D £15.
CC: MC Vi Am DC Swi Delt
How to get there: M1 J-29. West on A619 to Baslow, then north onto B6001 to Hathersage.

Hinckley, Leicestershire

Hanover International Hinckley
★★★★
A5 Watling Street, Hinckley,
Leicestershire, LE10 3JA
Tel: 01455 615737 Fax: 01455 635370
Email: sarah.todd@hanover-international.com
Web: www.hanover-international.com

HANOVER INTERNATIONAL

Unique, friendly modern hotel and extensive leisure club set in lovely countryside, with easy access to Midlands attractions, the NEC and motorway connections.
SB £102.50 DB £114 B £12.50 L £11.95
D £17.50. CC: MC Vi Am DC Swi Delt
How to get there: 300 yards from J-1 M69 which links M1 and M6.

Kings Hotel
★★
13–19 Mount Road, Hinckley, Leicestershire, LE10 1AD
Tel: 01455 637193 Fax: 01455 636201
Email: kingshinck@aol.com
Web: members.aol.com/kingshinck
Children minimum age: 10

This handsome privately owned hotel is in a central, yet quiet location, with its own car park and gardens. Lovely rooms and a much-acclaimed restaurant ensure a memorable stay.
SB £69.50 DB £79.50 HBS £85 HBD £65
B £10 D £20. CC: MC Vi Am DC Swi Delt
How to get there: From Hinckley town centre, follow signs for hospital. Hotel at bottom end of same road.

Holbeach, Lincolnshire

Cackle Hill House
♦♦♦♦
Cackle Hill Lane, Holbeach, Lincolnshire, PE12 8BS
Tel: 01406 426721 Fax: 01406 424659
Children minimum age: 10
SB £25 DB £40.
How to get there: From A17 at Holbeach roundabout, B1168 to Cackle Hill. Hotel 1/2 mile on right.

East Midlands

Kettering, Northamptonshire

Kettering Park

★★★★ ♙♙♙

Kettering Parkway, Kettering,
Northamptonshire, NN15 6XT
Tel: 01536 41666 Fax: 01536 416171
Web: www.shireinns.co.uk
SB £125 DB £145 L £6 D £20.
CC: MC Vi Am DC Swi

How to get there: Take A14 J-9.

Pennels Guest House

♦♦♦

175 Beatrice Road, Kettering,
Northamptonshire, NN16 9QR
Tel: 01536 481940
Fax: 01536 410798
Email: Pennelsgh@aol.com
Web: www.members.aol.com/pennelsgh
SB £21 DB £40 HBS £32.50 HBD £61 D £10.50.
CC: MC Vi Swi Delt

How to get there: From A14 J-7 follow Kettering
town centre/football ground. Pennels Guest
House is behind the football ground off
Rockingham Road.

Branston Hall Hotel

Branston Hall offers beautiful ensuite
accommodation in a characteristic and elegant
Country House set in 88 acres of wooded park
land and lakes. The Lakeside Restaurant offers
table d'hôte, an extensive à la carte menu and an
international wine list. Relax in our new indoor
pool, jacuzzi or spa and take advantage of the
hotel's peace and tranquility. We are 5 minutes
from the centre of historic Lincoln. For more
information or to request a brochure, call us.

Branston Park, Branston, Lincoln LN4 1PD
Tel: 01522 793305   Fax: 01522 790549
Email: brahal@enterprise.net
Website: www.scoot.co.uk/branston-hall

Leicester, Leicestershire

Leicester Stage

★★★

299 Leicester Road (A50), Wigston Fields,
Leicester, LE18 1JW
Tel: 0116 288 6161 Fax: 0116 257 3900/281 1874
Email: reservations@stagehotel.co.uk
Web: www.stagehotel.co.uk
SB £90 DB £100 HBS £105 HBD £130
B £10 L £12 D £17. CC: MC Vi Am DC Swi Delt

How to get there: From M1 J-21 outer ring road
SE (A563) for Oadby, Wigston. Right for
Northampton A50. Hotel ¼ mile on left.

Regency

★★★ ♙

360 London Road, Leicester, Leicestershire,
LE2 2PL
Tel: 0116 2709634 Fax: 0116 2701375
Web: www.smoothhound.co.uk/hotels/
regency1.html

Whatever the purpose of your stay, this
exquisitely restored Victorian town house hotel
will charm you with its grace and elegance.
SB £35 DB £54 CC: MC Vi Am Swi Delt

How to get there: On main A6, approximately
1½ miles from city centre. Close to universities.

Red Cow

★★

Hinckley Road, Leicester Forest East, Leicester,
Leicestershire, LE3 3PG
Tel: 0116 238 7878 Fax: 0116 238 6539

Stoneycroft Hotel

♦♦♦

5–7 Elmfield Avenue, off London Road,
Leicester, LE2 1RB
Tel: 0116 2707605 Fax: 0116 2706067
SB £39 DB £49 D £7.95. CC: MC Vi Am DC Swi Delt

Lincoln, Lincolnshire

Bentley Hotel & Leisure Club

★★★

Newark Road, South Hykeham, Lincoln,
Lincolnshire, LN6 9NH
Tel: 01522 878000 Fax: 01522 878001
Email: info@thebentleyhotel.uk.com
Web: www.thebentleyhotel.uk.com

Lincoln's newest and only hotel sporting a smart
leisure club. Indoor pool and large conference
facilities. Popular with both corporate and
leisure markets.
SB £62 DB £77 B £8.75 L £8.95 D £12.75.
CC: MC Vi Am DC Swi Delt Solo

How to get there: From A1, A46 for Lincoln.
After 10 miles, straight at first roundabout on
Lincoln bypass. Hotel 50 yards on left.

Branston Hall

★★★

Branston Park, Lincoln Road, Lincoln,
Lincolnshire, LN4 1PD
Tel: 01522 793305 Fax: 01522 790549
Email: brahal@enterprise.net
Web: www.scoot.co.uk/branston-hall
SB £59.50 DB £79.50 HBS £73.50
HBD £104.50 B £7.50 L £13.45 D £12.95.
CC: MC Vi Am DC Swi Delt Solo JCB

How to get there: B1188 3 miles south of Lincoln.
See advert on facing page

Golf Hotel

★★★

The Broadway, Woodhall Spa, nr Lincoln,
Lincolnshire, LN10 6SG
Tel: 01526 353535 Fax: 01526 353096
Web: www.principalhotels.co.uk
SB £65 DB £85 HBS £77 HBD £109
B £7.50 D £15.95. CC: MC Vi Am DC Swi Delt

How to get there: B1189 to Metheringham,
B1191 to Woodhall Spa. Golf Hotel is on main
street, 'The Broadway'.

The Grand

★★★

St Mary's Street, Lincoln, Lincolnshire, LN5 7EP
Tel: 01522 524211 Fax: 01522 537661
Email: reception@thegrandhotel.uk.com
Web: www.thegrandhotel.uk.com

Family-owned for over 70 years and renowned
throughout the county for its excellent cuisine.
Situated in the heart of the city.
SB £54 DB £69 HBS £45.50 HBD £91
B £7.50 L £9 D £13.75.
CC: MC Vi Am DC Swi Solo

How to get there: From A1 take A46. Signs for
Lincoln Central, then railway station.

Heritage Hotels – The White Hart

★★★

Bailgate, Lincoln, Lincolnshire, LN1 3AR
Tel: 01522 526222 Fax: 01522 531798
Email: heritagehotels-lincoln.whiteheart
@forte-hotels.com
Web: www.heritage-hotels.com
SB £50 DB £100 HBS £65 HBD £130
B £10.95 L £11.95 D £19.95.
CC: MC Vi Am DC Swi Delt JBC

How to get there: In Bailgate, midway between
the castle and the cathedral.

East Midlands

Castle Hotel

★★

Westgate, Lincoln, Lincolnshire, LN1 3AS
Tel: 01522 538801 Fax: 01522 575457
Email: rac@castlehouse.net
Web: www.castlehouse.net
Children minimum age: 10
SB £62 DB £79 HBS £77 HBD £109
B £5.95 D £17.90.
CC: MC Vi Am DC Swi Delt JCB Electron Solo

How to get there: Signs to 'Lawn Visitors Centre'. At mini-roundabout, turn left. Hotel on left at end of Westgate.

Four Seasons

Scothern Lane, Dunholme, Lincoln, Lincolnshire, LN2 3PQ
Tel: 01673 860108 Fax: 01673 862784

Archers Lodge

♦♦♦♦

133 Yarborough Road, Lincoln, Lincolnshire, LN1 1HR
Tel: 01522 520201 Fax: 01522 520201
Email: archerslodge@fsmail.net
SB £25 DB £40 HBS £32 HBD £54
CC: MC Vi Swi Delt

How to get there: Off A46 bypass onto A57, to traffic lights. Left onto B1273. Archers Lodge halfway uphill on left.

D'isney Place Little Gem

♦♦♦♦

Eastgate, Lincoln, Lincolnshire, LN2 4AA
Tel: 01522 538881 Fax: 01522 511321
Email: info@disneyplacehotel.co.uk
Web: www.disneyplacehotel.co.uk
SB £61.50 DB £79 CC: MC Vi Am DC Swi Delt

How to get there: A15 Lincoln north, left at traffic lights, 100 yards on right.

Tennyson

♦♦♦♦

7 South Park Avenue, Lincoln, Lincolnshire, LN5 8EN
Tel: 01522 521624 Fax: 01522 521624
Email: tennyson.hotel@virgin.net
Web: freespace.virgin.net/tennyson. hotel

This professionally run hotel offers its guests warmth and comfort in a setting that gives an easy walk to all the attractions of the city.

SB £29 DB £40 B £5 CC: MC Vi

How to get there: South of city, on the A15, 15 metres from the high street roundabout.

Admiral Guest House

♦♦♦

16–18 Nelson Street, Lincoln, Lincolnshire, LN1 1PJ Tel: 01522 544467
SB £22 DB £38 HBS £29 HBD £45 CC: MC Vi

How to get there: 5 minutes walk from university situated on Carholme Road, close to A57.

Bradford Guest House

♦♦♦

67 Monks Road, Lincoln, Lincolnshire, LN2 5HP
Tel: 01522 523947
SB £20 DB £35 HBS £26 HBD £47 B £1 D £6.

How to get there: 300 yards east of Lindum Road/Silver Street junction.

Halfway Farm Motel

♦♦♦

A46 Swinderby, Lincoln, Lincolnshire, LN6 9HN
Tel: 01522 868749 Fax: 01522 868082
Closed Christmas to New Year
SB £20 DB £40 CC: MC Vi Am DC Swi Delt

How to get there: On A46 Newark to Lincoln. Halfway between, opposite disused RAF base.

Pines Guest House

♦♦♦

104 Yarborough Road, Lincoln, LN1 1HR
Tel: 01522 532985 Fax: 01522 532985
SB £17 DB £33 HBD £46 D £6.

How to get there: West side of city. Accessible from Relief Road. A15 – A46, A158, A607, A57. Close to city centre and cathedral.

East Midlands

Westlyn Guest House

♦♦♦

67 Carholme Road, Lincoln, Lincolnshire,
LN1 1RT
Tel: 01522 537468 Fax: 01522 537468
Email: westlyn.bblincoln@easicom.com
Web: www.smoothhound.co.uk/hotels/
westlyn.html
Children minimum age: 3
SB £20 DB £35

How to get there: Signs to Lincoln Central. Pass racecourse. Over pedestrian lights, 150m on left.

Loughborough, Leicestershire

Quorn Country Hotel

★★★★ ♖ ♖ ♖

66 Leicester Road, Quorn, Leicestershire, LE12 8BB
Tel: 01509 415050 Fax: 01509 415557

Originally Leicestershire's most exclusive private club, created around the original 17th century listed building. This 4-star hotel is set amidst 4 acres of beautiful landscaped gardens. Award-winning restaurant and brasserie.
CC: MC Vi Am DC Swi Delt

How to get there: A6 Loughborough to Leicester road, exit for Quorn (Quorndon) village. Hotel near village hall and opposite police station.
See advert on the right

Quality Hotel & Suites Loughborough

★★★

New Ashby Road, Loughborough,
Leicestershire, LE11 0EX
Tel: 01509 211800 Fax: 01509 211868
Email: admin@gb613.u-net.com

Web: www.choicehotels.com
SB £94.75 DB £127.50 HBS £109.25
HBD £156.50 B £6.75 L £9.50 D £14.50.
CC: MC Vi Am DC Swi Delt

How to get there: M1 J-23. A512 for Loughborough town centre. Hotel approx 800m left.

Cedars Hotel

★★ ♖

Cedar Road, Loughborough, Leicestershire,
LE11 2AB
Tel: 01509 214459 Fax: 01509 233573

Great Central

★★

Great Central Road, Loughborough,
Leicestershire, LE11 1RW
Tel: 01509 263405 Fax: 01509 264130
Email: reception@greatcentralhotel.co.uk
Web: www.greatcentralhotel.co.uk
SB £34 DB £48 HBS £40 HBD £60
B £5 L £3 D £6.
CC: MC Vi Swi Delt

How to get there: Leave town centre on A6 to Leicester. A60 to Nottingham. 1st left into Great Central Road. Hotel on left.

Originally Leicestershire's most exclusive private club, created around the original 17th-century listed building. This award-winning 4-star hotel is set amid 4 acres of beautiful landscaped gardens. Stay in one of our individually designed bedrooms, including 3 suites. Your stay will be enhanced by the hotel's two AA award-winning restaurants where you can choose between the intimate alcoves of the Shires Restaurant with its classical cuisine or the light conservatory atmosphere of the Orangery Brasserie with its selection of contemporary dishes.

Charnwood House
66 Leicester Road, Quorn LE12 8BB
Tel: 01509 415050   Fax: 01509 415557

De Montfort

♦♦♦

88 Leicester Road, Loughborough,
Leicestershire, LE11 2AQ
Tel: 01509 216061 Fax: 01509 233667
SB £28.35 DB £38.40 D £7.
CC: MC Vi Am DC Swi Delt

How to get there: On A6 Leicester Road, 5 mins
from town centre.

Garendon Park

♦♦♦

92 Leicester Road, Loughborough,
Leicestershire, LE11 2AQ
Tel: 01509 236557 Fax: 01509 265559
Email: info@garendonparkhotel.co.uk
Web: www.garendonparkhotel.co.uk
SB £35 DB £45 HBS £41 HBD £57 D £6.50.
CC: MC Vi DC Swi Delt Solo

How to get there: Exit M1 J-23, A512 to
Loughborough. Right at 2nd roundabout, left at
3rd, left at lights. Hotel on right near lights.

Louth, Lincolnshire

Beaumont

★★★

Victoria Road, Louth, Lincolnshire, LN11 0BX
Tel: 01507 605005 Fax: 01507 607768
Privately-owned luxury hotel with a warm and

cosy atmosphere situated on the outskirts of
Louth. Its English charm is enhanced by the
Italian touch of the owners. Outstanding cuisine.
SB £45 DB £65 L £7.95 D £7.95.
CC: MC Vi Am Swi Delt

Looking for great dining? Look for RAC Hotels
and Guest Accommodation displaying the
RAC Dining Award symbol in this Guide.

Market Harborough, Leicestershire

Sun Inn & Restaurant

★★

Main Street, Marston, Trussell, LE16 9TY
Tel: 01858 465531 Fax: 01858 433155
Email: manager@suninn.com
Web: www.suninn.com
SB £69 DB £138 HBS £89 HBD £99
B £5 L £3 D £7. CC: MC Vi Am DC Swi Delt

Matlock, Derbyshire

Heritage Hotels – The New Bath

★★★

New Bath Road, Matlock Bath, Derbyshire,
DE4 3PX
Tel: 0800 404040 Fax: 01629 580268
Email: heritagehotels_bath.matlock.new_bath
@forte-hotels.com
Web: www.heritage-hotels.com
SB £64 DB £128 HBS £79 HBD £158
B £10.95 L £2.95 D £20.95.
CC: MC Vi Am DC Swi Delt Solo

How to get there: M1 J-28. A38, then A610. To
Little Chef at Ambergate. Turn right. Hotel
approximately 20 minutes along A6 on left.

Riber Hall

★★★

Matlock, Derbyshire, DE4 5JU
Tel: 01629 582795 Fax: 01629 580475
Email: info@riber-hall.co.uk
Web: www.riber-hall.co.uk
Children minimum age: 10
SB £95 DB £129 HBS £128.50 HBD £190.50
B £8 L £13 D £28.50.
CC: MC Vi Am DC Swi Delt JCB

How to get there: One mile off A615 at Tansley,
signed to Riber.

Coach House

♦♦♦

Home Farm, Main Road, Lea, nr Matlock,
Derbyshire, DE4 5GJ
Tel: 01629 534346
DB £45 B £5.95 L £6.50 D £6.50.
CC: MC Vi Swi Delt

How to get there: A6 from Derby for Matlock.
Turn for Crich at Cromford. After a mile, turn left

at Leabridge for Lea and Riber. The Coach House is ³/₄ mile on left.

Hillview

80 New Street, Matlock, Derbyshire, DE4 3FH
Tel: 01629 583662 Fax: 01629 583662
Email: hillview@quista.net
Children minimum age: 5
Closed November to February
SB £20 DB £40

How to get there: From Matlock centre (A6, Crown Square), proceed up hill, fourth right into New Street. Hillview on corner.

Jackson Tor House

76 Jackson Road, Matlock, Derbyshire, DE4 3JQ
Tel: 01629 582348 Fax: 01629 582348

Melbourne, Derbyshire

Melbourne Arms

92 Ashby Road, Melbourne, Derbyshire, DE73 1ES
Tel: 01332 864949

Melton Mowbray, Leicestershire

Stapleford Park

★★★★

Stapleford, Melton Mowbray, Leicestershire, LE14 2EF
Tel: 01572 787522 Fax: 01572 787322
Web: www.stapleford.co.uk

Neither words nor pictures can adequately describe this most imposing of Grade I Listed 15th-18th century stately home. Set in 500 acres of parkland, Stapleford Park boasts a lake and private 18-hole championship golf course.

SB £205 DB £205 D £44.
CC: MC Vi Am DC Swi

How to get there: From Melton Mowbray, follow ring road and signs for Grantham. Stay in left-hand lane until Grantham Road turns left: don't turn left, but drive through traffic lights. Signs for B676 to Stapleford. After 4 miles turn right at signpost to Stapleford.

Milford, Derbyshire

Strutt Arms

The Bridge, Milford, Derbyshire, DE56 0QW
Tel: 01332 840240 Fax: 01332 841758

Northampton, Northamptonshire

Northampton Marriott

★★★★

Eagle Drive, Northampton, Northants, NN4 7HW
Tel: 01604 768700 Fax: 01604 479231
Email: northampton@marriotthotels.co.uk
Web: www.marriott.com

Superbly located within the heart of Northamptonshire, with an abundance of great attractions nearby. Excellent shopping a short drive away. A relaxing and comfortable hotel.
SB £105.50 DB £116 B £10.50 L £15 D £22.75.
CC: MC Vi Am DC Swi

How to get there: M1 J-15. A508 /A45 to Northampton. Slip road to Delapre golf/Brackmills.

Quality Hotel Northampton

★★★

Ashley Way, Weston Favell, Northampton,
Northamptonshire, NN3 3EA
Tel: 01604 739955
Email: admin@gb070.u-net.com
Web: www.choicehotels.com

SB £91.50 DB £114 B £9.75 L £5.95 D £17.95.
CC: MC Vi Am DC Swi Delt

How to get there: M1 J-15. A508 to Nipton and
A45 to Wellingborough, then A43 to Kettering
and Weston Favell turn-off.

Whittlebury Hall

Whittlebury, near Towcester, Northamptonshire,
NN12 8QH
Tel: 01327 857857 Fax: 01327 857867
Email: sales@whittleburyhall.co.uk
SB £100 DB £130 B £11 L £16 D £27.50.
CC: MC Vi Am Swi Delt

How to get there: Near Silvertown and
Towcester, off the A413 in Whittlebury village
overlooking the golf course.

Poplars Hotel

◆◆◆◆

Cross Street, Moulton, Northampton,
Northamptonshire, NN3 7RZ
Tel: 01604 643983 Fax: 01604 790223
Email: poplars@btclick.com
SB £47.50 DB £59.50 HBS £60.50 HBD £83.50
D £13. CC: MC Vi Am

How to get there: 4 miles northeast of
Northampton in old part of Moulton village, just
off A43.

Nottingham, Nottinghamshire

Bestwood Lodge

★★★

Bestwood Country Park, Arnold, Nottingham,
Nottinghamshire, NG5 8NE
Tel: 0115 920 3011 Fax: 0115 967 0409

Novotel

★★★

Bostock Lane, Long Eaton, Derbyshire,
NG10 4EP
Tel: 0115 9465111 Fax: 0115 9465900
Email: h0507@accor-hotels.com
Web: www.novotel.com
DB £59 B £9.25 D £11. CC: MC Vi Am DC Swi Delt

How to get there: Between Nottingham and
Derby, M1 J-25. Direction Long Eaton.

Strathdon Hotel

★★★

Derby Road, Nottingham, Nottinghamshire,
NG1 5FT
Tel: 0115 941 8501 Fax: 0115 948 3725
Email: info@strathdon-hotel-nottingham.com
SB £79.50 DB £114 HBS £95.50 HBD £150
B £9.50 L £11 D £16. CC: MC Vi Am DC Swi Delt

How to get there: On the main road into Nottingham, off A52 from M1 J-25 (S) or J-26 (N).

Westminster Hotel

★★★

312 Mansfield Road, Nottingham,
Nottinghamshire, NG5 2EF
Tel: 0115 955 5000 Fax: 0115 955 5005
Email: mail@westminster-hotel.co.uk
Web: www.westminster-hotel.co.uk
SB £83.50 DB £107 HBS £98.50 HBD £137
B £7.50 L £5 D £15. CC: MC Vi Am DC Swi Delt

How to get there: M1 J-26. A610 to Nottingham
centre. Left onto A6130. Signs for A60 north
(Mansfield Road).
See advert opposite

Balmoral Hotel

★★

55–57 Loughborough Road, West Bridgford,
Nottingham, Nottinghamshire, NG2 7LA
Tel: 0115 9552992 Fax: 0115 9552991
Email: balmoralhotel55@hotmail.com
Web: www.smoothhound.co.uk
SB £27.50 DB £47.50 HBS £37.50 HBD £62.50
B £5 D £8.50.
CC: MC Vi Am Swi Delt Solo, JCB, Electron

How to get there: From south, M1 J-24. A453,
then B679, then A60. From north, M1 J-25. A52
then A60. Hotel close Trent Bridge and cricket
ground on A60.

Westminster Hotel

East Midlands

Conveniently located for Nottingham's tourist attractions, its celebrated shopping centre and wealth of sporting venues, our family owned and run hotel is decorated and equipped to the highest standards. Included in our 72 rooms are 2 Four-Poster bedded rooms and also 19 Superior rooms which are air-conditioned and offer the added attraction of king-size beds, dedicated PC/Fax connection points and, in the bathroom, the luxury of a shower unit which provides a relaxing steam shower. Dinner in the informal atmosphere of our highly acclaimed restaurant, where excellent food and good wines are sensibly priced, will simply add to the enjoyment of your stay. The hotel also has 5 meeting rooms, including a function suite for up to 60, all of which are air-conditioned.

312 Mansfield Road, Nottingham NG5 2EF
Tel: 0115 955 5000   Fax: 0115 955 5005
Email: mail@westminster-hotel.co.uk
Website: www.westminster-hotel.co.uk

The Westminster Hotel Ltd. Registered Office: 312 Mansfield Road, Nottingham NG5 2EF. Registered in England No. 2311762

Haven

★★

Grantham Road (A52), Whatton,
Nottinghamshire, NG13 9EU
Tel: 01949 850800 Fax: 01949 851454
SB £37.50 DB £49.50 B £6 L £5 D £6.
CC: MC Vi Am DC Swi Delt

How to get there: On A52, halfway between
Nottingham and Grantham, close to Holme
Pierrepont Watersports Centre.

Rufford Hotel

★★

Melton Road, West Bridgford, Nottingham,
Nottinghamshire, NG2 7NE
Tel: 0115 981 4202 Fax: 0115 945 5801

Stage Hotel

★★

5 Gregory Road, Nottingham, Nottinghamshire,
NG7 6LB
Tel: 01159 603261 Fax: 01159 691040
SB £44.50 DB £54.50 HBS £54.50 HBD £74.50
B £4.25 L £5.95 D £11.95.
CC: MC Vi Am DC Swi Delt JCB

How to get there: M1 J-26. A610 to city. Over
two roundabouts. Signs for Park and Ride onto
Gregory Boulevard.

Andrews Private Hotel

◆◆◆

310 Queens Road, Beeston, Nottingham,
NG9 1JA
Tel: 0115 925 4902 Fax: 0115 925 4902
Children minimum age: 9
SB £22 DB £40 HBS £30 HBD £57 D £8.50.

How to get there: M1 J25. A52 for Nottingham.
Over two roundabouts, right at second set of
lights onto B6006. Right at fourth lights, hotel
200m on right.

Fairhaven Private Hotel

◆◆◆

19 Meadow Road, Beeston, Rylands,
Nottingham, NG9 1JP
Tel: 0115 922 7509 Fax: 0115 943 6217
Email: booking@fairhaven.fsnet.co.uk
Web: www.fairhaven.fsnet.co.uk
SB £23 DB £44

How to get there: M1 J-25. A52 for Nottingham
for 4¹/₂ miles. Right at signposts for Beeston
town centre. Follow road for 1¹/₂ miles. Hotel on
left, 300 yards past Beeston rail station.

Royston Hotel

◆◆◆

326 Mansfield Road, Nottingham,
Nottinghamshire, NG5 2EF
Tel: 0115 962 2947 Fax: 0115 956 5018

Oakham, Rutland

Boultons

★★★

4 Catmose Street, Oakham, Rutland, LE15 6HW
Tel: 01572 722844 Fax: 01572 724473
Email: gm@boultonshotel.co.uk
Web: www.boultonshotel.co.uk

A welcoming country house ambience. Intimate
lounge bar and restaurant. Private dining and
meeting rooms. Friendly and attentive sevice.
A minute's drive into rolling countryside.
SB £35 DB £70 HBS £45 HBD £45 B £6.50
L £6.50 D £15. CC: MC Vi Am DC Swi Delt

How to get there: In Oakham town at junction
A606/A6003. From A1(N) B668. From A1(S)
A606. From Nottingham or Kettering A6003.

Scunthorpe, Lincolnshire

Forest Pines

★★★★

Ermine Street, Broughton, Brigg, Lincolnshire,
DN20 0AQ
Tel: 01652 650770 Fax: 01652 650495
Email: enquiries@forestpines.co.uk
Web: www.forestpines.co.uk
SB £90 DB £100 CC: MC Vi Am DC Swi Delt

How to get there: Onto M180 J-5. Exit J-4.
At roundabout take 1st exit to Scunthorpe, at
next roundabout take 2nd exit. Hotel on left-
hand side.

Hanover International Scunthorpe

★★★

Rowland Road, Scunthorpe, North Lincolnshire,
DN16 1SU

Tel: 01724 842223 Fax: 01724 280646

HANOVER INTERNATIONAL

This small, friendly hotel set in the heart of the
garden town of Scunthorpe is an ideal base to
explore an area of rural tranquility and natural
beauty.

SB £80 DB £87.50 B £7 L £5 D £14.
CC: MC Vi Am DC Swi Delt

♨ 🗓 🛏 ❊ 🍵 ⌨ ☎ P ⛌ ☪ 🐎 ♬ ❤ ▦ ⛏
How to get there: M180 J-3. Right at
roundabout. At next roundabout take third exit,
second left into Brumby Wood Lane. Straight
over next roundabout. Hotel on right.

Skegness, Lincolnshire

Crown

★★★

Drummond Road, Skegness, Lincolnshire,
PE25 3AB

Tel: 0500 007274 Fax: 01754 610847

Vine Hotel

★★★

Vine Road, Skegness, Lincolnshire, PE25 3DB

Tel: 01754 763018 Fax: 01754 769845

Crawford

♦♦♦

South Parade, Skegness, PE25 3HR

Tel: 01754 764215

Book with RAC Hotel Reservations and check
the latest offers available. Call 0870 603 9109
and quote 'RAC Guide 2001'

The Saxby

♦♦♦

Saxby Avenue, Skegness,
Lincolnshire, PE25 3LG

Tel: 01754 763905 Fax: 01754 763905
SB £24 DB £48 HBS £32 HBD £64
B £3.50 L £5 D £7. CC: MC Vi Delt

♿ ❊ ⊗ 🍵 ⌨ P ⛌ ☪ 🐎 ♬ ❤ ▦ ▮

Sleaford, Lincolnshire

Carre Arms

★★

1 Mareham Lane, Sleaford, Lincolnshire,
NG34 7JP

Tel: 01529 303156 Fax: 01529 303139
Email: cunago@carrearms.freeserve.co.uk
SB £50 DB £70 B £9.50 L £11.50 D £15.50.
CC: MC Vi Swi Delt

🍵 ⌨ 🍴 ☎ ⅃ P ⛌ ☪ 🐎 ♬ ❤ ▦ ▮
How to get there: 3 mins from Sleaford rail
station, easy access from Lincoln, Grantham
(A1), Boston (A15) and Newark (A1).

South Normanton, Derbyshire

Swallow Hotel

★★★★ ⓡ

Carter Lane East, South Normanton, Derbyshire,
DE55 2EH

Tel: 01773 812000 Fax: 01773 580032
To become Renaissance, Spring 2001.
SB £115 DB £130 B £9.75 L £12.95 D £18.95.
CC: MC Vi Am DC Swi Delt

♨ ♿ ❊ ⊗ 🍵 ⌨ ☎ ❊ ⅃ P ⛌ ☪ 🐎 ♬ ❤
👁 ▦ ▮ "Y" ⛾
How to get there: M1 J-28. A38 towards
Mansfield and first left down Carter Lane East.
Hotel 200 yards on left.

Spalding, Lincolnshire

Cley Hall

★★

22 High Street, Spalding, Lincolnshire,
PE11 1TX

Tel: 01775 725157 Fax: 01775 710785
Email: cleyhall@enterprise.net
SB £50 DB £85 B £8 L £6 D £17.
CC: MC Vi Am DC Swi Delt

♿ ⌨ ❊ ⊗ 🍵 ⌨ ☎ P ⛌ ☪ 🐎 ♬ ❤ ▦ ▮
How to get there: Hotel is on one-way system,
approached via Commercial Road/Albert Street
on A1073 to Peterborough.

East Midlands

Woodlands

★★

80 Pinchbeck Road, Spalding, Lincolnshire,
PE11 1QF

Tel: 01775 769933 Fax: 01775 711369

Travel Stop

♦♦

Locksmill Farm, 50 Cowbit Road, Spalding,
Lincolnshire, PE11 2RJ

Tel: 01775 767290 Fax: 01775 767716

Email: travelstopraclodg@btinternet.com

SB £40 DB £55 B £2.50 CC: MC Vi Am

♿ 🐾 🐕 ⊗ ⊜ 🖵 🔌 P 🚿 ☕ 🐎 🎠 🐟 ▮

How to get there: On B1173, ³/₄ mile from centre
of Spalding, by side of River Welland.

Stamford, Lincolnshire

George of Stamford

★★★ 🍴🍴🍴

71 St Martins, Stamford, Lincolnshire, PE9 2LB

Tel: 01780 750750 Fax: 01780 750701

Email: reservations@georgehotelofstamford.com

Web: www.georgehotelofstamford.com

SB £78 DB £103 B £8.50 L £14.50

CC: MC Vi Am DC Swi Delt

🏷 🐾 🖵 ☎ 🔌 P 🚿 ☕ 🐎 🎠 🐟 ▥ ▮▮▮

How to get there: A1, onto B1081 to Stamford at
roundabout. Hotel on left at first set of lights.

Crown

★★ 🍴

All Saints Place, Stamford, Lincolnshire,
PE9 2AG

Tel: 01780 763136 Fax: 01780 756111

Email: thecrownhotel@excite.com

This friendly town centre hotel offers a warm
welcome and excellent service. Popular with
locals, the restaurant provides high quality food
and the bar has a selection of real ales.

SB £50 DB £65 B £5.75 L £5 D £8.

CC: MC Vi Am DC Swi Delt

🏷 🐾 🖵 ☎ P 🚿 ☕ 🐎 🐟 🎠 🐟 ▮▮▮

How to get there: From A1 signs for Stamford
Town Centre. Crown next to All Saints Church.

Lady Anne's

★★

37–38 High Street, Saint Martins, Stamford,
Lincolnshire, PE9 2LJ

Tel: 01780 481184 Fax: 01780 65422

Candlesticks Hotel & Restaurant

♦♦

1 Church Lane, Stamford, Lincolnshire, PE9 2JU

Tel: 01780 764033 Fax: 01780 756071

Email: pinto@breathmail.net

A small family hotel run by Mr & Mrs Pinto for
25 years, providing freshly cooked food and
luxury bedrooms with fridge and Sky TV. Dine in
comfortable and elegant surroundings and enjoy
excellent cuisine at a price you can afford.

SB £35 DB £50.55 HBS £47.50 HBD £80
L £12. D £14.50.

CC: MC Vi Am Swi Delt

⊗ ⊜ 🖵 ☎ P 🚿 ☕ 🐎 🐟 🐟 ▥ ▮▮▮

How to get there: From A1 down St Martins
High Street. Left into Church Street by
St Martins Church.

Stretton, Leicestershire

Ram Jam Inn

★★

Great North Road, Stretton, nr Oakham,
Leicestershire, LE15 7QX

Tel: 01780 410776 Fax: 01780 410361

Email: rji@rutnet.co.uk

SB £53 DB £72 B £2.95 L £5.45 D £6.95.

CC: MC Vi Am Swi Delt Solo Electron

⊜ 🖵 ☎ P 🚿 ☕ 🐎 🐟 🐟 ▥ ▮▮▮

How to get there: On A1 north, look for hotel
sign. Through service station, just past B668
turn off. Southbound, take B668 exit and follow
signs for Oakham.

The motoring questionnaire

	Yes	No

1 When you're driving to a place in the UK or Europe that you've never been to before, would you like directions and a map created to help you?

2 Would you like to be told, while driving in your car, the latest traffic congestion hot spots and how to avoid them?

3 If driving abroad would you like to know if you need an International Drivers' Licence or special equipment?

4 Want to get competitive insurance quotes from a reputable company?

5 Have you ever considered how to be a safer driver?

6 Know someone who needs help to pass their driving test?

7 Are you wondering whether that used car will turn out to be a ringer?

8 Need to buy something for your motor?

If you answered yes to any of these questions please turn over...

A to B - we RAC to it

You said yes...

If you answered yes to any of the questions overleaf we're delighted to tell you that the RAC website has something for you.

You could be delighted too by winning a £500 holiday voucher (redeemable against short breaks, cruises, fly-drive holidays, package holidays, etc.) in our quarterly online prize draw.

Simply visit http://www.rac.co.uk/prizedrawof.htm to enter.

Motoring and Travel

RAC's easy-to-use website serves all your motoring and travel needs from products to advice, including the only free pan-European route planner with live traffic news.

Check it out at www.rac.co.uk

Join RAC

Plan Route

Check Traffic

Find Hotel

Prize Draw rules:

Last prize draw, end of 2001. The competition comprises one £500 gift voucher per quarter redeemable against RAC holidays. There is no cash prize or alternative. Entrants must be 18 years or over, and UK residents.
The competition is not open to RAC employees, suppliers, associated companies, or their families. Normal contest rules apply and decisions are final.

A to B - we RAC to it

Sutton in the Elms, Leicestershire

Mill On The Soar

★★

B4114 Coventry Road, Sutton in the Elms,
Leicestershire, LE9 6QD
Tel: 01455 282419 Fax: 01455 285937

Sutton-on-Sea, Lincolnshire

Grange and Links Hotel

★★★ ♟

Sea Lane, Sandilands, Mablethorpe,
Lincolnshire, LN12 2RA
Tel: 01507 441334 Fax: 01507 443033
Email: grangelinks@ic24.net
Web: www.grange+links.com
SB £59.50 DB £71.50 B £7.50 L £6 D £12.
CC: MC Vi Am DC Swi Delt

How to get there: From south, A16 to Spilsby
and Ulceby Cross. From north, A16 to Louth
and Ulceby Cross, then A1104 to Alford and
A1111 to Sutton-on-Sea.

Athelstone Lodge

♦ ♦ ♦

25 Trusthorpe Road, Sutton-on-Sea,
Lincolnshire, LN12 2LR
Tel: 01507 441521

Uppingham, Rutland

Lake Isle

★★ ♟ ♟

16 High Street East, Uppingham, Rutland,
LE15 9PZ
Tel: 01572 822951 Fax: 01572 822951
SB £55 DB £74 HBS £70 HBD £59
L £7 D £18.50. CC: MC Vi Am DC

How to get there: Via Queen Street to rear of
property for parking. On foot, via Reeves Yard.

Old Rectory

♦ ♦ ♦

Belton-in-Rutland, Uppingham, Rutland,
LE15 9LE
Tel: 01572 717279 Fax: 01572 717343
Email: bb@stablemate.demon.co.uk
SB £20 DB £38 B £7 CC: MC Vi

How to get there: From Leicester A47 take
1st turn to Belton-in-Rutland village. House
on left, approx 500m.

Weedon Bec, Northamptonshire

Globe Hotel

★★

High Street, Weedon Bec, Northamptonshire,
NN7 4QD
Tel: 01327 340336 Fax: 01327 349058

Woodhall Spa, Lincolnshire

Petwood House

★★★ ♟

Stixwould Road, Woodhall Spa, Lincolnshire,
LN10 6QF
Tel: 01526 352411 Fax: 01526 353473
Web: www.petwood.co.uk

A luxurious hotel, set in 30 acres, dating back to
the early 1900s. 50 en-suite bedrooms and
popular restaurant. 18 miles from Lincoln and
close to championship golf course.
SB £78 DB £105 HBS £93 HBD £135 B £8.50
L £12.50 D £18.50. CC: MC Vi Am DC Swi Delt

How to get there: From Sleaford, A153 to
Tattershall. Turn left onto B1192 to Woodhall
Spa. From Lincoln, travel south on B1188 and
B1191.

Worksop, Nottinghamshire

Charnwood

★★★ ♟

Sheffield Road, Blyth, Worksop,
Nottinghamshire, S81 8HF
Tel: 01909 591610 Fax: 01909 591429

Lion Hotel

★★★

112 Bridge Street, Worksop, Nottinghamshire,
S80 1HT
Tel: 01909 477925 Fax: 01909 479038

West Midlands

Tewkesbury

The West Midlands region encompasses the broadest range of counties in England, from the industrial to the agricultural. Surrounding the actual county of West Midlands (created in the late 1960s) are the similarly industrialised areas of the

Warwick Castle

Black Country of Staffordshire and north Warwickshire, but sharp contrast is provided by the rural and farming towns of Shropshire, Herefordshire, Worcestershire, south Warwickshire and Gloucestershire.

Shropshire epitomises the extremes; while largely agricultural, it also includes Ironbridge, near the modern town of Telford, which is regarded as the birthplace of the industrial revolution, thanks to Joseph Telford's innovative bridge spanning the River Severn.

On Shropshire's southern border, Ludlow has recently become known for its gourmet restaurants, yet its 930-year-old castle is an enduring tourist attraction.

Other well-known castles open to the public are Warwick on the delightful banks of the Avon, and Kenilworth. These are the places that inspired Shakespeare, but American visitors to the Bard's Stratford-upon-Avon may be amused to discover that John Harvard, founder of the US law college, was also born nearby.

A major export to the Americas is the hardy, naturally raised Hereford breed of cattle... although some may find the cider more attractive. Hereford Cider Museum traces the beverage's history from cottage brewing to the modern industrial process that converts local apples into the 68 million litres of liquid held in Hereford's cider vats. Hereford cathedral holds a Mappa Mundi from the fifth century, one of the original maps of the world that monks painstakingly copied before the advent of the printing press.

The heavy industry of the past used canals to transport coal, clay, iron ore, limestone and finished goods, but today the manmade waterways are navigated by holiday-makers. Birmingham's canal banks were among the first areas to be redeveloped in the 1990s; extensive reconstruction still in progress is helping the city centre to cast off its grim, grey image in favour of open spaces and clean, modern architecture. Beyond the city, concerts, trade shows and exhibitions at the National Exhibition Centre attract some five million visitors per year.

Staffordshire's biggest draw is undoubtedly Alton Towers' array of white-knuckle rides, but the county's historical nickname of 'The Potteries' still holds true. Spode, Royal Doulton and Wedgwood are synonymous with the finest earthenware, porcelain and bone china; each has a visitors' centre.

Southwards in Worcester is the Royal Porcelain Museum; the ancient city is also known for its glove-making, Saxon-era cathedral and the distinctive Worcestershire sauce. It hosts the Three Choirs Festival every three years, sharing Europe's oldest music festival with Hereford and Gloucester. The Cotswolds and Forest of Dean suggest Gloucestershire's rural nature, but the Jetage Museum reminds us that Sir Frank Whittle's engine was tested at Brockworth and that today's local aerospace companies are a legacy of the Gloster Aircraft Company.

West Midlands

Alveston, Gloucestershire

Alveston House

★★★ ☗☗
Alveston, Gloucestershire, BS35 2LA
Tel: 01454 415050 Fax: 01454 415425
Email: info@alvestonhousehotel.co.uk
Web: www.alvestonhousehotel.co.uk
SB £84.50 DB £94.50 HBS £104.25 HBD £134
B £5.75 L £9.50 D £19.75.
CC: MC Vi Am DC Swi Delt

How to get there: On main A38 at Alveston.

Balsall Common, West Midlands

Haigs

★★ ☗☗☗
273 Kenilworth Road, Balsall Common,
West Midlands, CV7 7EL
Tel: 01676 533004 Fax: 01676 535132
Closed Christmas to New Year

Family-run hotel recently refurbished to a high
standard. Award-winning restaurant. Ideally
situated 5 miles from the NEC and at hub of
Midland motorways. Close to Warwick and
Stratford-upon-Avon.
SB £63 DB £85 HBS £83 HBD £125 B £9.95
L £15.50 D £18.50. CC: MC Vi Am Swi Delt

How to get there: On A452.

Berkeley, Gloucestershire

Prince of Wales

★★★
Berkeley Road, Berkeley, GL13 9HD
Tel: 01453 810474 Fax: 01453 511370
SB £65 DB £81 B £6 L £10 D £10.
CC: MC Vi Am DC Swi Delt

How to get there: On the A38 between M5 J-13
and J-14.

Bewdley, Worcestershire

George Hotel

★★
Load Street, Bewdley, DY12 2AW
Tel: 01299 402117 Fax: 01299 401269
Email: enquiries@georgehotelbewdley.co.uk
Web: www.georgehotelbewdley.co.uk
SB £45 DB £63 HBS £54.50 HBD £79.50
B £6.50 L £9.95 D £12.50.
CC: MC Vi Swi Delt

How to get there: Exit M5 J-3, A456 to
Bewdley; M5 J-6, A449, A456 to Bewdley;
M42 J-1, A448, A456 to Bewdley.

Bibury, Gloucestershire

Bibury Court

★★★ ☗☗☗
Bibury, Gloucestershire, GL7 5NT
Tel: 01285 740337 Fax: 01285 740660
Email: reservations@biburycourt.co.uk
Web: www.biburycourt.co.uk
SB £85 DB £120 HBS £110 HBD £82.50
B £7.50 L £10 D £30.
CC: MC Vi Am DC Swi Delt

How to get there: Situated just off the B4425 in
the centre of the village, behind the church.

Birmingham

Birmingham Marriott

12 Hagley Road, Birmingham, B16 8SJ
Tel: 0121 452 1144 Fax: 0121 456 3442
SB £170 DB £195 HBS £202.50 HBD £260
B £12.75 L £18.50 D £32.50.
CC: MC Vi Am DC Swi Delt

How to get there: Approaching Five Ways
Roundabout from the city centre, take the 4th
exit into Calthorpe Road. Take the slip road on
the right after you pass the clock.

Burlington

★★★★ ☗
6 Burlington Arcade, 126 New Street,
Birmingham, B2 4JQ
Tel: 0121 643 9191 Fax: 0121 628 5005
SB £153.50 B £13.50 L £15.95 D £19.95.
CC: MC Vi Am DC Swi Delt

Copthorne

★★★★ ⓡ

Paradise Circus, Birmingham, West Midlands,
B3 3HJ
Tel: 0121 200 2727 Fax: 0121 200 1197
Email: sales.birmingham@mill-cop.com
Web: www.stay.with-us.com
B £12 L £14 D £18. CC: MC Vi Am DC Swi Delt
⚐ ⅃ ⅃⅃ ⊗ ⊜ ⬛ ☎ ⅃ ▣ ⚇ ⁙C ⚘ ♪ ⌇ ⌁
⌁⌁⌁ ⍭ ⍉
How to get there: Situated by Centenary
Square, approximately 10 minutes from M6 J-6,
follow city centre route (A38)

Great Barr Hotel

★★★

Pear Tree Drive, Great Barr, Birmingham,
B43 6HS
Tel: 0121 357 1141 Fax: 0121 357 7557
Email: sales@thegreatbarrhotel.co.uk
Web: www.thegreatbarrhotel.co.uk
SB £77.95 DB £93.95 HBS £95.45
HBD £128.95 B £6.95 L £12.95 D £17.50.
CC: MC Vi Am DC Swi Delt
⊜ ⬛ ☎ ▣⌁ ⚇ ⁙C ⚘ ♪ ⌁ ⌁⌁⌁ ⍭
How to get there: Exit M6 J-7, A34 to
Birmingham. Left at lights onto Newton Road.
After 1¼ miles, right into Pear Tree Drive.

Novotel Birmingham Airport

★★★

Birmingham International Airport, Birmingham,
West Midlands, B26 3QL
Tel: 0121 780 5700 Fax: 0121 782 2724
Email: h1158-gm@accor-hotels.com

SB £112 DB £121 B £10.50 L £14.50 D £19.50.
CC: MC Vi Am DC Swi Delt
⅃ ⅃⅃ ⚘ ⊗ ⊜ ⬛ ☎ ❋ ⅃ ▣⌁ ⚇ ⁙C ⚘ ♪ ⌁
⌁⌁⌁ ⍭ ℂ
How to get there: Exit M42 J-6, A45 to
Birmingham. Left slip-road, and follow signs to
airport terminal; the hotel is located immediately
opposite the terminal.

Novotel Birmingham Centre

★★★

70 Broad Street, Birmingham, B1 2HT
Tel: 0121 643 2000 Fax: 0121 643 9796
Email: h1077@accor-hotels.com
Web: www.novotel.com
SB £104 DB £114 B £10.25 L £10 D £15.
CC: MC Vi Am DC Swi Delt
⅃ ⅃⅃ ⚘ ⊗ ⊜ ⬛ ☎ ❋ ⅃ ▣ ⚇ ⁙C ⚘ ♪ ⌁
⌁⌁⌁ ⍭ ⍉
How to get there: Exit M6 J-6, follow A38(M).
Follow signs for Convention Centre; Novotel is
200m along street from Centre.

Portland

★★★

313 Hagley Road, Edgbaston, Birmingham,
West Midlands, B16 9LQ
Tel: 0121 455 0535 Fax: 0121 456 1841
Email: sales@portland-hotel.demon.co.uk
Web: www.birmingham.co.uk/portlandhotel
SB £52.45 DB £62.95 HBS £66.95 HBD £91.95
B £6.95 L £12.95 D £14.95.
CC: MC Vi Am DC Swi Delt
⅃⅃ ⊗ ⊜ ⬛ ☎ ▣⌁ ⚇ ⌁ ⌁⌁⌁ ⍭ ⍲
How to get there: Hotel is situated on A456,
Hagley Road into Birmingham city centre from
M5 J-3.

Quality Hotel (formerly Cobden)

★★★

116 Hagley Road, Birmingham, West Midlands,
B16 9NZ
Tel: 0121 454 6621 Fax: 0121 456 2935
Email: admin@gb605.u-net.com
Web: www.choicehotelseurope.com

SB £79.75 DB £101 HBS £94.25 HBD £130
B £9.75 L £7.50 D £14.50.
CC: MC Vi Am DC Swi Delt
⚐ ⅃ ⅃⅃ ⚘ ⚘ ⊗ ⊜ ⬛ ☎ ⅃ ▣⌁ ⚇ ⁙C ⚘
♪ ⚘ ⌁⌁⌁ ⍭ ⍲ SPA ⍭ ⍉
How to get there: Exit M6 J-6 and head for
central Birmingham. Right onto ring road and
right onto A456 to Kidderminster (Hagley Road).

West Midlands

Quality Inn & Suites

★★★

267 Hagley Road, Birmingham, West Midlands,
B16 9NA
Tel: 0121 454 8071 Fax: 0121 455 6149
Email: admin@gb606.u-net.com
Web: www.choicehotelseurope.com

Well-known friendly and comfortable hotel.
Free car park, own grounds. Fantastic central
location with ease to Cadbury World, Warwick
Castle, ICC, NEC etc. Rates available.
SB £79.95 DB £101 HBS £94.25 HBD £130
B £9.75 L £7.50 D £14.50.
CC: MC Vi Am DC Swi Delt

How to get there: Exit M6 J-6 and head for
central Birmingham. Right onto ring road. Turn
right onto A456 to Kidderminster (Hagley Road).

Quality Sutton Court

★★★

66 Lichfield Road, Sutton Coldfield,
West Midlands, B74 2NA
Tel: 0121 354 4991 Fax: 0121 355 0083
Email: reservations@sutton-court-hotel.co.uk
Web: www.sutton-court-hotel.co.uk/index.htm
SB £95 DB £118 HBS £112 HBD £153
B £9.50 D £17. CC: MC Vi Am DC Swi Delt

How to get there: Exit M42 J-9, A446 towards
Lichfield. A453 towards Sutton Coldfield, hotel
is on left at second set of lights.

Beechwood

★★

201 Bristol Road, Edgbaston, Birmingham,
B5 7UB
Tel: 0121 440 2133 Fax: 0121 446 4549
SB £35 DB £50
L £7.50 D £5. CC: MC Vi Am DC Swi Delt

How to get there: From city centre, proceed on
Bristol Road past traffic lights at McDonalds,
hotel is on right, one mile from city centre.

Greswolde Park

★★

980 Warwick Road, Acocks Green, Birmingham,
West Midlands, B27 6QG
Tel: 0121 706 4068 Fax: 0121 706 0649
Email: jeff@greswolde.freeserve.co.uk
Web: www.greswolde.freeserve.co.uk
SB £35 DB £45 L £6 D £6.
CC: MC Vi Swi Delt Solo

How to get there: Exit M42 J-6, A45 to
Birmingham. Fork left to Acocks Green, left at
island. Straight down to T-junction, turn right.
Second hotel on right.

Heath Lodge

★★

117 Coleshill Road, Marston Green,
Birmingham, B37 7HT
Tel: 0121 779 2218 Fax: 0121 779 2218
Email: reception@heathlodgehotel.
        freeserve.co.uk
Web: www.heathlodgehotel.freeserve.co.uk

Heath Lodge is a licensed family-run and
friendly hotel. It's only 1½ miles from NEC,
Birmingham Airport (long-term parking) and the
M6 J-4 and M42 J-6.
SB £54 DB £69 HBS £70 HBD £99 D £10.
CC: MC Vi Am Swi Delt

Hotel Clarine

★★

229 Hagley Road, Birmingham, B16 9RP
Tel: 0121 454 6514 Fax: 0121 456 2722
Email: reception@kyriadbirmingham.co.uk
Web: www.kyriadbirmingham.co.uk

Campanile hotels offer comfortable and convenient budget accommodation and a traditional French-style Bistro providing freshly cooked food for breakfast, lunch and dinner. All rooms en-suite with tea/coffee-making facilities, DDT and TV with Sky channels.
SB £40 DB £50 HBS £51 HBD £70 D £7.45.
CC: MC Vi Am DC Swi Delt

How to get there: M6 J-6, A38 for city centre. Over flyover, 3 underpasses, right at main lights, 2nd exit at roundabout. Hotel 1 mile on right.

Woodlands Hotel & Restaurant

★★

379-381 Hagley Road, Edgbaston, B17 8DL
Tel: 0121 420 2341 Fax: 0121 429 3935
Web: www.thewoodlandshotel.co.uk
CC: MC Vi Am

See advert on this page

Campanile

Travel Accommodation
Chester Street, Aston Locks, B6 4BC
Tel: 0121 359 3330 Fax: 0121 359 3330

Campanile hotels offer comfortable and convenient budget accommodation and a traditional French-style Bistro providing freshly cooked food for breakfast, lunch and dinner. All rooms en-suite with tea/coffee-making facilities, DDT and TV with Sky channels.
SB £45.90 DB £50.85 HBS £54 HBD £36 B £4.95 L £5.95 D £6.50.
CC: MC Vi Am DC Swi Delt

How to get there: Exit M6 J-6, A38. Take second exit (ring road), left at roundabout, then first left into Richard Street. From city centre, take M6 direction then ring road.

Bridge House

◆◆◆◆

49 Sherbourne Road, Acocks Green, Birmingham, West Midlands, B27 6DX
Tel: 0121 706 5900 Fax: 0121 624 5900
Email: enquiries@bridgehousehotel.co.uk
Web: www.bridgehousehotel.co.uk
Closed Christmas
SB £55 DB £70
CC: MC Vi Am DC Swi Delt

West Midlands

Central Guest House

1637 Coventry Road, South Yardley, B26 1DD
Tel: 0121 706 7757 Fax: 0121 706 7757
Email: mmou826384@aol.com
Web: www.centralguesthouse.freeserve.co.uk
SB £20 DB £40 HBS £20 HBD £40
CC: MC Vi Swi
How to get there: Situated 4 miles from NEC.

Comfort Inn

Station Street, Birmingham, B5 4DY
Tel: 0121 643 1134 Fax: 0121 643 3209
SB £60 DB £75 B £8 CC: MC Vi Am Swi Delt
How to get there: Exit M6 J-6, A38M to centre,
Queensway, turn onto Hill Street.

Gables Nest

1639 Coventry Road, South Yardley, B26 1DD
Tel: 0121 708 2712 Fax: 0121 707 3396
Email: mal-bb.gables@virgin.net
Web: www.guesthousebirmingham.co.uk
SB £20 DB £40 HBS £25 HBD £50
CC: MC Vi Am DC Swi Delt
How to get there: On A45 Coventry Road 4
miles from NEC and Birmingham airport.

Lyndhurst

135 Kingsbury Road, Erdington, B24 8QT
Tel: 0121 373 5695 Fax: 0121 373 5695

Tri-Star

Coventry Road, Elmdon, Birmingham, B26 3QR
Tel: 0121 782 1010 Fax: 0121 782 6131

Ideally situated 2 miles from Junction 6 of the
M42, and 1¹/₂ miles from Birmingham
International Airport and the NEC, the hotel
maintains a homely atmosphere at moderate
charge. Licensed bar. Ample parking.

SB £49 DB £59 B £5 L £3 D £6.
CC: MC Vi Am DC Swi Delt
How to get there: On main A45.

Rollason Wood

Wood End Road, Erdington, Birmingham,
West Midlands, B24 8BJ
Tel: 0121 373 1230 Fax: 0121 382 2578
Email: rollwood@globknet.co.uk

Friendly family-run hotel with 35 bedrooms.
Choose from economy, with shower, or fully en-
suite. Licensed bar and a la carte restaurant.
Weekend and weekly reductions.
SB £18 DB £32 D £6.
CC: MC Vi Am DC Swi Delt
How to get there: Exit M6 J-6, A5127, A4040.
Hotel ¹/₄ mile on left.

Bourton-on-the-Water, Gloucestershire

Chester House

Bourton-on-the-Water,
Gloucestershire, GL54 2BU
Tel: 01451 820286 Fax: 01451 820471
Email: juliand@chesterhouse.u-net.com
Web: www.bizare.demon.co.uk/chester
Closed December to January
SB £58 DB £77 HBS £74.95 HBD £55.45
B £6.50 D £10.95.
CC: MC Vi Am DC Swi Delt JCB, Solo
How to get there: In centre of village. Take left
road bridge spanning river, which leads to hotel
car park.

Old New Inn

★★

High Street, Bourton-on-the-Water,
Gloucestershire, GL54 2AF
Tel: 01451 820467 Fax: 01451 810236

Charming family-run 17th-century inn, home of
the famous model village, beautiful beer garden,
winter log fires. Restaurant, three bars, car park.
SB £38 DB £76 HBS £53 HBD £106
B £8 L £10 D £12. CC: MC Vi Swi
🐟🍵💻🅿🦷🎄🐎🎠🎅🚶

Ridge Guest House

♦♦♦♦

Whiteshoots, Bourton-on-the-Water,
Gloucestershire, GL54 2LE
Tel: 01451 820660 Fax: 01451 822448
Children minimum age: 6
SB £30 DB £45
🚫🍵💻🅿🦷🎄🐎🎅🎄
How to get there: Half a mile south of Bourton-
on-the-Water on the A429.

Polly Perkins Bed & Breakfast

♦♦♦

1 The Chestnuts, High Street,
Bourton-on-the-Water, GL54 2AN
Tel: 01451 820244 Fax: 01451 820558

Idyllic central position in Bourton. All rooms with
modern facilities. Breakfast served in our
daytime restaurant overlooking the River

Windrush and village green. Secure parking.
DB £50 CC: MC Vi Swi Delt
🚶⊗🍵💻🅿🦷🎄🐎🎅🎄🍽
How to get there: From A40 Northleach
roundabout take Fosse Way (A429) towards
Stow-on-the-Wold. Turn right into Lansdown, to
village centre.

Bridgnorth, Shropshire

Mill Hotel

★★★★

Alveley, nr Bridgnorth, Shropshire, WV15 6HL
Tel: 01746 780437 Fax: 01746 780850
SB £68 DB £80 HBS £92 HBD £63
B £7 L £14 D £23. CC: MC Vi Am DC Swi
🔷♿🛗🚶⊗🍵💻☎🅿🦷🎄🐎🎅🎄🍽
🚶 'ᵼ'
How to get there: Situated just off main A442,
midway between Kidderminster and Bridgnorth.

Old Vicarage

★★★ ♔♔♔

Worfield, Bridgnorth, Shropshire, WV15 5JZ
Tel: 01746 716497 Fax: 01746 716552
Email: admin@the-old-vicarage.co.uk
Web: www.oldvicarageworfield.com
SB £75 DB £115 HBS £105 HBD £150
B £10.50 L £18.50 D £22.50.
CC: MC Vi Am Delt
♿🚶🐾⊗🍵💻☎📞🅿🦷🎄🐎🎅🎄
🚶🚶
How to get there: The Old Vicarage is 1 mile
from the A454 and 2 miles from the A442 to the
east of Bridgnorth — look for the brown signs.

Parlors Hall Hotel

★★

Mill Street, Bridgnorth, Shropshire, WV15 5AL
Tel: 01746 761931 Fax: 01746 767058

Broadway, Worcestershire

Lygon Arms

★★★★ ♔♔♔♔

Broadway, Worcestershire, WR12 7DU
Tel: 01386 854405 Fax: 01386 854470
Email: shancox@the-lygon-arms.co.uk
Web: www.savoy-group.co.uk
SB £130 DB £175 HBS £140 HBD £140
B £14.50 L £22.50 D £39.50.
CC: MC Vi Am DC Swi Delt
🔷♿🚶🐾🍵💻☎📞🅿🦷🎄🐎🎅🎄🖼
🚶🚶🅿 'ᵼ'🔍🔍
How to get there: In the centre of Broadway
village, off the Broadway bypass.

West Midlands

Buckland Manor

★★★ ♗♗♗♗

Buckland, Broadway, Worcestershire, WR12 7LY
Tel: 01386 852626 Fax: 01386 853557
Email: buckland-manor-uk@msn.com
Children minimum age: 12

13th-century manor situated in the heart of the Cotswolds, in glorious grounds. Superb food and wines in award-winning restaurant. Luxury bedrooms with antiques and four-poster beds. SB £195 DB £205 B £7.50 L £7.25 D £7.25. CC: MC Vi Am DC Swi Delt

🗐 ⬛ ☎ 🅿 ⛳ ⚗ 🐎 🎋 😊 ⚙ 🔍 🎣

How to get there: 2 miles south of Broadway, on the B4632.

Dormy House Hotel

Located between the picturesque Cotswold villages of Chipping Campden and Broadway and only a few miles from Straford-upon-Avon, you'll find the 17th-century Dormy House Hotel. Enjoy the beautifully appointed rooms, superb restaurant and high standard of cuisine and service.
Stay for one night, a Champagne Weekend or a Carefree Midweek Break.

Willersey Hill, Broadway,
Worcestershire WR12 7LF
Tel: 01386 852711   Fax: 01386 858636
Email: reservations@dormyhouse.co.uk
Website: www.dormyhouse.co.uk

Dormy House

★★★ ♗♗♗

Willersley Hill, Broadway, WR12 7LF
Tel: 01386 852711 Fax: 01386 858636
Email: reservations@dormyhouse.co.uk
Web: www.dormyhouse.co.uk
Closed Christmas

Meticulously converted 17th-century Cotswold farmhouse combining traditional charm with all the modern comforts. Leisure facilities include: games room, gym, sauna/steam room, putting green and croquet lawn. SB £75 DB £150 B £10.50 L £19.95 D £32. CC: MC Vi Am DC Swi Delt

🔻 ♿ 🗐 🐎 ⚗ ⬛ ☎ 📞 🅿 ⛳ ⚗ 🐎 🎋 😊 ⚙ 🍶 🏹 🦽 ⚗

How to get there: From Broadway 1 mile up Fish Hill (A44), signs Saintbury/picnic area. After ½ mile fork left. Dormy House on left.
See advert on the left

Leasow House

♦♦♦♦

Laverton Meadow, Broadway, WR12 7NA
Tel: 01386 584526 Fax: 01386 584596
Email: leasow@clara.net
Web: www.leasow.co.uk

Cotswold stone farmhouse in quiet countryside location close to Broadway village. An ideal base for touring the beautiful Cotswolds and Shakespeare's Stratford-upon-Avon.

SB £43 DB £53 CC: MC Vi Am

How to get there: From Broadway, B4632 for Winchcombe. Right after 2 miles for Wormington and Dumbleton. Hotel first on right.

Windrush House

◆◆◆◆ ⍝ ⚘

Station Road, Broadway, WR12 7DE
Tel: 01386 853577 Fax: 01386 853790
Email: richard@broadway-windrush.co.uk
Web: www.broadway-windrush.co.uk
SB £30 DB £50 L £10 D £15.

How to get there: Near the start of Station Road at bottom of the village High Street.

Olive Branch Guest House

◆◆◆

78 High Street, Broadway, WR12 7AJ
Tel: 01386 853440 Fax: 01386 859070
Email: clive@theolivebranch.u-net.com
Web: www.theolivebranch.u-net.com
Closed January
SB £30 DB £50 CC: MC Vi Am Swi Delt

How to get there: Situated on the upper High Street, next to Teddy Bear Museum.

Bromsgrove, Worcestershire

Hanover International Bromsgrove

★★★★ ℞

Kidderminster Road, Bromsgrove, Worcestershire, B61 9AB
Tel: 01527 576600 Fax: 01527 878981
Email: enquiries@pine-lodge-hotel.co.uk

HANOVER INTERNATIONAL

Formerly Pine Lodge. This magnificent hotel has a distinctive Mediterranean flavour and charm

with an extensive leisure club and a wealth of local attractions in easy reach.
SB £120 DB £140 HBS £140 HBD £170
B £9.95 L £6 D £19.50.
CC: MC Vi Am DC Swi Delt

How to get there: From M5 J-4 or J-5, or M42 J-1, A38 into Bromsgrove town centre, then A488 for Kidderminster. Hotel is ¹/₂ mile out.

Avoncroft Guest House

◆◆◆◆ ⍝

77 Redditch Road, Stoke Heath, Bromsgrove, Worcestershire, B60 4JP
Tel: 01527 832819
SB £30 DB £45

Lower Bentley Farm

◆◆◆ ⍝

Lower Bentley Lane, Lower Bentley, Bromsgrove, Worcestershire, B60 4JB
Tel: 01527 821286 Fax: 01527 821193
Email: aj.gibbs@farmline.com
Web: www.lowerbentleyfarm.co.uk
SB £25 DB £42

How to get there: From Bromsgrove, A38 for Worcester. Take B4091 to Hanbury. After Navigation pub, turn right (signed Woodgate). First right, third left. Farm is first on left.

Bucknell, Shropshire

The Bow

◆◆◆◆ ⍝ ⚘

Adleymoor, Bucknell, Shropshire, SY7 0ES
Tel: 01547 530 878

West Midlands

Burton-upon-Trent, Staffordshire

Queens Hotel

★★★

One Bridge Street, Burton-upon-Trent,
Staffordshire, DE14 1SY
Tel: 01283 523800 Fax: 01283 523823
Email: hotel@burton-conferencing.com
Web: www.burton-conferencing.com

16th-century interior hides a hotel of friendly
service and modern facilities. From air-
conditioned conferencing to four-poster suites,
complementary parking and a free car wash.
SB £45 DB £59.50 HBS £59.50 HBD £89
B £6.50 L £6.95 D £14.95.
CC: MC Vi Am Swi Delt

How to get there: Town centre on corner of
Bridge Street and High Street. Exit M42 J-11
take A444. From A38 follow town centre.
See advert on facing page

Delter Hotel

◆◆◆

5 Derby Road, Burton-upon-Trent, DE14 1RU
Tel: 01283 535115
Fax: 01283 845261
Email: delterhotel@burtonontrenthotels.co.uk
Web: www.burtonontrenthotels.co.uk
SB £34 DB £47 HBS £46 HBD £69 D £11.50.
CC: MC Vi Swi Delt

How to get there: From A511 turn into Derby
Road at roundabout. Hotel 50 yards on left. Or,
from A38 join A5121 Burton north, straight over
two roundabouts. Hotel ½ mile on right.

Chaddesley Corbett, Worcestershire

Brockencote Hall

★★★ 🏵 🏵 🏵

Chaddesley Corbett, nr Kidderminster,
Worcestershire, DY10 4PY
Tel: 01562 777876 Fax: 01562 777872
Email: info@brockencotehall.com
Web: www.brockencotehall.com

Nestling in the heart of the Worcestershire
countryside, Brockencote Hall is set in 70 acres
of parkland with its own lake. Ideally situated to
visit Warwick Castle, Stratford-upon-Avon and
Ironbridge. The cooking is French and the Head
Chef, Didier Philipot masterminds his ideas into
mouthwatering delicacies.
SB £110 DB £135 HBS £137.50 HBD £95
CC: MC Vi Am DC Swi Delt

How to get there: Exit M5 J-4 or M42 J-1, into
Bromsgrove, then A448 for Kidderminster.
Hotel is situated 5 miles out of Bromsgrove,
on left-hand side.

Cheltenham, Gloucestershire

Cheltenham Park

★★★★

Cirencester Road, Charlton Kings, Cheltenham,
Gloucestershire, GL53 8EA
Tel: 01242 222021 Fax: 01242 226935

Heritage Hotels – The Queen's

★★★★

Promenade, Cheltenham, GL50 1NN
Tel: 0870 400 8107 Fax: 01242 224145
Web: www.heritage-hotels.com
SB £125 DB £165 B £11 L £9 D £22.
CC: MC Vi Am DC Swi Delt JCB

How to get there: Follow town centre signs from
A40 (Oxford) or A46. Hotel behind the town hall.

Carlton

★★★

Parabola Road, Cheltenham, Gloucestershire, GL50 3AQ

Tel: 01242 514453 Fax: 01242 226487

SB £65 DB £85 HBS £70 HBD £95 B £5.50 D £17.50. CC: MC Vi Am DC Swi Delt Solo Maestro JCB

How to get there: Follow signs to Town Hall. At Town Hall, take middle lane, across lights, past Ladies' College, left at lights and first right into Parabola Road.

Charlton Kings

★★★

London Road, Charlton Kings, Cheltenham, Gloucestershire, GL52 6UU

Tel: 01242 231061 Fax: 01242 241900

SB £61 DB £92 HBS £79 HBD £130 B £10 L £6.95 D £18.95.

CC: MC Vi Am Swi Delt JCB Solo

How to get there: First property on left as you enter Cheltenham from Oxford on A40.

George Hotel

★★★

41-49 St George's Road, Cheltenham, Gloucestershire, GL50 3DX

Tel: 01242 235751 Fax: 01242 224359

Email: hotel@stayatthegeorge.co.uk

Web: www.stayatthegeorge.co.uk

Town centre, privately owned Regency Hotel. Two-minute walk to fashionable shopping areas, theatre and antique shops. Perfect for both business and pleasurable breaks.

SB £65 DB £85 HBS £78.95 HBD £112.90 B £7.50 L £6.95 D £16.95.

CC: MC Vi Am DC Swi Delt

How to get there: Exit M5 J-11 and follow signs to Cheltenham. Left at TGI Fridays. Right into St George's Road. Hotel is on left.

The Queens Hotel & Conference Center

Behind the listed facade of this C16th hotel lies a true combination of tradition and technology. Our traditional service standards range from morning tea to washing your car. Combine this with in-house movies, ISDN data and "state of the art" conference facilities, offering air-conditioned luxury for meetings up to 50 in the heart of the Midlands Motorway Network - ideal as a central meeting place, for visiting the NEC or touring the Peak District

One Bridge Street, Burton upon Trent

Tel: 01283 523800

www.burton-conferencing.com

Greenway

★★★

Shurdington, Cheltenham, GL51 5UG

Tel: 01242 862352 Fax: 01242 862780

Email: greenway@btconnect.com

Children minimum age: 7

SB £120 DB £165 HBS £140 HBD £215 B £12 L £10 D £35. CC: MC Vi Am DC Swi Delt

How to get there: Located on the A46 Cheltenham to Stroud road, approx 1½ miles from city centre.

Hotel Kandinsky

★★★

Bayshill Road, Cheltenham, GL50 3AS

Tel: 01242 527788 Fax: 01242 226412

Email: kate@hotelkandinsky.com

Web: www.hotelkandinsky.com

SB £80 DB £105 B £3.50 L £12 D £12.

CC: MC Vi Am DC Swi Delt

How to get there: Exit M5 J-11, A40 for town centre. At 3rd roundabout, take 2nd exit into Bayshill Road. Hotel on corner of Bayshill and Parabola Road.

West Midlands

Hotel on The Park

★★★ 🐝🐝🐝

Evesham Road, Cheltenham, Gloucestershire,
GL52 2AH
Tel: 01242 518898 Fax: 01242 511526
Email: stay@hotelonthepark.co.uk
Web: www.hotelonthepark.co.uk
Children minimum age: 8
SB £86 DB £121.50 HBS £108 HBD £165.50
CC: MC Vi Am DC Swi Delt

How to get there: Head for town centre, join
one-way system. Follow signs to Evesham. Join
Portland Street, which becomes Evesham Road.
Hotel is on left.

Prestbury House Hotel & Restaurant

★★★ 🐝

The Burgage, Prestbury, Cheltenham,
Gloucestershire, GL52 3DN
Tel: 01242 529533 Fax: 01242 227076
Web: www.prestburyhouse.co.uk

300-year-old manor house hotel and restaurant
(open to non-residents), set in five acres of
secluded grounds. Cheltenham centre is 1½
miles away. Full conference and wedding
reception facilities.
SB £60 DB £80 HBS £75 HBD £110 B £10
L £14 D £14. CC: MC Vi Am DC Swi

How to get there: Follow any sign for
Cheltenham Racecourse on entering
Cheltenham. Hotel is ½ mile from racecourse
entrance, signposted from Prestbury village.

Wyastone

★★★ 🐝

Parabola Road, Montpellier, Cheltenham Spa,
Gloucester, GL50 3BG
Tel: 01242 245549 Fax: 01242 522659

Cotswold Grange

★★

Pittville Circus Road, Cheltenham,
Gloucestershire, GL52 2QH
Tel: 01242 515119 Fax: 01242 241537
Email: paul@cotswold-grange.fsnet.co.uk
Web: www.smoothhound.co.uk/hotels/
grangech.html

Closed Christmas to New Year
Friendly, family-run hotel situated in a quiet tree-
lined avenue within easy walking distance of the
town centre. Convenient for race course. Ample
car parking.
SB £50 DB £75 B £6 L £6 D £12.
CC: MC Vi Am DC Delt

How to get there: From the town centre, follow
signs for Prestbury. At roundabout on Prestbury
Road, turn right into Pittville Circus.

Acanthus Court

◆◆◆◆◆ 🍷

59 Leckhampton Road, Cheltenham,
Gloucestershire, GL53 0BS
Tel: 01242 576083 Fax: 01242 224579
Email: res@acanthus-court.co.uk
Web: www.acanthus-court.co.uk
Closed New Year to mid-January
SB £69 DB £79
CC: MC Vi Am DC Swi Delt JCB

How to get there: Exit M5 J-11. Follow signs for
A46 Stroud/Leckhampton. Acanthus Court is on
B4070 to Birdup Road.

Lypiatt House

◆◆◆◆◆ 🍷

Lypiatt Road, Cheltenham, Gloucestershire,
GL50 2QW
Tel: 01242 224994 Fax: 01242 224996

Beaumont House

 ✦✦✦✦

56 Shurdington Road, Cheltenham,
Gloucestershire, GL53 0JE
Tel: 01242 245986 Fax: 01242 520044
Email: rocking.horse@virgin.net
Web: www.smoothhound.co.uk/hotels/
beauchel.html
Children minimum age: 10
SB £48 DB £62 B £9.5 D £15.
CC: MC Vi Am Swi Delt JCB

Hollington House

 ✦✦✦✦

115 Hales Road, Cheltenham
Gloucestershire, GL52 6ST
Tel: 01242 256652 Fax: 01242 570280

Moorend Park

 ✦✦✦✦

Moorend Park Road, Cheltenham,
Gloucestershire, GL53 0LA
Tel: 01242 224441 Fax: 01242 572413
Email: moorendpark@freeuk.com
Web: moorendpark.freeuk.com
Closed Christmas to New Year
SB £44 DB £54 CC: MC Vi Am Swi Delt

How to get there: Located on the A46 from M5
J-11A. Take signs to Cheltenham. Hotel is on
first set of lights.

Broomhill Guest House

 ✦✦✦

218 London Road, Cheltenham,
Gloucestershire, GL52 6HW
Tel: 01242 513086 Fax: 01242 513086
SB £25 DB £40 B £5 CC: Am DC

How to get there: On A40 (Oxford) and A435
(Cirencester) junction, opposite Holy Apostles
Church, Charlton Kings.

Montpellier

 ✦✦✦

33 Montpellier Terrace, Cheltenham,
Gloucestershire, GL50 1UX
Tel: 01242 526009
Closed Christmas to New Year
SB £28 DB £48

How to get there: Exit M5 J-11. Follow A40 to
roundabout at Montpellier. Continue on A40.
Hotel is on right, 100m past roundabout.

Strayleaves

❖

282 Gloucester Road, Cheltenham, GL51 7AG
Tel: 01242 572303 Fax: 01242 572303
SB £35 DB £45 HBS £47 HBD £69

How to get there: Left from rear Cheltenham
railway station. 300 yards, second house on left.

Chipping Campden, Gloucestershire

Charingworth Manor

 ★★★ ♟♟

Chipping Campden, Gloucestershire, GL55 6NS
Tel: 01386 593555 Fax: 01386 593353
Email: charingworthmanor@
englishrosehotels.co.uk
Web: www.englishrosehotels.co.uk

An idyllic setting for a stylish and relaxed visit
where only the finest accommodation and
cuisine will suffice. Elegantly decorated rooms
enhanced with antiques and objets d'art
creating a stunning country house with award-
winning cuisine.
SB £115 DB £180 HBD £84.50 L £37.50
D £37.50. CC: MC Vi Am DC Swi Delt

How to get there: Exit M40 J-15, A429, B4035
for Chipping Camden. Manor is on the right.

Cotswold House

 ★★★ ♟♟♟♟

The Square, Chipping Campden,
Gloucestershire, GL55 6AN
Tel: 01386 840330 Fax: 01386 840310
Email: reception@cotswoldhouse.com
Web: www.cotswoldhouse.com
SB £75 DB £170 HBS £110 HBD £210
B £12.50 L £15 D £25. CC: MC Vi Am Swi Delt

How to get there: Exit M40 J-15, taking the
A429 south towards Cirencester. After 16 miles
turn right onto B4035, signposted Campden.

West Midlands

Seymour House

★★★ ♟

High Street, Chipping Campden, GL55 6AH
Tel: 01386 840429 Fax: 01386 840369
Email: enquiry@seymourhousehotel.com
Web: www.seymourhousehotel.com

Renovated, 17th-century Cotswold stone
building in town centre, with charming secluded
garden. Photographed by Nigel Hudson,
courtesy of the BTA.
SB £72.50 DB £95 HBS £92.50 HBD £135
CC: MC Vi Am Swi Delt

Three Ways House

★★★

Mickleton, Chipping Camden, GL55 6SB
Tel: 01386 438429 Fax: 01386 438118
Email: threeways@puddingclub.com
Web: www.puddingclub.com

Charming, Cotswold village hotel with 41
individually designed bedrooms, newly
refurbished and stylish restaurant. Conveniently
situated for Hidcote Manor Garden and
Stratford upon Avon. Seen on TV as Home of
the Pudding Club.
SB £67 DB £98 HBS £90 HBD £67
B £8 L £13 D £24. CC: MC Vi Am DC Swi Delt

How to get there: On B4632 in centre of village.

Lower Brook House Little Gem

♦♦♦♦

Lower Street, Blockley, GL56 9DS
Tel: 01386 700286 Fax: 01386 700286
Email: lowerbrookhouse@cs.com
Web: www.lowerbrookhouse.co.uk
SB £65 DB £96 B £7.50 L £12.50 D £20.
CC: MC Vi Swi Delt

How to get there: Between Moreton-in-Marsh
and Broadway (A44) take Blockley turning.
See advert on facing page

Nineveh Farm House

♦♦♦♦

Campden Road, Mickleton, Chipping Campden,
Gloucestershire, GL55 6PS
Tel: 01386 438923
Email: nineveh@easicom.com
Children minimum age: 5

Fine Georgian farmhouse with inglenooks and
beams set in large gardens and meadow.
Convenient for local inns, north Cotswold
villages, Hidcote Manor Garden, Stratford,
Warwick.
DB £50 HBS £40 CC: MC Vi

How to get there: Close to Mickleton village,
three miles from Chipping Campden (B4081).

Chipping Sodbury, Gloucestershire

Sodbury House

♦♦♦♦

Badminton Road, Old Sodbury, Gloucestershire,
BS37 6LU
Tel: 01454 312847
Email: sodhousehotel@tesco.net
Web: www.visitus.co.uk
Former 18th-century farmhouse set in extensive
grounds on the Cotswolds' edge, 12 miles from
Bath/Bristol. En-suite bedrooms with colour TV,
radio, hairdryer and trouser press.
SB £50 DB £78 CC: MC Vi Am DC

How to get there: Located 3 miles from M4 J-18, via A46, signposted Stroud. At traffic lights, turn left (A432), signposted Yate/Bristol.

Church Stretton, Shropshire

Denehurst
★★
Shrewsbury Road, Church Stretton,
Shropshire, SY6 6EU
Tel: 01694 722699 Fax: 01694 724110

Long Mynd
★★
Cunnery Road, Church Stretton,
Shropshire, SY6 6AG
Tel: 01694 722244 Fax: 01694 722718
Email: max@longmynd.co.uk
Web: www.longmynd.co.uk

The Long Mynd Hotel nestles in woodland overlooking the small country market town of Church Stretton. The views are breathtaking. Situated in the South Shropshire Hills, an Area of Outstanding Natural Beauty.
SB £55 DB £100 HBS £60 HBD £110 B £13.50 L £7.50 D £14.95. CC: MC Vi Am DC Swi
How to get there: From A49, turn into town centre, left by Lloyds TSB, then first right after mini-roundabout. Hotel is at the top on the left.

Lower Brook House

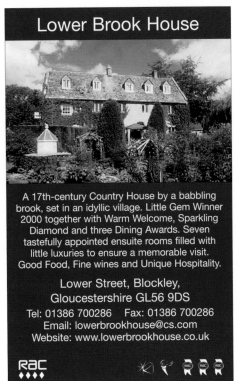

A 17th-century Country House by a babbling brook, set in an idyllic village. Little Gem Winner 2000 together with Warm Welcome, Sparkling Diamond and three Dining Awards. Seven tastefully appointed ensuite rooms filled with little luxuries to ensure a memorable visit. Good Food, Fine wines and Unique Hospitality.

**Lower Street, Blockley,
Gloucestershire GL56 9DS**
Tel: 01386 700286   Fax: 01386 700286
Email: lowerbrookhouse@cs.com
Website: www.lowerbrookhouse.co.uk

RAC
◆◆◆◆

West Midlands

Belvedere Guest House
◆◆◆◆
Burway Road, Church Stretton,
Shropshire, SY6 6DP
Tel: 01694 722232 Fax: 01694 722232
Email: belv@bigfoot.com
Web: www.s-h-systems.co.uk/hotels/
belveder.html

Belvedere is an old Edwardian house set in its own gardens on the outskirts of the village, yet very convenient for the Long Mynd.
SB £25 DB £50 CC: MC Vi Delt
How to get there: Turn west from A49 at Church Stretton. Belvedere is 1/2 mile on right.

Travellers Rest Inn

♦♦♦

Upper Affcot, Church Stretton, SY6 6RL
Tel: 01694 781275 Fax: 01694 781555
Email: reception@travellersrestinn.co.uk
Web: www.travellersrestinn.co.uk
SB £30 DB £50 L £5 D £7.
CC: MC Vi Am DC Swi Delt

How to get there: Situated on west side of A49,
5 miles south of Church Stretton.

Cirencester, Gloucestershire

Wild Duck Inn

★★

Drakes Island, Ewen, nr Cirencester,
Gloucestershire, GL7 6BY
Tel: 01285 770310 Fax: 01285 770924/770310
Email: wduckinn@aol.com
SB £55 DB £75

How to get there: From Cirencester take A429
towards Malmesbury and M4. At Kemble turn
left to Ewen. The Wild Duck is in the centre of
the village.
See advert below

The Bungalow

♦♦♦

93 Victoria Road, Cirencester,
Gloucestershire, GL7 1ES
Tel: 01285 654179 Fax: 01286 656159
Email: cbeard7@compuserve.com
SB £27 DB £37

How to get there: From town centre, church is
on left, proceed to traffic lights. Turn right into
Victoria Road. The Bungalow is two-thirds
down road on left.

Wimborne House

♦♦♦

91 Victoria Road, Cirencester, Gloucestershire,
GL7 1ES
Tel: 01285 643653 Fax: 01285 653890
Email: wimborneho@aol.com
Children minimum age: 10
Closed Christmas to New Year
SB £30 DB £40
How to get there: Leave A419 for Cirencester.
At traffic lights turn left into Victoria Road.
Wimborne House 300 yards on left.

The Wild Duck Inn
An attractive 15th-century inn of great character

The Wild Duck is a mellow Cotswold stone Elizabethan Inn. A typical local English inn with a warm and welcoming ambience, rich in colours and hung with old oil portraits of English ancestors. Large open log fires burn in the bar and the oak-panelled residents' lounge in winter time.

The garden is secluded, delightful and perfect for 'alfresco' dining in the summer. The bar offers six real ales and the wine list is extensive and innovative.

The country-style dining room offers fresh seasonal food; game in winter and fresh fish delivered overnight from Brixham in Devon, which can include such exotic fare as parrot fish and tilapia.

There are nine bedrooms, two of which have four-poster beds and overlook the garden. All rooms have direct dial telephone, colour TV and tea/coffee-making facilities.

Within one mile, The Wild Duck is surrounded by the Cotswold Water Park, with over 80 lakes providing fishing, swimming, sailing, water and jet skiing. Polo at Cirencester Park is a regular event and every March Cheltenham holds the Gold Cup Race Meeting. Horse trials at Gatcombe Park and Badminton are also held annually.

Location: From M4 take Junction 17 and follow Cirencester, turn right at Kemble and follow signs to Ewen

Drakes Island, Ewen, Near Cirencester GL7 6BY
Tel: 01285 770310 / 770364   Fax: 01285 770924   Email: wduckinn@aol.com

Codsall, Staffordshire

Moors Farm & Country Restaurant

Chillington Lane, Codsall, Staffordshire,
WV8 1QF
Tel: 01902 842330 Fax: 01902 847878
Email: enquiries@moorsfarmhotel.co.uk
Web: www.moorsfarm-hotel.co.uk
Children minimum age: 4
SB £36 DB £55 HBS £49 HBD £40.50
L £11 D £13. CC: MC Vi Swi Delt JCB Solo

How to get there: Take road from Codsall to
Codsall Wood. Turn right into Chillington Lane.
Turn right at T-junction. Entrance 200m on right.

Coleford, Gloucestershire

Cherry Orchard Farm

Newland, Coleford, Gloucestershire, GL16 8NP
Tel: 01594 832212
DB £36 B £6

How to get there: Hotel is on the B4231 1¹/₂
miles east of Redbrook, which is 3 miles south
of Monmouth on the A466.

Coleshill, Warwickshire

Grimstock Country House

★★★
Gilson Road, Gilson, Coleshill, Warwickshire,
B46 1AJ
Tel: 01675 462121 Fax: 01675 467646

Old Barn Guest House

◆◆◆
Birmingham Road, Coleshill, Warwickshire,
B46 1DP
Tel: 01675 463692 Fax: 01675 466275
SB £40 DB £68.50 CC: MC Vi Am DC Swi Delt

How to get there: Exit M6 J-4, A446 towards
Coleshill. Turn left at island onto B4114.
Old Barn ¹/₄ mile on left.

Guide dogs

If a Hotel or Guest Accommodation
does not display this 'dogs welcome'
symbol in its listing, the hotelier may
still be happy to welcome guests with guide
dogs, and you should contact the property to
discover whether this will be a problem.

Coln St-Aldwyns, Gloucestershire

New Inn At Coln

★★ ®®®
Coln St-Aldwyns, nr Cirencester,
Gloucestershire, GL7 5AN
Tel: 01285 750651 Fax: 01285 750657
Email: stay@new-inn.co.uk
Web: www.new-inn.co.uk
Children minimum age: 10

An exceptional 16th-century Coaching Inn set in
an idyllic Cotswold village. Wonderful food in
bar and restaurant. Quality bedrooms and
attentive, courteous staff. Great walking
countryside.
SB £68 DB £96 HBS £88 HBD £68.50 B £8.50
L £17.50 D £22.50. CC: MC Vi Am Swi Delt

How to get there: From Burford (A40), take
B4425 towards Bibury; turn left after Aldsworth.

Coventry, West Midlands

Brooklands Grange

★★★ ®
Holyhead Road, Coventry, West Midlands,
CV5 8HX
Tel: 02476 601601 Fax: 02476 601277
Email: lesley.jackson@virgin.net
Web: www.brooklands-grange.co.uk
SB £90 DB £105 B £12 L £12 D £15.
CC: MC Vi Am DC Swi Delt

How to get there: On the A4114 near Allesley
village roundabout, 1¹/₂ miles from city centre.

Heritage Hotels – The Brandon Hall

★★★
Brandon, Coventry, West Midlands, CV8 3FW
Tel: 0870 4008105 Fax: 0247 6544909
SB £112 DB £160 B £11.95 L £14.95 D £25.
CC: MC Vi Am DC Swi Delt

West Midlands

Novotel Coventry

★★★

Wilsons Lane, Lonford, Coventry, CV6 6HL
Tel: 02476 365000 Fax: 02476 362422
Email: h0506@accor-hotels.com
Web: www.accorhotel.com
SB £75.95 DB £84.90 HBS £90 HBD £105
B £8.95 L £10.50 D £15.50.
CC: MC Vi Am DC Swi Delt

♿ ⛰ 🐕 ⊗ ☕ 🖥 ☎ 🔌 🅿 ⚙ 🕯 🐎 🎠 🍴 🦀 ⚌
♙♙♙ ⚕ ⚘

How to get there: M6 J-3, B4113 for Bedworth,
3rd exit at roundabout, hotel is 20m on left.

Quality Hotel Stonebridge Manor

★★★

Birmingham Road, Allesley Village, Coventry,
West Midlands, CV5 9BA
Tel: 024 76403835 Fax: 024 76403081

Campanile Hotel Grille

Travel Accommodation
4 Wigston Road, Walsgrave, CV2 2SD
Tel: 02476 623311 Fax: 02476 603362

Typical Campanile bedroom

Campanile hotels offer comfortable and
convenient budget accommodation and a
traditional French-style Bistro providing freshly
cooked food for breakfast, lunch and dinner. All
rooms en-suite with tea/coffee-making facilities,
DDT and TV with Sky channels.
SB £38 DB £42 HBS £50 HBD £60 B £4.95
L £4.95 D £6.50. CC: MC Vi Am DC Swi Delt

♿ 🐕 ⊗ ☕ 🖥 ☎ 🔌 🅿 ⚙ 🎠 🍴 🦀 ⚌ ♙♙♙ ♙

How to get there: M6 J-2. A4600 for ³/₄ mile and
turn right on second roundabout.

Leacroft

♦ ♦ ♦

Leamoor Common, Winstanstow, Craven Arms,
Shropshire, SY7 8DN
Tel: 01694 781556 Fax: 01694 781556

Copthorne Hotel Merry Hill

★★★★

Level Street, Brierley Hill, Dudley, West
Midlands, DY5 1UR
Tel: 01384 482882 Fax: 01384 482773
Email: gill.talbot@mill-cop.com
Web: www.book.with-us.com

Modern 138-bedroom hotel in an attractive
waterfront setting in the heart of the Midlands.
Faradays bar & restaurant offers a wide range of
Mediterranean dishes.
SB £148.25 DB £171.50 HBS £163.25
HBD £201.50 B £13.25 L £7 D £14.
CC: MC Vi Am DC Swi Delt

♿ ⛰ ⊗ ☕ 🖥 ☎ 🔌 🅿 ⚙ 🕯 🐎 🎠 🍴 🦀 🔭 ⚌
♙♙♙ 🍴

How to get there: Exit M5 J-2, A4123 for
Dudley, 2¹/₂ miles follow signs for A461 to
Stourbridge/Merry Hill Centre.

Glenwood

♦ ♦ ♦

Croxton, Eccleshall, Staffordshire, ST21 6PF
Tel: 01630 620238
SB £20 DB £34

🐕 ⊗ ☕ 🅿 ⚙ 🎠 🐎 🍴 🦀

How to get there: Exit M6 J-14. Travel to
Eccleshall. Take B5026 to Loggerheads. After 3
miles, enter the village of Croxton. The Cottage
is on right.

Evesham Hotel

★★★ ℞

Cooper's Lane, off Waterside, Evesham,
Worcestershire, WR11 6DA
Tel: 01386 765566 Fax: 01386 765443

Email: reception@eveshamhotel.com
Web: www.eveshamhotel.com
SB £71 DB £98 B £7 L £10 D £21.
CC: MC Vi Am DC Swi Delt
♿ 🐾 ⊗ ⊜ ▭ ☎ 🅿 ♨ ℃ 🐴 ♫ ♻ ♨♨♨ ♨♨♨ ℮ ☒
How to get there: Cooper's Lane runs off the
road running along the River Avon.

Northwick

★★★

Waterside, Evesham, WR11 6BT
Tel: 01386 40322 Fax: 01386 41070
Email: enquiries@northwickhotel.co.uk
Web: www.northwickhotel.co.uk
SB £66 DB £90 HBS £70 HBD £110 B £7.50
L £14.50 D £22.50. CC: MC Vi Am DC Swi Delt
♿ ⊜ 🐾 ⊗ ⊜ ▭ ☎ ☏ 🅿 ♨ ℃ 🐴 ♫ ♻ ♨♨♨ ♨♨♨
How to get there: M5 J-9 to Evesham centre.
Right at bridge, signs for hotel ½ mile on right.

Mill at Harvington

★★ ₨ ₨
Anchor Lane, Harvington, Evesham,
Worcestershire, WR11 5NR
Tel: 01386 870688 Fax: 01386 870688
Children minimum age: 10

Tastefully converted beautiful Georgian house
and former baking mill, set in acres of parkland
on the banks of the River Avon, ½ mile from the
main road.
SB £63 DB £103 HBS £79 HBD £125 B £6.50
L £7.95 D £12. CC: MC Vi Am DC Swi Delt
⊜ ▭ ☎ 🅿 ♨ ℃ 🐴 ♫ ♻ ♨♨♨ ♨♨♨ 🔍 ⚓ 🚣
How to get there: Turn south off the
Norton/Bidford road opposite Harvington
village, 4 miles northeast of Evesham. Hotel 600
yards on left.

Park View

♦♦♦

Waterside, Evesham, Worcestershire,
WR11 6BS
Tel: 01386 442639
Email: mike.spires@btinternet.com
Web: www.parkview.hotel.btinternet.co.uk
SB £21.50 DB £41 CC: MC Vi Am Swi Delt

🐎 🅿 ♨ ℃ 🐴 ♫ ♻ ♨♨♨ ♨♨♨ ♂
How to get there: Hotel is ¼ mile southeast of
the town centre on Waterside (B4035) which
runs alongside the river.

Fownhope, Herefordshire

Green Man Inn

★★

Fownhope, Herefordshire, HR1 4PE
Tel: 01432 860243 Fax: 01432 860207
Web: www.smoothhound.co.uk/hotels/
greenman.html
SB £38.50 DB £64 HBS £45 HBD £90
B £6.25 L £7.50 D £10.95. CC: MC Vi Swi Delt
♿ ⊜ 🐾 ⊗ ▭ ☎ 🅿 ♨ ℃ 🐴 ♫ ♻ 👁 ♨♨♨
♨♨♨ 🆂🅿🅰 🍸 ☒
How to get there: Exit M50, A449 for Ledbury.
After 2 miles, left onto B4224 Fownhope for 5
miles. Green Man is in centre of village on left.

Gloucester, Gloucestershire

Gilberts Guest House

♦♦♦♦

Gilberts Lane, Brookthorpe, Gloucester,
Gloucestershire, GL4 0UH
Tel: 01452 812364 Fax: 01452 812364

Kings Head Inn

♦♦♦

Birdwood, Huntley, Gloucestershire, GL19 3EF
Tel: 01452 750348 Fax: 01452 750348
SB £25 DB £40 B £4 L £4 D £4.50.
⊜ ▭ 🅿 ♨ ℃ 🐴 ♫ ♻ 👁 ♨♨♨ ♨♨♨ ℮ ⚕
How to get there: Leave Gloucester for
Ross-on-Wye on A40. Hotel situated 6 miles out
of Gloucester on left at Birdwood. Flagpoles on
front.

Hampton-in-Arden, West Midlands

Cottage Guest House

♦♦♦

Kenilworth Road, Balsall Common,
Hampton-in-Arden, West Midlands, B92 0LW
Tel: 01675 442323 Fax: 01675 443323
Web: www.smoothhound.co.uk/cottage.html
SB £28 DB £44 B £10
♿ 🐾 ⊗ ⊜ ▭ 🅿 ♨ ℃ 🐴 ♫ ♻
How to get there: 3 miles from M42 and M6,
NEC, airport and rail station. Located on the
A452 to Balsall Common.

West Midlands

Hartlebury, Worcestershire

Yew Tree House

♦♦♦♦

Norchard, Crossway Green, Hartlebury,
Worcestershire, DY13 9SN
Tel: 01299 250921 Fax: 01299 250921

Hay-on-Wye, Herefordshire

Old Black Lion

★★

26 Lion Street, Hay-on-Wye, Herefordshire, HR3
5AD
Tel: 01497 820841

Henley-in-Arden, Warwickshire

Lapworth Lodge

♦♦♦

Bushwood Lane, Lapworth, Henley-in-Arden,
Warwickshire, B94 5PJ
Tel: 01564 783038 Fax: 01564 783635

Hereford, Herefordshire

Castle House

★★★★ Town House

Castle Street, Hereford, Herefordshire,
HR1 2NW
Tel: 01432 356321 Fax: 01432 365909
Email: info@castlehse.co.uk
Web: www.castlehse.co.uk
SB £90 DB £155 B £10.50 L £18.95 D £29.95.
CC: MC Vi Am Swi Delt

How to get there: Follow signs for city centre
and city centre east. At the end of St Owen
Street, take two right turns.
See advert on facing page

Belmont Lodge & Golf Course

★★★

Belmont, Hereford, HR2 9SA
Tel: 01432 352666 Fax: 01432 358090
Email: info@belmontlodge.co.uk
Web: www.belmontlodge.co.uk
SB £49.50 DB £67.50 HBS £62.50 HBD £93.50
B £6 L £4.50 D £13.
CC: MC Vi Am DC Swi Delt

How to get there: Belmont Lodge is situated on
the A456 Hereford to Abergavenny road,1 mile
from Hereford.

Heritage Hotels – Green Dragon

★★★

Forte Heritage, Broad Street, Hereford,
Herefordshire, HR4 9BG
Tel: 01432 272506 Fax: 01432 352139
SB £45 DB £90 HBS £60 HBD £120
B £12.50 L £5 D £7.50.
CC: MC Vi Am DC Swi Delt

Pilgrim Hotel

★★★

Ross Road, Hereford, Herefordshire, HR2 8HJ
Tel: 01981 540742 Fax: 01981 540620
Email: www.pilgrim540@aol.com
Web: www.pilgrimhotel.co.uk
SB £49.50 DB £75 HBS £71 HBD £89
B £7.50 L £9.75 D £15.75.
CC: MC Vi Am DC Swi Delt

How to get there: Situated midway between
Ross-on-Wye and Hereford, close to the A49 at
Much Birch.

Three Counties Hotel

★★★

Belmont Road, Hereford, Hereforshire, HR2 7BP
Tel: 01432 299955 Fax: 01432 275114
Web: www.threecountieshotel.co.uk

Modern hotel with a relaxing atmosphere and
beautiful scenery on the outskirts of the city.
Bedrooms set by a quiet garden.
SB £61.50 DB £79.50 B £4.50 D £17.50.
CC: MC Vi Am DC Swi Delt Solo

How to get there: 1¹/₂ miles outside Hereford
city on A465 — the main road to Abergavenny.

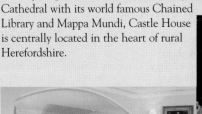

West Midlands

Aylestone Court

◆◆◆◆

Aylestone Hill, Hereford, HR1 1HS
Tel: 01432 341891 Fax: 01432 267691
Email: ayleshotel@aol.com
Web: aylestonecourthotel.homestead.com

Three storey Georgian building, Listed Grade II, tastefully renovated throughout. Spacious, comfortable public rooms and en-suite bedrooms. Lawns and gardens. 4 minutes walk to Hereford city centre.
SB £60 DB £90 B £7.50 L £16 D £22.
CC: MC Vi Am DC Swi Delt JCB
How to get there: At the bottom of Aylestone Hill (A456), marked Hereford City Centre (opposite train station).

Kenilworth, Warwickshire

Peacock Hotel

★★★

149 Warwick Road, Kenilworth, CV8 1HY
Tel: 01926 851156 Fax: 01926 864644
Email: peacockhotel@rafflesmalaysian.com
Web: www.peacockhotel.com

Small, luxurious hotel committed to providing outstanding quality and first class service at reasonable prices. Ideally located for weddings and functions with choice of three elegant restaurants, contemporary bar, gardens and ample parking. Weekend leisure breaks, optional tours and in-house coach service available.
SB £65 DB £80 HBS £84 HBD £59 L £3.95 D £9.75. CC: MC Vi Am DC Swi Delt JCB

Kidderminster, Worcestershire

Stone Manor

★★★★

nr Kidderminster, Stone, DY10 4PJ
Tel: 01562 777555 Fax: 01562 777834
Email: enquiries@stonemanorhotel.co.uk
Web: www.stonemanorhotel.co.uk
B £5.95 L £12.95 D £17.50.
CC: MC Vi Am DC Swi Delt

How to get there: From south M42 J-1, A38 and A448 to Kidderminster. From south M5 J-6, A449, A450 and A448. From north M5 J-3, A456 to A450 and A448.

Redfern

★★★

Lower Street, Cleobury Mortimer, Shropshire, DY14 8AA
Tel: 01299 270395 Fax: 01299 271011
Email: jon@red-fern.demon.co.uk
Web: www.red-fern.demon.co.uk
SB £65 DB £55 HBS £75 HBD £67
B £11 D £19.95. CC: MC Vi Swi Delt Solo

How to get there: Midway between Ludlow and Kidderminster (11 miles) on A4117.

Cedars

★★

Mason Road, Kidderminster, Worcestershire, DY11 6AL
Tel: 01562 515595 Fax: 01562 751103
SB £48 DB £59 HBS £60 HBD £80 B £7 D £12.
CC: MC Vi Am DC Swi Delt

How to get there: Follow directions to Telford and Bridgnorth on A442. At roundabout after Bewdley, turn left to police station. Hotel is 500m on left, opposite police station.

Properties displaying this symbol in the Guide have non smoking rooms available for guests. However, smokers should check in advance whether the Hotel or Guest Accommodation displaying this symbol actually allows smoking in any room.

Kington, Herefordshire

Burton Hotel

★★

Mill Street, Kington, Herefordshire, HR5 3BQ
Tel: 01544 230323 Fax: 01544 230323
Email: burton@hotelherefordshire.co.uk
Web: www.hotelherefordshire.co.uk
SB £42 DB £60 HBS £47 HBD £41
B £5.50 L £6.50 D £16. CC: MC Vi Am

How to get there: 14 miles from Leominster on the A44, driving due west. Three miles from the Welsh border.

Leamington Spa, Warwickshire

Angel Hotel

★★★

Regent Street, Leamington Spa, Warwickshire, CV32 4NZ
Tel: 01926 881296 Fax: 01926 881296
SB £35 DB £50 B £6 L £10.95 D £14.50.
CC: MC Vi Am DC Swi Delt

How to get there: Leamington Spa junction from M40, head for town centre. Turn off main parade opposite Barclay's Bank, up Holly Walk to archway car park.

Falstaff Hotel

★★★

16-20 Warwick New Road, Leamington Spa, Warwickshire, CV32 5JQ
Tel: 01926 312044 Fax: 01926 450574
Email: falstaff@meridianleisure.com
Web: www.meridianleisure.com
SB £70 DB £80 HBS £84 HBD £108
CC: MC Vi Am DC Swi Delt

Abbacourt

★★ ℛℛ

40 Kenilworth Road, Leamington Spa, Warwickshire, CV32 6JF
Tel: 01926 451755 Fax: 01926 886339
Email: abbacourt@maganto.freeserve.co.uk
SB £60 DB £80 HBS £75 HBD £95
B £6.95 L £4.50 D £4.50. CC: MC Vi Am Swi

How to get there: On the A452 Kenilworth road, 5 minutes walk from Leamington town centre.

Book with RAC Hotel Reservations and check the latest offers available. Call 0870 603 9109 and quote 'RAC Guide 2001'

Adams

★★

22 Avenue Road, Leamington Spa, Warwickshire, CV31 3PQ
Tel: 01926 450742 Fax: 01926 313110
SB £64 DB £68 B £6.50 L £18 D £22.
CC: MC Vi Am DC

How to get there: Situated on A452/A425. From M40 North, exit J-13, from South exit J-14. Follow signs to town centre.

Lansdowne

★★ ℛ

Clarendon Street, Leamington Spa, Warwickshire, CV32 4PF
Tel: 01926 450505 Fax: 01926 421313

Leominster, Herefordshire

Talbot Hotel

★★★

West Street, Leominster, Herefordshire, HR6 8EP
Tel: 01568 616347 Fax: 01568 614880

Town centre hotel, originally a 15th-century coaching house, beams and open fire. Ideal touring location, mid-Wales and Herefordshire. All bedrooms en-suite with modern-day facilities.
SB £48 DB £70 HBS £54 HBD £82
B £3 L £10.50 D £12.50.
CC: MC Vi Am DC Swi Delt JCB

How to get there: The Talbot Hotel is in the centre of Leominster, 26 miles from Worcester, Hereford 13 miles and Shrewsbury 40 miles.

Wharton Bank

♦♦

Leominster, Herefordshire, HR6 0NX
Tel: 01568 612575 Fax: 01568 616089

West Midlands

Lichfield, Staffordshire

Angel Croft

★★

Beacon Street, Lichfield, Staffordshire,
WS13 1AA
Tel: 01543 258737 Fax: 01543 415605

Coppers End Guest House

♦♦♦

Walsall Road, Muckley Corner, Lichfield,
Staffordshire, WS14 0BG
Tel: 01543 372910 Fax: 01543 360423
SB £25 DB £39 HBS £30 HBD £44 B £4
CC: MC Vi Am DC Delt

⊗ ⌂ ▭ ℙ ⚡ ℭ ⛄ ♁ ⚑ ⚓ ⓵

Long Compton, Warwickshire

Ascott House Farm

♦♦♦♦

Whichford, Shipston-on-Stour, Warwickshire,
CV36 5PP
Tel: 01608 684 655 Fax: 01608 684 539
Email: dp.haines.farms@farmline.com
Web: touristnetuk.com/wm/ascotthouse
Closed Christmas and New Year
SB £25 DB £42

⛄ ⌂ ▭ ℙ ⚡ ℭ ⛄ ♁ ⚓

How to get there: A3400 from Chipping Norton
to Long Compton. Right at end of village to
Whichford and Ascott. In Whichford ¹/₂ mile to
Ascott, then first right and first drive on right.

Lower Slaughter, Gloucestershire

Lower Slaughter Manor

★★★ ⚐ ⚐ ⚐

Lower Slaughter, Gloucestershire, GL54 2HP
Tel: 01451 820456 Fax: 01451 822150
Email: lowsmanor@aol.com
Web: www.lowerslaughter.co.uk
Children minimum age: 12
SB £175 DB £225 L £15 D £45.
CC: MC Vi Am DC Swi Delt

⛴ ▭ ☎ ℙ ⚡ ℭ ⛄ ♁ ⚓ ⚏ ⚑ ⚐ ✦

How to get there: From A429 Cirencester to
Stow-on-the-Wold road, just 2 miles from Stow,
follow signs to The Slaughters just past an Esso
garage. Entering the village, the Manor is on the
right.

Ludlow, Shropshire

Dinham Hall

★★★ ⚐ ⚐

Dinham, Ludlow, Shropshire, SY8 1EJ
Tel: 01584 876464 Fax: 01584 876019
SB £65 DB £110 B £7.50 L £26 D £26.
CC: MC Vi Am DC Swi Delt

⛴ ⛄ ⌂ ▭ ☎ ℙ ⚡ ℭ ⛄ ♁ ⚓ ⚏ ⓵

How to get there: From A49 Shrewsbury-
Hereford road, signs for town centre, signs for
Ludlow Castle, left in front Ludlow Castle:
Dinham Hall is 50m on left.

Number Twenty Eight `Little Gem`

♦♦♦♦♦

28 Lower Broad Street, Ludlow, Shropshire,
SY8 1PQ
Tel: 01584 876996 Fax: 01584 876860

Chadstone Guest House

♦♦♦♦ ⚐ ⚏ ⚑

Aston Munslow, Craven Arms, Shropshire,
SY7 9ER
Tel: 01584 841675 Fax: 01584 841620
Email: chasdstone.lee@btinternet.com
Children minimum age: 12

Friendly personal service, luxurious
accommodation, tastefully furnished and well
equipped bedrooms. Spacious lounge and
attractive dining room with panoramic views of
the Shropshire countryside.
SB £26 DB £52 HBS £40 HBD £80 D £15.

⊗ ⛄ ▭ ℙ ⚡ ℭ ⛄ ♁ ⚓ ⓵

How to get there: Turn east off A49 onto B4368
in Craven Arms. When in Aston Munslow, pass
Swan Inn; Chadstone 100m on right

The Church Inn

♦♦♦

Buttercross, Ludlow, Shropshire, SY8 1AW
Tel: 01584 872174 Fax: 01584 877146
How to get there: From A49 Shrewsbury-
Hereford road, signs for town centre. Inn is
behind the Buttercross in the centre.

Lydney, Gloucestershire

George Inn

◆◆◆

High Street, St Briavels, Lydney,
Gloucestershire, GL15 6TA
Tel: 01594 530228 Fax: 01594 530260
DB £45 CC: MC Vi DC Swi Delt
🐾🛢️🖥️📇🅿️🛋️🕯️🐎🎠🛏️🧺 ⅲ
How to get there: 6 miles from Chepstow on the
Lydney Road.

Malvern, Worcestershire

Holdfast Cottage

★★ 🅡🅡

Little Malvern, Malvern, Worcestershire,
WR13 6NA
Tel: 01684 310288 Fax: 01684 311117
Email: holdcothot@aol.com
Web: www.holdfast-cottage.co.uk
Closed early January

Enchanting wisteria-covered country house
hotel nestling into the foot of the Malvern Hills.
Award-winning restaurant, pretty en-suite
bedrooms, log fires, personal care and service
and a wonderfully warm and relaxing
atmosphere. Away Breaks available all week, all
year. Children and pets welcome.
SB £50 DB £90 HBS £74 HBD £66 D £24.
CC: MC Vi Swi
🐾⊗🛢️🖥️☎️🅿️🛋️🕯️🐎🎠🛏️🧺 ⅲ ▮
How to get there: Holdfast Cottage is situated
on the A4104 midway between the villages of
Welland and Little Malvern.

Malvern Hills Hotel

★★

Wynds Point, Malvern, Worcestershire,
WR13 6DW
Tel: 01684 540690 Fax: 01684 540327
Email: malhilhotl@aol.com
Web: www.malvernhillshotel.com
A character bedroomed country house hotel set

amidst the tranquillity of the Malvern Hills, with
direct access for walking. Excellent cuisine and
real ales. Pets welcome.
SB £40 DB £75 HBS £60 HBD £115
B £6.50 L £13 D £22.
CC: MC Vi Am DC Swi Delt
♿🛢️🐾⊗🛢️🖥️☎️🅿️🛋️🕯️🐎🎠🛏️🧺 ⅲ
ⅲ 🎧
How to get there: On A449 Malvern to Ledbury
road at junction with B4232 (opposite car park
for British Camp Iron Age hill fort).

Mount Pleasant

★★

Belle Vue Terrace, Malvern, Worcestershire,
WR14 4PZ
Tel: 01684 561837 Fax: 01684 569968
SB £49.50 DB £76 HBS £62.50 HBD £47.50
B £3.75 L £10.50 D £16.50.
CC: MC Vi Am DC Swi Delt
🛢️🖥️☎️🅿️🛋️🕯️🐎🎠🛏️🧺 ⅲ ▮

Thornbury House

★★

16 Avenue Road, Great Malvern,
Worcestershire, WR14 3AR
Tel: 01684 572273 Fax: 01684 577042/568548
Email: thornburyhousehotel@compuserve.com
SB £48 DB £70 HBS £48.50 HBD £48.50
B £8 D £5.
CC: MC Vi Am DC Swi Delt
🛢️🐾⊗🛢️🖥️🅿️🛋️🕯️🐎🎠🛏️🧺 ▮
How to get there: Follow signs for Great
Malvern Railway Station. Hotel is situated just
above the station.

Sidney House

◆◆◆

40 Worcester Road, Great Malvern,
Worcestershire, WR14 4AA
Tel: 01684 574994 Fax: 01684 574994
SB £20 DB £49 CC: MC Vi Am Swi Delt
🐾⊗🛢️🖥️🅿️🛋️🕯️🐎🎠🛏️🧺 ▮
How to get there: On the A449, 200m from the
town centre.

West Midlands

Market Drayton, Shropshire

Bear Hotel

★★

Hodnet, nr Market Drayton, TF9 3NH
Tel: 01630 685214 Fax: 01630 685787
SB £42.50 DB £62.50 B £7 L £10 D £15.
CC: MC Vi Am Swi Delt JCB

How to get there: At junction of A53/A442,
12 miles north of Telford.

Moreton-in-Marsh, Gloucestershire

Manor House

★★★ ☆☆

High Street, Moreton-in-Marsh, GL56 0LJ
Tel: 01608 650501 Fax: 01608 651481

Moreton House

★★★

High Street, Moreton-in-Marsh, GL56 0LQ
Tel: 01608 650747 Fax: 01608 652747
Email: moreton_house@msn.com
SB £24 DB £44 B £4 L £4.50
CC: MC Vi Swi Delt JCB

How to get there: Moreton House is in the
centre of Moreton-in-Marsh, at the junction of
the A429 and A44.

Crown Inn

High Street, Blockley, GL56 9EX
Tel: 01386 700245 Fax: 01386 700247
Email: info@thecrownatblockley.co.uk
Web: www.thecrownatblockley.co.uk
SB £70 DB £99 B £9.95 L £10 D £20. CC: MC
Vi Am DC Swi

How to get there: Located off the A44
Oxford/Evesham road between Moreton-in-
Marsh and Broadway.

Farriers Cottage

♦♦♦

44 Todenham, Moreton-in-Marsh,
Gloucestershire, GL56 9PF
Tel: 01608 652664 Fax: 01608 652668
Email: susanannwoolston@aol.com
Web: www.thefarrierscottage.co.uk
SB £25 DB £35

How to get there: Leave Moreton northbound on
A429. Take first right after railway bridge to
Todenham. Cottage opposite church and pub,
after three miles.

Nailsworth, Gloucestershire

Laurels at Inchbrook

♦♦♦

Inchbrook, Nailsworth, Gloucestershire,
GL5 5HA
Tel: 01453 834021 Fax: 01453 834021
Email: laurels@inchbrook.fsnet.co.uk
Web: www.smoothhound.co.uk/hotels/
thelaure.html
SB £30 DB £45 HBS £42 HBD £69
B £7 D £12.

How to get there: One mile north of Nailsworth,
3 miles south of Stroud. Just off the A46 on the
Inchbrook bends.

Newcastle-under-Lyme, Staffordshire

Borough Arms

★★

King Street, Newcastle-under-Lyme,
Staffordshire, ST5 1HX
Tel: 01782 629421 Fax: 01782 712388

Comfort Inn Newcastle-under-Lyme

★★

Liverpool Road, Newcastle-under-Lyme,
Staffordshire, ST5 9DX
Tel: 01782 717000 Fax: 01782 713669
Email: admin@gb617.u-net.com
Web: www.choicehotels.com

SB £55.25 DB £63 HBS £66 HBD £76.75
B £9.75 D £10.75.
CC: MC Vi Am DC Swi Delt

How to get there: Exit M6 J16, A500 for
Newcastle-under-Lyme, then the A34.

Nuneaton, Warwickshire

Ambion Court

♦♦♦♦

The Green, Dadlington, Nuneaton,
Warwickshire, CV13 6JB
Tel: 01455 212292 Fax: 01455 213141

Oakamoor, Staffordshire

Ribden Farm

 ◆◆◆◆

Oakamoor, Stoke-on-Trent, Staffordshire,
ST10 3BW
Tel: 01538 702830 Fax: 01538 702830
Email: chris@ribden.fsnet.co.uk
Web: www.ribdenfarm.com
SB £30 DB £44 CC: MC Vi Swi Delt Solo

How to get there: Situated on the B5417
Cheadle to Wardlow Road, on the right, ¹/₂ mile
before junction with A52. Ribden Farm is
second farm down drive.

Oswestry, Shropshire

Moreton Park Lodge

❖

Moreton Park, Gledrid, Chirk, LL14 5DG
Tel: 01691 776666 Fax: 01691 776655
Email: enquiries@moretonpark.com
Web: www.moretonpark.com
B £3.75 L £4.75 D £4.75.
CC: MC Vi Am Swi Delt Solo

How to get there: At intersection of A5 and
B5070, 3 miles north of Oswestry, 8 miles south
of Wrexham.
See advert on this page

Painswick, Gloucestershire

Painswick

★★★

Kemps Lane, Painswick, Gloucestershire,
GL6 6YB
Tel: 01452 812160 Fax: 01452 814059
Email: reservations@painswickhotel.com
Web: www.painswickhotel.com
SB £95 DB £120 HBS £100 HBD £95 B £8.5 L
£13 D £26. CC: MC Vi Am Swi Delt JCB

How to get there: Follow A46 to Painswick,
turning into St Mary's Street next to the church.
Follow the road around and turn right at The
March Hare. Hotel 200 yards on right.

If a Hotel or Guest Accommodation
does not display this 'dogs welcome'
symbol in its listing, the hotelier may
still be happy to welcome guests with guide
dogs, and you should contact the property to
discover whether this will be a problem.

Hambutts Mynd

◆◆◆

Edge Road, Painswick, GL6 6UP
Tel: 01452 812352 Fax: 01452 813862
Email: ewarland@aol.com
Children minimum age: 10. Closed February
SB £28 DB £46 CC: MC Vi Swi

How to get there: Entering Painswick from
Cheltenham, turn right at end of church wall.
From Stroud, take first left after car park.

Redditch, Worcestershire

Quality Hotel Redditch

★★★

Pool Bank, Southcrest, Redditch,
Worcestershire, B97 4JS
Tel: 01527 541511 Fax: 01527 402600
L £11.50 D £16.50.
CC: MC Vi Am DC Swi Delt

West Midlands

Campanile

Travel Accommodation

Far Moor Lane, Winyales Green, Redditch,
B98 0SD
Tel: 01527 510710 Fax: 01527 817269

Typical Campanile Bistro

Campanile hotels offer comfortable and
convenient budget accommodation and a
traditional French-style Bistro providing freshly
cooked food for breakfast, lunch and dinner. All
rooms en-suite with tea/coffee-making facilities,
DDT and TV with Sky channels.
SB £41.95 DB £41.95 HBS £50 HBD £66
CC: MC Vi Am DC Swi Delt

How to get there: Exit M42 J-3, A435 towards
Redditch. After 5 miles, take first exit onto
Coventry Road. Take first exit at roundabout
and stay in left lane.

Ross-on-Wye, Herefordshire

Chase Hotel

★★★ ℝ

Gloucester Road, Ross-on-Wye, HR9 5LH
Tel: 01989 763161 Fax: 01989 768330
Email: info@chasehotel.co.uk
Web: www.chasehotel.co.uk
Children minimum age: 12

Georgian Country House with extensive grounds
and gardens. The perfect rural location for
relaxation and comfort. Award-winning cuisine.

Event catering for up to 200 guests.
SB £70 DB £85 HBS £65 HBD £50
B £7.50 L £12.50 D £20. CC: MC Vi Swi Delt

How to get there: Exit M50 J-4, left for
Ross-on-Wye. A40 for Gloucester at 2nd
roundabout and right for town centre at 3rd
roundabout. Hotel on left.

Bridge House

★★

Wilton, Ross-on-Wye, Herefordshire, HR9 6AA
Tel: 01989 562655 Fax: 01989 567652
Email: alison@bhhotel.fsnet.co.uk

Peaceful family-run hotel, with extensive
riverside gardens, only 10 mins easy walk along
river to Ross-on-Wye town. Hospitality, service
and quality restaurant meals are our speciality.
SB £36 DB £55 HBS £51 HBD £86
B £7.50 D £15.50. CC: MC Vi Swi

How to get there: Before Wilton roundabout
(junction of A40 and A49).

Chasedale

★★

Walford Road, Ross-on-Wye, HR9 5PQ
Tel: 01989 562423 Fax: 01989 567900
Email: chasedale@supanet.co.uk
SB £33.50 DB £67 HBS £42 HBD £34 D £14.
CC: MC Vi DC Swi Delt JCB

How to get there: Half a mile from Ross-on-
Wye, south on B4234 Ross to Coleford road.

Saracens Head

★★

Symonds Yat East, Ross-on-Wye, HR9 6JL
Tel: 01600 890435 Fax: 01600 890034
Email: bookings@saracenshead.com
Web: www.saracenshead.com
Children minimum age: 9.
Closed December to January
SB £40 DB £60 B £6 L £6 D £10.

CC: MC Vi Swi Delt Electron Solo

How to get there: Exit A40 between Ross-on-Wye and Monmouth, signs to Symonds Yat East.
See advert on the right

Old Court

★

Symonds Yat West, Ross-on-Wye, HR9 6DA
Tel: 01600 890367 Fax: 01600 890964
Email: oldcourt@aol.com
Children minimum age: 12
SB £46.75 DB £73.50 B £10 D £22.
CC: MC Vi Am DC Swi Delt

How to get there: Midway between Ross-on-Wye and Monmouth.

Rosswyn

★

High Street, Ross-on-Wye, HR9 5BZ
Tel: 01989 562733 Fax: 01989 562733

Brynheulog

♦♦♦♦

Howle Hill, Ross-on-Wye, HR9 5SP
Tel: 01989 562051 Fax: 01989 562051

Garth Cottage

♦♦♦♦

Symonds Yat East, Herefordshire, HR9 6JL
Tel: 01600 890364 Fax: 01600 890364
Children minimum age: 12
Closed November to March
DB £48 HBD £80

How to get there: Leave A40 at Little Chef.
Follow signs for Symonds Yat East on B4229.

Sunnymount

♦♦♦♦

Ryefield Road, Ross-on-Wye, Herefordshire, HR9 5LU
Tel: 01989 563880

Inn On The Wye

♦♦♦

Kerne Bridge, Goodrich, nr Ross-on-Wye, Herefordshire, HR9 5QS
Tel: 01600 890872 Fax: 01600 890594
Web: www.theinnonthewye.co.uk
SB £36 DB £48 B £3.95 L £4.95 D £4.95.
CC: MC Vi Am DC Swi Delt

How to get there: 3 miles from Ross-on-Wye on the B4228 near Kerne Bridge.
See advert on the right

West Midlands

Vaga House

Wye Street, Ross-on-Wye, Herefordshire,
HR9 7BS
Tel: 01989 563024
Email: vagahouse@hotmail.com
Web: www.vagahouse.co.uk
SB £19 DB £23 HBS £29 HBD £55
B £3.50 D £4.25. CC: MC Vi Delt

How to get there: Situated at the top of Wye
Street, just below Tourist Information Centre.

The Whitehouse

Wye Street, Ross-on-Wye, Herefordshire,
HR9 7BX
Tel: 01989 763572 Fax: 01989 763572

Rugeley, Staffordshire

Cedar Tree

★★★

Main Road, Brereton, Rugeley, Staffordshire,
WS15 1DY
Tel: 01889 584241 Fax: 01889 575823

Attractive hotel with a warm, relaxed
atmosphere close to Lichfield and Cannock
Chase. All bedrooms are ensuite and well
appointed. Excellent restaurant and banqueting
facilities.
SB £42.50 DB £52.50 HBS £54 HBD £65 B £5
L £11.50 D £11.50. CC: MC Vi Am DC Swi Delt

How to get there: On A51 approximately 1 mile
from Rugeley town centre, 7 miles Lichfield.

Get your personalised route to the Hotel or
Guest Accommodation of your choice with
RAC's free on-line Route Planner facility —
visit www.rac.co.uk

Shrewsbury, Shropshire

Albright Hussey

★★★ ♟♟♟

Ellesmere Road, Shrewsbury,
Shropshire, SY4 3AF
Tel: 01939 290571 Fax: 01939 291143
Email: abhhotel@aol.com
Web: www.albrighthussey.co.uk
Children minimum age: 4
SB £79 DB £110 HBS £95 HBD £70.50
L £3.50 D £19.50. CC: MC Vi Am DC Swi Delt

How to get there: On A528 2½ miles north of
Shrewsbury. 400 yards from A49 bypass. On
leaving M54/A5, follow signs to Ellesmere.

Prince Rupert

★★★ ♟♟

Butcher Row, Shrewsbury,
Shropshire, SY1 1UQ
Tel: 01743 499955 Fax: 01743 357306
Email: post@prince-rupert-hotel.co.uk
Web: www.prince-rupert-hotel.co.uk
SB £85 DB £105 HBS £70 HBD £55
B £7.50 L £5 D £14. CC: MC Vi Am DC Swi Delt

How to get there: From the M54, signs for town
centre, over English Bridge, Wyle Cop, sharp
right into Fish Street. Hotel is 200m ahead.

Abbots Mead

★★

9–10 St Julians Friars, Shrewsbury,
Shropshire, SY1 1XL
Tel: 01743 235281 Fax: 01743 369133
Email: abbotsmead.hotel@virginnet.co.uk
Web: www.freespace.virginnet.co.uk/
                abbotsmead.hotel
SB £39 DB £56 HBS £54 HBD £86 B £5 D £15.
CC: MC Vi Am Swi Delt

How to get there: From M54, signs for town
centre, first sharp left, over English Bridge (by
Corn House Wine Bar), and hotel is on the left.

Nesscliffe

★★

Nesscliffe, Shrewshury, Shropshire, SY4 1DB
Tel: 01743 741430 Fax: 01743 741104
Email: nesscliffe@hotel01.fsnet.co.uk
SB £50 DB £60 B £6.50 L £4.50 D £6.95.
CC: MC Vi Swi Delt

How to get there: On the A5 between Oswestry
and Shrewsbury.

Shelton Hall

★★

Shelton, Shrewsbury, Shropshire, SY3 8BH
Tel: 01743 343982 Fax: 01743 241515

Solihull, West Midlands

Nailcote Hall

★★★★ ☂ ☂

Nailcote Lane, Berkswell,
Warwickshire, CV7 7DE
Tel: 024 76466174 Fax: 024 76470720
Email: info@nailcotehall.co.uk
Web: www.nailcotehall.co.uk

Charming Elizabethan house in 15 acres of
grounds. Relax in the Piano Bar Lounge, dine in
award-winning Oak Room Restaurant or
Mediterranean Rick's. Swimming pool, gym,
steam room, solarium, tennis, 9-hole golf course.
SB £145 DB £155 HBD £195
CC: MC Vi Am DC Swi Delt
🜨 ⅃ ⚏ ⚒ ☕ ☒ 🖵 ☎ ⚲ 🅿 ⚘ ⚡ ♞ ♄ 🐟 ☷
⚎ SPA ⟱ ⚐ ⚲ ☌ 🎬

Swallow St John's

★★★★

651 Warwick Road, Solihull,
West Midlands, B91 1AT
Tel: 0121 7113000 Fax: 0121 7113963
Email: solihull@swallow-hotels.co.uk
Web: www.swallowhotels.com
To become Renaissance, Spring 2001.
SB £150 DB £165 B £6 L £14.50 D £18.95
CC: MC Vi Am DC Swi Delt
🜨 ⅃ ⚏ ⚲ ⚒ ☕ 🖵 ☎ ⚲ 🅿 ⚘ ⚡ ♞ ♄ ⚲
🐟 ☷ ⚎ SPA ⟱ 🎬
How to get there: Exit M42 J-5, B4025 to
Solihull town centre. Drive through centre, over
roundabout, hotel on right.

Arden

★★★

Coventry Road, Bickenhill, Solihull,
West Midlands, B92 0EH
Tel: 01675 443221 Fax: 01675 443221

Flemings

★★

141 Warwick Road, Olton, Solihull,
West Midlands, B92 7HW
Tel: 0121 706 0371 Fax: 0121 706 4494
Email: reservations@flemingshotel.co.uk
Web: www.flemingshotel.co.uk
SB £32 DB £56 HBS £32 HBD £56
B £5 L £5 D £6.50. CC: MC Vi Am DC Swi Delt
⚲ ⚏ ⚒ 🖵 ☎ 🅿 ⚘ ⚡ ♞ ♄ ⚲ ⟱ ⚐ ⚬ ⚲
How to get there: Exit M42 J-5 for Solihull.
follow A41 to Olton. Turn right at T-junction.
Hotel is 2½ miles on right.

Stafford, Staffordshire

Quality Hotel Stafford

★★★

Pinfold Lane, Penkridge, Stafford,
Staffordshire, ST19 5QP
Tel: 01785 712459 Fax: 01785 715532
Email: admin@gb067.u-net.com
Web: www.qualityinn.com/hotel/gb067

SB £82 DB £110 HBS £90 HBD £120
B £9.95 L £11.50 D £16.95.
CC: MC Vi Am DC Swi Delt
🜨 ⚲ ⚏ ⚒ 🖵 ☎ ⚲ 🅿 ⚘ ⚡ ♞ ♄ ⚲ ⟱ ⚐
⚲ 🎬
How to get there: Exit M6 at either J-12 or J-13,
after 2 miles, at George and Fox pub, turn into
Pinfold Lane. Hotel on left-hand side.

Abbey

★★

65–68 Lichfield Road, Stafford,
Staffordshire, ST17 4LW
Tel: 01785 258531 Fax: 01785 246875
Closed Christmas and New Year
SB £35 DB £56 B £6 D £10.
CC: MC Vi Am Swi Delt
⚒ 🖵 ☎ 🅿 ⚘ ⚡ ♞ ⚲ ⚐
How to get there: Exit M6 J-13, for Stafford.
Turn right at Esso garage to roundabout, follow
Silkmore Lane. At 2nd roundabout take 2nd
exit. Hotel ¼ mile on right.

Albridge Hotel

★

72 Wolverhampton Road, Stafford, ST17 4AW
Tel: 01785 254100 Fax: 01785 223895
SB £26.95 DB £35.95 L £5.95 D £6.50.
CC: MC Vi Am DC Swi Delt

How to get there: Exit M6 J-13, signs for
Stafford. Hotel is on left after Telegraph Inn.

Leonards Croft

♦♦♦

80 Lichfield Road, Stafford,
Staffordshire, ST17 4LP
Tel: 01785 223676
Closed Christmas
SB £28 DB £48 CC: MC Vi

How to get there: Exit M6 J-13, A449, right at
Esso garage to roundabout. Hotel on A34, right.

Offley Grove Farm

♦♦♦

Adbaston, nr Eccleshall, Stafford,
Staffordshire, ST20 0QB
Tel: 01785 280205 Fax: 01785 250205
Email: accom@offleygrovefarm.freeserve.co.uk
Web: www.offleygrovefarm.freeserve.co.uk
SB £22 DB £40

How to get there: Situated between the villages
of Shebdon and Adbaston.

Staunton-on-Wye, Herefordshire

The Portway Inn

♦♦♦

The Brecon Road, Staunton-on-Wye HR4 7NH
Tel: 01981 500474

Stoke-on-Trent, Staffordshire

George Hotel

★★★

Swan Square, Burslem, Stoke-on-Trent,
Staffordshire, ST6 2AE
Tel: 01782 577544 Fax: 01782 837496
Email: georgestoke@btinternet.com
Web: www.georgehotelstock.cwc.net
Situated centrally for all local businesses,
pottery factories and tours. Alton Towers just 30
minutes drive. Award-winning restaurant,
friendly and comfortable surroundings.
SB £70 DB £90 B £7.95 L £10.95 D £16.95.
CC: MC Vi Am DC Swi Delt JCB

How to get there: Exit M6 J-15 or J-16, A500.
Left onto A53. Left at A50 junction.

North Stafford Hotel

★★★

Station Road, Stoke-on-Trent,
Staffordshire, ST4 2AE
Tel: 01782 744477 Fax: 01782 744580
Email: stuart.mcmanus@principalhotels.co.uk
Web: www.principalhotels.co.uk
SB £105 DB £130 HBS £115 HBD £140
B £10 L £9.95 D £16.95. CC: MC Vi Am DC Swi

How to get there: Exit M6 J-15, A555 ²/₃ mile,
signs for railway station, hotel directly opposite.

Hanchurch Manor   Little Gem

♦♦♦♦♦

Hanchurch, Stoke-on-Trent, ST4 8SD
Tel: 01782 643030 Fax: 01782 643035

The Olde House on the Green

♦♦♦♦

Fulford, Stoke-on-Trent, ST11 9QS
Tel: 01782 394555

Corrie Guest House

♦♦♦

13 Newton Street, Basford, Stoke-on-Trent,
Staffordshire, ST4 6JN
Tel: 01782 614838
Email: the.corrie@talk21.com

A warm and friendly welcome awaits you at this

fine Victorian house, ideally situated in the heart of the Potteries in a quiet location.
SB £22 DB £38
How to get there: From M6 take Junction 15 or 16 onto A500 towards Stoke. Take the A53 exit towards Newcastle-under-Lyme. Take the third left turn.

Rhodes
♦♦♦
42 Leek Road, Stoke-on-Trent, ST4 2AR
Tel: 01782 416320 Fax: 01782 416323
Email: rhodes.hotel@tesco.net
SB £20 DB £35 CC: MC Vi Delt
How to get there: On A52 Stoke to Leek 10 minutes from M6 J-15/16.

L.Beez Guest House
♦♦
46 Leek Road, Stoke-on-Trent, ST4 2AR
Tel: 01782 846727

Stonehouse, Gloucestershire

The Beacon Inn
♦♦♦
Haresfield, Stonehouse, GL10 3DX
Tel: 01452 728884

Stow-on-the-Wold, Gloucestershire

Wyck Hill House
★★★★
Burford Road, Stow-on-the-Wold, Cheltenham, Gloucestershire, GL54 1HY
Tel: 01451 831936 Fax: 01451 832243
Email: wychhill@wrengroup.com
Web: www.wyckhill.com
SB £105 DB £155 HBS £130 HBD £195
B £12.50 L £10 D £32.50.
CC: MC Vi Am DC Swi Delt
How to get there: On A424 towards Burford and Swindon, 3 miles south of Stow-on-the-Wold .

Fosse Manor
★★★
Stow-on-the-Wold, Cheltenham, Gloucestershire, GL54 1JX
Tel: 01451 830354 Fax: 01451 832486
Email: enquiries@fossemanor.co.uk
Web: www.fossemanor.co.uk
Closed Christmas

Rurally located Cotswold manor house in landscaped gardens.
SB £55 DB £98 HBS £78 HBD £156
B £8.50 L £12.50 D £25.
CC: MC Vi Am DC Swi Delt JCB
How to get there: 1 mile south of Stow-on-the-Wold on the A429 Warwick to Cirencester road.

Stow Lodge
★★★
The Square, Stow-on-the-Wold, GL54 1AB
Tel: 01451 830485 Fax: 01451 831671
Email: chris@stowlodge.com
Web: www.stowlodge.com

Closed Christmas and early January.
A friendly family-run Cotswold manor house hotel situated in its own grounds overlooking the Market Square of the historic town of Stow-on-the-Wold.
SB £60 DB £70 B £11 D £18.
CC: MC Vi DC Swi Delt
How to get there: The hotel is situated overlooking the Market Square and also has access off the A429 in Stow-on-the-Wold.

Limes

♦♦♦

Tewkesbury Road, Stow-on-the-Wold,
Gloucestershire, GL54 1EN
Tel: 01451 830034 Fax: 01451 830034
Closed Christmas
SB £26 DB £42

How to get there: Off A429 towards Evesham
and Broadway Road (A424). 300 yards on left.

Stratford-upon-Avon, Warwickshire

Heritage Hotels – The Alveston Manor

★★★★

Clopton Bridge, Stratford-upon-Avon,
Warwickshire, CV37 7HP
Tel: 01789 413205 Fax: 01789 413333
Email: gm1209@forte-hotels.com
Web: www.heritage-hotels.com
SB £131.75 DB £184 HBS £89 HBD £79
B £12 L £14 D £21. CC: MC Vi Am DC Swi Delt

How to get there: Exit M40 J-15, A46, A439 into
Stratford. Follow one-way system towards
Banbury/Oxford. Hotel situated just over bridge.

Heritage Hotels – The Shakespeare

★★★★

Chapel Street, Stratford-upon-Avon,
Warwickshire, CV37 6ER
Tel: 0870 400 8182 Fax: 01789 415411

Stratford Manor

★★★★

Warwick Road, Stratford-upon-Avon,
Warwickshire, CV37 0PY
Tel: 01789 731173 Fax: 01789 731131
Email: stratfordmanor@marstonhotels.com
Web: www.marstonhotels.co.uk
SB £110 DB £142 HBS £79.50 HBD £159 B £11
L £15.95 D £26. CC: MC Vi Am DC Swi Delt

How to get there: Exit M40 J-15, A46, A439 for
Stratford town centre. Hotel 1 mile on left.

MARSTON
HOTELS

Stratford Victoria

★★★★

Arden Street, Stratford-upon-Avon, CV37 6QQ
Tel: 01789 271000 Fax: 01789 271001
Email: stratfordvictoria@marstonhotels.com
Web: www.marstonhotels.co.uk

MARSTON
HOTELS

SB £98.50 DB £129 HBS £69.50 HBD £139
B £9.50 L £12.50 D £22.
CC: MC Vi Am DC Swi Delt

How to get there: Exit M40 J-15.

Welcombe

★★★★

Warwick Road, Stratford-upon-Avon, CV37 0NR
Tel: 01789 295252 Fax: 01789 414666
Web: www.welcombe.co.uk
SB £120 DB £180 B £9 L £14.50 D £32.50.
CC: MC Vi Am DC Swi Delt JCB

How to get there: Exit M40 J-15, A46, A439 for
3 miles. Hotel is on the right.

Grosvenor

★★★

Warwick Road, Stratford-upon-Avon, CV37 6YT
Tel: 01206 210001 Fax: 01206 212167
Email: sales@patenhotels.co.uk
Web: www.groshotelstratford.co.uk
SB £87.45 DB £107.40 HBD £60 B £8.95
L £11.50 D £16.50. CC: MC Vi Am DC Swi Delt

How to get there: A439 (A46) to Stratford. Hotel
is on Warwick Road (A439) in the centre.

Heritage Hotels – The Swan's Nest

★★★

Bridgefoot, Stratford-upon-Avon, CV37 7LT
Tel: 0870 400 8183 Fax: 01789 414547

Salford Hall

★★★

Abbots Salford, Warwickshire, WR11 5UT
Tel: 01386 871300 Fax: 01386 871301
Email: reception@salfordhall.co.uk
Web: www.salfordhall.co.uk
Closed Christmas
SB £80 DB £115 HBS £85 HBD £85 B £5.25
L £15.95 D £26.50. CC: MC Vi Am DC Swi Delt

How to get there: M40 J-15, A46 for 12 miles,
signs Salford Priors/Abbots Salford, 1½ miles.

Stratford Court

★★

Avenue Road, Stratford-upon-Avon,
Warwickshire, CV37 6UX
Tel: 01789 297799 Fax: 01789 262449

Avon View

♦♦♦♦

121 Shipston Road, Stratford-upon-Avon,
Warwickshire, CV37 9QL
Tel: 01789 297542 Fax: 01789 292936
SB £35 DB £60 HBS £48 HBD £85 D £13.
CC: MC Vi Am DC Swi Delt JCB

How to get there: South of river on A3400, or
walk from river bridge along old tramway walk.

Hampton Lodge Guest House

♦♦♦♦

38 Shipston Road, Stratford-upon-Avon,
Warwickshire, CV37 7LP
Tel: 01789 299374 Fax: 01789 299374
Email: reedbrew@aol.com
Web: www.hamptonlodge.co.uk
SB £45 DB £60 D £13. CC: MC Vi Am Swi Delt

How to get there: A3400 for Shipston, over
River Avon. Shipston Road is on right.

Hardwick House

♦♦♦♦

1 Avenue Road, Stratford-upon-Avon CV37 6UY
Tel: 01789 204307 Fax: 01789 296760
Email: hardwick@waveriver.co.uk
Web: www.stratford-upon-avon.co.uk/hardwick.
htm

Large Victorian house set in a quiet, mature,
tree-lined avenue, a few minutes walk from town
centre. Non-smoking bedrooms. Large car park.
SB £35 DB £55 CC: MC Vi Am Swi Delt

How to get there: Exit M40 J-15, A46, A439 to
centre. Right after 30mph sign into St Gregory's
Road. Hardwick House is 200m on the right.

Loxley Barn

♦♦♦♦

Stratford Road, Loxley, Stratford-upon-Avon,
Warwickshire, CV35 9JN
Tel: 01789 470028
Email: loxleybarn@hotmail.com
Web: members.tripod.co.uk/lizmac/
SB £30 DB £44

How to get there: From Wellesbourne, Loxley
Barn is 5th on right after church, sharing drive
with Loxley Farm. From Stratford, 4th on left.

Melita Private Hotel

♦♦♦♦

37 Shipston Road, Stratford-upon-Avon,
Warwickshire, CV37 7LN
Tel: 01789 292432 Fax: 01789 204867
Email: melita@email.msn.com
Web: www.stratford-upon-avon.co.uk/
melita.htm

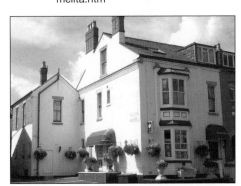

Beautifully appointed Victorian house offers a
friendly, cheerful service and excellent breakfast
menu. Ample parking, theatres and town centre 7
minute walk. En-suite, non-smoking bedrooms.
SB £49 DB £69 CC: MC Vi Am Swi Delt JCB

How to get there: On the A3400, south of town
centre. 150 yards from the Clopton Bridge.

Penryn Guest House

♦♦♦♦

126 Alcester Road, Stratford-upon-Avon,
Warwickshire, CV37 9DP
Tel: 01789 293718 Fax: 01789 266077
Email: penrynhouse@btinternet.com
Web: www.stratford-upon-avon/smoothhound.
co.uk/hotels/penry.html
SB £30 DB £50 CC: MC Vi Am DC Swi Delt
Solo, Maestro, JCB

How to get there: Exit M40 J-15, A46, A422 to
Stratford town centre. Penryn 1 mile on left.

West Midlands

Sequoia House

♦♦♦♦

51–53 Shipston Road, Stratford-Upon-Avon,
Warwickshire, CV37 7LN
Tel: 01789 268852 Fax: 01789 414559
Email: info@sequoiahotel.co.uk
Web: www.stratford-upon-avon.co.uk/
     sequoia.htm
Children minimum age: 5
SB £55 DB £69 CC: MC Vi Am DC Swi Delt
☻🕭🖵☎🅿️🐾🎠♞🏇🦮♨️🍴
How to get there: South of river on A3400,
Sequoia House is on the right.

Victoria Spa Lodge

♦♦♦♦

Bishopton Lane, Bishopton,
Stratford-upon-Avon, Warwickshire, CV37 9QY
Tel: 01789 267985 Fax: 01789 204728
Email: ptozer@victoriaspalodge.demon.co.uk
Web: www.stratford-upon-avon.co.uk/
     victoriaspa.htm

Explore the wonderful Cotswolds from this Grade
II listed lodge. Seven beautifully appointed ensuite bedrooms, with all modern facilities. Ample
parking. Completely non-smoking.
SB £52.50 DB £62.50 CC: MC Vi Swi Delt
☻🕭🖵🅿️🐾🎠♞🏇🦮

Cymbeline House

♦♦♦

24 Evesham Place, Stratford-upon-Avon,
Warwickshire, CV37 6HT
Tel: 01789 292958 Fax: 01789 292958

Ingon Bank Farm B&B

♦♦♦

Ingon Bank Farm, Warwick Road,
Stratford-upon-Avon, Warwickshire, CV37 0NY
Tel: 01789 292642 Fax: 01789 292642
Traditional farmhouse on a working farm, in a
quiet location two miles from Stratford-upon-
Avon. Comfortable en-suite bedrooms with all
facilities. Residents' lounge with open fire.

SB £25 DB £44
🐾☻🕭🖵🅿️🎠♞🏇🦮
How to get there: From Stratford, take A439
north towards Warwick for 2 miles. Ingon Bank
Farm is signposted on the left, 350 yards north
of the Snitterfield turning.

Marlyn

♦♦♦

3 Chestnut Walk, Stratford-upon-Avon,
Warwickshire, CV37 6HG
Tel: 01789 293752

Ambleside Guest House

♦♦

41 Grove Road, Stratford-upon-Avon,
Warwickshire, CV37 6PB
Tel: 01789 297239 Fax: 01789 295670

Nando's Guest House

♦♦

18 & 19 Evesham Place, Stratford-upon-Avon,
Warwickshire, CV37 6HT
Tel: 01789 204907 Fax: 01789 204907

Stroud, Gloucestershire

Bell Hotel

★★

Wallbridge, Stroud, Gloucestershire, GL5 3JA
Tel: 01453 763556 Fax: 01453 758611

Crown Inn

♦♦♦

Bath Road, Inchbrook, Stroud, Gloucestershire,
GL5 5HA
Tel: 01453 832914 Fax: 01453 832914
Web: www.inchbrook.cwc.net
SB £30 DB £45 B £2.50 L £4.95 D £4.95.
☻🕭🖵🅿️🐾🎠♞🏇🦮♨️🍴🎱🎧
How to get there: On the A46 between Stroud
and Nailsworth.

Downfield

♦♦♦

134 Cainscross Road, Stroud, GL5 4HN
Tel: 01453 764496 Fax: 01453 753150
Email: messenger@downfieldotel.demon.co.uk
Web: www.downfieldotel.demon.co.uk

A favourite for thousands of regular guests,
Maura and Nigel will give you a warm welcome
to this beautiful area of the south Cotswolds.
SB £40 DB £50 B £7 D £12.
CC: MC Vi Am Swi Delt

How to get there: Exit M5 J-13, A419 to Stroud.
After 5 miles, hotel situated on left.

Rose And Crown

♦♦♦

Nympsfield, Stonehouse, Stroud, GL10 3TU
Tel: 01453 860240 Fax: 01453 860240

Sutton Coldfield, West Midlands

New Hall Country House

★★★★ ଛ ଛ ଛ
Walmley Road, Sutton Coldfield, B76 1QX
Tel: 0121 378 2442 Fax: 0121 378 4637
Email: newhall@thistle.co.uk
Web: www.slh.com/newhall
Children minimum age: 8

The oldest moated manor house in England,
personally run. Now with health and beauty spa.
Offers a unique haven for the leisure and
business traveller.
SB £120 DB £146 HBS £146 HBD £192
£14.50 L £20 D £32.50.
CC: MC Vi Am DC Swi Delt

Moor Hall

★★★ ଛ
Moor Hall Drive, Sutton Coldfield, B75 6LN
Tel: 0121 308 3751 Fax: 0121 308 8974
Email: mail@moorhallhotel.co.uk
Web: www.moorhallhotel.co.uk

Country house hotel set in parkland yet within
easy reach of Birmingham and NEC. Restaurant
with RAC Dining Award, extensive conferencing
and leisure facilities. Ample free parking.
SB £105 DB £120 HBS £125 HBD £160
B £9.50 L £8.95 D £19.50. CC: MC Vi Am Swi

How to get there: From M42 J-9, A446, A453 to
Sutton Coldfield, right at lights into Weeford Rd.

Telford, Shropshire

Clarion, Madeley Court

★★★ ଛ ଛ
Castle Fields Way, Madeley Court, TF7 5DW
Tel: 01952 680068 Fax: 01952 684275
Email: admin@gb068.u-net.com

SB £105 DB £125 HBS £125 HBD £165
L £8 D £21. CC: MC Vi Am DC Swi Delt JCB

How to get there: Exit M54 J-4, A442 for
Kidderminster to Castlefields roundabout.

The Hundred House

★★ ♟♟

Bridgenorth Road, Norton, Telford, TF11 9EE
Tel: 01952 730353 Fax: 01952 730355
Email: hphundredhouse@compuserve.com
SB £69 DB £95 HBS £90 HBD £115 B £7.95
L £16.95 D £25. CC: MC Vi Swi Delt JCB

How to get there: Situated 6 miles south of
Telford on A442 between Telford/Bridgenorth.

White House

★★ ♟

Wellington Road, Muxton, Telford, TF2 8NG
Tel: 01952 604276 Fax: 01952 670336

Tetbury, Gloucestershire

Calcot Manor

★★★ ♟♟♟

nr Tetbury, Gloucestershire, GL8 8YJ
Tel: 01666 890891 Fax: 01666 890894
Email: reception@calcotmanor.co.uk
Web: www.calcotmanor.co.uk
Charming Cotswold stone manor house
originally dating back to the 15th century.

SB £115 DB £150 L £13.50 D £20.
CC: MC Vi Am DC Delt0

How to get there: 3 miles outside Tetbury, on
the crossroads of the A4135 and A46.

The Hare & Hounds

★★★

Westonbirt, Tetbury, Gloucestershire, GL8 8QL
Tel: 01666 880233 Fax: 01666 880241
SB £76 DB £91 HBS £96 HBD £130
CC: MC Vi Am DC Swi Delt

How to get there: On A433 2½ miles south.
See advert on below

Tavern House `Little Gem`

♦♦♦♦♦   ⤜ ⍭

Willesley, Tetbury, Gloucestershire, GL8 8QU
Tel: 01666 880444 Fax: 01666 880254
Children minimum age: 10
SB £49.50 DB £69 B £7.95 CC: MC Vi

⊗ ⨄ ☐ ☎ 🅿 ⍤ ⍒ 🐎 ♉ ⛩

How to get there: M4 J-118, A46, A433, 4 miles.
Willesley after Didmarton. Tavern House on right.

Tewkesbury, Gloucestershire

Chestal Cottage

♦♦♦   ⤜

High Street, Kemerton, Tewkesbury,
Gloucestershire, GL20 7HP
Tel: 01386 725717 Fax: 01242 261655
Email: pettman@supanet.co.uk
SB £25 DB £34

⊗ ⨄ ☐ ⍤ ⍒ 🐎 ⛩

How to get there: Chestal Cottage is situated on
the main street, next door to the village shop.

Thornbury, Gloucestershire

Thornbury Castle

★★★ ♙♙♙

Thornbury, Gloucestershire, BS35 1HH
Tel: 01454 281182 Fax: 01454 416188
Email: thornburycastle@compuserve.com
Web: www.thornburycastle.com
Closed 4 days in early January
SB £105 DB £130 B £8.95 L £16.50 D £39.50.
CC: MC Vi Am DC Swi Delt

◬ ⍾ ⨄ ☐ ☎ 🅿 ⍤ ⍒ 🐎 ♉ ⛩ ⌗ ⑃

How to get there: A38 to Thornbury High Street,
left into Castle St. behind St Mary's church.
See advert on the right above

Tutbury, Staffordshire

Ye Olde Dog & Partridge

★★★ ♙♙

High Street, Tutbury, Burton-upon-Trent,
Staffordshire, DE13 9LS
Tel: 01283 813030 Fax: 01283 813178
Email: info@yeoldedogandpartridge.co.uk
Closed Christmas to New Year
SB £55 DB £70 B £6 L £5.95 D £5.95.
CC: MC Vi Am Swi

⍾ 🦌 ⊗ ⨄ ☐ ☎ ☏ 🅿 ⍤ ⍒ 🐎 ♉ ⛩ ⑃

How to get there: Exit M1 J-24, A50, A511 for
Burton-on-Trent and follow signs for Tutbury.
See advert on right

Thornbury Castle

This beautiful 16th-century castle, once
owned by Henry VIII, stands in 15 acres of
regal splendour. Surrounded by its vineyard
and Tudor Garden, it is renowned for being
one of the finest Country House Hotels in
England. The recipient of many prestigious
awards for its fine food and excellent
accommodation.

Thornbury, Gloucestershire BS35 1HH
Tel: 01454 281182 Fax: 01454 416188
Email: thornburycastle@compuserve.com
Website: www.thornburycastle.com

Ye Olde Dog & Partridge

One of England's oldest and finest coaching
inns, situated in the historic village of Tutbury.
This warm and friendly hotel offers luxury
accommodation and excellent dining facilities
in both the famous Carvery and Brasserie
Restaurants. All 20 bedrooms have been
individually designed and furnished to the
highest standards. Short breaks available all year.

High Street, Tutbury, Staffordshire DE13 9LS
Tel: 01283 813030   Fax: 01283 813178
Email: info@yeoldedogandpartridge.co.uk

West Midlands

Upper Slaughter, Gloucestershire

Lords Of The Manor

★★★ ♔♔♔♔

Upper Slaughter, Gloucestershire, GL54 2JD
Tel: 01451 820243 Fax: 01451 820696
Email: lordsofthemanor@btinternet.com
Web: www.lordsofthemanor.com
Children minimum age: 9

A 17th-century former rectory set amidst eight acres of gardens. Comfortable surroundings and fine cuisine make it an ideal base to explore the Cotswolds.
SB £99 DB £145 HBD £89 B £11 L £15.95
D £34. CC: MC Vi Am DC Swi Delt JCB

Upton-upon-Severn, Worcestershire

White Lion

★★★ ♔

High Street, Upton-upon-Severn,
Worcestershire, WR8 0HJ
Tel: 01684 592551 Fax: 01684 593333

Uttoxeter, Staffordshire

Oldroyd Guest House

♦♦♦

18-22 Bridge Street, Uttoxeter, Staffordshire,
ST14 8AP
Tel: 01889 562763 Fax: 01889 568916

Walsall, West Midlands

Quality Boundary Hotel

★★★

Birmingham Road, Walsall, West Midlands,
WS5 3AB
Tel: 01922 633609 Fax: 01922 635727
Email: boundryhotel@talk21.com

SB £90 DB £85 B £7.95 L £5 D £10.
CC: MC Vi Am DC Swi Delt

How to get there: M6 J-7, A34 for Walsall. Hotel is 1½ miles on left towards Walsall.

Quality Hotel and Suites Walsall

★★★

Wolverhampton Road West, Bentley, Walsall,
West Midlands, WS2 0BS
Tel: 01922 724444 Fax: 01922 723148
Email: admin@gb622.u-net.com
Web: www.qualityinn/hotel/gb622

B £7.50 L £6.95 D £11.95.
CC: MC Vi Am DC Swi Delt JCB

How to get there: Located at J-10 of M6.

Abberley

★★

29 Bescot Road, Walsall, WS2 9AD
Tel: 01922 627413 Fax: 01922 720933
Email: abberley.hotel@virgin.net
Web: www.abberleyhotel.co.uk
SB £44.95 DB £64.95 HBS £58.95 HBD £92.95
B £5.95 L £6.95 D £13.95.
CC: MC Vi Am Swi Delt

How to get there: Exit M6 J-9, signs to Walsall. At lights bear left. Hotel then visible on right.

Royal

★★

Ablewell Street, Walsall, WS1 2EL
Tel: 01922 24555 Fax: 01922 30028

Warwick, Warwickshire

Chesford Grange

★★★

Chesford Bridge, Kenilworth, CV8 2LD
Tel: 01926 515106 Fax: 01926 855272
Email: karen.everitt@principalhotels.co.uk
Web: www.principalhotels.co.uk
SB £120 DB £135 HBS £54 HBD £108 B £10.50
L £11.95 D £18.50. CC: MC Vi Am DC Swi Delt

How to get there: Exit M40 J-15, A46 for Coventry, A452 Leamington, right at roundabout to Leamington; hotel is 250 yards on right.

Glebe
★★★
Church Street, Barford, Warwick, CV35 8BS
Tel: 01926 624218 Fax: 01926 624625

Warwick Arms
★★
17 High Street, Warwick, Warwickshire,
CV34 4AT
Tel: 01926 492759 Fax: 01926 410587

Croft Guest House
♦♦♦♦
Haseley Knob, Warwick, Warwickshire,
CV35 7NL
Tel: 01926 484447 Fax: 01926 484447
Email: david@croftguesthouse.co.uk
Web: www.croftguesthouse.co.uk
SB £34 DB £48 CC: MC Vi Am
Delt
How to get there: From A46 follow A4177 for 4
miles to second roundabout. Turn right (still
A4177). After ¹/₂ mile turn right to Haseley Knob
village.

King's Head Inn
♦♦♦
39 Saltisford, Warwick, Warwickshire, CV34 4TD
Tel: 01926 775177 Fax: 01926 775166
Email: thekingsheadwarwick@hotmail.com
Web: www.thekingsheadwarwick.co.uk
SB £50 DB £60 B £4 L £6 D £11.
CC: MC Vi Swi

Old Rectory
♦♦♦
Vicarage Lane, Sherbourne, Warwick, CV35 8AB
Tel: 01926 624562 Fax: 01926 624995
SB £35 DB £45 HBS £50 HBD £60 D £15.
CC: MC Vi DC Swi Delt

How to get there: Exit M40 J-15. Follow A46 to
Stratford. Hotel is ¹/₄ mile down on left.

24 Coton End
♦♦
Warwick, Warwickshire, CV34 4NP
Tel: 01926 491355

Whitchurch, Shropshire

Dukes
♦♦♦♦
Halghton, Whitchurch, Shropshire, SY13 3DU
Tel: 01948 830269
Email: gilberts@thedukes.fsbusiness.co.uk
SB £30 DB £54
How to get there: At Whitchurch, take A525 for
Wrexham. After 6 miles, turn left for Horseman's
Green. Proceed past houses, then turn right for
Halghton. The hotel is on right after ¹/₂ mile.

Roden View Guest House
♦♦♦♦
Dobson Bridge, Whixall, Whitchurch,
Shropshire, SY13 2QL
Tel: 01348 710320 Fax: 01348 710320
SB £18 DB £36 HBS £28 HBD £56 B £5 L £10
D £10. CC: Cheque

How to get there: From Whitchurch, B5476 for
Wem. After 5 miles, pass Bull & Dog Pub. Next
right and travel for 2 miles, left at T-junction.
Over canal bridge, Roden View on left.

Whittington, Shropshire

Ye Olde Boot Hotel
★
Castle Street, Whittington, Shropshire,
SY11 4DF
Tel: 01691 662250

Wolverhampton, West Midlands

Connaught Hotel
★★★
Tettenhall Road, Wolverhampton,
West Midlands, WV1 4SW
Tel: 01902 24433 Fax: 01902 710353

Novotel Wolverhampton
★★★
Union Street, Wolverhampton, WV1 3JN
Tel: 01902 871100 Fax: 01902 870054
Email: h1188@accor-hotels.com
Children minimum age: 16
SB £81 DB £90 HBS £97 HBD £122 B £9 L £13
D £16. CC: MC Vi Am DC Swi Delt
How to get there: From M6, M5, M54, follow
signs to Woverhampton town centre, then
railway station. Hotel on St George's ring road.

Quality Hotel

★★★ ⓡ

Penn Road, Wolverhampton, West Midlands,
WV3 0ER
Tel: 01902 429216 Fax: 01902 710419
Email: admin@gb069.u-net.com
Web: www.qualityinn.com/hotel/gb069

SB £92.75 DB £116.50 HBS £100 HBD £130
B £9.75 L £10.50 D £16.95.
CC: MC Vi Am DC Swi Delt

How to get there: Exit M6 J-10, A454 to
Wolverhampton. At town centre, signs for A449
Kidderminster. Hotel is ¼ mile on right.

Barons Court

★★

142 Gold Thorn Hill, Wolverhampton, WV2 3JE
Tel: 01902 341751 Fax: 01902 340033
Email: info@baronscourthotel.com
Web: www.baronscourthotel.com
Children minimum age: 10

This country house hotel situated near the
centre of town retains its Edwardian charm and
character. Original oak floors and beams.
Graceful dining room, innovative menu.
SB £45 DB £60 HBS £57.50 HBD £63.50
B £5 D £12.50. CC: MC Vi Swi Delt

How to get there: Take A449 Kidderminster road
from Wolverhampton ring road. At 3rd set of
lights (1 mile) turn left into Goldthorn Hill.

Worcester, Worcestershire

Heritage Hotels – The Giffard

★★★

High Street, Worcester, WR1 2QR
Tel: 0870 400 8133 Fax: 01905 723458

Maximillian

★

Shrub Hill Road, Worcester, WR4 9EF
Tel: 01905 23867 Fax: 01905 724935
Email: maximillian.hotel@tinyworld.co.uk
SB £40 DB £53 HBS £55 HBD £83
CC: MC Vi Am DC Swi Delt

How to get there: At first roundabout in
Worcester from M5 J-7, straight on, second
roundabout right, third straight on, fourth left,
fifth straight on. Through tunnel, turn right. Hotel
after traffic lights.

Manor Arms Country Inn

♦♦♦

Abberley Village, Worcestershire, WR6 6BN
Tel: 01299 896507 Fax: 01299 896723
Email: themanorarms@btconnect.com
Web: www.themanorarms.co.uk
SB £38 DB £50 B £6 L £5 D £10. CC: MC Vi

How to get there: Leave A443 at Abberley and
follow signs to 'Norman Church' and Abberley
Village. As you enter the village the Manor Arms
is located on the left, opposite the church.

Park House

♦♦♦

12 Droitwich Road, Worcester,
Worcestershire, WR3 7LJ
Tel: 01905 21816 Fax: 01905 612178

Wotton-Under-Edge, Gloucestershire

Burrows Court

♦♦♦

Nibley Green, North Nibley, Gloucestershire,
GL11 6AZ
Tel: 01453 546230 Fax: 01453 544536
Email: p.f.rackley@tesco.net
Web: www.burrowscourt.co.uk
Closed January to February
SB £35 DB £52 CC: MC Vi

How to get there: From the A38 Bristol to
Gloucester road, turn off at sign to Blanchworth,
North Nibley, Stinchcombe. Hotel opposite
North Nibley village sign.

Save 20%
on 12 issues of *Top Gear*
Britain's best motoring magazine

Why Subscribe...

- Save 20% on 12 issues of *Top Gear*
- Free delivery – every issue delivered straight to your door
- Be the first – read *Top Gear* magazine before it goes on sale in the shops
- Never miss an issue
- Avoid any price rises for a whole year

What you get...

- The UK's best motoring magazine
- Comprehensive new and used car buying information
- Road tests on all the latest models
- Features on a wide range of motoring topics from off-roading to rally driving
- Comment from *Top Gear* columnists

Subscribe now... Subscribing to Top Gear couldn't be easier.

To receive 12 issues of the best motoring magazine around for the very special price of **£31.68** call our credit card hotline on **01795 414 714**, quoting code RACG00.

Northeast

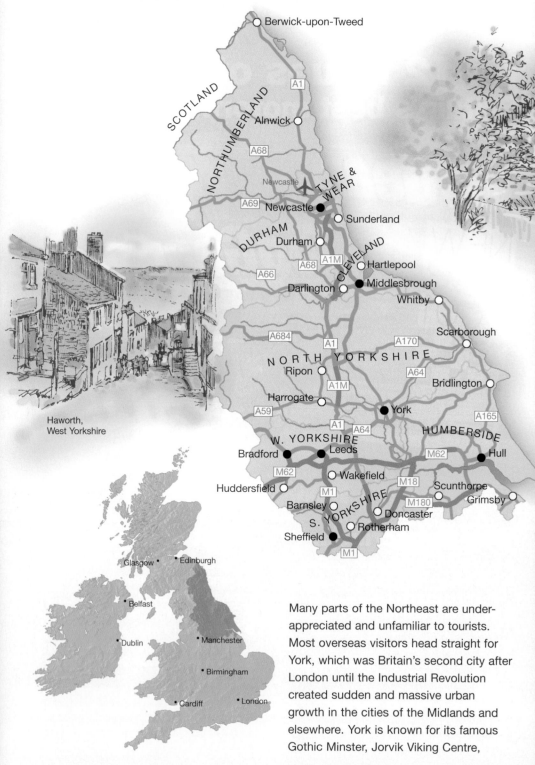

Berwick-upon-Tweed

SCOTLAND

NORTHUMBERLAND

A1

Alnwick

A68

Newcastle

TYNE & WEAR

A69 Newcastle

Sunderland

DURHAM

Durham

A68 A1M

Hartlepool

CLEVELAND

A66

Darlington Middlesbrough

Whitby

A684

A1 A170

Scarborough

N O R T H   Y O R K S H I R E

Ripon

A64

Bridlington

A1M

Harrogate

A59

York

A165

A1 A64

HUMBERSIDE

W. YORKSHIRE

Bradford Leeds

M62 Hull

M62

Wakefield

M18

Huddersfield

M1

Scunthorpe

Barnsley

S. YORKSHIRE

M180 Grimsby

Doncaster

Sheffield Rotherham

M1

Haworth,
West Yorkshire

Glasgow   Edinburgh

Belfast

Dublin   Manchester

Birmingham

Cardiff   London

Many parts of the Northeast are under-
appreciated and unfamiliar to tourists.
Most overseas visitors head straight for
York, which was Britain's second city after
London until the Industrial Revolution
created sudden and massive urban
growth in the cities of the Midlands and
elsewhere. York is known for its famous
Gothic Minster, Jorvik Viking Centre,

Newcastle-upon-Tyne

restored medieval streets, its racecourse and riverside gardens.

Yorkshire, which is comprised of the counties of North Yorkshire, West Yorkshire, South Yorkshire and Humberside (which largely replaced the old East Riding of Yorkshire), has two superb National Parks: the Yorkshire Dales and the North York Moors, both known for their ruggedly beautiful landscape, stone-built villages and, in the latter case, stunning coastline. Seaside towns such as Scarborough exude a graceful Victorian ambience, as does the spa town of Harrogate, while smaller places like Robin Hood's Bay complement the rugged coastline that becomes spectacular as it climbs into Northumberland.

In the 19th century Yorkshire was known for its socially-conscious industrial entrepreneurs, and just outside Bradford is the purpose-built millworkers' village of Saltaire, a commendable Victorian endeavour in creating good housing and social amenities for industrial workers and their families.

Literary fans will revel in a visit to Haworth, hometown of the Brontë sisters and full of artifacts and memorabilia associated with their lives. Haworth is geared for tourism, with over a quarter of a million coming each year.

Visitors to Leeds and Sheffield will find impressive city centres utterly transformed from the gloomy industrial conurbations they were just a few decades ago. Leeds boasts the Royal Armouries Museum and Sheffield has the National Centre for Popular Music, as well as the Peak District National Park just outside its suburbs.

North of Yorkshire County Durham offers a change in character. For centuries the Northeast ruled itself as an independent region and served as a bulwark to successive invasions. It was normally around Durham that the English halted invading Scots. The Roman Hadrian's Wall is accessible to sightseers in many places, and the moody silhouette of Bamburgh Castle will be familiar to many visitors through the countless published photographs of it.

The city of Durham centres on a loop in the River Wear and boasts a fine Cathedral where St Cuthbert is interred, surrounded by the massive piers of Romanesque construction, and a castle – home to the bishops of Durham until 1836. Durham University is the third oldest in England and gives the city a cultured and academic feel.

Newcastle-upon-Tyne is effectively the Northeast's capital and is famous for its independent spirit. The city's heart has been revitalised, and now includes the pleasant Quayside and the MetroCentre, as well as the high-tech International Centre for Life, a biotechnology research complex open to the public. In 2001 the Baltic Flour Mill is due to be reopened as a visual arts focus.

Alnwick, Northumberland

Bondgate House

♦♦♦

20 Bondgate Without, Alnwick, Northumberland, NE66 1PN
Tel: 01665 602025 Fax: 01665 602554
Email: kenforbes@lineone.net
Web: www.bondgatehouse.ntb.org.uk
SB £25 DB £47 HBS £38 HBD £73
CC: MC Vi Swi Delt JCB Eurocard

How to get there: Leave A1 at Alnwick turnoff. Head for town centre. Bondgate House Hotel is 200yds on right past war memorial.

Ampleforth, North Yorkshire

Shallowdale House   Little Gem

♦♦♦♦♦

West End, Ampleforth, North Yorkshire, YO62 4DY
Tel: 01439 788325 Fax: 01439 788885
Children minimum age: 12.
Closed Christmas to New Year
SB £44 DB £64 HBS £65 HBD £106
CC: MC Vi Delt

How to get there: At the west end of Ampleforth, on the turning to Hambleton.

Austwick, North Yorkshire

Austwick Country House

★★

Austwick, Settle, North Yorkshire, LA2 8BY
Tel: 01524 251224 Fax: 01524 251224
Email: austwickh@cs.com

The Yorkshire Dales' best kept secret. A Georgian Country House Hotel dating from 1750. Furnished with English and Oriental Antiques. RAC Dining Award restaurant. Twelve exclusive ensuite bedrooms.

SB £45 DB £100 HBS £65 HBD £140
L £5.50 D £20. CC: MC Vi Swi

How to get there: A65 Skipton to Kendal. Three miles past Settle right at Cross Street Pub into National Park. ³/₄ mile over bridge, hotel on the left.

Bamburgh, Northumberland

Waren House

★★★

Waren Mill, Belford, Northumberland, NE70 7EE
Tel: 01668 214581 Fax: 01668 214484
Email: enquiries@warenhousehotel.co.uk
Web: www.warenhousehotel.co.uk
Children minimum age: 14
SB £80.50 DB £115 HBS £95 HBD £58.50
B £14.50 D £18.45.
CC: MC Vi Am DC Swi Delt

How to get there: 14 miles south of Berwick-upon-Tweed. Take B1342, off the A1, to Waren Mill Hotel on southwest corner of Bodle Bay.

Lord Crewe Arms

★★

Front Street, Bamburgh, Northumberland, NE69 7BL
Tel: 01668 214243 Fax: 01668 214273

Barnard Castle, County Durham

Old Well Inn

♦♦♦

21 The Bank, Barnard Castle, County Durham, DL12 8PH
Tel: 01833 690130 Fax: 01833 690140
Email: reservations@oldwellinn.co.uk
Web: www.oldwellinn.co.uk
SB £48 DB £60 B £5 L £3 D £8.
CC: MC Vi Am Swi Delt

How to get there: Centre of Barnard Castle below the Market Cross, in the Antique Quarter.

Batley, West Yorkshire

Alder House

★★

Towngate Road, Healey Lane, Batley, West Yorkshire, WF17 7HR
Tel: 01924 444777 Fax: 01924 442644
Email: info@alderhousehotel.co.uk
Web: www.alderhousehotel.co.uk

SB £47.50 DB £55 B £6.95 L £7.95 D £16.
CC: MC Vi Am DC Swi Delt

Beadnell, Northumberland

Low Dover Bed & Breakfast

◆◆◆◆

Low Dover, Harbour Road, Beadnell,
Northumberland, NE67 5BJ
Tel: 01665 720291 Fax: 01665 720291
Email: kathandbob@lowdover.co.uk
Web: www.lowdover.co.uk
Children minimum age: 12

Relax in our splendid beach-side home.
Immaculate ground-floor suites. Enjoy breakfast
with panoramic sea views across Beadnell Bay.
Beautiful garden, golden beach 50 yards.
Superb website. Also superior self-catering
ETC four diamonds.
DB £52
CC: MC Vi Swi Delt

How to get there: Signs to Beadnell Harbour.
Low Dover is last house on right, by the beach.

Bedale, North Yorkshire

Elmfield Country House

◆◆◆◆◆

Arrathorne, Bedale, North Yorkshire, DL8 1NE
Tel: 01677 450558 Fax: 01677 450557
Email: bed@elmfieldhouse.freeserve.co.uk
Web: www.countryhouseyorkshire.co.uk
SB £35 DB £50 HBS £47 HBD £74 D £12.
CC: MC Vi Swi Delt

How to get there: From A1, A684 into Bedale,
on towards Leyburn after Patrick Brompton.
Right at crossroads for Richmond. Elmfield is
1½ miles on right.

Southfield

◆◆◆

96 South End, Bedale, North Yorkshire,
DL8 2DS
Tel: 01677 423510
SB £22 DB £44

How to get there: A1 to Bedale. Left at 'White
Bear'. Hotel 400yds on right, with privet hedge
and white stone front.

Belford, Northumberland

Blue Bell

★★★

Market Square, Belford, Northumberland,
NE70 7ND
Tel: 01668 213543 Fax: 01668 213787
Email: bluebel@globalnet.co.uk
Web: www.bluebellhotel.com
SB £39 DB £78 HBS £49 HBD £98 B £7 L £7
D £23. CC: MC Vi Am Swi Delt

See advert below

The
Blue Bell
Hotel

Perfectly situated between Northumberland's
magnificent coastline and superb National
Parks, the Hotel offers delightful ensuite
bedrooms, excellent cuisine in three individual
restaurants and an RAC Dining Award for food.
Short breaks for golf, birdwatching and walking
are available all year round.

Market Place, Belford, NE70 7NE
Tel: 01668 213543   Fax: 01668 213787
Email: bluebel@globalnet.co.uk
Website: www.bluebellhotel.com

Northeast

Bellingham, Northumberland

Riverdale Hall

★★ ♖

Bellingham, Northumberland, NE48 2JT
Tel: 01434 220254 Fax: 01434 220457
Email: iben@riverdalehall.demon.co.uk

A stone-built 19th century mansion with a modern wing set in five acres of grounds alongside the North Tyne River.
SB £48 DB £84 HBS £67 HBD £122 B £9.95 L £10.95 D £19.95. CC: MC Vi Am DC Swi Delt

How to get there: Off B6320 after bridge onto C200. Hotel is 150yds on left.

Berwick-upon-Tweed, Northumberland

Kings Arms

★★★

Hide Hill, Berwick-upon-Tweed,
Northumberland, TD15 1EJ
Tel: 01289 307454 Fax: 01289 308867
Email: greathouseat@btconnect.com
Web: www.greathouseatsonning.com
SB £59.50 DB £79.50 HBS £74.50 HBD £109.50 B £8.50 L £6.50 D £12.50.
CC: MC Vi Am DC Swi

How to get there: Town centre. Enter High Street from south over bridge, from north on A1. First right turn past the Guildhall.
See advert on facing page bottom

Queen's Head

★

Sandygate, Berwick-upon-Tweed,
Northumberland, TD15 1EP
Tel: 01289 307852 Fax: 01289 307858
SB £35 DB £60 HBS £50 HBD £90
B £6.50 L £9.50 D £15. CC: MC Vi Swi

How to get there: Main street, pass town hall, first right into Hide Hill. Hotel at bottom of hill.

Beverley, Humberside

Tickton Grange

★★★ ♖♖

Tickton, Beverley, Humberside, HU17 9SH
Tel: 01964 543666 Fax: 01964 542556
Email: maggy@tickton-grange.demon.co.uk
Web: www.ticktongrange.co.uk
B £8.50 L £15.95 D £25.
CC: MC Vi Am DC Swi Delt

How to get there: 3 miles from Beverley on A1035.

Manor House

★★ ♖♖♖

Northlands, Walkington, Beverley, Humberside, HU17 8RT
Tel: 01482 881645 Fax: 01482 866501
Email: derek@the-manor-house.co.uk
Web: www.the-manor-house.co.uk
Children minimum age: 12
SB £78.50 DB £97 B £4.50 D £18.50.
CC: MC Vi Swi Delt

How to get there: On the Newbald Road between Walkington and Bishop Burton, 2 miles west of Beverley.

Eastgate Guest House

♦♦♦ ✍

7 Eastgate, Beverley, Humberside, HU17 0DR
Tel: 01482 868464 Fax: 01482 871899
SB £25 DB £38

How to get there: Close to train and bus stations, within sight of Beverley Minster.
See advert on facing page top

Bingley, West Yorkshire

Five Rise Locks

♦♦♦♦ ♖✍

Beck Lane, Bingley, West Yorkshire, BD16 4DD
Tel: 01274 565296 Fax: 01274 568828

Formerly a wealthy Victorian mill owner's house, now in the rural setting of the canal conservation area. Each bedroom is individually designed and tastefully furnished. Enjoy freshly prepared food complemented by an imaginative wine list in elegant, yet relaxing surroundings.
SB £50 DB £60 B £7.50 L £9 D £14.
CC: MC Vi Swi Delt

🐕🕙🍽☕🖥☎🧳🅿♿🐾❄🐴♬🍴♻♨🍴🍷

How to get there: From Bingley, turn onto Park Road. Continue for ¼ mile. At crossroads sign turn left. Hotel on left.

Bishop Auckland, County Durham

Helme Park Hall
★★★
Near Fir Tree, Bishop Auckland, Co Durham, DL13 4NW
Tel: 01388 730970 Fax: 01388 730970

Short breaks

Northeast

Greenhead Country House

◆◆◆◆ ⚘ ♈

Fir Tree, Crook, Bishop Auckland,
County Durham, DL15 8BL
Tel: 01388 763143 Fax: 01388 763143
Email: info@the-greenhead-hotel.co.uk
Web: www.the-greenhead-hotel.co.uk
Children minimum age: 13

The Birbecks offer clean, comfortable
accommodation set in acres of open
countryside. Great hospitality ensuring guests'
comfort. "Richly deserves the 'Warm Welcome'
and 'Sparkling Diamond' awards" – RAC report,
2000.
SB £42 DB £55 CC: MC Vi Am Swi Delt
🛏 🛉 ⊗ ☕ ☐ 🅿 🛎 ♦
How to get there: A1 to A68 into Fir Tree.
Turn right at pub. Hotel 500yds on left.

Blanchland, Northumberland

Lord Crewe Arms

★★ ⓡ

Consett, Blanchland, Northumberland, DH8 9SP
Tel: 01434 675251 Fax: 01434 675337

Bolton Abbey, North Yorkshire

Devonshire Arms

★★★ ⓡ ⓡ ⓡ

Bolton Abbey, nr Skipton, North Yorkshire,
BD23 6AJ
Tel: 01756 710441 Fax: 01756 710564
Email: sales@thedevonshirearms.co.uk

SB £125 DB £175 B £12 L £10 D £42.
CC: MC Vi Am DC Swi Delt
🔱 🚪 🛏 🍴 ⊗ ☐ ☎ ✳ 🅿 🛎 ♨ 🐴 ♬ 🐕 👁
👥 👪 🅂🄿🄰 ⅋ 🍷 ⚲ 🎣
How to get there: 5 miles east of Skipton on
B6160, just 250yds north of junction with A59.

Boroughbridge, North Yorkshire

Crown

★★★ ⓡ

Horsefair, Boroughbridge, North Yorkshire,
YO51 9LB
Tel: 01423 322328 Fax: 01423 324512
Web: www.crownboroughbridge.co.uk

Former coaching inn with 37 bedrooms, all ensuite. Leisure facilities which include pool, gym
and beauty therapist. Large secure private car
park. Excellent conference facilities, bars and
restaurant.
SB £65 DB £80 HBS £77.50 HBD £115 B £7.50
L £4.95 D £19.95. CC: MC Vi Am DC Swi Delt
🔱 🏋 🛏 ⊗ ☕ ☐ ☎ 🅿 🛎 ♨ 🐴 ♬ 🐕 👁 👥
👪 🍷 🎣

How to get there: A1(M) J-48. Road into Boroughbridge. Follow signs into town; hotel is on T-junction. Car park is at rear.

Rose Manor

★★★
Horsefair, Boroughbridge, North Yorkshire, YO51 9LL
Tel: 01423 322245 Fax: 01423 314106
Email: rosemanorhotel@ukf.net
Web: www.rosemanorhotel.co.uk

Elegant country house hotel set in secluded grounds with large private car park. Within one mile of Boroughbridge exit on A1(M). Excellent conference and function facilities.
SB £79.50 DB £110 B £6.95 L £10.75 D £18.
CC: MC Vi Am Swi Delt
🛥️ ☕ ☎ 🅿 🎠 ♥ ♨️
How to get there: Within 1 mile of A1(M) J-48 for Boroughbridge.

Bradford, West Yorkshire

Cedar Court

★★★★ 🍽️🍽️
Mayo Avenue, Off Rooley Lane, Bradford, West Yorkshire, BD5 8HZ
Tel: 01274 406606 Fax: 01274 406600
Email: sales@cedar-court.com
Web: www.cedar-court.com
SB £108.75 DB £118.50 HBS £128.25
HBD £157.50 B £4.50 L £10.50 D £19.50.
CC: MC Vi Am DC
🛥️ ♿ ☕ ☎ 🅿 🎠 ♨️ SPA
How to get there: M62 J-26. M606 to Bradford. Take 3rd exit off roundabout at end of M606. First sharp right at traffic lights.

Midland

★★★
Forster Square, Bradford, West Yorkshire, BD1 4HU
Tel: 01274 735735
Fax: 01274 720003
Email: info@midland-hotel-bradford.com
SB £79 DB £89 HBS £94 HBD £119
B £5.50 L £12.95 D £12.95.
CC: MC Vi Am DC Swi Delt

PEEL HOTELS PLC

🛥️ ☕ ☎ 🅿 🎠 ♥ ♨️
How to get there: Head towards Bradford city centre, following signs for Forster Square station. Hotel 50 yards from station.

Novotel Bradford

★★★
6 Roydsdale Way, Bradford, BD4 6SA
Tel: 01274 683683 Fax: 01274 651342
Email: h0510@accor-hotels.com
Web: www.novotel.com
Children minimum age: 16
SB £59.50 DB £68 HBS £73 HBD £87.10
B £5.50 L £10.50 D £10.50.
CC: MC Vi Am DC Swi Delt
♿ ☕ ☎ 🅿 🎠 ♥ ♨️
How to get there: M62 J-26 , then M606 J-2. Right off sliproad and next right.

Quality Hotel Victoria

★★★
Bridge Street, Bradford, BD1 1JX
Tel: 01274 728706 Fax: 01274 736358
Email: admin@gb654.u-net.com
Web: www.qualityvictoriahotel.co.uk

SB £84.75 DB £109.50 HBS £99.25
HBD £138.50 B £9.75 L £11.50 D £14.50.
CC: MC Vi Am DC Swi Delt JCB
♿ ☕ ☎ 🅿 🎠 ♥ ♨️
How to get there: From all directions, follow signs for city centre and Bradford Interchange. Hotel directly opposite the interchange.

Northeast

Park Drive

★★

12 Park Drive, Bradford, West Yorkshire,
BD9 4DR
Tel: 01274 480194 Fax: 01274 484869
Email: info@parkdrivehotel.co.uk
Web: www.parkdrivehotel.co.uk
SB £49 DB £59 HBS £62.50 HBD £43 D £13.50.
CC: MC Vi Am DC Swi Delt

How to get there: Off A650 Keighley Road into
Emm Lane at Lister Park, then take 2nd right.

Bridlington, Humberside

Expanse

★★★

North Marine Drive, Bridlington, Humberside,
YO15 2LS
Tel: 01262 675347 Fax: 01262 604928
Email: expanse@brid.demon.co.uk
Web: www.expanse.co.uk
SB £48 DB £76 HBS £58 HBD £96 B £6.50
L £9.95 D £16. CC: MC Vi Am Swi Delt

New Revelstoke

★★★

1-3 Flamborough Road, Bridlington,
Humberside, YO15 2HU
Tel: 01262 672362 Fax: 01262 672362

Monarch

★★

South Marine Drive, Bridlington, Humberside,
YO15 3JJ
Tel: 01262 674447 Fax: 01262 670060
Closed January to February
SB £36 DB £72 HBS £44 HBD £88
CC: MC Vi Swi Delt Solo

How to get there: On South Beach, opposite Spa
Theatre, by Lifeboat Station – South Marine Drive.

Bay Ridge

♦♦♦

Summerfield Road, Bridlington, Humberside,
YO15 3LF
Tel: 01262 673425

For your complete reassurance, only RAC
Hotels and Guest Accommodation have been
assessed on your behalf by our team of
independent inspectors for quality, facilities
and service.

Langdon

♦♦♦

13/16 Pembroke Terrace, Bridlington,
Humberside, YO15 3BX
Tel: 01262 400124
Closed November to March
SB £25 DB £50 HBS £32 HBD £64
CC: MC Vi Swi Delt

How to get there: Between harbour and Spa
Royal Hall and Theatre.

Park View

♦♦

9-11 Tennyson Avenue, Bridlington,
Humberside, YO15 2EU
Tel: 01262 672140 Fax: 01262 672140

Burnsall, North Yorkshire

Red Lion Inn

★★

By The Bridge, Burnsall, North Yorkshire, BD23
6BU
Tel: 01756 720204 Fax: 01756 720292
Email: redlion@daelnet.co.uk
Web: www.redlion.co.uk
SB £66 DB £100 HBS £85 HBD £150
B £8 L £8 D £10.
CC: MC Vi Am DC Swi Delt Solo Connect

How to get there: From A59 Harrogate/Skipton
road at Bolton Abbey, B6160 for Burnsall/
Grassington. Hotel 5 miles down this road.

Cleethorpes, Humberside

Kingsway

★★★

Kingsway, Cleethorpes, Humberside, DN35 0AE
Tel: 01472 601122 Fax: 01472 601381
Web: www.kingsway-hotel.com
Children minimum age: 5. Closed Christmas
SB £68 DB £84 B £8 L £12.75 D £14.95.
CC: MC Vi Am DC Swi Delt

Short breaks

Many Hotels and Guest Accommodation offer
special weekend rates and mid-week breaks.
If not quoted in the property's entry, call
RAC Hotel Reservations on 0870 603 9109
to find out what may be on offer.

Corbridge, Northumberland

Lion of Corbridge

★★★

Bridge End, Corbridge, Northumberland,
NE45 5AX
Tel: 01434 632504 Fax: 01434 632571
Email: lionofcorbridge@talk21.com
SB £48 DB £74 B £5.50 L £5 D £10.
CC: MC Vi Am DC Swi Delt Maestro JCB Solo
Electron

How to get there: From Newcastle A69 signed to
Hexham. Take bypass route into Corbridge. Hotel
on south side of river, after crossing bridge.

Angel Inn

★★ ♞

Main Street, Corbridge, Northumberland,
NE45 5LA
Tel: 01434 632119 Fax: 01434 632119
SB £49.50 DB £74 B £5.50 L £6.25 D £6.25.
CC: MC Vi Am DC Swi Delt

How to get there: 1/2 mile off A69, signed
Corbridge.

Cornhill-on-Tweed, Northumberland

Collingwood Arms

★★

Cornhill-on-Tweed, Northumberland, TD12 4UH
Tel: 01890 882424 Fax: 01890 883644

Darlington, County Durham

St George

★★★

Tees-side Airport, Darlington, County Durham,
DL2 1RH
Tel: 01325 332631 Fax: 01325 333851

Clow Beck House | Little Gem

♦♦♦♦♦ ♞ ✕ ♝

Monk End Farm, Croft-on-Tees, Darlington,
County Durham, DL2 2SW
Tel: 01325 721075 Fax: 01325 720419
Email: david@clowbeckhouse.co.uk
Web: www.clowbeckhouse.co.uk
Closed Christmas to New Year
SB £47 DB £75 D £9.
CC: MC Vi Am Swi Delt

How to get there: Follow brown tourist signs on
all roads leading to Croft-on-Tees.

Doncaster, South Yorkshire

Regent

★★★

Regent Square, Doncaster, South Yorkshire,
DN1 2DS
Tel: 01302 364180 Fax: 01302 322331
Email: admin@theregenthotel.co.uk
Web: www.theregenthotel.co.uk

A charming Victorian building overlooking a
secluded Regency park. The hotel is ideally
situated within easy reach of Doncaster's
vibrant town centre and only minutes away from
the historic racecourse.
SB £63 DB £89 B £7.35 L £4.50 D £12.50.
CC: MC Vi Am DC Swi Delt

How to get there: Follow brown signs to racecourse. Into Bennetthorpe Road. After 1/2 mile,
hotel is on right.

Wentbridge House

★★★ ♞♞

Wentbridge, nr Pontefract, West Yorkshire,
WF8 3JJ
Tel: 01977 620444 Fax: 01977 620148
Email: info@wentbridgehouse.co.uk
Web: www.wentbridgehouse.co.uk
SB £75 DB £90 HBS £98 HBD £113 B £7.50 L
£12.50 D £23.
CC: MC Vi Am DC Swi Delt

How to get there: Wentbridge House is 1/2 mile
off the A1 and 4 miles south of the A1/A162
interchange.

See advert on following page

Northeast

Wentbridge House Hotel

This fine Georgian manor house dates from 1700 and is set in 20 acres of the beautiful Went Valley, four miles south of the A1/M62 interchange. Award winning cuisine and wines in beautiful surroundings.

Wentbridge, Pontefract WF8 3JJ
Tel: 01977 620444   Fax: 01977 620148
Email: info@wentbridgehouse.co.uk
Website: www.wentbridgehouse.co.uk

Campanile

Travel Accommodation
Bawtry Road, Doncaster Leisure Park, South Yorkshire, DN4 7PD
Tel: 01302 370770 Fax: 01302 370813

Typical Campanile Bistro

A lodge-style hotel situated close to the town centre. Ideal for all people, from business and leisure to conferences. Restaurant open to non-residents.
SB £41.95 DB £46.90 HBS £50 HBD £60 B £4.95 L £2.95 D £6.50. CC: MC Vi Am DC Swi Delt
How to get there: M18 J-3. Tourist signs for Racecourse and Leisure Park. Hotel behind Dome Leisure Park.

Canda Lodge

♦♦♦♦
Hampole Balk Lane, Skellow, Doncaster, South Yorkshire, DN6 8LF
Tel: 01302 724028 Fax: 01302 727999
SB £35 DB £40 CC: MC Vi Delt
How to get there: On A1 south, Skellow exit, or northbound, Pontefract exit (A639), then A1 south.

Almel

♦♦
20/24 Christchurch Road, Doncaster, South Yorkshire, DN1 2QL
Tel: 01302 365230 Fax: 01302 341434
SB £32 DB £42 CC: MC Vi Am Swi Delt
How to get there: M18 J-3. Right at Market Roundabout. Left after traffic lights. Hotel at bottom of road.

Driffield, East Yorkshire

Bell in Driffield

★★★
Market Place, Driffield, Humberside, YO25 6AN
Tel: 01377 256661 Fax: 01377 253228
Children minimum age: 12.
SB £79 DB £105 HBD £63 B £7.95 L £3 D £15.
CC: MC Vi Am DC Swi Delt
How to get there: M62 J-37. Signs for Driffield. In Driffield, turn right at traffic lights. Car park 50yds on left.

White Horse Inn

♦♦♦
Main Street, Hutton Cranswick, Driffield, East Yorkshire, YO25 9QN
Tel: 01377 270383/136 Fax: 01377 270383

An inn situated by the village pond and green, with proprietors Clive and Mary Tomlinson

offering you a warm and friendly welcome. An ideal base for touring the Yorkshire Wolds.
SB £29.50 DB £45 L £5 D £5.
CC: MC Vi Am Delt

How to get there: Off M62 at Howden, A614 into Driffield. A164 for Beverley and, 3 miles south, turn left into Hutton Cranswick. Hotel 500 yards down main street on left, opposite green.

Durham, County Durham

Royal County
★★★★ ♔♔
Old Elvet, Durham, County Durham, DH1 3JN
Tel: 0191 386 6821 Fax: 0191 386 7238
To become Marriott, Spring 2001.
SB £110 DB £125 B £12.50 L £13.50 D £19.50.
CC: MC Vi Am DC Swi Delt

How to get there: Off A1(M), A690 to Durham. Straight over first roundabout, at second turn left. At traffic lights turn left and hotel is on left.

Eden Arms
★★★ ♔♔
Rushyford, County Durham, DL17 0LL
Tel: 01388 720541 Fax: 01388 721871
Email: edenarms.swallow@whitbread.com
Web: www.swallow-hotels.co.uk

This 17th-century coaching inn retains its character and provides a very charming and intimate atmosphere, the perfect base for exploring the beautiful surrounding countryside.
SB £48 DB £115 HBS £70 HBD £139 D £20.
CC: MC Vi Am DC Swi Delt JCB

How to get there: A1(M) J-60 onto A689. After two miles, at roundabout take second left.

Ramside Hall
★★★
Carrville, Durham, County Durham, DH1 1TD
Tel: 0191 386 5282 Fax: 0191 386 0399
B £8 L £6 D £12. CC: MC Vi Am DC Swi Delt

How to get there: 400yds from A1M /A690 junction towards Sunderland. Turn right just after railway bridge.

Swallow Three Tuns
★★★ ♔♔
New Elvet, County Durham, DH1 3AQ
Tel: 0191 3751504 Fax: 0191 3842093

This 16th-century coaching inn retains many original features such as Tudor beams, oak panelling and open fireplaces. An excellent base in the centre of Durham city.
B £9.95 L £7.95 D £19.50.
CC: MC Vi Am DC Swi Delt

Hallgarth Manor
★★
Pittington, Durham, County Durham, DH6 1AB
Tel: 0191 372 1188 Fax: 0191 372 1249
B £6 L £13.50 D £17.95.
CC: MC Vi Am DC Swi Delt Solo

How to get there: A1(M) J-62 to A690 Sunderland. After one mile turn right. Half mile to crossroads – straight over. After one mile turn left into Hallgarth.

See advert on following page

Epworth, Humberside

Red Lion
★★
Market Place, Epworth, Humberside, DN9 1EU
Tel: 01427 872208 Fax: 01427 874330

Northeast

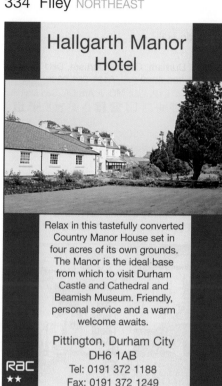
Filey, North Yorkshire

The Downcliffe House

★★

The Beach, Filey, North Yorkshire, YO14 9LA
Tel: 01723 513310

Seafield

♦♦♦

9-11 Rutland Street, Filey, North Yorkshire, YO14 9JA
Tel: 01723 513715
SB £20 DB £40 HBS £26 HBD £52 D £6.
CC: MC Vi Delt
♿ ☻ ⌾ 💻 🅿 ✂ 🐾 🛏 ♨ ♟ 🛍 ⚱ 🍴
How to get there: Follow signpost to Filey from A64. At crossroads in town centre turn right. Second left into Rutland Street.

Goathland, North Yorkshire

Inn on the Moor

★★★

Goathland, North Yorkshire, YO22 5LZ
Tel: 01947 896296 Fax: 01947 896484
Email: innonthemoor@btconnect.com
Web: www.innonthemoor.com

Closed December 24 – January 2
SB £35 DB £70 HBS £50 HBD £100 B £6 L £5
D £10.
CC: MC Vi Am DC Swi Delt

♿ ⚙ 🐾 ☕ 🖥 ☎ 🅿 ✂ ⚜ 🐴 🎋 🦆 ♨ ⛱

How to get there: Off main Whitby-Pickering road
(A169), 14 miles Pickering and 9 miles Whitby.
See advert on facing page bottom

Goole, Humberside

Clifton
★★
115 Boothferry Road, Goole, Humberside,
DN14 6AR
Tel: 01405 761336 Fax: 01405 762350
Email: cliftonhotel@telincs.co.uk
Closed Christmas
SB £44 DB £52 B £3.95 D £7.95.
CC: MC Vi Am DC Swi Delt Solo

🐾 ☕ 🖥 ☎ ☎ 🅿 ✂ ⚜ 🐴 🎋 🦆 ♨ ⛱ ⛱

How to get there: M62 J-36. Follow Goole Town
Centre signs. At second traffic lights, turn right
into Boothferry Road. Hotel is 500yds on left.

Grimsby, Humberside

Humber Royal
★★★
Littlecoates Road, Grimsby, Humberside,
DN34 4LX
Tel: 01472 240024 Fax: 01472 241354

Halifax, West Yorkshire

Rock Inn
★★★
Holywell Green, Halifax, West Yorkshire,
HX4 9BS
Tel: 01422 379721 Fax: 01422 379110
Email: cjrockinn@aol.com
Web: www.rockinnhotel.com
SB £67 DB £67 B £8.95 L £6 D £15.
CC: MC Vi Am DC Swi Delt

🦢 ♿ ⚙ 🐾 ❌ ☕ 🖥 ☎ ☎ 🅿 ⚜ 🐴 🎋 🦆
⛱ ⛱ 📶

How to get there: M62 J-24, 1½ miles towards
Blackley.

Shibden Mill Inn
◆◆◆◆
Shibden Mill Fold, Shibden, Halifax,
West Yorkshire, HX3 7UL
Tel: 01422 365840 Fax: 01422 362971

Harrogate, North Yorkshire

Balmoral
★★★★ ☕☕☕
Franklin Mount, Harrogate, North Yorkshire,
HG1 5EJ
Tel: 01423 508208 Fax: 01423 530652
Email: info@balmoralhotel.co.uk
Web: www.balmoralhotel.co.uk
SB £85 DB £100 B £6.50 L £6 D £12.50.
CC: MC Vi Am Swi Delt

⚙ 🐾 ☕ 🖥 ☎ 🅿 ✂ ⚜ 🐴 🎋 🦆 ⛱

How to get there: Signs for Harrogate Conference
Centre. Hotel 100 yards past centre on right.

Cedar Court
★★★★ ☕
Park Parade, Harrogate, North Yorkshire,
HG1 5AH
Tel: 01423 858585 Fax: 01423 504950
Email: sales@cedarcourt.karoo.co.uk
Web: www.cedarcourthotels.co.uk
SB £60 DB £80 HBS £65 HBD £45 B £9.95
L £12.50 D £18.50. CC: MC Vi Am DC Swi Delt

🦢 ♿ ⛰ ⚙ 🐾 ❌ ☕ 🖥 ☎ ☎ 🅿 ✂ ⚜ 🐴 🎋
🦆 ⛱ ⛱ 🍸

How to get there: Off Knaresborough Road in
high Harrogate, overlooking 'Stray' parkland.

The Majestic
★★★★
Ripon Road, Harrogate, North Yorkshire,
HG1 2HU
Tel: 01423 568972 Fax: 01423 502283
Email: majestic@paramount-hotels.co.uk
SB £105 DB £135 B £10 L £14.50 D £19.95
CC: MC Vi Am DC Swi Delt

🦢 ♿ ⛰ ⚙ 🐾 ❌ ☕ 🖥 ☎ ☎ 🅿 ✂ ⚜ 🐴
🦢 ⛱ ⛱ 🧖 🍸 📷 🔍

How to get there: A1(M) J-58. A68 to Bishop
Auckland. Roundabout – straight on.
Hotel ¼ mile on left.

Northeast

Boars Head

★★★ ♔♔♔

Ripley, Harrogate, North Yorkshire, HG3 3AY
Tel: 01423 771888 Fax: 01423 771509
Email: reservations@boarsheadripley.co.uk
Web: www.ripleycastle.co.uk

Elegantly restored coaching inn provides outstanding food, fine wines, friendly attentive service with comfortable and relaxing surroundings. In historic village location and beautiful Dales countryside.
SB £95 DB £115 B £6.50 L £10 D £7.50.
CC: MC Vi Am DC Swi Delt

How to get there: The Boars Head is 3 miles north of Harrogate on the A61, 10 minutes from the A1.

Grants Hotel & Chimney Pots Bistro

★★★ ♔

3-13 Swan Road, Harrogate, North Yorkshire, HG1 2SS
Tel: 01423 560666 Fax: 01423 502550
Email: enquiries@grantshotel-harrogate.com
Web: www.grantshotel-harrogate.com

Award winning hotel situated in the heart of Harrogate close to town centre and Valley Gardens. Affiliated to Academy Health and Leisure Club. Fine fresh food in Chimney Pot Bistro.

SB £99 CC: MC Vi Am DC Swi Delt JCB

How to get there: From south, take A61 past Betty's tea room on left, down hill to traffic lights, and straight across then 1st left into Swan Road.

Harrogate Spa

★★★

West Park, Harrogate, North Yorkshire, HG1 1LB
Tel: 01423 564601 Fax: 01423 507508
SB £89 DB £97 B £7.50 L £7.50 D £15.
CC: MC Vi Am DC Swi Delt

How to get there: From A61 follow signs for city centre. Turn right into Albert Street and right into hotel.

Hob Green

★★★ ♔♔

Markington, Harrogate, North Yorkshire, HG3 3PJ
Tel: 01423 770031 Fax: 01423 771589
Email: hobgreen.hotel@virgin.net

Set in 800 acres of beautiful rolling countryside, a charming and elegant hotel known locally for its excellent restaurant. The main rooms, furnished with antiques, enjoy a stunning view of the valley below.
SB £85 DB £95 HBS £90 HBD £140
B £9 L £9.95 D £22.50.
CC: MC Vi Am DC Swi Delt

How to get there: Between Harrogate and Ripon on A61 turn towards Markington at Wormald Green, following brown information road signs.

St George

★★★

Ripon Road, Harrogate, North Yorkshire, HG1 2SY
Tel: 01423 561431 Fax: 01423 530037
SB £95 DB £120 B £9.75 L £11.50 D £12.50.

CC: MC Vi Am DC Swi Delt Solo

How to get there: From A1 south, take A59, A658 and A661 signed to Harrogate. Turn left at roundabout and third exit of next roundabout. A61 is signed to Ripon.

The White House
★★★ ☕☕

10 Park Parade, Harrogate, North Yorkshire, HG1 5AH
Tel: 01423 501388 Fax: 01423 527973

Ascot House
★★ ☕

53 Kings Road, Harrogate, North Yorkshire, HG1 5HJ
Tel: 01423 531005 Fax: 01423 503523
Email: admin@ascothouse.com
Web: www.harrogate.com/ascot
Closed New Year
SB £49.50 DB £76 HBS £59.50 HBD £49
B £17.50 D £15.50.
CC: MC Vi Am DC Swi Delt

How to get there: Follow signs for town centre and conference/exhibition centre. Hotel on left as you drive up Kings Road, about 500yds from Conference Centre.

Low Hall
★★ ☕

Ripon Road, Killinghall, Harrogate, North Yorkshire HG3 2AY
Tel: 01423 508598 Fax: 01423 560848

Charming privately owned and run hotel and restaurant dating from 1672, with modern ensuite facilities and with restaurant and bistro menu.
SB £49.50 DB £59.50 HBS £60 HBD £80
CC: MC Vi Am DC Swi Delt

Imperial

Prospect Place, Harrogate, HG1 1LA
Tel: 01423 565071 Fax: 01423 508427
SB £95 DB £109 HBS £113 HBD £137
B £10 L £12.95 D £18.
CC: MC Vi Am Swi

How to get there: A1(M) J-47. Follow signs for Harrogate. On reaching Harrogate, turn left at first roundabout, right at next. Hotel 250 yards on right.

Alexa House
♦♦♦♦

26 Ripon Road, Harrogate, North Yorkshire, HG1 2JJ
Tel: 01423 501988 Fax: 01423 504086
Email: alexahouse@msn.com
Web: www.alexahouse.co.uk
SB £50 DB £65 D £15. CC: MC Vi Am Swi Delt

How to get there: ½ mile` from crossroads of A59 and A61, towards Harrogate town centre.

Arden House
♦♦♦♦

69/71 Franklin Road, Harrogate, North Yorkshire, HG1 5EH
Tel: 01423 509224 Fax: 01423 561170
Email: prop@ardenhousehotel.free-online.co.uk
Web: www.ardenhousehotel.co.uk
SB £32 DB £58 D £17. CC: MC Vi Am Swi Delt

How to get there: On entering Harrogate, signs for Conference and Exhibition Centre. At Conference Centre on Kings Road, left into Strawberry Dale Avenue, then left into Franklin Road.

Northeast

Ashley House

◆◆◆◆

36-40 Franklin Road, Harrogate,
North Yorkshire, HG1 5EE
Tel: 01423 507474 Fax: 01423 560858
Email: ron@ashleyhousehotel.com
Web: www.ashleyhousehotel.com

Only 5 minutes walk from the town centre.
Comfortable, well-equipped bedrooms and a
cosy bar specialising in single malt whiskies. A
warm welcome and friendly service await you.
Contact Ron or Linda to reserve your room.
SB £42.50 DB £65
CC: MC Vi Am DC Swi Delt

Grafton

◆◆◆◆

1-3 Franklin Mount, Harrogate, North Yorkshire,
HG1 5EJ
Tel: 01423 508491 Fax: 01423 523168
Email: enquiries@graftonhotel.co.uk
Web: www.graftonhotel.co.uk
SB £45 DB £74 B £9 L £10 D £17.50.
CC: MC Vi Am DC Swi Delt

How to get there: Follow signs to Harrogate
International Centre. Continue along Kings Road
for 300yds. Turn right into Franklin Mount.

Shannon Court

◆◆◆◆

65 Dragon Avenue, Harrogate, North Yorkshire,
HG1 5DS
Tel: 01423 509858 Fax: 01423 530606
Email: shannon@hotels.harrogate.com
Web: www.harrogate.com/shannon
Closed Christmas to New Year
SB £30 DB £55 CC: MC Vi Swi

How to get there: 5 minutes from town centre in
High Harrogate, located off the Skipton Road
(A59).

Gillmore

◆◆◆

98 King's Road, Harrogate, North Yorkshire,
HG1 5HH
Tel: 01423 503699 Fax: 01423 563223
Email: gillmoregh@aol.com
SB £25 DB £44 D £9. CC: MC Vi Swi Delt

How to get there: 2 minutes walk from
Conference Centre. Kings Road is located
between A59 and A61.

Glenayr

◆◆◆

19 Franklin Mount, Harrogate, North Yorkshire,
HG1 5EJ
Tel: 01423 504259 Fax: 01423 504259
DB £45 B £2.50 CC: MC Vi Swi Delt

How to get there: From A61, turn onto Kings
Road. Pass Conference Centre. Proceed
through traffic lights and take second turning on
right.

Mrs Murray's Guest House

◆◆◆

67 Franklin Road, Harrogate, North Yorkshire,
HG1 5EH
Tel: 01423 505857 Fax: 01423 530027

Hebden Bridge, West Yorkshire

Carlton

★★★

Albert Street, Hebden Bridge, West Yorkshire,
HX7 8ES
Tel: 01422 844400 Fax: 01422 843117
Email: ctonhotel@aol.com
SB £56 DB £75 B £8 L £6 D £12.95.
CC: MC Vi Am DC Swi Delt

How to get there: Just off the A646 in the centre
of Hebden Bridge.

Helmsley, North Yorkshire

Feversham Arms

★★★

1 High Street, Helmsley, York, YO62 5AG
Tel: 01439 770766 Fax: 01439 770346
Email: reception
        @feversham-helmsley.fsnet.co.uk

Warm, historic inn, elegantly modernised with
attractive patio, swimming pool, tennis court

and walled gardens. Ground floor and four-poster bedrooms. Fine food and wines. Bonanza breaks.
SB £55 DB £80 HBS £63 HBD £43
B £8 L £15 D £20.

How to get there: From A1, A168 dual carriageway to Thirsk, then A170. Or, at A1 junction with A64, take A64 to York north bypass, then B1363.

Heritage Hotels – The Black Swan
★★★ ☻☻
Market Place, Helmsley, North Yorkshire,
YO6 5BJ
Tel: 01439 770466 Fax: 01439 770174
Email: heritagehotels_helmsley.blackswan
@forte-hotels.com
Web: www.heritage-hotels.com
SB £60 DB £120 HBS £75 HBD £150 B £12
L £6 D £26.50. CC: MC Vi Am DC Swi Delt

How to get there: Helmsley is 15 miles east of Thirsk on A170 for Scarborough. Hotel in centre.

Pheasant
★★★
Harome, Helmsley, North Yorkshire, YO62 5JG
Tel: 01439 771241 Fax: 01439 771744
Children minimum age: 5
Closed December to February
SB £45 DB £90 HBS £67 HBD £133
B £10 L £6.50 D £20. CC: MC Vi Am Swi Delt

How to get there: Leave Helmsley on A170 for Scarborough. After 1/4 mile, turn right signposted Harome. Hotel on opposite corner from church.

Crown
★★
Market Place, Helmsley, North Yorkshire,
YO62 5BJ
Tel: 01439 770297 Fax: 01439 771595
SB £35 DB £70 HBS £49 HBD £98
B £6.95 L £11 D £15.95. CC: MC Vi Swi Delt

How to get there: In the market square in the centre of Helmsley.

Feathers
★★
Market Place, Helmsley, North Yorkshire,
YO6 5BH
Tel: 01439 770275 Fax: 01439 771101
SB £45 DB £60 B £5 L £5 D £10.
CC: MC Vi Swi Delt

How to get there: On A170 Thirsk to Scarborough road facing Market Square.

Hexham, Northumberland

Langley Castle
★★★ ☻☻
Langley-on-Tyne, Hexham, Northumberland,
NE47 5LU
Tel: 01434 688888 Fax: 01434 684019
Email: manager@langleycastle.com
Web: www.langleycastle.com
SB £94.50 DB £115 HBS £99.50 HBD £131
B £9.50 L £12.50 D £28.50.
CC: MC Vi Am DC Swi Delt

How to get there: By car, A69 to Hagdon Bridge, then 2 miles south on A686 to Langley Castle.
See advert on following page

Northeast

Swallow George

★★★ ⌘⌘⌘

Chollerford, Northumberland, NE46 4EW
Tel: 01434 681611 Fax: 01434 681727
Email: georgehotel@chollerford.fsbusiness.co.uk
Web: www.georgehotel-chollerford.com

This delightful country hotel with riverside gardens has excellent accommodation, a reputation for fine cuisine and full leisure facilities.
SB £70 DB £90 HBS £90 HBD £130 B £9.75 L £15 D £25.95. CC: MC Vi Am DC Delt

Langley Castle

A genuine 14th-century castle set in woodland estate. All rooms with private facilities, some boasting features such as window seats set into 7ft thick walls, and four-poster beds.
The magnificent drawing room complements the intimate Josephine Restaurant. The exclusive nature of the castle makes Langley the perfect destination for discovering Northumberland.

Langley-on-Tyne, Hexham NE47 5LU
Tel: 01434 688888   Fax: 01434 684019
Email: manager@langleycastle.com
Website: www.langleycastle.com

How to get there: From A1 at Newcastle, onto A69 past Hexham, A6079 to Chollerford.

Blackcock Inn

◆◆◆

Falstone, Kielder Water, Northumberland, NE48 1AA
Tel: 01434 240200 Fax: 01434 240200
Email: blackcock@falstone.fsbusiness.co.uk
Web: www.smoothhound.co.uk/
hotels/black.html
SB £28 DB £50 B £3.50 L £3.95 D £5.95.
CC: MC Vi Swi Delt

How to get there: Falstone can be accessed off the C200 road from Bellingham which can be accessed off the A68 or the B6320.

Rose & Crown Inn

◆◆◆

Main Street, Slaley, Hexham, Northumberland, NE47 0AA
Tel: 01434 673263 Fax: 01434 673305
Email: rosecrowninn@supanet.com
SB £27.50 DB £45 B £5.50 L £7 D £11.
CC: MC Vi Am Swi Delt Solo Electron

How to get there: From A68, take B6306. Inn on left after approximately 4 miles.

Holmfirth, West Yorkshire

White Horse Inn

◆◆

Scholes Road, Jackson Bridge, Holmfirth, Huddersfield, West Yorkshire, HD7 7HF
Tel: 01484 683940
Web: www.holme-valley.co.uk
SB £25 DB £40 B £4 L £4 D £4.

How to get there: Leave M1 southbound at Junction 39. Take A616 to Derby Dale. OR, from M1 northbound, leave at Junction 35A, and take A616 to Huddersfield.

Hornsea, East Yorkshire

Merlstead

◆◆◆

Hornsea, East Yorkshire, HU18 1NB
Tel: 01964 533068 Fax: 01964 536975
SB £30 DB £45 HBS £42 HBD £70 CC: MC Vi

Huddersfield, West Yorkshire

Bagden Hall

★★★

Wakefield Road, Scissett, Huddersfield,
West Yorkshire, HD8 9LE
Tel: 01484 865330 Fax: 01484 861001
Email: info@bagdenhall.demon.co.uk
Web: www.bagdenhall.demon.co.uk

Traditional country house hotel, set in 40 acres
of beautiful parkland and boasting a superb
9-hole golf course.
SB £60 DB £80 HBS £78 HBD £58 B £7.50
L £8.95 D £18. CC: MC Vi Am DC Swi Delt
How to get there: On A636 between Scissett
and Denbydale. Only 10 minutes drive from M1.

Briar Court

★★★

Halifax Road, Birchencliffe, Huddersfield,
West Yorkshire, HD3 3NT
Tel: 01484 519902 Fax: 01484 431812
Email: briarcourthotel@btconnect.com
Web: www.briarcourthotel.co.uk

Modern hotel, refurbished throughout with 48
bedrooms, Zanzibar Wine & Coffee Lounge and
conference and wedding facilities. Home of Da
Sandro Ristorante – authentic Italian cuisine
served in an unrivalled atmosphere.
SB £59 DB £69 B £5 L £5 D £10.
CC: MC Vi Am DC Swi Delt Solo

How to get there: Located on A629, just 300yds
from M62 J-24, also within easy reach of M1.

George

★★★ ⓡ

St George Square, Huddersfield,
West Yorkshire, HD1 2JA
Tel: 01484 515444 Fax: 01484 435056
Email: sam.mcmillan@principalhotels.co.uk
Web: www.principalhotels.co.uk
SB £73 DB £91 HBS £85.50 HBD £116 B £8.50
L £10.95 D £15.95. CC: MC Vi Am DC Swi Delt

How to get there: M62 J-24 and follow signs for
Huddersfield town centre. Hotel by train station.

Hanover International Huddersfield

★★★

Penistone Road, Kirkburton, Huddersfield, West
Yorkshire, HD8 0PE
Tel: 01484 607783 Fax: 01484 607961
Web: www.hanover-international.com

HANOVER INTERNATIONAL

A former spinning mill full of charm and
character, the Brasserie 209 offers contemporary cuisine in stylish surroundings. Ideally
situated for 'Last of the Summer Wine' country.
SB £45 DB £75 HBS £80 HBD £90
B £8.50 D £18.95. CC: MC Vi Am DC Swi Delt

The Huddersfield

★★★

33–47 Kirkgate, Huddersfield, West Yorkshire,
HD1 1QT
Tel: 01484 512111 Fax: 01484 435262
SB £52 DB £70 B £5 L £6 D £12.
CC: MC Vi Am DC Swi Delt

See advert following page

Northeast

Dalton Bed & Breakfast

♦♦♦ ✗

2 Crossley Lane, Dalton, Huddersfield, West
Yorkshire, HD5 9SX
Tel: 01484 540091 Fax: 01484 540091
SB £20 DB £40

How to get there: Hotel is situated 2 miles
south-east of town centre, 3 miles from
M62 J-25, 13 miles from M1 J-38.

Hull, Humberside

Humber Crown

★★★

Ferriby High Road, North Ferriby, Hull,
Humberside, HU14 3LG
Tel: 01482 645212

Portland

★★★

Paragon Street, Hull, Humberside, HU1 3PJ
Tel: 01482 326462 Fax: 01482 213460

Please mention the RAC Inspected guide
when you make your booking at an RAC
Hotel or Guest Accommodation.

THE

HUDDERSFIELD

HOTEL & ENTERTAINMENT COMPLEX

Town Centre location. Award winning high
security overnight parking. Renowned for
friendliness. All-day Continental Brasserie open
7 days and nights. Rosemary Lane Bistro
serving Dinner every evening. Our own local
style Pub, the Boy & Barrel Inn, with
entertainment most evenings. All rooms ensuite
with all facilities.

Kirkgate, Huddersfield,
West Yorkshire HD1 1QT
Tel: 01484 512111   Fax: 01484 435262

Quality Hotel Hull

★★★

Ferensway, Hull, Humberside, HU1 3UF
Tel: 01482 325087 Fax: 01482 323172
Email: admin@gb611.u-net.com
Web: www.choicehotels.com
SB £75 DB £90 B £9.95 L £4.95 D £13.50.
CC: MC Vi Am DC Swi Delt

How to get there: M62 onto M63, onto Clive
Sullivan Way. Left at roundabout (A1079). Follow
signs for railway station. Hotel 200yds on left.

Willerby Manor

★★★ ✗

Well Lane, Willerby, Hull, Humberside,
HU10 6ER
Tel: 01482 3652616 Fax: 01482 653901
Email: info@willerbymanor.co.uk
Web: www.willerbymanor.co.uk
SB £82.75 DB £107.50 CC: MC Vi Am Swi Delt

How to get there: M62 into A63. Exit Beverley
and Humber Bridge to Willerby. At roundabout
third exit, hotel signs from next roundabout.

Comfort Inn Hull

★★

11 Anlaby Road, Hull, Humberside, HU1 2PJ
Tel: 01482 323299 Fax: 01482 214730
Email: admin@gb631.u-net.com
Web: www.choicehotels.com
SB £55 DB £60 B £7.75 D £8.95.
CC: MC Vi Am DC Swi Delt

Rowley Manor

★★ ✗

Little Weighton, Hull, Humberside, HU20 3XR
Tel: 01482 848248 Fax: 01482 849900

Campanile

Travel Accommodation
Beverley Road, Freetown Way, Hull,
Humberside, HU2 9AN
Tel: 01482 325530 Fax: 01482 587538

Typical Campanile bedroom

The hotel is situated in the city centre of Hull,
and consists of a French bistro restaurant, with
conference facilities and disabled access.
SB £44.90 DB £49.85 HBS £48 HBD £64.20
B £4.95 L £2.95 D £6.15.
CC: MC Vi Am DC Swi Delt

⚓ ঠ 🐾 ⊗ ⑤ ▢ ☎ 📞 P➧ 🐎 🕯 🎠 ⌂ 🦢
♨ ⅲ

How to get there: From M62 follow A63 into
Hull, passing Humber Bridge on right. Pass a
flyover, follow signs for city centre A1079. At
junction of Freetown Way and Beverley Road,
straight across lights and turn right.

Earlsmere
♦ ♦ ♦
76-78 Sunnybank, Hull, HU3 1LQ
Tel: 01482 341977 Fax: 01482 473714
Email: su@earlsmerehotel.karoo.co.uk
SB £18 DB £32
CC: MC Vi DC Swi Delt

ঠ 🐾 ⊗ ⑤ ▢ 🕯 🎠 🐎 ⌂ 🦢 ∣

Ilkley, West Yorkshire

Rombalds
★★★ ☗ ☗
11 West View, Wells Road, Ilkley,
West Yorkshire, LS29 9JG
Tel: 01943 603201 Fax: 01943 816586
Email: reception@rombalds.demon.co.uk
Web: www.rombalds.co.uk

Standing between the town and the moors, this
elegantly furnished hotel provides comfortable
lounges, well-equipped bedrooms and an
attractive restaurant service with award-winning
cuisine.

SB £55 DB £80 HBS £68 HBD £85
B £6.95 L £8.95 D £9.95.
CC: MC Vi Am DC Swi Delt JCB

⚓ 🐾 ⊗ ⑤ ▢ ☎ P 🕯 🎠 🐎 ⌂ 🦢 ♨ ∣∣ ∣

How to get there: On Leeds/Skipton A65, left at
second main lights, follow signs for Ilkley Moor.
Hotel 600 yards on left.

Ingleton, North Yorkshire

Springfield Country House
♦ ♦ ♦   🐾
Main Street, Ingleton, North Yorkshire, LA6 3HJ
Tel: 01524 241280 Fax: 01524 241280
Closed Christmas

A family-run detached Victorian villa with a
fountain at the front, set in its own grounds
backing onto the River Greta, with panoramic
views.
SB £23 DB £44 HBS £34 HBD £68 D £11.
CC: MC Vi Am DC Delt

🐾 ⑤ ▢ P 🕯 🎠 🐎 ⌂ 🦢 🥄

How to get there: On A65(T), 11 miles from NW
Settle. Springfield is 100 yards from A65(T).

Northeast

Keighley, West Yorkshire

Dalesgate

★★

406 Skipton Road, Utley, Keighley, West
Yorkshire, BD20 6HP
Tel: 01535 664930 Fax: 01535 611253
Email: stephen.e.atha@btinternet.com
Web: www.dalesgate.co.uk
SB £45 DB £65 HBS £52 HBD £80
B £6.95 D £12.95. CC: MC Vi Am DC Delt
How to get there: From Keighley town centre
follow signs for Skipton. Straight across
roundabout. Hotel in Utley, 1¹/₂ miles on right.

Kettlewell, North Yorkshire

Langcliffe Little Gem

♦♦♦♦

Kettlewell, North Yorkshire, BD23 5RJ
Tel: 01756 760 243

Knaresborough, North Yorkshire

Abbey Garth

♦♦♦♦

28 Abbey Road, Knaresborough,
North Yorkshire, HG5 8HX
Tel: 01423 862043
Web: www.gocities.com/abbey_garth
Children minimum age: 10
DB £42.50
How to get there: From A1(M) A59 Harrogate.
Right at B6163 Calcutt/Knaresborough. Over
river turn right into Abbey Road.

Newton House

♦♦♦♦

5–7 York Place, Knaresborough, North
Yorkshire, HG5 0AD
Tel: 01423 863539 Fax: 01423 869748
Email: newtonhouse@btinternet.com
Web: www.harrogate.com/newton
SB £35 DB £55 HBS £52.50 HBD £90 D £17.50.
CC: MC Vi Swi Delt JCB Electron
How to get there: A59 turn-off A1(M), follow
signs to Knaresborough for 2¹/₂ miles. On right
hand side just before third set of traffic lights.

Looking for great dining? Look for RAC Hotels
and Guest Accommodation displaying the
RAC Dining Award symbol in this Guide.

Yorkshire Lass

♦♦♦

High Bridge, Harrogate Road, Knaresborough,
North Yorkshire, HG5 8DA
Tel: 01423 862962 Fax: 01423 869091
Email: yorkshirelass@knaresborough.co.uk
Web: www.knaresborough.co.uk/yorkshirelass
SB £42.50 DB £49.50 B £6 L £6 D £12.50.
CC: MC Vi Swi Delt
How to get there: On A59 between Knares-
borough and Harrogate, opposite Mother
Shipton's Cave.

Lastingham, North Yorkshire

Lastingham Grange

★★★

Lastingham, North Yorkshire, YO6 6TH
Tel: 01751 417345

Leeds, West Yorkshire

42 The Calls

★★★★★ Town House
42 The Calls, Leeds, Yorkshire, LS2 7EW
Tel: 01132 440099 Fax: 01132 344100
Email: hotel@42thecalls.co.uk
Web: www.42thecalls.co.uk
Closed Christmas
SB £109.50 DB £151 B £8.95
CC: MC Vi Am DC Swi Delt
How to get there: City centre signs onto the city
centre loop. Turn left at junction 15. Number 42
then immediately on your right.

Hotel Metropole

★★★★

King Street, Leeds, West Yorkshire, LS1 2HQ
Tel: 01132 450841 Fax: 01132 425156
Web: www.principalhotels.co.uk
B £2.95 L £5 D £5. CC: MC Vi Am DC Swi Delt
How to get there: From all motorways, follow
signs for city centre. Join Wellington Street, then
King Street. Metropole on right.

Le Meridien Queen's

★★★★

City Square, Leeds, LS1 1PL
Tel: 0870 400 8696 Fax: 0113 242 5154
Web: www.lemeridien-hotels.com
SB £127 DB £149 HBS £145 HBD £184

B £11.75 L £16 D £17.50.
CC: MC Vi Am DC Swi Delt

⚓ ♿ 📶 ⊗ 🍵 🖵 ☎ 🄿 🐾 ❄ 🎠 🐕 ♬ 🍴 ♨ ⛲ 🍴

How to get there: From M621 signs for Holbeck and City Centre. Continue under railway bridge and take first left towards Granary Wharf Market.

Chevin Lodge Country Park

★★★

Yorkgate, Otley, West Yorkshire, LS21 3NU
Tel: 01943 467818 Fax: 01943 850335
Email: reception@chevinlodge.co.uk
Web: www.chevinlodge.co.uk
SB £65 DB £110 HBS £78 HBD £68
B £6 L £12 D £20. CC: MC Vi Am Swi Delt

⚓ ♿ 🐱 🍵 🖵 ☎ 🄿 🐾 ❄ 🎠 🐕 ♬ 🍴 ♨ ⛲ 🍴 🍴 SPA
🍷 🚬 🔍 🎿 🚤

How to get there: On rural road off A658 Leeds/Bradford airport to Harrogate, 2 miles airport.
See advert below

Golden Lion

★★★

2 Lower Briggate, Leeds,
West Yorkshire,
LS1 4AE

PEEL HOTELS PLC

Tel: 0113 243 6454 Fax: 0113 242 9327
Email: info@goldenlionhotel-leeds.com
SB £99 DB £109 HBS £111 HBD £133
L £8.95 D £15.95. CC: MC Vi Am DC Swi Delt

📶 🚬 ⊗ 🍵 🖵 ☎ 📞 🄿 🐾 ❄ 🎠 🐕 ♬ 🍴 ♨ ⛲ 🍴

How to get there: Half mile M621 J-3, for city centre. On loop road J-16. Station 5 minutes walk.

Merrion

★★★

Merrion Centre, Wade Lane, Leeds,
West Yorkshire, LS2 8NH
Tel: 0113 243 9191 Fax: 0113 242 3527
Email: info@merrion-hotel-leeds.com
SB £111 DB £139 B £9.25 L £5.50 D £14.75.
CC: MC Vi Am DC Swi Delt

♿ 📶 🚬 ⊗ 🍵 🖵 ☎ 🄿 🐾 ❄ 🎠 🐕 ♬ 🍴 ♨ ⛲ 🍴

How to get there: Signs for city centre. Join inner loop road and exit at J-7 into Wade Lane.

Milford Lodge

★★★

A1 Great North Road, Peckfield, Leeds,
LS25 5LQ
Tel: 01977 681800 Fax: 01977 681245
Email: enquiries@mlh.co.uk
Web: www.mlh.co.uk
B £3.95 L £3.95 D £16. CC: MC Vi Am DC Swi

♿ 🚬 ⊗ 🍵 🖵 ☎ ❄ 📞 🄿 🐾 ❄ 🎠 🐕 ♬ 🍴
⛲ 🍴

How to get there: A1 south, junction A63 from Leeds, 6 miles north A1/M62 intersection.

Pinewood

◆◆◆◆

78 Potternewton Lane, Leeds, West Yorkshire, LS7 3LW
Tel: 01132 622561 Fax: 01132 622561

A most comfortable, welcoming small hotel of distinction. Rooms are attractively decorated and well-furnished with many extra touches enhancing guest comfort.
SB £38 DB £48 HBS £49.95 HBD £35.95
D £11.95. CC: MC Vi Am Delt

🍵 🖵 🐾 🎠 🐕 ♬ 🍴 ♨ 🍴

How to get there: Exit centre on A61 for Harrogate. 2 miles on, at first roundabout turn right. Hotel is 600yds on left.

Northeast

Broomhurst

◆◆◆

12 Chapel Lane, off Cardigan Road, Headingley, Leeds, LS6 3BW
Tel: 01132 786836 Fax: 01132 307099

Comfortable, family-run hotel in a quiet, pleasantly wooded conservation area. 1½ miles from city centre. Close to universities, cricket ground and Bechets Park. Tea & coffee-making facilities and colour TV in all rooms.
SB £25 DB £35 HBS £35 HBD £45 D £10.50.
CC: MC Vi Swi Delt

Leeming Bar, North Yorkshire

The Lodge at Leeming Bar

★★

Bedale, Leeming Bar, North Yorkshire, DL8 1DT
Tel: 01677 422122 Fax: 01677 424507

White Rose

★★

Bedale Road, Leeming Bar, Northallerton, DL7 9AY
Tel: 01677 422707 Fax: 01677 425123
Email: royston@whiterosehotel.co.uk
Web: www.whiterosehotel.co.uk
SB £38 DB £48 CC: MC Vi Am DC Swi Delt

How to get there: 12 miles south of Scotch Corner, take A684 turning right for Northallerton. We are ½ mile along on left.

Non smoking policy   RΛC

Properties displaying this symbol in the Guide have non smoking rooms available for guests. However, smokers should check in advance whether the Hotel or Guest Accommodation displaying this symbol actually allows smoking in any room.

Levisham, North Yorkshire

Moorlands   Little Gem

◆◆◆◆◆

Levisham, Pickering, North Yorkshire, YO18 7NL
Tel: 01751 460229 Fax: 01751 460229
Email: ronaldoleonardo@aol.com
Web: www.yorkshireholidays.com/
moorlands.htm
Children minimum age: 15.
Closed December to March

A beautifully restored Victorian country house in four acres of wooded gardens with stunning views across the valley. Ideal base for walking, cycling or touring the beautiful North York Moors.
SB £35 DB £70 CC: MC Vi

How to get there: A169 from Pickering, turn left. Through Lockton into Levisham. First house on right.

Leyburn, North Yorkshire

Wensleydale Heifer

★★

West Witton, Wensleydale, North Yorkshire, DL8 4LS
Tel: 01969 622322 Fax: 01969 624183

Historic 17th-century inn. Comfortable bedrooms, including four posters. Award-winning restaurant, bistro and bar food. Children

and pets welcome. Excellent walking and local attractions.
SB £60 DB £80 HBS £75 HBD £120
CC: MC Vi Am DC Swi Delt
How to get there: The inn is on the A684 trans-Pennine road from Leyburn to Hawes.

Golden Lion
★
Market Square, Leyburn, North Yorkshire, DL8 5AS
Tel: 01969 622161 Fax: 01969 623836

Liversedge, West Yorkshire

Healds Hall
★★
Leeds Road, Liversedge, West Yorkshire, WF15 6JA
Tel: 01924 409112 Fax: 01924 401895
Email: healdshall@ndirect.co.uk

Family run hotel with award winning restaurant and exciting new bistro. Wedding and conference facilities.
SB £59 DB £75 HBS £75 HBD £105
B £5 L £6.95 D £6.95. CC: MC Vi DC Swi Delt
How to get there: On A62 between Leeds and Huddersfield. Near M1 J-40 and M62 J-26/27.

Malham, North Yorkshire

Buck Inn
★★
Malham, Skipton, North Yorkshire, BD23 4DA
Tel: 01729 830317 Fax: 01729 830670
SB £33.50 DB £57 L £5.25 D £5.25.
CC: MC Vi Am Swi Delt
How to get there: A65 Skipton–Settle. Turn right in Gargrove, sign Malham, and on for seven miles to Malham. Inn is in the village centre.

Malton, North Yorkshire

Burythorpe House
★★★
Burythorpe, Malton, North Yorkshire, YO17 9LB
Tel: 01653 658200 Fax: 01653 658204

Green Man
★★★
15 Market Street, Malton, North Yorkshire, YO17 7LY
Tel: 01653 600370 Fax: 01653 696006
Email: greenman@englishrosehotels.co.uk
Web: www.englishrosehotels.co.uk
SB £60 DB £90 HBS £35.50 HBD £35.50 B £10 L £12.50 D £15.50. CC: MC Vi Am DC Swi Delt
How to get there: A64 from A1/M1. Exit for Malton at start of bypass. First left past Talbot Hotel.

Talbot
★★
Yorkersgate, Malton, North Yorkshire, YO17 7AJ
Tel: 01653 694031 Fax: 01653 693355
Email: talbothotel@englishrosehotels.co.uk
Web: www.englishrosehotels.co.uk
SB £49.50 DB £90 HBS £32.50 HBD £32.50 B £10 L £10 D £16.95. CC: MC Vi Am DC Swi Delt
How to get there: From A64 take road into Malton: the hotel is on right.

Wentworth Arms
★
Town Street, Malton, North Yorkshire, YO17 0HD
Tel: 01653 692618 Fax: 01653 692618
SB £25 DB £50 B £5 L £7.50 D £15.
CC: MC Vi Am Swi Delt
How to get there: Off A64 Malton bypass for Malton. Hotel on right, 400yds from A64.

Morpeth, Northumberland

Linden Hall
★★★
Longhorsley, Morpeth, Northumberland, NE65 8XF
Tel: 01670 516611 Fax: 01670 788544
Email: stay@lindenhall.co.uk
Web: www.lindenhall.co.uk
SB £69.50 DB £49.50 B £9 L £15.50 D £24.50.
CC: MC Vi Am DC Swi Delt
How to get there: Off the A697 between the villages of Longhorsley and Longframlington.

Northeast

Newcastle-upon-Tyne, Tyne & Wear

Copthorne Newcastle

★★★★ 🛏 🛏

The Close, Quayside, Newcastle-upon-Tyne,
Tyne & Wear, NE1 3RT
Tel: 0191 222 0333 Fax: 0191 230 1111

Situated on the banks of the Tyne. Bedrooms,
restaurants and bar boast superb river views.
Guests benefit from complimentary use of Spirit
Leisure Club and car parking.

Newcastle Marriott

★★★★ 🛏 🛏

Gosforth Park, Gosforth, Newcastle-upon-Tyne,
Tyne & Wear, NE3 5HN
Tel: 0191 2364111 Fax: 0191 2368192
Children minimum age: 14
SB £123 DB £131 B £8 L £17 D £18.
CC: MC Vi Am DC Swi Delt

How to get there: From south follow A1 until 5
miles north of Newcastle. From north follow A1
western bypass for Newcastle. Turn off A1 to
Wideopen (A1056). First left at roundabout and
hotel is straight ahead.

Vermont

★★★★ 🛏 🛏 🛏

Castle Garth, Newcastle, NE1 1RQ
Tel: 0191 233 1010 Fax: 0191 233 1234
Email: info@vermont-hotel.co.uk
SB £145 DB £165 B £10.50 L £8 D £14.
CC: MC Vi Am DC Swi Delt

How to get there: City Centre by high-level
bridge and the castle.

Book with RAC Hotel Reservations and check
the latest offers available. Call 0870 603 9109
and quote 'RAC Guide 2001'

Novotel Newcastle

★★★

Ponteland Road, Kenton, Newcastle,
Tyne & Wear, NE3 3HZ
Tel: 0191 214 0303 Fax: 0191 214 0633
Email: h1118@accor-hotels.com
Web: www.novotel.com
SB £84.50 DB £94 HBS £95 HBD £105
B £9.50 L £9.95 D £9.95.
CC: MC Vi Am DC Swi Delt

How to get there: From A1 take A696 junction.
At roundabout take Kingston Park turnoff; at
mini-roundabout again take Kingston Park.
Novotel on right.

Swallow Hotel Gateshead

★★★

High Street, Gateshead, Tyne & Wear, NE8 1PE
Tel: 0191 477 1105 Fax: 0191 478 1638
SB £85 DB £105 B £6.95 L £10.25 D £23.
CC: MC Vi Am DC Swi Delt

How to get there: Northbound A1, take A167 at
Angel Of The North. Follow signs. Southbound
A1, take A186 to Gateshead. Follow signs after
Civic Centre.

Swallow Imperial Newcastle

★★★

Jesmond Road, Jesmond,
Newcastle-upon-Tyne, Tyne & Wear, NE2 1PR
Tel: 0191 231 5511 Fax: 0191 212 1069
Email: jesmond@swallow-hotels.co.uk
SB £90 DB £115 HBS £110 HBD £145 B £9.75
L £11.50 D £19.50. CC: MC Vi Am DC Swi Delt

How to get there: Just off A167. Signs for coast
A1058.

The Caledonian

★★★

Osborne Road,
Newcastle-upon-Tyne,
Tyne & Wear, NE2 2AT

PEEL HOTELS PLC

Tel: 0191 281 7881 Fax: 0191 281 6241
SB £89 DB £99 HBS £101 HBD £124
B £8.95 L £4.99 D £15.
CC: MC Vi Am DC Swi Delt

How to get there: From A1, Jesmond signs. Left
into Osborne Road. Or from Tyne Tunnel, Newcastle signs (A1058). Left into Osborne Road.

Cairn

★★

97 Osborne Road, Jesmond,
Newcastle-Upon-Tyne, Tyne & Wear, NE2 2TA
Tel: 0191 281 1358 Fax: 0191 281 9031

Chirton House

◆◆◆

46 Clifton Road, Newcastle-upon-Tyne,
Tyne & Wear, NE4 6XH
Tel: 0191 273 0407 Fax: 0191 273 0407
SB £26 DB £37 CC: MC Vi Swi Delt Solo

How to get there: Exit A1 Newcastle West. On
West Road (A186) 2 miles. At hospital, right into
Grainger Park Rd. Left into Clifton Road.

Pateley Bridge, North Yorkshire

Roslyn

◆◆◆

King Street, Pateley Bridge, North Yorkshire,
HG3 5AT
Tel: 01423 711374 Fax: 01423 711374
Email: roslynhotelatpateley@talk21.com
Web: www.nidderdale.co.uk/roslynhotel
SB £40 DB £50 HBS £51 HBD £72 D £11.

How to get there: Turn right off Main Street.
Hotel 250yds on left of King Street.

Peterlee, County Durham

Hardwicke Hall Manor

★★

Heslenden Road, Blackhall, Peterlee,
County Durham, TS27 4PA
Tel: 01429 836326 Fax: 01429 837676

Pickering, North Yorkshire

Blacksmith's Country Inn

★★★ ◈◈

Hartoft End, Rosedale Abbey, Pickering,
North Yorkshire, YO18 8EN
Tel: 01751 417331 Fax: 01751 417167
Email: blacksmiths.rosedale@virgin.net
Web: www.blacksmithsinn-rosedale.co.uk
SB £41.50 DB £63 HBS £56.50 HBD £93
B £6 L £10 D £16. CC: MC Vi Swi Delt

How to get there: From Pickering A170 for Helmsley. Right at Wrelton. Hartoft signposted.
See advert on the right

Pontefract, West Yorkshire

Rogerthorpe Manor

★★★ ◈

Thorpe Lane, Badsworth, Pontefract,
West Yorkshire, WF9 1AB
Tel: 01977 643839 Fax: 01977 645704
Email: ops@rogerthorpemanor.co.uk
SB £80 DB £95 HBS £95 HBD £125
B £9.95 L £14.95 D £14.95. CC: MC Vi Am DC

See advert on the following page

Redworth, County Durham

Redworth Hall

★★★★ ◈◈

Redworth, County Durham, DL5 6NL
Tel: 01388 772442 Fax: 01388 775112
Email: redworthhall@paramount-hotels.co.uk
Web: www.paramount-hotels.co.uk
SB £105 DB £135 HBS £85 HBD £65 B £10.50
L £11.95 D £12. CC: MC Vi Am DC Swi Delt

How to get there: A1(M) J-58. A68 to Bishop
Auckland roundabout. Straight on, hotel ¼ mile
on left.

Blacksmith's Country Inn

Lovely 16th-century hostelry, fully refurbished
but retaining all the ambience of years past.
Cosy lounges, superb food and wine in
wonderful surroundings. Quality ensuites,
some ground floor, panoramic views, ideal
walking base.

Hartoft End, Rosedale Abbey,
Pickering, North Yorkshire YO18 8EN
Tel: 01751 417331   Fax: 01751 417167
Email: blacksmiths.rosedale@virgin.net
Website: www.blacksmithsinn-
rosedale.co.uk

Northeast

Richmond, North Yorkshire

Quality Hotel Scotch Corner
★★★

Junction A1/A66, nr Richmond, North Yorkshire, DL10 6NR
Tel: 01748 850900 Fax: 01748 852417
Email: admin@gb609.u-net.com
Web: www.qualityinn.com/hotel/gb609

SB £83.75 DB £106.50 HBS £100.75 HBD £60.25 B £8.95 L £9.95 D £15.95.
CC: MC Vi Am DC Swi Delt

How to get there: Off Scotch Corner roundabout on A1/A66 junction on northbound side of A1.

Bridge House
★★

Catterick Bridge, Richmond, North Yorkshire, DL10 7PE
Tel: 01748 818331 Fax: 01748 818331
SB £40 DB £60 HBS £55 HBD £90 B £6 L £8.50

D £15. CC: MC Vi Am DC Swi Delt

How to get there: Either Catterick exits off A1. Approx 4 miles south of Scotch Corner, hotel opposite Catterick racecourse.

Frenchgate
★★

59–61 Frenchgate, Richmond, North Yorkshire, DL10 7AE
Tel: 01748 822087 Fax: 01748 823596
SB £39 DB £65 HBS £53 HBD £46.50
CC: MC Vi Am DC Swi Delt

How to get there: A6108 to Richmond, past schools to roundabout. Straight on, past lights, left at roundabout, next left, 100 yards on left.

Ripon, North Yorkshire

Unicorn
★★

Market Place, Ripon, North Yorkshire, HG4 1BP
Tel: 01765 602202 Fax: 01765 690734
Email: admin@unicorn-hotel.co.uk
Web: www.unicorn-hotel.co.uk
Closed Christmas
SB £47 DB £67 HBS £58 HBD £96

B £7 L £7.95 D £14.95.
CC: MC Vi Am DC Swi Delt
🐕🐎🕭🖥☎🅿✂🕊🐎🎠♫🐟🦆♨♨♨ ⅱⅰ
How to get there: 4 miles from A1 on A61.
Located in market place, city centre.

Romaldkirk, County Durham

Rose & Crown
★★ 🐓🐓
Romaldkirk, Barnard Castle, County Durham,
DL12 9EB
Tel: 01833 650213 Fax: 01833 650828
Email: hotel@rose-and-crown.co.uk
Web: www.rose-and-crown.co.uk
Closed Christmas

An 18th-century stone-built traditional coaching
inn set on the middle green in one of Teesdale's
loveliest locations.
SB £62 DB £86 L £13.95 D £25.
CC: MC Vi Swi Delt
🕭🐕🐎🖥☎✆🅿✂🕊🐎🎠♫🐟♨♨♨ ⅰⅰⅰ
How to get there: B6277 Barnard Castle road.

Rotherham, South Yorkshire

Hellaby Hall
★★★★ 🐓
Old Hellaby Lane, Hellaby, Rotherham,
South Yorkshire, S66 8SN
Tel: 01709 702701

Best Western Elton
★★★
Main Street, Bramley, Rotherham,
South Yorkshire, S66 0SF
Tel: 01709 545681 Fax: 01709 549100
Email: bestwestern.eltonhotel@btinternet.com
SB £63.35 DB £78.70 HBS £83.35
HBD £123.35 B £5.50 L £12.50 D £20.
CC: MC Vi Am DC Swi Delt JCB
🍸🕭🐕🐎🖥☎🅿✂🕊🐎♫
♨♨♨ ⅰⅰⅰ

How to get there: ¼ mile from M18 J-1. A631
Rotherham. Right into Ravenfield. Hotel at end
of Bramley village.

Consort
★★★
Brampton Road, Thurcroft, Rotherham,
South Yorkshire, S66 9JA
Tel: 01709 530022 Fax: 01709 531529

Marriott
★★★ 🐓
West Bawtry Road, Rotherham, South Yorkshire,
S60 4NA
Tel: 01709 830630 Fax: 01709 830549
To become Courtyard by Marriott, Spring 2001.
SB £95 DB £125 B £9.75 L £12.50 D £19.
CC: MC Vi Am DC Swi Delt
🍸🕭🎢🍷🖥☎✆🅿✂🕊🐎♫🐟🦆👁
♨♨♨ ⅰⅰⅰ 🎾🔲
How to get there: M1 J-33. Signs for Rotherham
A630. Left at next roundabout, see hotel on right.

Brecon
★★
Moorgate Road, Rotherham, South Yorkshire,
S60 2AY
Tel: 01709 828811 Fax: 01709 513030

The Brecon's excellent reputation has been built
up since 1963 by giving a friendly atmosphere,
where all our staff care for your well-being.
SB £46.50 DB £55 HBS £62.50 HBD £86.50
CC: MC Vi Am DC Swi Delt
🕭🐕🐎🍷🖥☎🅿✂🕊🐎♫🐟🦆♨♨♨ ⅰ ⅰ
How to get there: M1 J-33. Signs to Bawtry
(A631). After ½ mile, left at lights for A618. Hotel
1 mile on right.

Northeast

Brentwood

★★

Moorgate Road, Rotherham, South Yorkshire,
S60 2TY
Tel: 01709 382772 Fax: 01709 820289
SB £45 DB £50 B £6 L £6 D £6.
CC: MC Vi Am DC Swi Delt Solo

How to get there: M1 J-33. Right at island
(A631). 1 mile to crossroads. Left onto A618.
Continue 1 mile, hotel on left past hospital.

Campanile

Travel Accommodation

Lowton Way off Denby Way, Hellaby Industrial
Estate, Rotherham, South Yorkshire, S66 8RY
Tel: 01709 700255 Fax: 01709 545169

Typical Campanile Bistro

The Campanile offers its nationwide tradition of
a relaxed atmosphere in the Bistro Restaurant,
with comfortable rooms. Conference, business
or weekend stays all catered for.
SB £43.45 DB £48.40 B £4.95 L £3.50 D £6.95.
CC: MC Vi Am DC Swi Delt

How to get there: M18 at J-1, M1 J-32. At
roundabout turn towards Bawtry. Turn left at
lights, then second left.

Saltburn, Cleveland

Grinkle Park

★★★

Grinkle Lane, Easington, Saltburn-By-The-Sea,
Cleveland, TS13 4UB
Tel: 01287 640515 Fax: 01287 641278
Email: grinkle.parkhotel@bass.com
Web: www.grinklepark.co.uk

Refurbished 19th century house. Set in 35 acres
of parkland. Drive lined with rhododendrons and
azaleas. Perfect location to get away from it all.
SB £81.50 DB £100 HBS £82.95 HBD £60.75
B £7 L £13 D £20. CC: MC Vi Am DC Swi Delt

How to get there: Situated 9 miles from
Guisborough, signed left off main A171
Guisborough to Whitby road.

Scarborough, North Yorkshire

Ganton Greyhound

★★★★

Main Road, Ganton, nr Scarborough, YO12 4NX
Tel: 01944 710116 Fax: 01944 712705
Email: gantongreyhound@supanet.com
Ganton Greyhound is situated alongside Ganton
championship golf course in the village of
Ganton. Built originally as a farmhouse it has
beamed ceilings.
SB £25 DB £50 B £6 L £6 D £7.
CC: MC Vi Am DC Swi

How to get there: Alongside A64 at Ganton, 9
miles from Scarborough, 35 miles from York.

Ambassador

★★★

Centre of The Esplanade, South Cliff,
Scarborough, North Yorkshire, YO11 2AY
Tel: 01723 362841 Fax: 01723 366166
Stunning sea view Victorian hotel offering 59
ensuite bedrooms with full facilities. Heated
swimming pool, spa, steam room and solarium.

Nightly entertainment. Lift. Free parking.
SB £28 DB £56 HBS £38 HBD £76
B £5 L £2 D £14.95. CC: MC Vi Am DC Swi Delt
♿ ♨ 🐾 🐕 🍴 💻 ☎ 📞 🅿 ✂ ⛪ 🐴 🎠 ☩ 🦮 🌊 ♨♨♨
♨♨♨ ⛵

How to get there: On A64, right at roundabout opposite B&Q, right at next roundabout, then immediately left down Avenue Victoria to cliff top.

Clifton
★★★
Queens Parade, Scarborough, North Yorkshire, YO12 7HX
Tel: 01723 875691 Fax: 01723 371780
Email: cliftonhotel@englishrosehotels.co.uk
Web: www.englishrosehotels.co.uk
SB £55 DB £90 HBS £35.50 HBD £35.50
L £11.50 D £16.50. CC: MC Vi Am DC Swi Delt
♿ ♨ 🍴 🌊 💻 ☎ 🅿 ✂ ⛪ 🐴 🦮 🌊 ♨♨♨ ♨♨♨
How to get there: A64 from A1/M1. Left at Scarborough rail station and right at Peasholm Park. Hotel opposite Alexandra Bowls Centre.

Crown
★★★
Esplanade, Scarborough, North Yorkshire, YO11 2AG
Tel: 01723 357450 Fax: 01723 362271
Email: richardfrank@scarboroughhotel.com
Web: www.scarboroughhotel.com

Famous hotel (1835) perched on the esplanade with exhilarating views of south bay.

Entertainment, bars, patio, free leisure 400yds away, Crown Leisure from February.
SB £30 DB £56 HBS £40 HBD £76
B £8.95 L £2.95 D £16.95.
CC: MC Vi Am DC Swi Delt
♿ ♨ ♨ 🍴 🐾 🐕 🌊 💻 ☎ 📞 🅿 ✂ ⛪ 🐴 ☩
🦮 🌊 ♨♨♨ ♨♨♨ 🍴 ⛵ ☩

How to get there: At south end of Valley Bridge (A165), turn east across Valley Bridge Parade onto Belmont Road. Continue to cliff top, hotel on right.

East Ayton Lodge
★★★
Moor Lane, East Ayton, Scarborough, North Yorkshire, YO13 9EW
Tel: 01723 864227 Fax: 01723 862680
SB £49 DB £65 HBS £71.50 HBD £116
B £5 L £8 D £15. CC: MC Vi Am Swi Delt
♿ ♨ 🐕 🌊 💻 ☎ 🅿 ✂ ⛪ 🐴 ☩ 🦮 ♨♨♨ ♨♨♨
How to get there: From A170 from Pickering turn left over bridge.

Esplanade
★★★
Belmont Road, Scarborough, North Yorkshire, YO11 2AA
Tel: 01723 360382 Fax: 01723 376137

Hackness Grange
★★★
North Yorkshire Moors National Park, Hackness, North Yorkshire, YO13 0JW
Tel: 01723 882345 Fax: 01723 882391
Web: www.englishrosehotels.co.uk
SB £77.50 DB £135 HBS £65.50 HBD £54.50
B £12.50 L £12.50 D £25.
CC: MC Vi Am DC Swi Delt
♨ 🌊 💻 ☎ 🅿 ✂ ⛪ 🐕 ☩ 🦮 ♨♨♨ ♨♨♨ 🔍 ☩ ⛵
How to get there: From A1/M1 take A64. Enter Scarborough, follow B1261 and Hackness sign on right. At Hackness, turn left for hotel.

Guide dogs   RaC

If a Hotel or Guest Accommodation does not display this 'dogs welcome' symbol in its listing, the hotelier may still be happy to welcome guests with guide dogs, and you should contact the property to discover whether this will be a problem.

Northeast

Hotel St Nicholas

★★★

St Nicholas Cliff, Scarborough, North Yorkshire, YO11 2EU

Tel: 01723 364101 Fax: 01723 500538

An ideal location for business or leisure. RAC 3 star hotel, which offers a range of superb conference rooms, leisure club with indoor swimming pool, security car parking and a choice of excellent cuisine complemented by the finest wines.

SB £57 DB £75 HBS £67 HBD £99

B £8 L £9.95 D £17. CC: MC Vi Am DC Swi Delt

How to get there: A64 into town centre. Right at first lights, left at second lights. Over small roundabout and take second turn on right.

Palm Court

★★★

St Nicholas Cliff, Scarborough, North Yorkshire, YO11 2ES

Tel: 01723 368161 Fax: 01723 371547

SB £41 DB £76 HBS £46 HBD £92 B £6 L £9.25 D £13.50. CC: MC Vi Am DC Swi Delt

How to get there: Signs for town centre, then town hall. Hotel is en-route.

Wrea Head Country Hotel

★★★

off Barmoor Lane, Scalby, Scarborough, North Yorkshire, YO13 0PB

Tel: 01723 378211 Fax: 01723 371780

Email: wreaheadhotel@englishrosehotels.co.uk

Web: www.englishrosehotels.co.uk

SB £75 DB £120 HBS £59.50 HBD £49.50

L £12.50 D £25. CC: MC Vi Am DC Swi Delt

How to get there: A64 from A1/M1. On entering Scarborough, take A171 (Whitby Road). Pass Scalby and turn left. Hotel drive on left, after pond.

Bradley Court

★★

7–9 Filey Road, Scarborough, North Yorkshire, YO11 2SE

Tel: 01723 360476 Fax: 01723 376661

Email: info@bradleycourthotel.co.uk

Web: www.bradleycourthotel.co.uk

SB £35 DB £60 HBS £40 HBD £75

B £10 D £15. CC: MC Vi DC Swi Delt

How to get there: A64 into Scarborough. Right at mini-roundabout after B&Q. On to next mini-roundabout, turn left, hotel 50yds further on.

Brooklands

★★

Esplanade Gardens, South Cliff, Scarborough, YO11 2AW

Tel: 01723 376576 Fax: 01723 376576

Web: www.brk-hotel.co.uk

Closed January

Brooklands Hotel is situated on the South Cliff, less than one minute's walk to spa and beach tramway. All bedrooms centrally heated and lift to all floors.

SB £20 DB £40 HBS £25 HBD £50 B £5 D £10. CC: MC Vi Swi Delt

How to get there: From A64 to York, turn left for South Cliff, right at mini-roundabout, left onto Victoria Avenue, to Esplanade. Left, then second left onto Esplanade Gardens.

Gridley's Crescent

★★ ®®

The Crescent, Scarborough, North Yorkshire, YO11 2PP

Tel: 01723 360929 Fax: 01723 354126

Email: reception@crescent-hotel.co.uk

Web: www.crescent-hotel.co.uk

Children minimum age: 6

SB £45 DB £80 B £9.50 L £10 D £16.50.

CC: MC Vi Am Swi

How to get there: In Scarborough town centre, signs to Brunswick Centre, Museum & Art Gallery. At Centre, turn right into The Crescent.

Red Lea

★★

Prince of Wales Terrace, South Cliff, Scarborough, North Yorkshire, YO11 2AJ
Tel: 01723 362431 Fax: 01723 371230
Email: redlea@globalnet.co.uk
SB £36 DB £72 HBS £48 HBD £96
B £6 L £9 D £12. CC: MC Vi Am Swi Delt
How to get there: Signs for South Cliff. Hotel is located off the Esplanade near cliff lift.

Ryndle Court

★★

47 Northstead Manor Drive, Scarborough, North Yorkshire, YO12 6AF
Tel: 01723 375188 Fax: 01723 375188
Email: enquiries@ryndlecourt.co.uk
Web: www.ryndlecourt.co.uk
Closed November, January
SB £32 DB £58 HBS £40 HBD £76 B £6 L £9.50
D £10. CC: MC Vi Am DC Swi Delt JCB, Solo
How to get there: Signs marked 'North B41 and Leisure Parks' to Northstead Manor Drive.
See advert below right

Southlands

★★

15 West Street, Scarborough, North Yorkshire, YO11 2QW
Tel: 01723 361461 Fax: 01723 376035

Sunningdale

★★

105 Peasholm Drive, Scarborough, North Yorkshire, YO12 7NB
Tel: 01723 372041
Email: sunningdale@barclays.net
Web: www.sunningdale-scarborough.co.uk

Sunningdale is a modern family-run hotel, on

the north side of Scarborough, opposite Peasholm Park, close to the North Bay and all its attractions.
SB £26 DB £52 HBS £34 HBD £68 D £8.
CC: MC Vi Am Swi Delt
How to get there: Into Scarborough, left at rail station onto Northway, down Columbus Ravine to Peasholm Park. Hotel is on left.

Ashcroft

♦♦♦

102 Columbus Ravine, Scarborough, North Yorkshire, YO12 7QZ
Tel: 01723 375092
SB £20 DB £40 HBS £26 HBD £52
CC: MC Vi
How to get there: In North Bay area, 500 yards up Columbus Ravine from Peasholm Park.

Blacksmiths Arms

♦♦♦

High Street, Cloughton, Scarborough, North Yorkshire, YO13 0AE
Tel: 01723 870244

Northeast

Boundary

124–126 North Marine Road, Scarborough,
North Yorkshire, YO12 7HZ
Tel: 01723 376737

Granby Hotel

Queen Street, Scarborough, North Yorkshire,
YO11 1HL
Tel: 01723 373031 Fax: 01723 373031
Closed Oct to March
SB £24 DB £42 HBS £31 HBD £56 B £4 D £7.
How to get there: Queen St to right as you head
for castle and town centre.

Olivers

34 West Street, South Cliff, Scarborough,
North Yorkshire, YO11 2QP
Tel: 01723 368717
Email: olivers@scarborough.co.uk
SB £25 DB £37 HBS £33 HBD £26.50 CC: Am
How to get there: Approaching Scarborough on
A165 turn right down Avenue Victoria. Take next
right onto West Street. Olivers is on the left.

Parade

29 Esplanade, Scarborough, North Yorkshire,
YO11 2AQ
Tel: 01723 361285
Children minimum age: 2.
Closed November to April
SB £26 DB £52 HBS £37 HBD £74 D £11.
CC: MC Vi Swi Delt
How to get there: From town centre A165 Filey
Rd, across Valley Bridge, second left (Albion Rd),
follow to Esplanade, hotel 100 yards on right.

Sefton

18 Prince of Wales Terrace, South Cliff,
Scarborough, North Yorkshire, YO11 2AL
Tel: 01723 372310
Closed November to February
SB £22 DB £44 HBS £27 HBD £54 B £3 L £4 D £7.

The Phoenix

157 Columbus Ravine, Scarborough,
North Yorkshire, YO12 7QZ
Tel: 01723 368319

Tudor House

164/166 North Marine Road, Scarborough,
North Yorkshire, YO12 7HZ
Tel: 01723 361270

Wheatcroft Lodge

156-158 Filey Road, Scarborough,
North Yorkshire, YO11 3AA
Tel: 01723 374613
Closed Christmas
SB £21.50 DB £43 CC: MC Vi Delt
How to get there: On A165 Scarborough to
Bridlington Road 2 miles south of Scarborough
centre, near South Cliff Golf Club.

West Lodge

38 West Street, Scarborough, North Yorkshire,
YO11 2QP
Tel: 01723 500754
SB £18 DB £36 HBS £25 HBD £50
CC: MC Vi Delt
How to get there: From rail station, sign for Filey
over bridge. Church on right. West St opposite.

Vintage

Scotch Corner, North Yorkshire, DL10 6NP
Tel: 01758 824424 Fax: 01758 826272
Closed Christmas to New Year

Family-run roadside hotel overlooking open
countryside. Open plan rustic style bar and
restaurant. Ideal overnight stop or base for
visiting Yorkshire Dales/Moors.
SB £39 DB £50 HBS £47 HBD £40
B £4 L £9 D £16. CC: MC Vi Am DC Swi Delt

How to get there: Leave A1 at Scotch Corner. Take A66 towards Penrith, Vintage Hotel 200yds on left.

Seahouses, Northumberland

Bamburgh Castle

★★

Seahouses, Northumberland, NE68 7SQ
Tel: 01665 720283 Fax: 01665 720848
Web: www.bamburghcastlehotel.ntb.org.uk
SB £40.95 DB £73.90 HBS £49.90 HBD £49.90
B £12 L £5 D £14.95.

Beach House

★★ 🍴

Seafront, Seahouses, Northumberland, NE68 7SR
Tel: 01665 720337 Fax: 01665 720921
Email: reservations@beachhousehotel.co.uk
Web: www.beachhousehotel.co.uk
Closed January
SB £36 DB £72 HBS £50 HBD £100

How to get there: East off A1 (Berwick to Alnwick) to Seahouses. Hotel on the seafront.

Olde Ship

★★ 🍴

9 Main Street, Seahouses, Northumberland, NE68 7RD
Tel: 01665 720200 Fax: 01665 721383
Email: theoldeship@seahouses.co.uk
Web: www.seahouses.co.uk
Children minimum age: 10
Closed December to January

A stone's throw from the harbour, this friendly family-run hotel has tremendous character, with its cosy public areas and corridors adorned with nautical and period memorabilia.
SB £34 DB £68 HBS £49 HBD £98
B £5.50 L £9.50 D £15. CC: MC Vi Swi Delt

How to get there: 5 miles north of Alnwick on A1. Take the B1340 to Seahouses. The hotel is perched at the harbour top.

Sedgefield, Cleveland

Hardwick Hall

★★★

Sedgefield, Cleveland, TS21 2EH
Tel: 01740 620253 Fax: 01740 622771
Web: www.hardwickhall.co.uk

July 2001 sees the completion of a major redevelopment of this historic hotel. Thirty-six superb additional bedrooms provide accommodation of the very highest quality.
SB £68 DB £78 HBS £86 HBD £96 B £10
CC: MC Vi Am DC Swi Delt

How to get there: Just north of the A117/A689 roundabout at Sedgefield, minutes from A1(M) J-60 and A19.

Settle, North Yorkshire

Plough Inn

★★

Wigglesworth, North Yorkshire, BD23 4RJ
Tel: 01729 840243 Fax: 01729 840243
Email: steve@the-plough-
        wigglesworth.freeserve.co.uk
Web: www.the-plough-wigglesworth.
        freeserve.co.uk
SB £36 DB £56 HBS £52.50 HBD £89
B £7.50 L £5.95 D £12.95.
CC: MC Vi Swi Delt

How to get there: Take the B6478 of the A65 at Long Preston and follow signs to Wigglesworth.

Northeast

Golden Lion

♦ ♦ ♦

Duke Street, Settle, Yorkshire, BO24 9DU
Tel: 01729 822203 Fax: 01729 824103
Email: bookings@goldenlion.yorks.net
Web: www.yorkshirenet.co.uk/stayat/goldenlion

A traditional busy inn with restaurant, offering 14 comfortable bedrooms and log fires. Prime location for Dales, Three Peaks and Settle-Carlisle railway.
SB £33 DB £64 HBS £45 HBD £88
B £6.50 L £9.25 D £9.25.
CC: MC Vi Swi Delt Electron JCB Solo

How to get there: As you enter Settle town centre from south, hotel is on right-hand side of road, just before market square.

Sheffield, South Yorkshire

Swallow

★ ★ ★ ★

Kenwood Road, Sheffield, South Yorkshire, S7 1NQ
Tel: 01142 583811 Fax: 01142 500138
To become Marriott, Summer 2001.
SB £95 DB £120 CC: MC Vi Am DC Swi Delt

How to get there: M1 J-33. Travel 6 miles to city centre. Follow signs for A61 South, to Nether-edge Hotels.

Charnwood

★ ★ ★

10 Sharrow Lane, Sheffield, South Yorkshire, S11 8AA
Tel: 0114 2589411 Fax: 0114 2555107
Email: king@charnwood.force9.co.uk
Closed December 25 to January 1.
This charming Georgian residence has elegant public areas and conference facilities, charming bedrooms and two excellent restaurants. Situated 1½ miles southwest of

the city centre, only 10 mins by car from Derbyshire's Peak District National Park.
SB £75 DB £90 B £7.75 L £15.25 D £15.25.
CC: MC Vi Am DC Swi Delt

Novotel Sheffield

★ ★ ★

Arundel Gate, Sheffield, Yorkshire, S1 2PR
Tel: 01142 781781 Fax: 01142 787799
Email: h1348-gm@accor-hotels.com
SB £91.95 DB £102 B £9.95 L £4.95 D £11.50.
CC: MC Vi Am DC Swi

How to get there: In the heart of the city, 5 mins from M1 J-33 via A57, Parkway. 10 mins from Sheffield airport, close to rail station.

Cooke House   Little Gem

♦ ♦ ♦ ♦ ♦

78 Brookhouse Hill, Sheffield, South Yorkshire, S10 3TB
Tel: 0114 2308186 Fax: 0114 263 0241

The Briary   Little Gem

♦ ♦ ♦ ♦ ♦

12 Moncrieffe Road, Nether Edge, Sheffield, South Yorkshire, S7 1HR
Tel: 0114 255 1951 Fax: 0114 221 7716
Email: briary@briary.fq.co.uk
Children minimum age: 13
SB £35 DB £52 B £5 D £17. CC: MC Vi Delt

How to get there: Right off A621 from Abbeydale Road at Yorkshire Bank traffic lights, up Sheldon Road to next lights, right onto Moncrieffe Road.

Etruria House

♦ ♦ ♦

91 Crookes Road, Broomhill, Sheffield, South Yorkshire, S10 5BD
Tel: 01142 662241 Fax: 01142 670853
Email: etruria@waitrose.com
SB £38 DB £52 CC: MC Vi

How to get there: M1 J-33. A57 for Glossop for 2 miles. At traffic lights in Broomhill, turn right. Hotel 200 yards on left.

Hunter House

♦♦♦

685-691 Ecclesall Road, Sheffield,
South Yorkshire, S11 8TG
Tel: 0114 2662709 Fax: 0114 2686370
Email: ma@hhh.freeserve.co.uk
Web: www.hunterhousehotel.com
SB £32 DB £50 D £6.50.
CC: MC Vi Am Swi Delt

How to get there: From Sheffield town centre take A624 to Bakewell. Hotel on Ecclesall Road at Hunters Bar roundabout.

Lindrick

♦♦♦

226 Chippinghouse Road, Sheffield,
South Yorkshire, S7 1DR
Tel: 0114 258 5041 Fax: 0114 255 4758

Skipton, North Yorkshire

Hanover International Skipton

★★★

Keighley Road, Skipton, North Yorkshire,
BD23 2TA
Tel: 01756 700100 Fax: 01756 700107
Email: hihskipton@totalise.co.uk
Web: www.hanover-international.com

HANOVER INTERNATIONAL

Offers stunning views of the Yorkshire Dales, with a state registered nursery and extensive leisure club. Brasserie H2O has an enviable reputation for mouth-watering cuisine.
SB £60 DB £70 HBS £80 HBD £100
B £7 D £16.95.
CC: MC Vi Am DC Swi Delt Solo JCB

How to get there: To Skipton from A629. Signs for centre. Hotel on right on entering Skipton.

Skipton Park Guest'Otel

♦♦♦

2 Salisbury Street, Skipton, North Yorkshire,
BD23 1NQ
Tel: 01756 700640 Fax: 01756 700641
Email: derekchurch@skiptonpark.freeserve.co.uk
Web: www.milford.co.uk/go/skiptonpark.html
SB £35 DB £48

South Cave, East Yorkshire

Rudstone Walk

♦♦♦♦

South Cave, East Yorkshire, HU15 2AH
Tel: 01430 422230 Fax: 01430 424552

South Shields, Tyne & Wear

Sea Hotel

★★★

Sea Road, South Shields, Tyne & Wear,
NE33 2LD
Tel: 0191 427 0999 Fax: 0191 454 0500

Stockton-on-Tees, Cleveland

Swallow Hotel Stockton

★★★★ 🍴🍴

10 John Walker Square, Stockton-on-Tees,
Cleveland, TS18 1AQ
Tel: 01642 679721 Fax: 01642 601714
Email: stockton@swallow-hotels.co.uk
Web: www.swallow-hotels.com
SB £115 DB £120 HBS £135 HBD £160 B £9.95
L £12.50 D £19.95. CC: MC Vi Am DC Swi

How to get there: From A19, A66 to Stockton town centre. Park in long stay Castlegate car park. Rear entrance to hotel on sixth floor.

Claireville

★★

519 Yarm Road, Easglesclife, Cleveland,
TS16 9BG
Tel: 01642 780378 Fax: 01642 784109
Email: reception@clairev.demon.co.uk
Web: www.clairev.demon.co.uk
SB £50 DB £65 B £5 L £10 D £12.
CC: MC Vi Am DC Swi Delt

How to get there: A135 between A66 (Stockton-on-Tees) and A19 at Yarm. By Eaglescliffe Golf
Course.

Sunnyside

★★

580-582 Yarm Road, Eaglescliffe, Cleveland,
TS16 0DF
Tel: 01642 780075 Fax: 01642 783789
Web: www.sunnysidehotel.co.uk
SB £43 DB £55 HBS £55 HBD £75 D £10.
CC: MC Vi Am DC Swi Delt

How to get there: On A135 between Stockton-on-Tees and Yarm. A135 access from A19 and A66.

Sunderland, Tyne & Wear

Marriott Sunderland

★★★★

Queens Parade, Sunderland, Tyne & Wear,
SR6 8DB
Tel: 0191 529 2041 Fax: 0191 529 3843
SB £99 DB £130 B £9.95 L £9.95 D £9.95.
CC: MC Vi Am DC Swi Delt

Quality Hotel

★★★

Junction A19/A184, Witney Way, Boloon, nr
Sunderland, NE35 9PE
Tel: 0191 519 1999 Fax: 0191 519 0655
Email: admin@gb621.u-net.com
Children minimum age: 14

SB £92.75 DB £128.50 HBS £107.25 HBD £148
B £9.75 L £8.25 D £14.50.
CC: MC Vi Am DC Swi Delt

How to get there: On the junction between A19
and A184, 7 miles from Newcastle train station.

Tunstall Lodge

★★

Burdon Lane, Burdon, Tyne & Wear, SR3 2QB
Tel: 0191 5210353 Fax: 0191 5236887
SB £45 DB £65 HBS £56 HBD £87
B £7.50 L £4 D £10.95. CC: MC Vi Am Swi Delt

How to get there: Off A19 onto A690. Sign for
Doxford Park. Proceed to Burdon roundabout.
Turn right and hotel is 100yds on left.

Thirsk, North Yorkshire

Angel Inn

★★

Long Street, Topcliffe, Thirsk, North Yorkshire,
YO7 3RW
Tel: 01845 577237 Fax: 01845 578000
SB £45 DB £60 B £7.75 L £10.95 D £14.95.
CC: MC Vi Swi Delt

How to get there: Just off A168, 3 miles from
A1(M) J-49. 3 miles from A19.

Sheppard's

★★

Church Farm, Front Street, Sowerby, Thirsk,
North Yorkshire, YO7 1JF
Tel: 01845 523655 Fax: 01845 524720

Tynemouth, Tyne & Wear

Grand

★★★

Grand Parade, Tynemouth, Tyne & Wear,
NE30 4ER
Tel: 0191 293 6666 Fax: 0191 293 6665
Email: info@grand-hotel.demon.co.uk
Web: www.grand-hotel.demon.co.uk
SB £70 DB £75 HBS £85.75
B £8.50 L £14.75 D £15.75.
CC: MC Vi Am DC Swi Delt

How to get there: From A1, A19 then A1058.
Signs for Tynemouth. At seafront, turn right.
Grand Hotel is approx 1/2 mile.

If you're looking for great dining when staying
away, look for RAC Hotels and Guest
Accommodation displaying the RAC Dining
Award symbol in this Guide.

Park

★★★

Grand Parade, Tynemouth, Tyne & Wear,
NE30 4JQ
Tel: 0191 257 1406 Fax: 0191 257 1716
CC: MC Vi Am DC Swi Delt

Wakefield, West Yorkshire

Cedar Court

★★★★

Denby Dale Road, Wakefield, West Yorkshire,
WF4 3QZ
Tel: 01924 276310 Fax: 01924 280221
Email: johnh@cedarcourthotels.co.uk
Web: www.cedarcourthotels.co.uk
SB £105 DB £115 HBS £120 HBD £145 B £9
L £12.50 D £18. CC: MC Vi Am DC Swi Delt

How to get there: Off M1 J-39, by roundabout
under motorway.

St Pierre

★★★

Barnsley Road, Newmillerdam, Wakefield,
West Yorkshire, WF2 6QG
Tel: 01924 255596 Fax: 01924 252746

Campanile

Travel Accommodation
Monckton Road, Wakefield, West Yorkshire,
Tel: 01924 201054 Fax: 01924 201055

Typical Campanile bedroom

Campanile hotels offer comfortable and
convenient budget accommodation and a
traditional French style Bistro providing freshly
cooked food for breakfast, lunch and dinner. All
rooms ensuite with tea/coffee making facilities,
DDT and TV with Sky channels.
B £4.95 L £2.95 D £11.25.
CC: MC Vi Am DC Swi Delt Solo

How to get there: M1 J-39. Towards Wakefield
Centre on A636, hotel is 1 mile on left, on
Monkton Road Industrial Estate.

Warkworth, Northumberland

Warkworth House

★★

16 Bridge Street, Warkworth, Northumberland,
NE65 0XB
Tel: 01665 711276 Fax: 01665 713323
Email: welcome@warkworthhousehotel.co.uk
Web: www.warkworthhousehotel.co.uk
SB £55 DB £90 HBS £69 HBD £109 B £10.95
L £10.95 D £17.95. CC: MC Vi Am DC Swi Delt

How to get there: From A1, B6345 and signs for
Warkworth Castle. Hotel on B1068 near bridge.

Washington, Tyne & Wear

Campanile, Washington

Travel Accommodation
Emerson Road, District 5, Washington, Tyne &
Wear, NE37 1LE
Tel: 0191 416 5010 Fax: 0191 416 5023

Typical Campanile Bistro

Campanile hotels offer comfortable and
convenient budget accommodation and a
traditional French style Bistro providing freshly
cooked food for breakfast, lunch and dinner. All
rooms ensuite with tea/coffee making facilities,
DDT and TV with Sky channels.
SB £44.90 DB £49.85 HBS £52 HBD £68.20
B £4.95 L £4.95 D £5.95. CC: MC Vi Am DC Swi

How to get there: A1(M) north J-64. A195 signs
Washington. First left (Emerson Rd) and follow
signs.

Northeast

Whitby, North Yorkshire

Old West Cliff

★★

42 Crescent Avenue, Whitby, North Yorkshire,
YO21 3EQ
Tel: 01947 603292 Fax: 01947 821716
Email: oldwestcliff@telinco.co.uk
Web: www.oldwestcliff.telinco.co.uk
Closed January
SB £31.50 DB £52 HBS £43.50 HBD £76
CC: MC Vi Am DC Swi Delt
How to get there: Approach Whitby, signs for
West Cliff. Hotel off central exit Crescent
Gardens, opposite Spa and Pavillion complex.

Saxonville

★★ ☕

Ladysmith Avenue, Whitby, North Yorkshire,
YO21 3HX
Tel: 01947 602631 Fax: 01947 820250
Email: saxonville@onyxnet.co.uk
Web: www.yorkshirenet.co.uk/saxonville
Closed December to February
SB £40 DB £80 HBS £51 HBD £102
B £9.50 D £20.50. CC: MC Vi Swi Delt
How to get there: Signs for Whitby/West Cliff. At
Metropole Towers turn inland into Argyle Road.
Saxonville first turning on right.

White House

★★

Upgang Lane, Whitby, North Yorkshire,
YO21 3JJ
Tel: 01947 600469 Fax: 01947 821600

Glendale Guest House

♦♦♦♦

16 Crescent Avenue, Whitby, North Yorkshire,
YO21 3ED
Tel: 01947 604242

Seacliffe

♦♦♦♦

North Promenade, Whitby, North Yorkshire,
YO21 3JX
Tel: 01947 603139 Fax: 01947 603139
Email: julie@seacliffe.fsnet.co.uk
Web: www.seacliffe.co.uk
SB £39.50 DB £65 HBS £54.50 HBD £95
B £7.50 D £15.
CC: MC Vi Am DC Swi Delt
How to get there: Follow signs for West Cliff and
West Cliff car park. Hotel located on seafront.

Heatherdene

♦♦♦

The Common, Goathland, Whitby,
North Yorkshire, YO22 5AN
Tel: 01947 896334

Sandbeck

♦♦♦

2 Crescent Terrace, West Cliff, Whitby, North
Yorkshire, YO21 3EL
Tel: 01947 604012 Fax: 01947 606402
Email: dysonsandbeck@tesco.net
Closed Dec
DB £42.60 CC: MC Vi Am Swi Delt JCB Solo
How to get there: A169/A171, signs for West Cliff.

Whitley Bay, Tyne & Wear

Windsor

★★★

South Parade, Whitley Bay, Tyne & Wear,
NE26 2RF
Tel: 0191 251 8888 Fax: 0191 297 0272
Email: info@windsor-hotel.demon.co.uk
SB £65 DB £70 HBS £80 HBD £100 D £14.75.
CC: MC Vi Am DC Swi Delt Solo
How to get there: From A1, join A19. Signs for
A1058. On seafront turn left, approx 2 miles.

York House Hotel & Studios

♦♦♦♦ ☕

30 Park Parade, Whitley Bay, Tyne & Wear,
NE26 1DX
Tel: 0191 2528313 Fax: 0191 2513953
Email: reservations@yorkhousehotel.com
Web: www.yorkhousehotel.com
SB £35 DB £50 HBS £42.50 HBD £75 D £12.50.
CC: MC Vi Am Swi Delt
How to get there: On two sites 200yds apart.
York House Hotel on Park Parade, York House
Studios on Park Avenue, both off A193.

Wooler, Northumberland

Tankerville Arms

★★

Cottage Road, Wooler, Northumberland,
NE71 6AD
Tel: 01668 281581 Fax: 01668 281387
Email: enquiries@tankervillehotel.co.uk
Web: www.tankervillehotel.co.uk
SB £45 DB £80 B £5 L £5.95 D £10.

CC: MC Vi Swi Delt

🏔🐾🐕🖥☎🅿⛱☳🐎🐎🎿♨♨♨

How to get there: On northern outskirts of Wooler on A697. Midway between Edinburgh and Newcastle-upon-Tyne.

Yarm, Cleveland

Crathorne Hall
★★★★ 🍴🍴🍴
nr Yarm, Crathorne, Cleveland, TS15 0AR
Tel: 01642 700398 Fax: 01642 700456

Impressive Edwardian mansion in classical style with oak-panelled rooms and fine antiques. Set in 15 acres of wooded grounds.
SB £80 DB £140 HBS £90 HBD £160 B £9.50 L £14.50 D £27.50. CC: MC Vi Am DC Swi Delt

🏔🐾🐕🖥☎🅿⛱🐎🐎🎿♨♨♨

How to get there: From A1 north, A19 Teesside exit. Crathorne signposted off A19 at Yarm/Teeside airport exit. Crathorne 1 mile slip road.

York, North Yorkshire

Royal York
★★★★
Station Road, York, North Yorkshire, YO2 2AA
Tel: 01904 653681 Fax: 01904 653271
Email: julia.bodmer@principalhotels.co.uk
SB £136.95 DB £168.90 HBS £156.95
HBD £208.90 CC: MC Vi Am DC Swi Delt

🏔🐕🖥☎🅿⛱🐎🐎🎿♨♨♨

How to get there: M1 J-32, M18 then J-2 onto A1 (north). From A1, A64 to York, A1036 to centre.

Swallow Hotel
★★★★ 🍴
Tadcaster Road, York, YO2 2QQ
Tel: 01904 701000 Fax: 01904 702308
To become Marriott, Spring 2001.
SB £99 DB £140 CC: MC Vi Am DC Swi Delt

🏔🐕♨🖥🐾🐕🖥☎🅿⛱🐎🐎
🎿♨♨♨

How to get there: On A1036, 1 mile from city centre.

Ambassador
★★★ 🍴
123 The Mount, York, North Yorkshire, YO24 1DU
Tel: 01904 641316 Fax: 01904 640259
Email: stay@ambassadorhotel.co.uk
Web: www.ambassadorhotel.co.uk

Beautiful bedrooms and award-winning Greys Restaurant, where the food is simple and delicious. Easy walk to the city centre or racecourse. Ample car parking.
SB £90 DB £118 HBS £110 HBD £158
B £7 L £12 D £18. CC: MC Vi Am DC Swi Delt

🏔♨🖥🐕🖥☎🅿⛱🐎🐎🎿
♨♨♨

How to get there: From A64 take A1036 (York). Past racecourse, hotel on right, before lights.

Dean Court
★★★ 🍴
Duncombe Place, York, North Yorkshire, YO1 2EF
Tel: 01904 625082 Fax: 01904 620305
Email: info@deancourt-york.co.uk
Web: www.deancourt-york.co.uk
SB £82.50 DB £125 HBS £99 HBD £160
B £7.50 L £9.75 D £15.
CC: MC Vi Am DC Swi Delt JCB

🏔♨🖥🐕🖥☎🅿⛱🐎🐎🎿♨♨♨

How to get there: From outer ring road, take A64 York North, then A1237 A19 Thirsk, then Clifton (inner ring road) to city centre and Minster.

Northeast

Grange

★★★ ⚘⚘⚘
Clifton, York, North Yorkshire, YO30 6AA
Tel: 01904 644744 Fax: 01904 612453
Email: info@grangehotel.co.uk
Web: www.grangehotel.co.uk

Exclusive Regency townhouse just minutes from the Minster and city centre. Luxurious accommodation, 3 superb restaurants and award winning food. Excellent conference facilities. Private car park.
SB £99 DB £125 HBS £89 HBD £59
B £8.50 L £11.50 D £25.
CC: MC Vi Am DC Swi Delt

How to get there: On A19 York to Thirsk road, 500yds from city centre.

Judges Lodging

★★★
9 Lendal, York, North Yorkshire, YO1 8AQ
Tel: 01904 638733 Fax: 01904 679947
Email: judgeshotel@aol.com
Web: www.judges_lodging.co.uk

Privately owned. Offers impressive Minster views, spa baths, 14 ensuite beds, some four-poster. Secure on-site parking. Leave your car and explore the history of York on-foot.
SB £75 DB £100 HBS £85 HBD £120 B £5 L £5
D £10. CC: MC Vi Am Swi Delt

How to get there: In the heart of York.

Middlethorpe Hall

★★★ ⚘⚘⚘⚘
Bishopthorpe Road, York, North Yorkshire,
YO2 1QB
Tel: 01904 641241 Fax: 01904 620176
Email: info@middlethorpe.com
Web: www.middlethorpe.com
Children minimum age: 8
SB £119.50 DB £184 B £10.50 L £15.50 D £34.
CC: MC Vi Swi Delt

How to get there: From A64 join A1036 signs York/Racecourse. Then follow smaller signs to Bishopthorpe and Middlethorpe.

Monk Fryston Hall

★★★
Monk Fryston, North Yorkshire, LS25 5DU
Tel: 01977 682369 Fax: 01977 683544
Email: reception@monkfryston-hotel.com
Web: www.monkfryston-hotel.com
SB £81 DB £102 L £10 D £23.
CC: MC Vi Am DC Swi Delt

How to get there: Less than 5 minutes drive from A1 on A63 – 3 miles east off A1 in North Yorkshire.
See advert on facing page top

Monkbar

★★★
Monkbar, York, North Yorkshire, YO31 7JA
Tel: 01904 638086 Fax: 01904 629195
Email: sales@monkbar-hotel.co.uk
Web: www.monkbar-hotel.co.uk

Situated at the heart of York, The Monkbar overlooks the castle walls and Minster. Delightful courtyard garden. Private car parking.
SB £85 DB £125 B £9.50 L £12.50 D £17.95.
CC: MC Vi Am DC Swi Delt

How to get there: On York inner ring road next to city walls at Monkbar entrance to York.

Mount Royale

★★★

The Mount, York, YO24 1GU
Tel: 01904 628856 Fax: 01904 611171
Email: reservation@mountroyale.co.uk
Web: www.mountroyale.co.uk
SB £85 DB £95 B £7.50 D £25.
CC: MC Vi Am DC Swi Delt

How to get there: Southbound M1, take A64 to York. Second turn off for York (A1036 west). At traffic lights left. After 3 miles, hotel at top of hill.

See advert on this page bottom

Novotel York

★★★

Fishergate, York, YO10 4FD
Tel: 01904 611660 Fax: 01904 610925
Email: h0949@accor-hotels.com
Web: www.accorhotel.com
SB £89.45 DB £105 HBS £105 HBD £125 B £6.95 L £7.95 D £13.95. CC: MC Vi Am DC Swi Delt JCB Solo Electron

How to get there: A19 exit from A64. A19 for city centre, following signs. Novotel York on left.

Parsonage Country House

★★★

Escrick, York, North Yorkshire, YO19 6LF
Tel: 01904 728111 Fax: 01904 728151
Email: sales@parsonagehotel.co.uk
Web: www.parsonagehotel.co.uk
SB £95 DB £110 HBS £110 HBD £140 B £10 L £7 D £19.75.
CC: MC Vi Am DC Swi Delt

How to get there: In village of Escrick on A19 between York and Selby.

Abbots Mews

★★

Marygate Lane, Bootham, York, YO3 7DE
Tel: 01904 634866 Fax: 01904 612848
SB £37.50 DB £65 HBS £50 HBD £90 D £12.50.
CC: MC Vi Am DC Swi Delt JCB Solo

How to get there: A19 into York. Just before Bootham Bar and lights at Exhibition Square, right into Marygate. At end of Marygate, right and right again. Hotel overlooks car park.

Monk Fryston Hall Hotel

Monk Fryston Hall is a 16th-century listed manor house set in spacious, secluded grounds, yet has easy access from A1, M62 M1 Link, in the Vale of York. Oak-panelled reception rooms, mullioned windows and log fires offer every comfort and an impressive welcome. Suitable for conferences, business or leisure. Pets welcome. Open all year.

Room and breakfast from £81.00–£135.00 (single) £102–£155 (double) VAT included.
Weekend break, dinner, bed and breakfast (2 nights) from £124.00 pp.
Sunday special: Dinner, bed and breakfast £49.99 pp.

Monk Fryston, N. Yorkshire LS25 5DU
Tel: 01977 682369 Fax: 01977 683544
Email: reception@monkfryston-hotel.com
Website: www.monkfryston-hotel.com

Mount Royale

The Mount Royale is ideally placed for visitors to the city of York.

With a restaurant overlooking the garden offering the best of international cuisine.

The Mount, York YO24 1GU
Tel: 01904 628856 Fax: 01904 611171
Email: mountroyale@mountroyale.co.uk
Website: www.mountroyale.co.uk

Alhambra Court

★★ ℞

31 St Marys, Bootham, York, North Yorkshire,
YO30 7DD
Tel: 01904 628474 Fax: 01904 610690

Ideal location, a quiet cul-de-sac five minutes
walk to the city centre. Offers well appointed
bedrooms, comfortable lounges, a bar and a
non-smoking restaurant. Private car park. Lift.
SB £35 DB £50 HBS £48.50 HBD £77 D £13.50.
CC: MC Vi Swi Delt JCB

⌁ ⬚⊗◔▢☎P♿℃ⅉⱨ♥⛉†
How to get there: From city wall of Bootham
Bar, 2nd turning on left off Bootham (A19 Thirsk).

Beechwood Close

★★

19 Shipton Road, York, North Yorkshire,
YO30 5RE
Tel: 01904 658378 Fax: 01904 647124
Email: bch@selcom.co.uk
Web: www.beechwood-close.co.uk
SB £47 DB £79 HBS £52.25 HBD £89.50
B £6.75 L £8 D £14.
CC: MC Vi Am DC Swi Delt Solo

◔▢☎P♿℃ⅉⱨ♥⛉†
How to get there: From Outer Ring Road
(A1237), turn to city centre at A19 Thirsk
roundabout. Hotel 1 mile on right, just inside
30mph zone.

Cottage

★★

3 Clifton Green, York, North Yorkshire, YO3 6LH
Tel: 01904 643711 Fax: 01904 611230

Heworth Court

★★

Heworth Green, York, North Yorkshire,
YO31 7TQ
Tel: 01904 425156 Fax: 01904 415290
Email: hotel@heworth.co.uk
Web: www.visityork.com

A traditional English hotel within one mile of
York Minster with ensuite hotel accommodation,
four-posters, whisky bar, candle-lit restaurant
and ample parking.
Web: www.visityork.com
SB £48 DB £90 HBS £65 HBD £45 B £7.50
L £9.95 D £11.95. CC: MC Vi Am DC Swi Delt

⬙⬚⊗◔▢☎❱P♿℃ⅉⱨ♥⬚†
How to get there: Drive around outer ring road
(York bypass) and turn into York from Scarbo-
rough roundabout on A1036 east. Hotel on left.

Hudsons

★★ ℞

60 Bootham, York, North Yorkshire, YO3 7BZ
Tel: 01904 621267 Fax: 01904 654719

Kilima

★★

129 Holgate Road, York, North Yorkshire,
YO24 4AZ
Tel: 01904 625787 Fax: 01904 612083
Email: sales@kilima.co.uk
Web: www.kilima.co.uk
SB £58 DB £86 HBS £73 HBD £126 B £7.50
L £13.50 D £13.50. CC: MC Vi Am DC Swi Delt

♿⬚⊷⊗◔▢☎P♿℃ⅉⱨ♥⛉ SPA
🍴 🛈
How to get there: A59 Harrogate road (W city).

Knavesmire Manor

★★

302 Tadcaster Road, York, North Yorkshire,
YO24 1HE
Tel: 01904 702941 Fax: 01904 709274
Email: kanvesmire@easynet.co.uk
Web: www.knavesmire-manor.co.uk

Once a Rowntree family home, the hotel offers tropical indoor pool, uninterrupted views of the famous York racecourse, ensuite bedrooms and Two Rosette restaurant.
SB £32.50 DB £65 HBS £44.50 HBD £89
B £3.50 D £14.50. CC: MC Vi Am Swi Delt

How to get there: A64 off A1, near Tadcaster. Signs to York West, then signs to Bishopthorpe or Racecourse. Hotel opposite Knavesmire racecourse.

Savages
★★
St Peter's Grove, Clifton, York, North Yorkshire, YO30 3AQ
Tel: 01904 610818 Fax: 01904 627729
SB £24.50 DB £49 HBS £34.50 HBD £69
B £7.50 D £11.50. CC: MC Vi Am DC Swi Delt

How to get there: Off A19 to Thirsk, approx 10 minutes walk from York Minster at end of St Peter's Grove.

Arndale
◆◆◆◆
290 Tadcaster Road, York, North Yorkshire, YO24 1ET
Tel: 01904 702424 Fax: 01904 709800
SB £50 DB £80 CC: MC Vi Swi Delt

How to get there: From A64 take York West 1036 road. City centre signs. Hotel approx 1 mile from A64 on left overlooking racecourse.
See advert on the right

Ascot House
◆◆◆◆
80 East Parade, York, North Yorkshire, YO31 7YH
Tel: 01904 426826 Fax: 01904 431077
Email: j+k@asot-houe-york.demon.co.uk

SB £25 DB £50
CC: MC Vi DC Swi Delt

How to get there: From northeast, junction A1237 and A64 (ringroad) take A1036. Turn left for Heworth after 30mph sign, then right at traffic lights into East Parade.

Arndale Hotel

A Victorian gem set in beautiful walled grounds overlooking racecourse and within easy walking distance of city, with ample private parking and on main bus route. Lovely bedrooms individually furnished with antiques. Pretty Victorian bathrooms many with whirlpool baths. Spacious drawing room with honesty bar. Also exquisite Garden Rooms.

290 Tadcaster Road, York YO24 1ET
Tel: 01904 702424   Fax: 01904 709800

Ashbourne House

139 Fulford Road, York, North Yorkshire,
YO1 4HG
Tel: 01904 639912 Fax: 01904 631332
Email: ashbourneh@aol.com
SB £30 DB £40 CC: MC Vi Am DC
⊗☺🖵☎P🛏🕯🐎♿🛎🍴
How to get there: On A19 road south (York to Selby), one mile from city centre.

Bloomsbury

127 Clifton, York, North Yorkshire, YO3 6BL
Tel: 01904 634031

Curzon Lodge & Stable Cottages

23 Tadcaster Road, Dringhouses, York, North Yorkshire, YO24 1QE
Tel: 01904 703157 Fax: 01904 703157
Web:
www.smoothhound.co.uk/hotels/curzon.html
Children minimum age: 7

Relax and unwind in a unique atmosphere at this charming 17th century former farmhouse and stables overlooking York racecourse. Close to centre. Parking in grounds. Personal service.
SB £45 DB £59
CC: MC Vi Swi Delt Solo Electron JCB Maestro
🖨⊗☺🖵P🛏🕯🐎♿
How to get there: From A64, A1036 for city centre, 2 miles on right between Forte Post House hotel and York Swallow Hotel.

Eastons

90 Bishopthorpe Road, York, North Yorkshire, YO23 1JS
Tel: 01904 626646 Fax: 01904 626165
Children minimum age: 5
Closed Christmas to New Year
Award-winning hotel situated 300 yards from the city walls. William Morris décor, period furnishings, original paintings, all rooms ensuite. Extensive Victorian breakfasts. Car park.
SB £39.50 DB £42
⊗☺🖵P🛏🕯🐎♿
How to get there: A64, then A1036. Signs for Bishopthorpe. First left in village into Church Lane. At end of road turn left. Hotel 2 miles on right opposite church.

Hazelwood

24-25 Portland Street, Gillygate, York, North Yorkshire, YO31 7EH
Tel: 01904 626548 Fax: 01904 628032
Email: admin@thehazelwoodyork.com
Web: www.thehazelwoodyork.com
Children minimum age: 8

SB £35 DB £65 CC: MC Vi Swi Delt
🖨⊗☺🖵P🛏🕯🐎♿🛎🍴
How to get there: Just 400yds from York Minster in residential side street, off inner ring road (Gillygate).
See advert on opposite page

Holly Lodge

304–306 Fulford Road, York, North Yorkshire, YO1 4DD
Tel: 01904 646005
Web: www.thehollylodge.co.uk

Beautifully appointed Grade II listed building, 10 minutes stroll to centre. Convenient for all

York's attractions. On-site parking. All rooms en-suite overlooking garden or terrace. Booking recommended. 1½ miles A64/A19 intersection.
SB £48 DB £58 CC: MC Vi Delt

⊗ ☒ ▯ Ⓟ ✾ ℃ ⛷ ♬ ⛵

How to get there: Corner Fulford road and Wenlock, 1½ miles towards centre from A19/A64 intersection. 10 minutes walk on A19 south from centre.

Holmwood House

♦♦♦♦

114 Holgate Road, York, North Yorkshire, YO24 4BB
Tel: 01904 626183 Fax: 01904 670899
Email: holmwood.house@dial.pipex.com
Web: www.holmwoodhousehotel.co.uk
Children minimum age: 8

Elegant Victorian house.
SB £55 DB £80 CC: MC Vi Am Swi Delt

🖼 ⊗ ☒ ▯ ☎ ↳ Ⓟ ✾ ℃ ⛷ ♬ ⛵ ⚏ ╏

How to get there: On A59 Harrogate to York road, 300 yards past The Fox.

Acorn Guest House

♦♦♦

1 Southlands Road, York, North Yorkshire, YO2 1NP
Tel: 01904 620081 Fax: 01904 613331
Email: acorn.gh@btinternet.com
DB £40 CC: MC Vi

⊗ ☒ ▯ ☎ ✾ ℃ ⛷ ♬ ⛵

How to get there: Off A64, A1036 to city centre. After ⅔ mile, right into Scarcroft Rd. Then take 6th right. Scott St leads to Southlands Rd.

Bank House

♦♦♦

9 Southland Road, York, North Yorkshire, YO23 1NP
Tel: 01904 627803
SB £22 DB £40

🐈 ⊗ ☒ ▯ ✾ ℃ ⛷ ♬ ⛵

How to get there: Bank House is on Southland Road off Bishopthorpe Road, 5 minutes walk from York city centre (Southbank area).

Blue Bridge

 ◆◆◆

Fishergate, York, North Yorkshire, YO10 4AP
Tel: 01904 621193 Fax: 01904 671571
Email: info@bluebridgehotel.co.uk
Web: www.bluebridgehotel.co.uk
SB £40 DB £60 HBS £50 HBD £80 D £10.
CC: MC Vi Swi JCB Solo

How to get there: On A19 York to Selby road,
2 miles from outer ring road on right. Five
minutes walk city centre.

Carlton House

◆◆◆

134 The Mount, York, YO24 1AS
Tel: 01904 622265
Email: rac@carltonhouse.co.uk
Web: www.carltonhouse.co.uk
SB £30 DB £54

How to get there: Turn off A64 York-Leeds road
onto A1036. Hotel just beyond the racecourse,
through traffic lights on left.

Georgian Guest House

◆◆◆

35 Bootham, York, North Yorkshire, YO3 7BT
Tel: 01904 622874 Fax: 01904 635379
Email: georgian.house@virgin.net
Web: www.georgianhouse.co.uk
Children minimum age: 8
SB £24 DB £44 B £8 CC: MC Vi

How to get there: Into York on A19, Georgian
House on left, in city centre.

Ivy House Farm

◆◆◆

Hull Road, Kexby, North Yorkshire, Y041 5LQ
Tel: 01904 489368

Situated on the A1079 east of York, with easy
access to the Yorkshire wolds, dales, moors and
east coast. Comfortable accommodation with

lounge, dining room and gardens, with TV and
hot and cold water in all rooms.
SB £20 DB £36

How to get there: Leave York on A1079 Hull
Road., Ivy House Farm is on right about 5 miles
from town centre.

Linden Lodge

◆◆◆

6 Nunthorpe Avenue, Scarcroft Road, York,
YO2 1PF
Tel: 01904 620107 Fax: 01904 620985

Linden Lodge is 10 mins walk from city centre,
railway station and racecourse. With a mix of
doubles, singles and family rooms, all with tea-
and coffee-making facilities and colour televisions.
SB £25 DB £52

Monkgate Guest House

◆◆◆

65 Monkgate, York, YO31 7PA
Tel: 01904 655947
Email: jmb@monkgate.swinternet.co.uk
Web: www.monkgateguesthouse.co.uk
SB £25 DB £54 CC: MC Vi

How to get there: Avoid city centre, stay on A64
until Scarborough/Marlton roundabout. Left
onto A1036 that leads to bottom of Monkgate.

Priory

♦ ♦ ♦

126–128 Fulford Road, York, North Yorkshire,
YO10 4BE
Tel: 01904 625280 Fax: 01904 637330
Email: liz@priory-hotelyork.co.uk
Web: www.priory-hotelyork.co.uk

A prominent family-run hotel, set in secluded
gardens, with free parking to residents and only
a few minutes walk from the city centre.
SB £45 DB £70 HBS £55 HBD £90
B £5 D £8.95. CC: MC Vi Am DC Swi Delt

How to get there: On A19 to Selby on south
side of city. No 9 bus or 1½ miles from station.

St Denys

♦ ♦ ♦

St Denys Road, York, North Yorkshire, YO1 1QD
Tel: 01904 622207 Fax: 01904 624800
Email: info@stdenyshotel.co.uk
Web: www.stdenyshotel.co.uk
SB £40 DB £60 CC: MC Vi Swi JCB Solo

How to get there: A1079 for York/Hull, 2½ miles
from outer ring road, through Walmgate Bar.
After ½ mile, left on one way system. Hotel is
on left, 2 minutes walk from city centre.

St Georges

♦ ♦ ♦

6 St Georges Place, York, YO24 2DR
Tel: 01904 625056 Fax: 01904 625009
Email: sixstgeorg@aol.com
Web: members.aol.com/sixstgeorg

Victorian residence in quiet cul-de-sac opposite
York's beautiful racecourse. Ten minute walk to
city walls. Ideally placed for access and all
places of interest.
SB £30 DB £48 HBS £37 HBD £31 D £7.
CC: MC Vi Am DC Swi Delt
How to get there: From south, take 1036. Turn

left as racecourse ends on right. From north, on
A59 turn right after Iron Bridge. Turn right again
and second right.

Winston House

♦ ♦ ♦

4 Nunthorpe Drive, Bishopthorpe Road, York,
North Yorkshire, YO23 1DY
Tel: 01904 653171
Children minimum age: 8
DB £18

How to get there: 10 minutes walk in direction
of city centre from Railway Station. Take A64 to
York, and Tadcaster road to Bishopthorpe road.

Northwest

A595 Carlisle

A595

Maryport ○

Workington ○ **M6** ○ Penrith

A66

Keswick ○

A66

Lake District Brough ○

Ambleside ○

A595

Windermere ○

Kendal ○

Ulverston ○ **A6**

○ **A65**

Barrow-in-Furness ○

○ Lancaster

LANCASHIRE

Blackpool ○ **M55** Preston ● **M65** ○ Burnley

Lytham St Anne's ○ ○ Blackburn

Southport ○ **M61** ○ **M66** Rochdale

Bolton ○ **M62**

A565 **M6** _MANCHESTER_ ○ Oldham

MERSEYSIDE Salford ○ ● Manchester

Liverpool ● **M62**

Warrington ○ ○ Stockport

Birkenhead ○ **M63**

M53 **M56** _Manchester_

○ Macclesfield

● Chester **M6** **A54**

Crewe

A41 **A49** ○

WALES **CHESHIRE**

SCOTLAND

CUMBRIA

Blackpool

Glasgow ● ● Edinburgh

● Belfast

● Dublin ● Manchester

● Birmingham

● Cardiff ● London

The Northwest of England has something for everyone. The region offers visitors the traditional seaside resorts of Blackpool and Morecambe, Manchester – Britain's third largest city, and the breathtaking scenery of the Lake District, within easy reach of the cultural centre of Liverpool.

Sandy beaches stretch from West Kirby on Merseyside in the south to Allonby Bay

The Lake District

(964 metres) and Scafell Pike (978 metres).

The Northwest's appeal is not limited to the Lake District, many visitors are attracted to the vibrant cities of Manchester and Liverpool. Dominated by its docks – once the centre of British maritime commerce – Liverpool has reinvented itself through extensive civic redevelopment. It is famous for a rich musical heritage, exemplified by the Beatles, but also houses a splendid Victorian art collection in the Walker Gallery and boasts an outpost of the Tate.

Nearby Manchester has one of the most thriving cultural scenes in Britain, with swathes of the city being redeveloped for the Commonwealth Games to be held here in 2002. Much of Manchester's historic architecture is Victorian; while some gothic buildings remain, the city saw its most rapid expansion as a major cotton-milling centre during the Industrial Revolution, the 'dark, satanic mills' of Blake's poem 'Jerusalem'.

Cheshire's county town, Chester, some 40 miles south of Liverpool, provides a contrast to the larger northern cities. While the imposing walls encircling its Tudor-to-Victorian town buildings are medieval, the Roman influence on the city they called Deva – after the River Dee – is evident. Once the base for the Twentieth Legion, Chester is home to the largest Roman amphitheatre in Britain. There is plenty else to see: the cathedral, castle and excellent Chester Zoo are inviting attractions. And the nearby Lady Leverhulme Gallery at Port Sunlight – a masterpiece of compact museum architecture – houses a fine collection of Pre-Raphaelite paintings at the heart of a wonderful Industrial Revolution worker's model village.

in the north. However, the main attraction of the region is undoubtedly the Lake District National Park, in the county of Cumbria. Just 30 miles in diameter, the area boasts 16 lakes offering scenic walks, spectacular waterfalls and abundant watersports. Bowness, in the south, Cumbria's most popular resort, sits on the banks of Windermere, largest and best known of the lakes. Coniston Water and Grasmere are two other notable lakes in the south. Centrally placed in the Lake District, the small town of Ambleside is a popular base for walking.

To the north, Derwent Water lies close to the town of Keswick, while the peaks of Scafell Pike, Skiddaw and Blencathra loom large over it. Keswick itself is home to the Cumberland Pencil Museum, which takes local graphite as its theme, recounting not only the story of its discovery but also of its subsequent importance to the local pencil-making industry. Keswick is also the starting point for walks to the summit of Skiddaw – at 931 metres (3,055 feet) the fourth highest peak in the Lake District after Helvellyn (950 metres), Scafell

Alderley Edge, Cheshire

Alderley Edge

★★★ 🐾🐾🐾

Macclesfield Road, Alderley Edge,
Cheshire, SK9 7BJ
Tel: 01625 583033 Fax: 01625 586343
Email: sales@alderley-edge-hotel.co.uk
Web: www.alderley-edge-hotel.co.uk
SB £110 DB £145.50 B £8.50 L £14.50
D £25.50. CC: MC Vi Am DC Swi Delt

How to get there: Located on B5087, just 400
yards from Alderley Edge village.

Alston, Cumbria

Lowbyer Manor Country House

★★

Alston, N. Pennines, Cumbria, CA9 3JX
Tel: 01434 381230 Fax: 01434 382937
Web: www.lowbyermanor.ntb.org.uk
SB £36 DB £72 HBS £45 HBD £90
B £10.50 D £16.50. CC: MC Vi Am DC

How to get there: Exit M6 J-40, A686. Hotel out
of Alston on A686 towards Newcastle.

Altrincham, Cheshire

Cresta Court

★★★

Church Street, Altrincham, Cheshire, WA14 4DP
Tel: 0161 927 7272 Fax: 0161 926 9194
Email: info@cresta-court.co.uk
Web: www.cresta-court.co.uk
B £8.95 L £7.50 D £12.50.
CC: MC Vi Am DC Swi Delt

How to get there: M56, A56 through Altrincham
and two sets of lights. Cresta Court Hotel is on
the right, past second set of lights.

Quality Hotel Altrincham

★★★ 🐾

Langham Road, Bowdon, Altrincham, Cheshire,
WA14 2HT
Tel: 0161 928 7121 Fax: 0161 927 7560
Email: admin@gb064.u-net.com
Web: www.choicehotels.com

SB £95 DB £115 HBS £110 HBD £145 B £7.75
L £7.50 D £17.95. CC: MC Vi Am DC Swi Delt

How to get there: Exit M6 J-19, A556 towards
Manchester onto A56. Turn left onto B5161.
Hotel one mile on right.

The Lodge At The Bull's Head

★★

Wicker Lane, Hale Barns, Altrincham,
Cheshire, WA15 0HG
Tel: 0161 903 1300 Fax: 0161 903 1301

Old Packet House

♦♦♦

Navigation Road, Broadheath, Altrincham,
Cheshire, WA14 1LW
Tel: 0161 929 1331
Web: www.cheshireinns.co.uk
SB £39.50 DB £67.50 B £7.50 L £4.50 D £8.95.
CC: MC Vi Swi Delt

How to get there: On A56 towards Manchester,
at junction of Navigation Road and Broadheath.

Ambleside, Cumbria

Ambleside Salutation

★★★ 🐾

Lake Road, Ambleside, Cumbria, LA22 9BX
Tel: 01539 432244 Fax: 01539 434157
Email: enquiries@hotelambleside.uk.com
Web: www.hotelambleside.uk.com

Situated in the centre of Ambleside and the
Lake District. Newly refurbished rooms, some
non-smoking. Delightful restaurant and lounge.
New for 2000 is our gym.
SB £39 DB £78 HBS £53 HBD £106
B £7.50 D £19. CC: MC Vi Am DC Swi Delt JCB

How to get there: Exit M6 J-36, A591 into
Ambleside one-way system. Right lane at lights.
Hotel on brow of hill on left corner.

Langdale Hotel & Country Club

★★★

Langdale Estate, Great Langdale, LA22 9JD
Tel: 01539 438026 Fax: 01539 437394
Email: marketing@langdale.co.uk
Web: www.langdale.co.uk
SB £130 DB £210 HBS £150 HBD £250 B £8.50
L £12 D £20. CC: MC Vi Am Swi Delt

How to get there: Exit M6 J-36, A591, B593. At
Skelwith Bridge turn right onto B5343.
See advert on the right

Nanny Brow Country House

★★★ 🏆🏆

Clappersgate, Ambleside, Cumbria, LA22 9NF
Tel: 01539 432036 Fax: 01539 432450
Email: reservations@nannybrow.co.uk
Web: www.nannybrow.co.uk
SB £55 DB £110 HBS £75 HBD £150
B £7.50 D £25. CC: MC Vi Am DC Swi Delt JCB

How to get there: 1½ miles outside Ambleside
on A593.
See advert on the right (below)

Wateredge

★★★ 🏆

Waterhead Bay, Ambleside, Cumbria, LA22 0EP
Tel: 01539 432332 Fax: 01539 431878
Email: contact@wateredgehotel.co.uk
Web: www.wateredgehotel.co.uk
Children minimum age: 7
Closed December to January

The family-run Wateredge is delightfully situated
on the shores of Windermere, with gardens to
the lake edge. Beautiful lake views and relaxed,
friendly atmosphere.
SB £48 DB £74 HBS £68 HBD £114 B £10
L £3.25 D £29.90. CC: MC Vi Am Swi Delt

How to get there: ½ mile south of Ambleside on
A591 at Waterhead, next to the Steamer Pier.

Northwest

Queens

★★

Market Place, Ambleside, Cumbria, LA22 9BU
Tel: 01539 432206 Fax: 01539 432721
SB £25 DB £50 CC: MC Vi Am Swi Delt
How to get there: Exit M6 J-36, A591. The hotel
is in the town centre.

Skelwith Bridge

★★

Skelwith Bridge, Cumbria, LA22 9NJ
Tel: 01539 432115 Fax: 01539 434254
Email: skelwithbr@aol.com
Web: www.skelwithbridgehotel.co.uk
SB £33.50 DB £61 HBS £50 HBD £94
B £7.75 L £10.45 D £19.45. CC: MC Vi Swi Delt
How to get there: Exit M6 J-36, A591 to
Ambleside, A592 2½ miles to Skelwith Bridge.

Rowanfield Country House   Little Gem

♦♦♦♦♦

Kirkstone Road, Ambleside, Cumbria, LA22 9ET
Tel: 01539 433686 Fax: 01539 431569
Email: email@rowanfield.com
Web: www.rowanfield.com
Children minimum age: 8
Closed January to February
DB £62 HBD £54 D £23.
CC: MC Vi Swi Delt Electron
How to get there: ¾ mile up road signposted
Kirkstone almost opposite Ambleside's car park.

Borrans Park

♦♦♦♦

Borrans Road, Ambleside, Cumbria, LA22 0EN
Tel: 01539 433454 Fax: 01539 433003
Email: info@borranspark.co.uk
Web: www.borranspark.co.uk
Children minimum age: 7
SB £60 DB £70 HBS £80 HBD £55 D £20.
CC: MC Vi Swi Delt
How to get there: A591 from Windermere, left at
Waterhead lights. Hotel is ½ mile on right.

Elder Grove

♦♦♦♦

Lake Road, Ambleside, Cumbria, LA22 0DB
Tel: 01539 432504 Fax: 01539 432504
Email: mcdougall-eldergrove@hotmail.com
SB £32 DB £68 CC: MC Vi Swi Delt JCB Solo
How to get there: Opposite BP petrol station at
the start/end of the one-way system.

High Green Gate Guest House

♦♦♦

nr Sawrey, Ambleside, Cumbria, LA22 0LF
Tel: 01539 436296
Closed November to March
SB £29 DB £52 HBS £39 HBD £72 B £7 D £10.
How to get there: On B5285 between
Hawkshead and Bowness via Ferry.

Appleby-in-Westmorland, Cumbria

Appleby Manor Country House

★★★

Roman Road, Appleby-in-Westmorland,
Cumbria, CA16 6JB
Tel: 01768 351571 Fax: 01768 352888
Email: reception@applebymanor.co.uk
Web: www.applebymanor.co.uk
SB £72 DB £104 HBS £82 HBD £62
B £9 L £10 D £17.
CC: MC Vi Am DC Swi Delt JCB
How to get there: Situated ½ mile from the town
centre on the hill towards A66, Appleby Manor
overlooks the castle.

Royal Oak Inn

★★

Bondgate, Appleby-in-Westmorland,
Cumbria, CA16 6UN
Tel: 01768 351463 Fax: 01768 352300
Email: m.m.royaloak@btinternet.com
Web: www.mortal-man-inns.co.uk/royaloak

A lovely genuine old inn, the Royal Oak in
Appleby stands out for its good food and drink,
and above all its atmosphere.
SB £36 DB £72.90 HBS £45 HBD £50
B £5.50 L £6 D £10. CC: MC Vi Am Swi Delt

Courtfield

◆◆◆

Bongate, Appleby-in-Westmorland,
Cumbria, CA16 6UP
Tel: 017683 51394

Arnside, Cumbria

Willowfield Hotel

◆◆◆◆

The Promenade, Arnside, Cumbria, LA5 0AD
Tel: 01524 761354
Email: kerr@willowfield.net1.co.uk
Web: www.smoothhound.co.uk/hotels/
willowfi.html
SB £25 DB £52 HBS £39 HBD £80 D £14.
CC: MC Vi Swi

How to get there: From Milnthorpe, B5282 to
Arnside, right at T-junction on entering village
and right again at Albion public house.

Ashton-under-Lyne, Lancashire

York House

★★
York Place, Ashton-under-Lyne, OL6 7TT
Tel: 0161 330 5895 Fax: 0161 343 1613
Email: enquiries@yorkhouse-hotel.co.uk
Web: www.yorkhouse-hotel.co.uk
SB £65 DB £80 CC: MC Vi Am DC Swi Delt

Welbeck House

◆◆◆

324 Katharine Street, Ashton-under-Lyne,
Lancashire, OL6 7BD
Tel: 0161 344 0751 Fax: 0161 343 4278
Email: welbeck5000@breathemail.net
Web: www.smoothhound.co.uk/hotels/
welbeck.html
SB £32 DB £46 D £8. CC: MC Vi DC Delt

Barrow-in-Furness, Cumbria

Abbey House

★★★
Abbey Road, Barrow-in-Furness, LA13 0PA
Tel: 01229 838282 Fax: 01229 820403

When booking at an RAC Hotel or Guest
Accommodation, please mention this Guide.

Bassenthwaite, Cumbria

Lakeside Guest House

◆◆◆◆

Dubwath, Bassenthwaite Lake,
Cumbria, CA13 9YD
Tel: 01768 776358
SB £31 DB £46

How to get there: Exit M6 J-40, A66 west to the
northern end of Bassenthwaite lake. 400m after
dual carriageway turn right at the sign to Castle
Inn. Hotel 400m on left.
See advert on following page

Beeston, Cheshire

The Wild Boar Hotel & Restaurant

★★★
Whitchurch Road, Beeston, nr Tarporley,
Cheshire, CW6 9NW
Tel: 01829 260309 Fax: 01829 261081

Birkenhead, Merseyside

Riverhill Hotel

★★★
Talbot Road, Oxton, Birkenhead,
Merseyside, L43 2HJ
Tel: 0151 653 3773 Fax: 0151 653 7162

Blackburn, Lancashire

Clarion Hotel & Suites

★★★★
Whalley Road, Billington, Clitheroe,
Lancashire, BB7 9HY
Tel: 01254 822556 Fax: 01254 824613
Email: admin@gb065.u-net.com

SB £101 DB £124 HBS £120 HBD £164
B £10 L £ 7.50 D £20.
CC: MC Vi Am DC Swi

How to get there: Exit M6 J-31 and follow signs
to Blackburn (A677). Take the A59 to Clitheroe.
Straight over next roundabout, through traffic
lights, 2nd exit next roundabout, hotel 1/2 mile
on right.

Northwest

The Lake District

Overlooking the picturesque northern Lake Bassenthwaite in the quieter part of the Lake District National Park, Lakeside Guest House is conveniently situated between Keswick and Cockermouth, the birthplace of poet William Wordsworth. It is a peaceful location for the serious walker and within walking distance of a bird reserve, nature trails, forest walks, golf, fishing and sailing at the nearby Bassenthwaite Sailing Club. 8 comfortably furnished rooms, 7 ensuite, with colour TV, radio, alarm, hairdryer, shoe cleaning and tea/coffee-making facilities.

Lakeside Guest House

Dubwath, Bassenthwaite
Cumbria CA13 9YD
Tel: 017687 76358

RAC
◆◆◆◆

Mytton Fold Hotel & Golf Complex

★★★

Langho, nr Blackburn, Lancashire, BB6 8AB
Tel: 01254 240662 Fax: 01254 248119
Email: mytton_fold.hotel@virgin.net
Web: www.myttonfoldhotel.co.uk
SB £52 DB £82 B £6.50 L £6.50 D £11.
CC: MC Vi Am Swi Delt

How to get there: Exit M6 J-3, A59 signposted Whalley and Clitheroe for 10 miles. At second roundabout follow Whalley sign (minor road). Gateway is about 500 yards on right.

Millstone

★★

Church Lane, Mellor, Blackburn,
Lancashire, BB2 7JR
Tel: 01254 813333 Fax: 01254 812628
Email: gmmill@shireinns.co.uk
Web: www.shireinns.co.uk
SB £88 DB £105 HBS £98 HBD £125 B £11.95
L £6.50 D £11.95. CC: MC Vi Am DC Swi Delt

How to get there: Exit M6 J-3, A59 towards Clitheroe. After 3 miles, turn right at roundabout. Head for Mellor.

Dunkenhalgh

❖

Blackburn Road, Clayton-le-Moors, Accrington,
nr Blackburn, Lancashire, BB5 5JP
Tel: 01254 398021 Fax: 01254 872230
Email: info@dunkenhalgh.macdonald.
hotels.co.uk
Web: www.macdonaldhotels.co.uk
SB £70 DB £85 HBS £72.5 HBD £57.50
B £10.50 L £12.50 D £15.50.
CC: MC Vi Am DC Swi Delt

How to get there: Exit M6 J-29, M65 to J-7, left at roundabout, left at lights, left into hotel drive.

Blackpool, Lancashire

Imperial

★★★★

North Promenade, Blackpool, Lancashire,
FY1 2HB
Email: imperialblackpool@paramount-
hotels.co.uk
Web: www.paramount-hotels.co.uk
Tel: 01253 623971 Fax: 01253 751784
SB £104 DB £156 HBS £85 HBD £65

B £9.50 L £10.50 D £20.50.
CC: MC Vi Am DC Swi Delt

How to get there: On Promenade 1 mile past Blackpool Tower on right side.

Brabyns
★★
Shaftesbury Avenue, North Shore, Blackpool, Lancashire, FY2 9QQ
Tel: 01253 354263 Fax: 01253 352915
SB £30 DB £50 HBS £40 HBD £35
B £6 L £7.50 D £12. CC: MC Vi Am

How to get there: Exit M55 J-4. Proceed on Preston New Road to box junction. Turn right into Whitegate Drive, then onto Devonshire Road. Take 3rd left after island. Hotel on left.

Carlton
★★
North Promenade, Blackpool, FY1 2EZ
Tel: 01253 628966 Fax: 01253 752587
SB £30 DB £50 HBS £35 HBD £55
B £5 D £10. CC: MC Vi Am DC Swi

How to get there: On the seafront north of North Pier, between Metropole and Imperial hotels.

Gables Balmoral
★★
Balmoral Road, Blackpool, Lancashire, FY4 1HP
Tel: 01253 345432 Fax: 01253 406058

Headlands
★★
611–613 New South Promenade, Blackpool, Lancashire, FY1 1NJ
Tel: 01253 341179 Fax: 01253 342047
Email: headlands@blackpool.net
Web: www.theheadlands.blackpool.net
Closed January 2–16
SB £32 DB £64 HBS £38.50 HBD £77 B £8.50
L £10.50 D £14.50. CC: MC Vi Am DC Swi

How to get there: Right at Promenade, 1/2 mile.

Revill's
★★
190–194 North Promenade, Blackpool, Lancashire, FY1 1RJ
Tel: 01253 625768 Fax: 01253 624736
Email: revills.hotel@blackpool.net
Web: www.blackpool.net/www/revills
SB £28 DB £46 HBS £35 HBD £60
CC: MC Vi Swi Delt

Stretton
★★
206–214 North Promenade, Blackpool, Lancashire, FY1 1RU
Tel: 01253 625688 Fax: 01253 752534
Email: strettonhotel@btconnect.com
Web: www.strettonhotel.co.uk

The Stretton is highly recommended and is situated opposite the North Pier. Close to all amenities, it offers excellent cuisine and friendly, courteous service.
SB £24.50 DB £24.50 HBS £30.50 HBD £30.50
B £4.25 L £6.95 D £7.95.
CC: MC Vi Am DC Swi Delt

How to get there: Exit M6 J-32 to M55 to Blackpool. Right onto promenade. Hotel is 100m past North Pier.

Warwick
★★
603 New South Promenade, Blackpool, Lancashire, FY4 1NG
Tel: 01253 342192 Fax: 01253 405776
Closed January
SB £20 DB £40 HBS £29 HBD £58
CC: MC Vi Am Swi Delt JCB

How to get there: From the end of the M55 follow the A5230 to South Shore. Turn right at promenade. Hotel is 1/2 mile on right.

Old Coach House
◆◆◆◆◆
50 Dean Street, Blackpool, Lancashire, FY4 1BP
Tel: 01253 349195 Fax: 01253 344330
Email: blackpool@theoldcoachhouse.
        freeserve.co.uk
Web: www.theoldcoachhouse.freeserve.co.uk
SB £35 DB £50 HBS £45 HBD £70
B £5 D £10. CC: MC Vi Am Swi

How to get there: Exit M6 J-32, take M55 to large roundabout. Go straight over, take next right, left at lights, left at next lights, 2nd right before Texaco, hotel on right.

Northwest

Burlees

◆◆◆◆
40 Knowle Avenue, North Shore, Blackpool,
Lancashire, FY2 9TQ
Tel: 01253 354535 Fax: 01253 354535
Email: enquiries@burleeshotel.co.uk
Web: www.burleeshotel.co.uk
Closed November to February
SB £24 DB £48 HBS £33.50 HBD £67
CC: MC Vi Swi Delt
How to get there: 1³/₄ miles north of Tower, right
at Uncle Tom's Cabin. Burlees is 300yds on left.

Sunray

◆◆◆◆
42 Knowle Avenue, off Queens Promenade,
Blackpool, Lancashire, FY2 9TQ
Tel: 01253 351937 Fax: 01253 593307
Email: sunray@cwcom.net
SB £30 DB £60 HBS £42.50 HBD £85
CC: MC Vi Am
How to get there: 1³/₄ miles north of Tower, right
at Uncle Tom's Cabin. Sunray is 300yds on left.

Beaucliffe

◆◆◆
20–22 Holmfield Road, North Shore,
Blackpool, Lancashire, FY2 9TB
Tel: 01253 351663

Garville B & B

◆◆◆
3 Beaufort Avenue, North Shore, Blackpool,
Lancashire, FY2 9HQ
Tel: 01253 351004 Fax: 01253 351004
Children minimum age: 3. Closed January
SB £22 DB £40
How to get there: From Tower, 2¹/₂ miles north
to Red Bank Road, right at lights, first on left.

Langwood

◆◆◆
250 Queens Promenade, Bispham, FY2 9HA
Tel: 01253 351370

Sunny Cliff

◆◆◆
98 Queens Promenade, Blackpool, FY2 9NS
Tel: 01253 351155
Closed November to March
SB £21 DB £42 HBS £27 HBD £54 D £6.
How to get there: 1¹/₂ miles from North Pier on
A584, towards Bispham.

Wilmar

◆◆◆
42 Osborne Road, Blackpool, FY4 1HQ
Tel: 01253 346229
Children minimum age: 11
SB £17.5 DB £35 HBS £23 HBD £46
How to get there: On Promenade, pass South
Pier towards Pleasure Beach, left after
pedestrian lights. Wilmar 150m on left.

Windsor Park

◆◆◆
96 Queens Promenade, Blackpool, FY2 9NS
Tel: 01253 357025 Fax: 01253 357025
Closed November 5 to December 24,
    January 2 to Easter

The Windsor Park Hotel is situated in one of the
most sought after areas of the Fylde coast.
Queens Promenade overlooks the North Shore
cliffs and looks out over the Irish Sea.
SB £17 DB £34 HBS £22.50 HBD £45
CC: MC Vi Delt
How to get there: North along the Promenade to
Gyn Square roundabout. Continue on Queens
Promenade (north) for approximately half a
mile. Hotel on right hand side.

Knowlsley

◆◆
68 Dean Street, Blackpool, Lancashire, FY4 1BP
Tel: 01253 343414

Villa Private Hotel

◆◆
9–11 Withnell Road, Blackpool,
Lancashire, FY4 1HF
Tel: 01253 343314

Roker

◆
563 New South Promenade, Blackpool,
Lancashire, FY4 1NF
Tel: 01253 341853

Bolton, Manchester

The Beaumont

★★★

Beaumont Road, Bolton, Manchester, BL3 4TA
Tel: 01204 651511 Fax: 01204 61064

Egerton House

★★★ ♙♙

Blackburn Road, Egerton, Bolton,
Manchester, BL7 9PL
Tel: 01204 307171 Fax: 01204 593030

Borrowdale, Cumbria

Borrowdale Gates Country House

★★★ ♙♙

Grange-in-Borrowdale, Keswick,
Cumbria, CA12 5UQ
Tel: 01768 777204 Fax: 01768 777254
Email: hotel@borrowdale-gates.com
Web: www.borrowdale-gates.com
Closed January

Delightful and charming lakeland house, nestling
peacefully in wooded gardens with breathtaking
views of Borrowdale. Relaxing and comfortable
with an 'away from it all' atmosphere.
SB £45 DB £85 HBS £60 HBD £115
L £7.50 D £31. CC: MC Vi Am Swi Delt
♿♨♫♦🅿🐎🎠♞🐴♘♙♙
How to get there: B5289 from Keswick 4 miles.
Right over double hump-backed bridge into
Grange. Hotel ½ mile through village on right.

Borrowdale

★★★

Borrowdale, Keswick, Cumbria, CA12 5UV
Tel: 01768 777224 Fax: 01768 777338
Email: theborrowdalehotel@yahoo.com
SB £50 DB £120 HBS £60 HBD £140
B £8.50 L £2.50 D £19.95. CC: MC Vi Swi Delt
🔥🐎♨♦🅿🐎🎠♞🐴♘♙♙
How to get there: 3 miles from the market town
of Keswick at the head of Lake Derwent Water.

Scafell Hotel

Situated in the heart of the Borrowdale Valley,
the Scafell Hotel was formerly a coaching inn
frequented by travellers making the journey
over Honister Pass from Keswick to
Cockermouth. Tastefully modernised with
24 ensuite bedrooms, it still retains its old
charm and character. The restaurant (open to
non-residents) is renowned for its fine food
and wines; 5-course table d'hôte & Late
Supper menu. Fully licensed, with Cocktail
and Riverside Bar selling real ale, both well
noted for bar lunches.

Rosthwaite, Borrowdale,
Cumbria CA12 5XB

Tel: 017 687 77208 Fax: 017 687 77280
Email: scafellhotel@aol.com
Website: www.scafell.co.uk

To make an on-line booking at an RAC
inspected Hotel or Guest Accommodation,
visit www.rac.co.uk/hotels

Scafell Hotel

★★ ♙

Rosthwaite, Borrowdale, Cumbria, CA12 5XB
Tel: 017 687 77208 Fax: 017 687 77250
Email: scafellhotel@aol.com
Web: www.scafell.co.uk/hotel
SB £41.50 DB £83 HBS £63.50 HBD £127
B £8.75 L £9.75 D £25.95.
CC: MC Vi Swi Delt
🐟♿🍴♦🅿🐎🎠♞🐴♘♙♙
See advert above

Greenbank Country House

♦♦♦♦ ✿♈

Borrowdale, Keswick, Cumbria, CA12 5UY
Tel: 01768 777215
Children minimum age: 2
Closed Christmas and January
SB £32 DB £64 HBS £44 HBD £88
CC: MC Vi Swi
🔥☺♨🅿🐎🎠♞🐴♘♦♨♙
How to get there: Take A66 to Keswick. Follow
signs to Borrowdale on B5289 for approximately
3½ miles.

Brampton, Cumbria

Farlam Hall

★★★ 🍐🍐🍐

Brampton, Cumbria, CA8 2NG
Tel: 01697 746234 Fax: 01697 746683
Email: farlamhall@dial.pipex.com
Web: www.farlamhall.co.uk
Children minimum age: 5
HBS £120 HBD £230 B £12 D £31.
CC: MC Vi Swi

♿ 🗎 🐾 🖥 ☎ 🅿 👤 🔌 🐎 ♬ 🦪 ♨ 👥 🍾 🍷

How to get there: On A689 Brampton to Alston road. NOT in Farlam village.

Abbey Bridge Inn

♦♦♦

Lanercost, Brampton, Cumbria, CA8 2HG
Tel: 01697 72224 Fax: 01697 72224

Burnley, Lancashire

Higher Trapp Country House

★★★ 🍐

Trapp Lane, Simonstone, nr Burnley, BB12 7QW
Tel: 01282 772781 Fax: 01282 772782
Email: reception@highertrapphotel.co.uk
Web: www.highertrapphotel.co.uk
SB £55 DB £80 CC: MC Vi Swi Delt

🏊 ♿ 🗎 😊 🛏 🖥 ☎ 🅿 👤 🔌 🐎 ♬ 🦪 👥 🍾

How to get there: Exit M65 J-8, A678, A671 for Clitheroe. Right into School Lane, 1 mile on left.

Oaks Hotel

★★★ 🍐

Colne Road, Reedley, Burnley, BB10 2LF
Tel: 01282 414141 Fax: 01282 433401
Email: oaks@shireinns.co.uk
Web: www.shireinns.co.uk
SB £96 DB £116 B £11.50 L £5.50 D £22.
CC: MC Vi Am DC Swi Delt

🏊 🗎 🐾 😊 🛏 🖥 ☎ 📞 🅿 👤 🔌 🐎 ♬ 🦪 👥 🍾 🍷 🚬

How to get there: Exit M65 J-12. Right for Brierfield. After 1 mile, Oaks Hotel is on left.

Comfort Inn Burnley

★★

Keirby Walk, Burnley, Lancashire, BB11 2DH
Tel: 01282 427611 Fax: 01282 436370
Email: admin@gb608.u-net.com
Web: www.choicehotels.com

SB £35 DB £50 HBS £55 B £7.75
CC: MC Vi Am DC Swi Delt

🎚 🗎 🐾 😊 🛏 🖥 ☎ 🅿 👤 🔌 🐎 ♬ 🦪 ♨ 👥 🍾

How to get there: Exit M65 J-10. Follow signs for Townley Hall. Town centre location, opposite Sainsbury's.

Bury, Manchester

Bolholt

★★★

Walshaw Road, Bury, Manchester, BL8 1PU
Tel: 0161 762 4000 Fax: 0161 762 4100

Buttermere, Cumbria

Bridge

★★ 🍐

Buttermere, Lake District, Cumbria, CA13 9UZ
Tel: 01768 770252 Fax: 01768 770215
Email: enquiries@bridge-hotel.com
Web: www.bridge-hotel.com
HBS £50 HBD £100 CC: MC Vi Swi

🗎 🐾 😊 🛏 ☎ 🅿 👤 🔌 🐎 ♬ 🦪 👥

How to get there: Take A66 around Keswick. Turn off at Braithwaite. Head over 'Newlands Pass'. This brings you down into Buttermere and the hotel.

Carlisle, Cumbria

Central Plaza

★★★

Victoria Viaduct, Carlisle, Cumbria, CA3 8AL
Tel: 01228 520256 Fax: 01228 514657
Email: info@centralplazahotel.co.uk
Web: www.centralplazahotel.co.uk

Elegant, Victorian-style, city centre hotel.
SB £65 DB £75 B £4.50 L £1.95
CC: MC Vi Am DC Swi Delt Solo

🎚 🗎 🐾 😊 🛏 🖥 ☎ 👤 🔌 🐎 ♬ 🦪 👥 🍾

Crown Hotel

★★★

Wetheral, Carlisle, Carlisle, Cumbria, CA4 8ES
Tel: 01282 414141 Fax: 01282 835586
Email: jane@shireinns.co.uk
Web: www.shireinns.co.uk
SB £102 DB £122 CC: MC Vi Am DC Swi

How to get there: Exit M6 J-42 and follow B6263 to Wetheral, turn right in village.

Crown & Mitre

★★★

4 English Street, Carlisle, Cumbria, CA3 8HZ
Tel: 01228 525491 Fax: 01228 514553
SB £84 DB £109 HBS £98.50 HBD £138
B £7.95 L £4.95 D £14.50.
CC: MC Vi Am DC Swi Delt

How to get there: Exit M6 J-42, A6 to centre. Left at lights, sharp right into Blackfriars Street.

Cumbria Park

★★★

32 Scotland Road, Carlisle, CA3 9DG
Tel: 01228 522887 Fax: 01228 514796
Closed Christmas
SB £74 DB £95 HBS £89 HBD £125
B £7.50 L £12.50 D £15.95.
CC: MC Vi Am DC Swi Delt JCB

How to get there: Exit M6 J-44. Hotel is 1¹/₂ miles down main road into Carlisle on left.

Swallow Hilltop

★★★

London Road, Carlisle, Cumbria, CA1 2PQ
Tel: 01228 529255 Fax: 01228 525238
Email: carlisle@swallow-hotels.co.uk
Web: www.swallowhotels.com
SB £95 DB £110 B £9.75 L £12 D £18.50.
CC: MC Vi Am DC Swi Delt

How to get there: Exit M6 J-42, A6. Swallow Hilltop Hotel is 2 miles on left, up a hill.

County

★★

9 Botchergate, Carlisle, Cumbria, CA1 1PQ
Tel: 01228 531316 Fax: 01228 401805
Email: countyh@cairn-hotels.co.uk
Web: www.cairn-hotels.co.uk
SB £57.45 DB £74.95 HBS £75.45
HBD £110.95 B £4.99 L £4.95 D £18.

CC: MC Vi Am DC Swi Delt

How to get there: Exit M6 J-43 for Carlisle. After Tesco, cross 4 sets of lights, first left (Cecil St), first right (Mary St). Hotel car park on right.

Graham Arms

★★

English Street, Longtown, nr Carlisle, CA6 5SE
Tel: 01228 791213 Fax: 01228 791213
Email: hotel@cumbria.com
Web: www.cumbria.com
SB £32 DB £52 B £4.25 L £6 D £8.
CC: MC Vi Am Swi

How to get there: Exit M6 J-44, for Galashiels-Borders Tourist Route. Graham Arms is 400m on the right as you enter this small town.

Pinegrove

★★

262 London Road, Carlisle, Cumbria, CA1 2QS
Tel: 01228 524828 Fax: 01228 810941
Closed Christmas Day
SB £48 DB £60 B £6 D £4.75.
CC: MC Vi Am DC Swi Delt

How to get there: Exit M6 J-42, A6. Hotel on left 1¹/₂ miles.

East View Guest House

♦♦♦

110 Warwick Road, Carlisle, Cumbria, CA1 1JU
Tel: 01228 522112 Fax: 01228 522112
Web: www.eastviewguesthouse.com
Closed Christmas

Newly decorated guest house, easy to find from motorway, railway and bus stations. Enjoy local Cumberland sausage served in our attractive dining room.
SB £25 DB £40

How to get there: Exit M6 J-43. 1¹/₄ miles towards city, East View is on left side of road.

Vallum House Garden

♦ ♦ ♦

Burgh Road, Carlisle, Cumbria, CA2 7NB
Tel: 01228 521860

Family and friendly hotel with all the comforts of home, excellent food and cheery surroundings, plus car park. Situated in its own natural gardens on the Western rim of Carlisle on the road to Burgh-By-Sands on the site where Romans camped.

SB £35 DB £50 B £5 L £7 D £10.
CC: MC Vi DC Swi Delt

How to get there: On west side of city, 1½ miles from town centre.

Crabwall Manor Hotel

Four-star country house hotel, set in 9 acres of its own gardens, ideally situated just 1½ miles from Chester. 48 individually designed, luxurious bedrooms, award-winning restaurant and £2 million leisure club and beauty retreat. Close to Chester, North Wales and Liverpool and only 100 yards from the Mollington Grange Golf Club.

Parkgate Road, Mollington, Chester, Cheshire CH1 6NE
Tel: 01244 851666   Fax: 01244 851400
Email: sales@crabwall.com

Carnforth, Lancashire

Royal Station

★

Market Street, Carnforth, Lancashire, LA5 9BT
Tel: 01524 733636 Fax: 01524 720267

Chester, Cheshire

Chester Grosvenor

★ ★ ★ ★ ★   🛡 🛡 🛡

56 Eastgate Street, Chester, CH1 1LT
Tel: 01244 324024 Fax: 01244 313246
Email: chesgrov@chestergrosvenor.co.uk
Web: www.chestergrosvenor.co.uk
B £10.50 L £25 D £45.
CC: MC Vi Am DC Swi Delt JCB

How to get there: M56 J-15 to M53, exit J-12 for A56, signs for Chester and city centre hotels.

Carden Park

★ ★ ★ ★   🛡 🛡 🛡

Carden, nr Chester, Cheshire, CH3 9DQ
Tel: 01829 731000 Fax: 01829 731032
Email: reservations@cardenpark.co.uk
CC: MC Vi Am DC Swi Delt

How to get there: Exit M56 onto M53 for Chester. Take A41 to junction for Whitchurch, stay on A41 for 8 miles. At Broxton roundabout, left onto A534 for Wrexham and continue for 1½ miles.

Crabwall Manor

★ ★ ★ ★   🛡 🛡 🛡

Parkgate Road, Mollington, Chester, Cheshire, CH1 6NE
Tel: 01244 851666 Fax: 01244 851000/400
Email: sales@crabwall.com
Web: www.crabwall.com

SB £125 DB £150 B £10 L £20 D £20.
CC: MC Vi Am DC Swi Delt

How to get there: At the end of the M56, follow signs for Queensferry/North Wales for approximately ½ mile, left at the roundabout. Crabwall Manor is 1¾ miles down this road, on the left.
See advert on the left

De Vere St David's Park

★★★★ ♖ ♖ ♖

St David's Park, Ewloe, nr Chester, CH5 3YB
Tel: 01244 520800 Fax: 01244 520930
Email: reservations@stdavidspark.co.uk
B £10.95 L £13.95 D £19.50.
CC: MC Vi Am DC Swi

How to get there: From Chester, A55 to North
Wales for 12 miles, A494. Just past the
Queensferry junction, take the left sliproad,
B5127 to Buckley.

Queen

★★★★ ♖

City Road, Chester, Cheshire, CH1 3AH
Tel: 01244 305000 Fax: 01244 318483
Web: www.principalhotels.co.uk
SB £90 DB £110 HBS £68 HBD £136 B £10.95
L £12.50 D £19.95. CC: MC Vi Am DC Swi

How to get there: Follow signs for station, hotel
is opposite.

Broxton Hall

★★★ ♖

Whitchurch Road, Broxton, Cheshire, CH3 9JS
Tel: 01829 782321 Fax: 01829 782330
Email: reservations@broxtonhall.co.uk
Web: www.broxtonhall.co.uk
SB £70 DB £85 HBS £90 HBD £700
B £6.50 L £17 D £26.50.
CC: MC Vi Am DC Delt

How to get there: Off A41 Chester-Whitchurch
road at Broxton roundabout where the road
crosses the Wrexham-Nantwich road (A534).
See advert on this page

Gateway To Wales

★★★

Welsh Road, Sealand, nr Chester,
Cheshire, CH5 2HX
Tel: 01244 830332 Fax: 01244 836190
SB £60 DB £85 HBS £75 HBD £95
B £8.50 L £3.95 D £16.50.
CC: MC Vi Am DC Swi Delt

How to get there: From the A55 take the A494.
Four miles from Chester.

Broxton Hall
Country House
Hotel and Restaurant

RAC ★★★

17th-century Broxton Hall, 10 miles south of
medieval Chester. Easy access to North Wales
and Snowdonia. Country House ambience,
French and English cuisine, 5 acres of gardens.
Log fires in winter. All bedrooms ensuite.

Which? Good Hotel Guide and Johansen
recommended.

**Whitchurch Road, Broxton, Chester,
Cheshire CH3 9JS**
Tel: 01829 782321 Fax: 01829 782330
Email: reservations@broxtonhall.co.uk
Website: www.broxtonhall.co.uk

Green Bough

★★★ ♖

60 Hoole Road, Hoole, Chester, CH2 3NL
Tel: 01244 326241 Fax: 01244 326265
Email: greenboughhotel@cwcom.net
Web: www.smoothhound.co.uk/hotels/
greenbo.html
Children minimum age: 11
SB £65 DB £85 HBS £85 HBD £125
L £10 D £20. CC: MC Vi Am DC Swi Delt

How to get there: Exit M53 J-12, A56 to Chester
city. Hotel is 1 mile from motorway.
See advert on following page

Grosvenor Pulford

★★★ ♖

Wrexham Road, Pulford, Chester, CH4 9DG
Tel: 01244 570560 Fax: 01244 570809
Email: enquiries@grosvenorpulfordhotel.co.uk
Web: www.grosvenorpulfordhotel.co.uk
SB £70 DB £90 HBS £75 HBD £60 B £4.95
L £5.95 D £10. CC: MC Vi Am DC Swi Delt Solo

How to get there: Exit M53/A55 for A483
Chester, then B5445, hotel is 2 miles on right.
See advert on following page

Northwest

Green Bough Hotel

Ideally situated only 1km from the city centre with ample off-road parking. This homely and relaxing family-run hotel provides a quality personal, professional service. The award winning restaurant with its Savoy-trained chef produces a daily menu using local fresh foods. All bedrooms are non-smoking.

60 Hoole Road, Hoole,
Chester CH2 3NL
Tel:01244 326241   Fax: 01244 326265
Email: greenboughhotel@cwcom.net
Website: www.SmoothHound.co.uk/hotels/
greenbo.html

Grosvenor Pulford Hotel

18 metre swimming pool • Whirlpool • Sauna
Aromatherapy Steam Room • Solarium. Fully
equipped gymnasium. Hair and Beauty salon.
Snooker Room. 72 ensuite bedrooms with all
the modern conveniences.
Bar snacks and à la Carte meals served daily.
Conference and Banqueting facilities for
between 10 and 240 delegates. Wedding
Receptions our speciality. Ideally located only
five minutes from Chester city centre.

Wrexham Road, Pulford,
Chester CH4 9DG
Tel: 01244 570560   Fax: 01244 570809
Email: enquiries@grosvenorpulford.co.uk
Website: www.grosvenorpulfordhotel.co.uk

Heritage Hotels – The Blossoms

★★★
St John Street, Chester, Cheshire, CH1 1HL
Tel: 0870 400 8108 Fax: 01244 346433
SB £52 DB £104 HBS £67 HBD £134 B £9.95
L £5.45 D £12.95. CC: MC Vi Am DC Swi Delt
How to get there: St John Street is off Eastgate
Street at centre of shopping area.

Llyndir Hall

★★★
Llyndir Lane, Rossett, Clwyd, LL12 0AY
Tel: 01244 571648 Fax: 01244 571258
Email: llyndirhall@pageant.co.uk
Web: www.pageant.co.uk
SB £70 DB £80 HBS £88 HBD £120 B £5.50
L £10.95 D £18. CC: MC Vi Am Swi Delt

Northop Hall Country House

★★★
Northop Hall Village, nr Mold, CH7 6HJ
Tel: 01244 816181 Fax: 01244 814661
Email: northop@hotel-chester.com
Web: www.hotel-chester.com

Set in nine secluded acres of tranquil gardens
and woodlands, the historic Northop Hall
Country House Hotel represents the perfect
venue for that 'get away' weekend or special
occasion.
SB £50 DB £65 HBS £124 HBD £178 B £9.50
L £10.50 D £15.95. CC: MC Vi Am DC Swi Delt
How to get there: M56, A494 for North Wales.
Exit Davids Park, right at roundabout, first right,
left at mini roundabout. Hotel is 200m further.

Rowton Hall Hotel & Health Club

★★★
Whitchurch Road, Rowton, Chester, CH3 6AD
Tel: 01244 335262 Fax: 01244 335464
Email: catherinefoster@rowtonhall.co.uk
SB £75 DB £95 HBS £97 HBD £140

B £9.50 L £14.50 D £22.50.
CC: MC Vi Am DC Swi Delt

How to get there: M56, M53 J-12, 3rd exit off roundabout. Follow A41 to Rowton Hall sign.
See advert below

Chester Court
★★
48 Hoole Road, Chester, Cheshire, CH2 3NL
Tel: 01244 345014 Fax: 01244 344795
Email: chestercourthotel@classic.msn.com
Web: www.chestercourt.u-net.com
SB £45 DB £70 D £8. CC: MC Vi Am Swi Delt

How to get there: Exit M53 J-12, A56 (Hoole Road), hotel on right opposite All Saints Church.

Dene
★★
95 Hoole Road, Chester, Cheshire, CH2 3ND
Tel: 01244 321165 Fax: 01244 350277
Email: denehotel@btconnect.com
Web: www.denehotel.com
SB £45 DB £57 HBD £79.50 B £6.95 D £7.95.
CC: MC Vi Am Swi Delt

How to get there: Take Junction 12 of the M53. Follow signs for A56 Hoole Road. The Dene Hotel is about 500m on left.

Redland

64 Hough Green, Chester, CH4 8JY
Tel: 01244 671024 Fax: 01244 681309

A delightful hotel, with a unique Victorian ambience, conveniently situated only one mile from the city centre of Chester and with the advantage of ample parking.
SB £45 DB £65

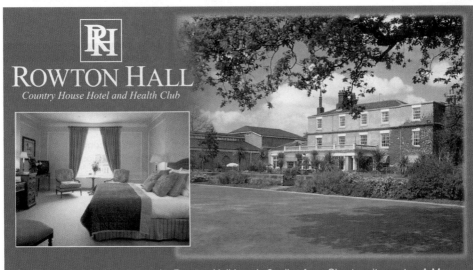

ROWTON HALL
Country House Hotel and Health Club

Set in 8 acres of private grounds, Rowton Hall is only 3 miles from Chester city centre. A Manor House built in the Georgian period, Rowton Hall is now a fine country house hotel that retains many original features. With 38 luxurious bedrooms, the Langdale Restaurant providing quality service and excellent cuisine, a superb Health Club, conference facilities and outdoor activities, your stay at Rowton Hall is sure to be memorable.

Rowton Hall Hotel, Whitchurch Road, Rowton, Cheshire CH3 6AD
Tel: 01244 335262   Fax: 01244 335464

RAC
★★★

Northwest

Stone Villa

♦♦♦♦ ✍

3 Stone Place, Chester, Cheshire, CH2 3NR
Tel: 01244 345014 Fax: 01244 345015
Email: adam@stonevilla.freeserve.co.uk
Web: www.smoothhound.co.uk
SB £35 DB £28 CC: MC Vi Swi Delt
⊛⌂🖥🅿🐾🕯🐎🃏🛥
How to get there: M53, A56 past church on left,
cross lights, second left into Stone Place, car
park end of cul-de-sac.

Glen Garth Guest House

♦♦♦

59 Hoole Road, Chester, CH2 3NJ
Tel: 01244 310260
Email: glengarth@chester63.fsnet.co.uk
SB £27 DB £44
⊛⌂🖥🅿
How to get there: M53, A56, guest house is
situated on the right, 1 mile from the junction.

Devonia Guest House

♦

33–35 Hoole Road, Chester, Cheshire, CH2 3NH
Tel: 01244 322236

Malvern Guest House

♦

21 Victoria Road, Chester, Cheshire, CH2 2AX
Tel: 01244 380865

Chorley, Lancashire

Pines

★★★

Preston Road, Clayton-le-Woods, Lancashire,
PR6 7ED
Tel: 01772 388551 Fax: 01772 629002
Email: info@thepineshotel.fsbusiness.co.uk
SB £70 DB £80 B £7.50 L £10
CC: MC Vi Am DC Swi Delt
⌚&🖨⊛⌂🖥📞📞🅿🐾🕯🐎🃏🛥
🎿🎿
How to get there: Exit M6 J-29 to Preston
South. Right at roundabout. Follow A6. After 4th
mini-roundabout, hotel is immediately on left.

Parr Hall Farm

♦♦♦♦ ✍

Parr Lane, Eccleston, Chorley,
Lancashire, PR7 5SL
Tel: 01257 451917 Fax: 01257 453749
Email: parrhall@talk21.com
SB £25 DB £40 CC: MC Vi Delt
⊛⌂🖥🅿🐾🕯🐎🃏🛥

Clitheroe, Lancashire

Brooklyn Guest House

♦♦♦♦

32 Pimlico Road, Clitheroe, BB7 2AH
Tel: 01200 428268
Email: rg@classicfm.net
SB £27.50 DB £43 HBS £37 HBD £31.50
D £10. CC: MC Vi Swi Delt JCB Solo
⊛⌂🖥🐾🕯🐎🃏🛥🍴
How to get there: North of centre, near BP
garage: take Waddington Road, 200m, right at
smaller roundabout.

Cockermouth, Cumbria

Trout

★★★ ♟

Crown Street, Cockermouth, CA13 0EJ
Tel: 01900 823591 Fax: 01900 827514
Email: enquiries@trouthotel.co.uk
Web: www.trouthotel.co.uk
SB £79.95 DB £89.95 HBS £102 HBD £109.95
B £8.50 L £10.95 D £18.95.
CC: MC Vi Am DC Swi Delt
⌚&🐎⊛⌂🖥📞🅿🐾🕯🐎🃏🛥🎿🎿🎿
🐟↘
How to get there: Exit M6 J-40 (Penrith), A66 to
Keswick. In Cockermouth, Crown Street is a
continuation of Main Street.

Coniston, Cumbria

Coniston Lodge   Little Gem

♦♦♦♦♦ ♟ ✍ ♟ Little Gem
Station Road, Coniston, Cumbria, LA21 8HH
Tel: 01539 441201 Fax: 01539 441201
Email: robinson@conistonlodge.freeserve.co.uk
Web: www.coniston-lodge.com
Children minimum age: 10. Closed January

An RAC Little Gem winner. Beautiful scenery,
peaceful surroundings, fine home cooking and a
very warm welcome.

SB £47.50 DB £81 HBS £56 HBD £119
D £19. CC: MC Vi Am

🛋️🌐☕🖥️☎️📞🅿️🐎🎠🎻🍴🎾🚶🧍

How to get there: Leave A593 at crossroads, up hill, 100m on left. Park under the building.

Crown

◆◆◆

Coniston, Cumbria, LA21 8EA
Tel: 01539 441243 Fax: 01539 441804
Email: enntiidus@crownhotel.co.uk
SB £35 DB £60 HBS £50 HBD £90
B £6 L £6 D £15. CC: MC Vi Am DC Swi Delt

🌐🖥️☎️🅿️🎠🎻🍴🎾🧍🧍 🎵

How to get there: Exit M6 J-36, A590 to Windermere, Ambleside, A593 to Coniston.

Dalston, Cumbria

Dalston Hall

★★★ 🍴

Dalston, Cumbria, CA5 7JX
Tel: 0228 710271 Fax: 0228 711273

Darwen, Lancashire

Whitehall Hotel & Restaurant

★★★

Springbank, Whitehall, Darwen, BB3 2JU
Tel: 01254 701595 Fax: 01254 773426
Email: hotel@thewhitehallhotel.freeserve.co.uk
SB £55 DB £65 HBS £70.5 HBD £96 B £7.50
L £12.50 D £16.95. CC: MC Vi Am Swi Delt

🛋️♿🌐☕🖥️☎️📞🅿️🐎🎠🎻🍴🎾🧍🧍
🎵🎿📠

How to get there: Just off A666 between Blackburn and Bolton, close to M65 J-4.

Egremont, Cumbria

Blackbeck Inn

★★

nr Egremont, Cumbria, CA22 2NY
Tel: 01946 841661 Fax: 01946 841007

Popular local inn with an excellent reputation. 21 en-suite bedrooms. Special weekend rates, eg. £59.95 per couple per night, carvery dinner, bed and breakfast.
SB £54.49 DB £75.48 B £3.50 L £2.95 D £2.95.
CC: MC Vi Am DC Swi Delt

♿🛋️🐾🌐☕🖥️☎️📞🅿️🐎🎠🎻🍴🎾🧍🧍🧍

How to get there: On A595 between Calderbridge and Egremont.

Ellesmere Port, Cheshire

Quality Hotel Chester

★★★

Berwick Road, Welsh Road, Little Sutton,
Ellesmere Port, Cheshire, L66 4PS
Tel: 051 339 5121 Fax: 051 339 3214

Garstang, Lancashire

Crofters

★★★ 🍴

A6 Cabus, Garstang, Lancashire, PR3 1PH
Tel: 01995 604128 Fax: 01995 601646
SB £46 DB £58 B £6 L £10.25 D £13.85.
CC: MC Vi Am DC Swi Delt Solo

🐾☕🖥️🗄️☎️🅿️🐎🎠🎻🍴🎾🧍🧍🧍 🎵

How to get there: Situated midway between Preston and Lancaster, on the A6 trunk road, near the market town of Garstang.

Northwest

Grange-over-Sands, Cumbria

Graythwaite Manor

★★★

Fernhill Road, Grange-over-Sands, LA11 7JE
Tel: 01539 532001 Fax: 01539 535549
Email: office@graythwaitemanor.co.uk
Web: www.graythwaitemanor.co.uk
Closed January 8–29

A lovely family-run country house set in
extensive gardens and woodland overlooking
bay and hills. Charming bedrooms, some
ground floor, generous lounges with antiques
and log fires. Excellent cuisine and wine cellar.
SB £55 DB £99 HBD £136 B £7.50 L £12
D £18. CC: MC Vi Am Swi Delt JCB Maestro
How to get there: B5277 through Grange. Right
opposite fire station into Fernhill Road.

Netherwood

★★★

Lindale Road, Grange-over-Sands, LA11 6ET
Tel: 01539 532552 Fax: 01539 534121
Email: blawith@aol.com
Web: www.netherwood-hotel.co.uk
SB £55 DB £110 HBS £79 HBD £79 B £8.50
L £16.50 D £24. CC: MC Vi Swi Delt
How to get there: Exit M6 J-36, A590 for
Barrow-in-Furness, follow signs for for Holker
Hall on B5277. Netherwood is on the right just
before the rail station.

Elton

◆◆◆◆

Windermere Road, Grange-over-Sands,
Cumbria, LA11 6EQ
Tel: 01539 532838
Closed January to February
SB £29 DB £48 HBS £40 HBD £35
How to get there: 50m after rail station, right
exit at mini-roundabout. Hotel 200m on left.

Grasmere, Cumbria

Wordsworth

★★★★

Grasmere, Cumbria, LA22 9SW
Tel: 01539 435592 Fax: 01539 435765
Email: enquiry@wordsworth-grasmere.co.uk
Web: www.grasmere-hotels.co.uk

Set in the heart of Lakeland, in magnificent
surroundings, the Wordsworth has a reputation
for the high quality of its food, accommodation
and hospitality.
SB £90 DB £150 HBS £110 HBD £105
B £12.50 L £19.50 D £32.50. CC: MC Vi Am DC

Gold Rill

★★★

Red Bank Road, Grasmere, Cumbria, LA22 9PU
Tel: 01539 435486 Fax: 01539 435486

Grasmere Red Lion

★★★

Red Lion Square, Grasmere, LA22 9SS
Tel: 01539 435456 Fax: 01539 435579
Email: enquiries@hotelgrasmere.uk.com
Web: www.hotelgrasmere.uk.com

Beautifully refurbished hotel in the heart of the
Lake District. All rooms en-suite — many with
jacuzzi bath. Good food, friendly staff, leisure
facilities and hairdressing salon.

SB £41 DB £82 HBS £55 HBD £110 B £7.50
D £19. CC: MC Vi Am DC Swi Delt JCB

♿ 🛗 🐴⊗☕🖥️💻☎️📞🅿️♨️🎠🐎🍴🐕🦅
♨♨ SPA ⛷️ ☕

How to get there: From South: exit M6 J-36,
A591 to Grasmere. North: exit at J-40, A66 for
Keswick, left (Windermere), A591 to Grasmere.

Heritage Hotels – The Swan
★★★ ☕

Keswick Road, Grasmere, Cumbria, LA22 9RF
Tel: 0870 400 8132 Fax: 01539 435741
SB £63 DB £63 HBS £72 HBD £72

♿☕🐴⊗☕🖥️☎️📞🅿️♨️🎠🐎🍴🐕♨♨

How to get there: From M6, take the A591 to
Kendal. At Kendal take the A590 to Grasmere.

Rothay Garden
★★★ ☕☕

Broadgate, Grasmere, Cumbria, LA22 9RJ
Tel: 015394 35334 Fax: 015394 35723
Email: rothay@grasmere.com
Web: www.grasmere.com
SB £65 DB £130 HBS £75 HBD £150
L £5.95 D £22. CC: MC Vi Swi Delt

☕🐴🖥️☎️📞🅿️♨️🐕♨♨

How to get there: Adjacent to park in Grasmere.
From North: M6 J-40 for Keswick, A591 to
Grasmere. South: M6 J-36 through Windermere
to Grasmere.

Grasmere
★★ ☕

Broadgate, Grasmere, Cumbria, LA22 9TA
Tel: 01539 435277 Fax: 01539 435277
Email: enquiries@grasmerehotel.co.uk
Web: www.grasmerehotel.co.uk
Children minimum age: 12
Closed January 2 to February 13
SB £30 DB £60 HBS £50 HBD £80 D £18.50.
CC: MC Vi Am Swi Delt

♿☕🐴⊗☕🖥️☎️📞🅿️♨️🎠🐎🍴🐕♨♨

Moss Grove
★★

Grasmere, Cumbria, LA22 9SW
Tel: 01539 435251 Fax: 01539 435691
Email: martinw@globalnet.co.uk
Web: www.mossgrove.co.uk
Closed December and January
SB £48 DB £105 HBS £63 HBD £135
B £6 D £13. CC: MC Vi Swi Delt JCB

☕⊗☕🖥️☎️🅿️♨️🎠🐕🦅 i

How to get there: From South, take M6 J-36,
then A591 and left to village. Moss Grove Hotel
on right just past church. From North, take M6
J-40, A66 Keswick, A591 Grasmere and right
into village. Hotel on left opposite church.

Hampson Green, Lancashire

Hampson House
★★

Galgate, Hampson Green, Lancashire, LA2 0JB
Tel: 01524 751158 Fax: 01524 751779

Hawkshead, Cumbria

Sawrey House   Little Gem
♦♦♦♦♦   ☕☕☕⚜️☕

nr Sawrey, Hawkshead, Cumbria, LA22 0LF
Tel: 01539 436387 Fax: 01539 436010
Email: shirley@sawrey-house.com
Web: www.sawrey-house.com
Children minimum age: 8. Closed January
SB £45 DB £90 HBS £65 HBD £65
B £7.50 D £29. CC: MC Vi Delt

♿🐴⊗☕🖥️☎️🅿️♨️🎠🐎🍴🐕♨♨ i

How to get there: On B5285 from Hawkshead
towards Windermere car ferry.

Grizedale Lodge
♦♦♦♦   ☕⚜️

Grizedale, Cumbria, LA22 0QL
Tel: 01539 436532 Fax: 01539 436572
Email: enquiries@grizedale-lodge.com
Web: www.grizedale-lodge.com
Children minimum age: 5

A comfortable and elegant former shooting
lodge tucked away in the heart of the
magnificent Grizedale Forest Park, midway
between Coniston Water and Windermere.
SB £35 DB £60 L £5 CC: MC Vi Am Swi

♿☕🐴⊗☕🖥️🅿️♨️🎠🐎🍴🐕♨ i

How to get there: From Windemere and
Ambleside, follow signs to Hawkshead, then
signs to Grizedale and visitors' centre. Turn right
onto Nowby Bridge Road.

Northwest

Ivy House

♦♦♦♦

Ambleside, Hawkshead, Cumbria, LA22 0NS
Tel: 01539 436204

Hawkshead Hill, Cumbria

Highfield House Country

★★ 🐾

Hawkshead Hill, Cumbria, LA22 0PN
Tel: 01539 436344 Fax: 01539 436793

Heywood, Manchester

Birch

★★

Manchester Road, Birch, Heywood, OL10 2QD
Tel: 01706 366137 Fax: 01706 621000
Email: thebirch@globalnet.co.uk
Web: www.hotels-manchester.co.uk
SB £60 DB £70 B £6 L £17 D £17.
CC: MC Vi Am DC Swi Delt
⚓ 占 🐾 ☜ 🖵 ☎ 🅿 ⅋ 〰 🐴 ⛏ 🌴 ♨ ⅏ ⅏
How to get there: Exit M62 J-19. Head for
Heywood. Turn left at Texaco Garage. Turn left
at T-junction. Hotel ¾ mile on left.

Holmes Chapel, Cheshire

Old Vicarage

★★★ 🐾🐾

Knutsford Road, Cranage, Holmes Chapel,
Cheshire, CW4 8EF
Tel: 01477 532041 Fax: 01477 535728
Email: oldvichotel@aol.com
SB £72.5 DB £85 CC: MC Vi Am DC Swi
占 ☜ ☕ 🖵 ☎ ☏ ⅋ 〰 🐴 ⛏ 🌴 ♨ ⅏ ⅏
How to get there: Situated on the A50 only
1 mile from J-18 on the M6.

Holmrook, Cumbria

Lutwidge Arms

★★

Holmrook, Cumbria, CA19 1UH
Tel: 01946 724230 Fax: 01946 724100
Email: sales@lutwidgewestcumbria.com
Web: www.lutwidgewestcumbria.com
SB £40 DB £53 HBS £35 HBD £70
B £6 L £5 D £12. CC: MC Vi Swi Delt JCB
占 🐾 ☜ 🖵 ☎ 🅿 ⅋ 〰 🐴 ⛏ 🌴 ♨ ⅏ ⅏
How to get there: On A595 at Holmrook, three
miles south of Gosforth.

Hoole, Cheshire

Ba Ba Guest House

♦♦♦

65 Hoole Road, Hoole, Cheshire, CH2 3NJ
Tel: 01244 315047 Fax: 01244 315046

Kendal, Cumbria

Stonecross Manor

★★★

Milnthorpe Road, Kendal, Cumbria, LA9 5HP
Tel: 01539 733559

Heaves

★★

Levens, nr Kendal, Cumbria, LA8 8EF
Tel: 01539 560396 Fax: 01539 560269
Email: hotel@heaves.freeserve.co.uk
Web: www.heaveshotel.co.uk

Spacious Georgian mansion in ten acres of
formal gardens and woodland. Four miles from
Exit 36 of M6 and Kendal. Family owned and
run. Library and billiard room.
SB £32 DB £56 HBS £46 HBD £42
B £4 L £9.75 D £14.
CC: MC Vi Am DC Swi Delt JCB
🖾 🐾 ☜ 🖵 🅿 ⅋ 〰 🐴 ⛏ ♨ ⅊ ⁄.
How to get there: Exit M6 J-36, A590 Barrow &
South Lakes. After 3 miles follow A590 to
roundabout, again take A590. Take second
juction on right (Sizergh), signs on left after turn.

Lane Head House Country

♦♦♦♦♦ 🐾

Helsington, Kendal, Cumbria, LA9 5RJ
Tel: 01539 731283 Fax: 01539 721023
Children minimum age: 6
Family run 17th-century manor house in private
grounds with magnificent panoramic views
across River Kent Valley to fells. Ideally situated
on south side of Kendal.
SB £45 DB £75 D £12.

CC: MC Vi Am Swi Delt JCB Solo Maestro

⊛ ☕ ▯ ☎ **P** ⚸ ⁑ 🎠 🎠 🍴 🦆 ⚒ ❗

How to get there: Exit M6 J-36, A590/A591 for Kendal, A6, then first left opposite BP garage.

Garnett House Farm

♦♦♦

Burneside, Kendal, Cumbria, LA9 5SF

Tel: 01539 724542 Fax: 01539 724542

Closed Christmas to New Year

DB £40

⊛ ☕ ▯ **P** ⚸ ⁑ ☕ 🎠 🍴 🦆

How to get there: Exit M6 J-36, A591 to Windermere, right on dual carriageway at Ratherheath crossroads. Hotel ½ mile on left.

Keswick, Cumbria

Dale Head Hall

★★★ ℞

Lake Thirlmere, Keswick, Cumbria, CA12 4TN

Tel: 01768 772478 Fax: 01768 771070

Derwentwater

★★★ ℞

Portinscale, Keswick, Cumbria, CA12 5RE

Tel: 01768 772538 Fax: 01786 771002

Email: derwentwater.hotel@dial.pipex.com

A traditional Lakeland building, furnished and decorated in a Victorian style. Set in 16 acres on the shores of Lake Derwentwater. Panoramic lake views from many bedrooms.

CC: MC Vi Am DC JCB

🦆 🐾 🔑 **P** ⚒

See advert on following page

Keswick Country House

★★★

Station Road, Keswick, Cumbria, CA12 4NQ

Tel: 01768 772020 Fax: 01768 771300

Email: crafferty@principalhotels.co.uk

Web: www.principalhotels.co.uk

SB £72 DB £124 HBS £80 HBD £140

CC: MC Vi Am DC Swi Delt

⬦ ⑊ 🦆 🐾 ☕ ▯ ☎ **P** ⚸ ⁑ ☕ 🎠 🍴 🦆 ⚒ ❗ ⚒ ⚲

How to get there: Within short walking distance of Keswick town centre and Derwent Water lake.

Queen's

★★★

Main Street, Keswick, Cumbria, CA12 5JF

Tel: 01768 773333 Fax: 01768 771144

Email: book@queenshotel.co.uk

Web: www.queenshotel.co.uk

Closed Christmas

Situated in the geographical centre of Cumbria, the Queen's offers friendly, efficient service, a popular restaurant, fully decked out bar with log stove and conservatory-style roof.

SB £33 DB £66 B £7.5 D £11.

CC: MC Vi Am DC Swi Delt JSB

⑊ 🦆 ☕ ▯ ☎ **P** ⚸ ⁑ ☕ 🍴 🦆 ⚒ ❗

How to get there: From M6 J-40, head west along A66, take Keswick turn off, hotel is in market square.

Applethwaite Country House

★★

Applethwaite, Keswick, Cumbria, CA12 4PL

Tel: 01768 772413

Chaucer House

★★

Derwentwater Place, Keswick, CA12 4DR
Tel: 01768 772318 Fax: 01768 775551
Email: enquiries@chaucer-house.demon.co.uk
Web: www.chaucer-house.co.uk
Closed December to January
SB £31 DB £62 HBS £45 HBD £90
B £8.50 D £13. CC: MC Vi Am Swi Delt JCB

How to get there: From A591 turn into Manor
Brow. The road is signed Keswick via Manor
Brow. Hotel is opposite church of St John's at
the bottom of the road.

Crow Park

★★

The Heads, Keswick, Cumbria, CA12 5ER
Tel: 01768 772208 Fax: 01768 774776
SB £30.50 DB £61 HBS £44.50 HBD £89
B £5 D £11. CC: MC Vi Delt

How to get there: 200 metres from town centre,
overlooking park and lake.

Highfield

★★

The Heads, Keswick, Cumbria, CA12 5ER
Tel: 01768 772508
Email: highfieldkeswick@talk21.com
Children minimum age: 8. Closed January
SB £35 DB £60 HBS £52 HBD £94
B £5 L £5 D £18.50. CC: MC Vi Am Swi Delt

How to get there: Leave A66, 2nd exit at
roundabout. Left to T-junction. Left then right at
mini-roundabout. The Heads is 4th turning right.

Ladstock Country House

★★

Thornthwaite, Keswick, Cumbria, CA12 5RZ
Tel: 01768 778210 Fax: 01768 778088
Email: enquiries@keswickhotel.co.uk
Web: www.keswickhotel.co.uk

Ladstock is a fine, grand country house set
amid landscaped gardens, overlooking Skiddaw
and related Fells, also Bassenthwaite Lake. An
ideal centre for walking, touring or long breaks,
also ideal for weddings or conferences.
SB £45 DB £80 HBS £62 HBD £116
B £10 D £16.50. CC: MC Vi Am

Lairbeck

★★

Vicarage Hill, Keswick, Cumbria, CA12 5QB
Tel: 01768 773373 Fax: 01768 773144
Email: info3@lairbeckhotel-keswick.co.uk
Web: www.lairbeckhotel-keswick.co.uk
Children minimum age: 5. Closed Jan to Feb
SB £30 DB £60 HBS £46 HBD £92
D £16. CC: MC Vi Swi Delt

How to get there: Exit M6 J-40, A66. After 16
miles, ignore 1st exit to Keswick. At roundabout
turn left, then immediately right.

Lyzzick Hall

★★

Underskiddaw, Keswick, Cumbria, CA12 4PY
Tel: 01768 772277 Fax: 01768 772278
Email: lyzzickhall@netscapeonline.co.uk
Web: www.gocumbria.co.uk
Closed mid-January to mid-February

In a stunning location 2 miles north of Keswick,
family-run with acclaimed cuisine and a relaxing
atmosphere. Rambling gardens and a superb
indoor swimming pool.
SB £56 DB £92 HBS £58 HBD £116
D £22. CC: MC Vi Swi Delt

How to get there: 2 miles north of Keswick on
the A591, 19 miles west from J-40 (Penrith exit)
on the M6.

Middle Ruddings

★★

Braithwaite, Keswick, Cumbria, CA12 5RY
Tel: 01768 778436 Fax: 01768 778436

Northwest

Morrel's Restaurant & Rooms

★★

34 Lake Road, Keswick, Cumbria, CA12 5DQ
Tel: 01768 772666
Email: info@morrels.co.uk
Web: www.lakedistricthotel.co.uk
SB £30 DB £60 B £5 D £15.
CC: MC Vi Swi Delt

How to get there: Exit M6 J-40, A66 to Keswick then take signs to the lake. Morrel's is on left by roundabout.

Swinside Lodge

★ 🐾 🐾 🐾

Grange Road, Newlands, Keswick, CA12 5UE
Tel: 01768 772948 Fax: 01768 772948
Email: info@swinsidelodge-hotel.co.uk
Web: www.swinsidelodge-hotel.co.uk
Children minimum age: 10
SB £62 DB £94 HBS £87 HBD £144
D £25. CC: MC Vi Swi Delt Solo Electron

How to get there: From Keswick, A66 for Cockermouth, left for Portinscale for 2 miles, signposted Grange, not Swinside.
See advert below

Swinside Lodge Hotel

Beautifully situated in an idyllic location at the foot of Cat Bells and just five minutes walk from Lake Derwentwater, Swinside Lodge offers peace and tranquility. This informal licensed country house hotel provides the highest standards of comfort, service and hospitality, and is renowned both locally and nationally for its superb award-winning cuisine.

Grange Road, Newlands,
Keswick, Cumbria CA12 5UE
Tel: 017687 72948   Fax: 017687 72948
Email: info@swinsidelodge-hotel.co.uk
Website: www.swinsidelodge-hotel.co.uk

Thwaite Howe

 ♣

Thornthwaite, nr Keswick, Cumbria, CA12 5SA
Tel: 01768 778281 Fax: 01768 778529
Web: www.keswickhotels.itgo.com
Children minimum age: 12
Closed January to February

Exquisite small country house hotel nestling against Thornthwaite Forest with views across Derwent valley to Skidaw and mountains. Excellent food and good wines.
SB £55 DB £70 HBS £72 HBD £104
CC: MC Vi Swi

How to get there: A66 past Keswick. Left at Thornthwaite. After Thornthwaite Gallery car park fork right to hotel at top of hill.

Acorn House

♦♦♦♦

Ambleside Road, Keswick, Cumbria, CA12 4DL
Tel: 01768 772553 Fax: 01768 775332
Email: enq@acornhouse.demon.co.uk
Web: www.acornhouse.com
Children minimum age: 8
Closed November to February
SB £28.50 DB £52 CC: MC Vi Swi Delt

How to get there: 400m from town centre, opposite St John's Church on Ambleside Road.

Dalegarth House

♦♦♦♦

Portinscale, Keswick, Cumbria, CA12 5RQ
Tel: 01768 772817 Fax: 01768 772817
Email: john@dalegarthhousehotel.
freeserve.co.uk
Children minimum age: 5
SB £30 DB £60 HBS £43 HBD £86
D £20. CC: MC Vi Swi Delt

How to get there: Approach Portinscale from A66, pass Farmers Arms. Dalegarth approx 100m on left, behind Dorothy Well.

Greystones

◆◆◆◆

Ambleside Road, Keswick, Cumbria, CA12 4DP
Tel: 01768 773108
Email: greystones@keslakes.freeserve.co.uk
Children minimum age: 10
SB £25 DB £50 CC: MC Vi Delt
🌐🗲💻🅿️🍳🕯️🐎🎬🛏️🏊‍♀️🍴
How to get there: Exit M6 J40, A66 to Keswick,
A591 (Windermere), first right into Manor Brow.
Greystones ¹/₂ mile on right.

Honister House

◆◆◆◆

1 Borrowdale Road, Keswick, CA12 5DD
Tel: 01768 773181 Fax: 0870 1202948
Email: philandsueh@aol.com
Closed December to January

A warm welcome awaits you at our 18th-
century home. We are centrally located close to
all local amenities. We especially cater for
walkers, cyclists and families. Drying room and
cycle storage. Special breaks and brochure
available.
DB £18.28
🌐🗲💻🅿️🍳🕯️🐎🎬🛏️
How to get there: From Tourist Information
office Honister is 400 yards along lake road, on
left-hand side, opposite 'George Fisher's'.

Parkfield No Smoking Guest House

◆◆◆◆

The Heads, Keswick, Cumbria, CA12 5ES
Tel: 01768 772328
Email: parkfield@kencomp.net
Web: www.kencomp.net/parkfield
Closed January to March
SB £30 DB £52 CC: MC Vi
🌐🗲💻🅿️🍳🕯️🐎🎬🛏️
How to get there: From A66 or A591, follow
road through town and turn left at mini-
roundabout. After 500m, turn right onto The
Heads. Parkfield is on left.

Ravensworth

◆◆◆◆

29 Station Street, Keswick, Cumbria, CA12 5HH
Tel: 01768 772476 Fax: 01768 775287
Email: info@ravensworth-hotel.co.uk
Web: www.ravensworth-hotel.co.uk
Children minimum age: 6. Closed January

An elegant town house offering quality
accommodation, an exquisite breakfast and an
exceedingly warm welcome. An ideal location
for an exploration of town and fells.
SB £35.50 DB £53
CC: MC Vi DC Swi Delt JCB Solo
🌐🗲💻🅿️🍳🎬🐎🛏️🏊‍♀️🍴🍴
How to get there: Exit M6 J-40, A66 then A591
to Keswick. On reaching the war memorial, turn
left into Station Street and the hotel is
immediately on the right.

Northwest

Rickerby Grange

♦♦♦♦

Portinscale, nr Keswick, Cumbria, CA12 5RH
Tel: 01768 772344 Fax: 01768 775588
Email: val@ricor.demon.co.uk
Web: www.ricor.demon.co.uk
Children minimum age: 5

A small and friendly hotel in the pretty village of Portinscale. Waking distance to Keswick and Lake Derwentwater. Easy access to all parts of the Lakes, ample parking, resident proprietor.
SB £28 DB £56 HBS £41 HBD £82 D £14.50.
CC: MC Vi Swi Delt
How to get there: Bypass Keswick on A66 Cockermouth road. Turn left at Portinscale sign. Pass Farmers Arms Inn on left, and turn down 2nd lane to the right.

Shemara Guest House

♦♦♦♦

27 Bank Street, Keswick, Cumbria, CA12 5JZ
Tel: 01768 773936
Children minimum age: 2
SB £25 DB £22 CC: MC Vi Swi Delt JCB
How to get there: From A66, go into Keswick, over pedestrian crossing. Pass car park on left; guest house is on right.

Sunnyside Guest House

♦♦♦♦

25 Southey Street, Keswick, Cumbria, CA12 4EF
Tel: 01768 772446 Fax: 01768 774447
Email: raynewton@survey.u-net.com
Web: www.survey.u-net.com
Closed mid-December
SB £24 DB £38
How to get there: From M6 take A66 west, turn off for Keswick, right at T-junction, left at war memorial. Sunnyside 100 yards on left.

Tarn Hows

♦♦♦♦

3–5 Eskin Street, Keswick, Cumbria, CA12 4DH
Tel: 01768 773217 Fax: 01768 773217
Email: david@tarnhows40.freeserve.co.uk
Children minimum age: 6
SB £24.50 DB £41 HBS £36 HBD £64 D £11.50.
How to get there: Left after Conservative Club into Greta Street and continue into Eskin Street.

Swiss Court Guest House

♦♦♦

25 Bank Street, Keswick, Cumbria, CA12 5JZ
Tel: 01768 772637 Fax: 01768 780146
Email: info@swisscourt.co.uk
Web: www.swisscourt.co.uk
SB £20 DB £40 CC: MC Vi Swi Delt
How to get there: On main road in Keswick, opposite Bell Close car park and police station.

Knutsford, Cheshire

Cottons

★★★★

Manchester Road, Knutsford, WA16 0SU
Tel: 01282 414141 Fax: 01282 835586
SB £125 DB £145 CC: MC Vi Am DC Swi
How to get there: 1 mile from M6 J-19 on A50.

Mere Court

★★★★

Warrington Road, Mere, Knutsford, WA16 0RW
Tel: 01565 831000 Fax: 01565 831001
Email: sales@merecourt.co.uk
Web: www.merecourt.co.uk
SB £85 DB £95 B £9.95 L £14.95 D £22.50.
CC: MC Vi Am DC Swi Delt
See advert on facing page

Longview

★★

Manchester Road, Knutsford, WA16 0LX
Tel: 01565 632119 Fax: 01565 652402
Email: longview_hotel@compuserve.com
Web: www.longviewhotel.com
SB £50 DB £68 CC: MC Vi Am DC
How to get there: Exit M6 J-19, A556 for Chester. Left at lights after 1 mile. Left after 1¾ miles at roundabout, hotel is 150 yards on right.

Dog Inn

◆◆◆◆

Well Bank Lane, Over Peover, Knutsford,
Cheshire, WA16 8UP
Tel: 01625 861421 Fax: 01625 864800
Web: www.cheshireinns.co.uk
SB £55 DB £75 B £7.50 L £4.50 D £9.95.
CC: MC Vi Am Swi Delt

How to get there: From Knutsford, follow A50
Holmes Chapel Road. Turn left at 'Whipping
Stocks'. Proceed for 2 miles.

Lancaster, Lancashire

Lancaster House

★★★★

Green Lane, Ellel, Lancaster, LA1 4GJ
Tel: 01524 844822 Fax: 01524 844766
Email: lanchouse@elhmail.co.uk
Web: www.elh.co.uk
CC: MC Vi Am DC Swi Delt Solo

How to get there: Exit M6 J-33, right at
roundabout, 2 miles to signpost on right.

Little Hayfield, Cheshire

Pool Cottage

◆◆◆

Park Hall, Little Hayfield, High Peak, SK22 2NN
Tel: 01663 742463
SB £18 DB £30

How to get there: Approach Little Hayfield on
A624. From south, proceed over 4 sets of
rumble strips. Take first right.

Liverpool, Merseyside

Liverpool Marriott City Centre

★★★★

One Queen Square, Liverpool, L1 1RH
Tel: 0151 476 8000 Fax: 0151 474 5000
SB £110 DB £130 HBS £134 HBD £178
B £9.75 L £10.95 D £25.
CC: MC Vi Am DC Swi Delt Solo

How to get there: Follow M62 to end, follow
signs for city centre, then Lime Street Station.
Turn right when Lime Street is on left: Marriott is
on the left.

Mere Court Hotel

This attractive Edwardian country house hotel
stands in 7 acres of mature gardens, with an
ornamental lake, in the most desirable part of
the Cheshire countryside. The 1903 house
offers individually designed four-posters,
some with double jacuzzi spa baths, and king-
size Lakeside rooms furnished to the same
standard. The lakeside Arboreum Restaurant,
offers du Jour and à la carte menus.

Warrington Road, Mere, Knutsford,
Cheshire WA16 0RW
Tel: 01565 831000 Fax: 01565 831001
Email: sales@merecourt.co.uk
Website: www.merecourt.co.uk

Campanile

Travel Accommodation
Wapping & Curloner Street, Queens Dock,
Liverpool, L8 4AJ
Tel: 0151 709 8104 Fax: 0151 709 8725

Campanile hotels offer comfortable and
convenient budget accommodation and a
traditional French-style Bistro providing freshly
cooked food for breakfast, lunch and dinner. All
rooms en-suite with tea/coffee-making facilities,
DDT and TV with Sky channels.
SB £45.90 DB £50.86 HBS £53 HBD £69.80
B £4.95 L £5.25 D £10.85.
CC: MC Vi Am DC Swi Delt

How to get there: Follow brown signs for Albert
Dock. Hotel is located next to Queens Dock.

The Gladstone

Lord Nelson Street, Liverpool, L3 5QB
Tel: 0151 709 7050 Fax: 0151 707 0352

Aachen

89-91 Mountpleasant, Liverpool, L3 5TB
Tel: 0151 709 3477 Fax: 0151 709 1126/3633
Email: fpwaachen@netscapeonline.co.uk
Web: www.merseyword.com/aachen
Closed Christmas to New Year
SB £26 DB £40 HBS £47 HBD £74 D £12.75.
CC: MC Vi Am DC Swi Delt JCB
How to get there: Follow signs city centre to
Mountpleasant car park.

Blenheim Guest House

37 Aigburth Drive, Sefton Park, Liverpool,
Merseyside, L17 4JE
Tel: 0151 727 7380 Fax: 0151 727 5833

Loweswater, Cumbria

Grange Country House

Loweswater, Cumbria, CA13 0SU
Tel: 01946 861211

Lytham St Annes, Lancashire

Clifton Arms
★★★★

West Beach, Lytham St Annes, FY8 5QJ
Tel: 01253 739898 Fax: 01253 730657
Email: welcome@cliftonarms.com
Web: www.cliftonarms.com

The historic Clifton Arms Hotel is situated
overlooking Lytham Green. The elegant decor

and surroundings create a stylish hotel whilst
retaining its reputation for friendly hospitality.
SB £90 DB £112 HBS £60 HBD £120
B £9.75 L £14.50 D £25.
CC: MC Vi Am DC Swi Delt
How to get there: Exit M55 J-4, follow signs for
A584. Hotel is situated on the seafront at
Lytham St Annes.

Chadwick

★★★

South Promenade, Lytham St Annes,
Lancashire, FY8 1NP
Tel: 01253 720061 Fax: 01253 714455
Email: sales@chadwickhotel.com
Web: www.chadwickhotel.com

Family-run seafront award-winning hotel and
leisure complex renowned for good food,
service and comfort.
SB £46 DB £68 HBS £56 HBD £44.50
CC: MC Vi Am DC Swi Delt
How to get there: From M6 to M55, then follow
signs to Lytham St Annes. Hotel is on the
Promenade at St Annes.

Fernlea
★★★

11–17 South Promenade, St Annes-on-Sea,
Lancashire, FY8 1LU
Tel: 01253 726726 Fax: 01253 721561
Email: enquiries@thefernleahotel.co.uk
Web: www.thefernleahotel.co.uk
SB £40.50 DB £81 HBS £51.50 HBD £103
B £7.50 D £11.50.
CC: MC Vi Am Swi
How to get there: Seafront location on
promenade, close to main shopping centre.
See advert on facing page

Lindum

★★

63–67 South Promenade, Lytham St Annes,
Lancashire, FY8 1LZ
Tel: 01253 721534 Fax: 01253 721364
Email: info@lindumhotel.co.uk
Web: www.lindumhotel.co.uk
SB £36 DB £60 HBS £50 HBD £45 B £8
L £9.50 D £15. CC: MC Vi Am Swi Delt

How to get there: Situated on the main
promenade (A584) at St Annes.

Endsleigh

◆◆◆

315 Clifton Drive South, Lytham St Annes,
Lancashire, FY8 1HN
Tel: 01253 725622 Fax: 01253 729977
SB £23 DB £46 HBS £32 HBD £64

How to get there: First Hotel east of St Annes
Square shopping centre.

Strathmore

◆◆◆

305 Clifton Drive South, Lytham St Annes,
Lancashire, FY8 1HN
Tel: 01253 725478
Children minimum age: 9
SB £23 DB £46 HBS £28 HBD £56
B £4 L £4 D £5.

How to get there: 200m along main Blackpool
to Preston road.

Macclesfield, Cheshire

Shrigley Hall

★★★★
Shrigley Park, Pott Shrigley, Macclesfield,
Cheshire, SK10 5SB
Tel: 01625 575757 Fax: 01625 573323
Email: shrigleyhall@paramount-hotels.co.uk
Web: www.paramount-hotels.co.uk
SB £110 DB £140 D £24.
CC: MC Vi Am DC Swi Delt

How to get there: Through Macclesfield into
Bollington. Follow signs for Pott Shrigley.

If you're looking for great dining when staying
away, look for RAC Hotels and Guest
Accommodation displaying the RAC Dining
Award symbol in this Guide.

Superb sea front position featuring
Nivens Health Club with indoor swimming
pool, gymnasium, squash, sauna, jacuzzi,
four-poster bedroom suites
and great food and service

11-17 South Promenade,
St. Annes-on-Sea, Lancashire FY8 1LU
Tel: 01253 726726   Fax: 01253 721561
Email: fernhotel@aol.com
Website: www.thefernleahotel.co.uk

Moorhayes House

◆◆◆

27 Manchester Road, Tytherton, Macclesfield,
Cheshire, SK10 2JJ
Tel: 01625 433228 Fax: 01625 429878
Email: helen@moorhayeshouse.freeserve.co.uk
SB £38 DB £55 CC: MC Vi Swi Delt Solo JCB

How to get there: North from Macclesfield on
A538, signposted Tytherington. Moorhayes is on
left, ½ mile from town.

Northwest

Manchester

Copthorne Manchester

★★★★

Clippers Quay, Salford Quay,
Manchester, M5 2XP
Tel: 0161 873 7321 Fax: 0161 877 8110
Email: manchester@mill-cop.com
Web: www.mill-cop.com

At this four-star property guests enjoy spacious comfort within a peaceful location overlooking the waterfront. Ideally situated minutes from the motorway with complementary car parking.
B £12.95 L £17 D £21.
CC: MC Vi Am DC Swi Delt

How to get there: M602, A57/A5063 to Salford. A5063 onto Trafford Road. Turn right into Clippers Quay. Hotel on right, next to cinema.

Le Meridien Victoria & Albert

★★★★

Water Street, Manchester, M3 4JQ
Tel: 0870 400 8585 Fax: 0161 834 2484
Web: www.lemeridien-hotels.com
B £14.50 L £9.95 D £14.95.
CC: MC Vi Am DC Swi Delt

How to get there: M6, M26, M602 Manchetser. Exit M602 for A57 Manchester, continue through lights, 2nd set lights turn left onto Water Street.

Palace

★★★★

Oxford Street, Manchester, M60 7HA
Tel: 0161 288 1111 Fax: 0161 288 2222
Web: www.principalhotels.co.uk
B £11.50 L £12.50 D £17.95.
CC: MC Vi Am DC Swi Delt

How to get there: Follow signs for Piccadilly/Universities. Turn onto Whitworth Street, and left onto Oxford Street. The Palace Hotel is located on your left.

Jury's Inn Manchester

★★★

56 Great Bridgewater Street,
Manchester, M1 5LE
Tel: 00353 16070055 Fax: 00353 16609625
Email: dorothy_cusack@jurysdoyle.com
Web: www.jurysdoyle.com
CC: MC Vi Am DC

Novotel Manchester West

★★★

Worsley Brow, Worsley, Manchester, M28 2YA
Tel: 0161 799 3535 Fax: 0161 703 8207
Email: h0807@accor-hotels.com
Web: www.novotel.com
Children minimum age: 16
B £9.50 L £10.50 D £16.50.
CC: MC Vi Am DC Swi Delt

Stanneylands

★★★

Stanneylands Road, Wilmslow,
Cheshire, SK9 4EY
Tel: 01625 525225 Fax: 01625 537282
Email: enquiries@stanneylandshotel.co.uk
Web: www.stanneylandshotel.co.uk

The Stanneylands Hotel is a strikingly handsome house set in beautiful gardens, the oak-panelled dining room serving outstanding cuisine and fine wines.
SB £98.50 DB £119 CC: MC Vi Am DC Swi Delt

How to get there: Exit M56 J-5, follow signs to Styal. Follow B5166, B5358, hotel signposted on right-hand side.

Willow Bank

★★★

Wilmslow Road, Fallowfield, M14 6AF
Tel: 0161 224 0461 Fax: 0161 257 2561
Email: willowbankhotel@feathers.uk.com

Web: www.feathers.uk.com
SB £54.95 DB £74.95 HBS £62.50 HBD £90
B £5.95 D £10.95. CC: MC Vi Am DC Swi Delt

How to get there: M56 to end (A5103). Right at 5th lights. Left at 2nd lights into Wilmslow Road. Hotel 500 yards on left.

Albany
★★

21 Albany Road, Chorlton, M21 0AY
Tel: 0161 8816774 Fax: 0161 8629405
SB £59.50 DB £69.50 HBS £75 HBD £101
B £7.95 L £12.95 D £16.95.
CC: MC Vi Am DC Swi Delt

How to get there: Off A6010, 250 yards east of junction with B5217. Also, 1 mile west of A5103.

Comfort Inn, Manchester
★★

Hyde Road, Birch Street, West Gorton, Manchester, M12 5NT
Tel: 0161 220 8700 Fax: 0161 220 8848
Email: admin@gb615.u-net.com

SB £56.50 DB £64 HBS £68 HBD £90 B £8.75
L £9.75 D £12.75. CC: MC Vi Am DC Swi Delt

How to get there: Off A57 2¹/₂ miles southeast of city centre

Campanile
❖ Travel Accommodation

55 Ordsall Lane, Regent Road, Salford, Manchester, M5 4RS
Tel: 0161 833 1845 Fax: 0161 833 1847

Campanile hotels offer comfortable and convenient budget accommodation and a

traditional French-style Bistro providing freshly cooked food for breakfast, lunch and dinner. All rooms en-suite with tea/coffee-making facilities, DDT and TV with Sky channels.
SB £46 DB £51 HBS £57 HBD £73 B £4.95
L £5.95 D £11.25. CC: MC Vi DC Swi Delt

How to get there: Exit M6 J-21a onto M62 to Manchester, then M602 Salford. Continue over roundabout onto Regent Road. Hotel on right, after Sainsbury's.

Highbury
◆◆◆◆

113 Monton Road, Eccles, Manchester, M30 9HQ
Tel: 0161 787 8545 Fax: 0161 787 9023

Family-run high standard hotel, 15 mins from Manchester city centre and 20 mins from airport. 16 rooms en-suite, TV, radio, telephone, tea/coffee, trouserpress, hairdryer, evening meals, licensed bar, parking.
SB £25 DB £35 D £8. CC: MC Vi Am Swi Delt

How to get there: Exit M60 J-12, then M602 J-2. Left for A576 Guilder Brook, second left Half Edge Lane into Monton Road. Hotel ¹/₂ mile on left.

Imperial
◆◆◆

157 Hathersage Road, Manchester, M13 0HY
Tel: 0161 225 6500 Fax: 0161 225 6500
Email: imperialhotel.manchester@
          tinyworld.co.uk
Web: www.hotelimperialmanchester.co.uk
Closed Christmas to New Year
SB £33 DB £50 B £5 D £8.
CC: MC Vi Am DC Swi Delt

How to get there: Approximately 1 mile south of city centre. By Manchester Royal Infirmary and Manchester University.

Northwest

Victoria Park

4-6 Park Crescent, Victoria Park, M14 5RE
Tel: 0161 224 1399 Fax: 0161 225 4949
Email: vhp.manchester@claranet.co.uk
Web: www.vhp.manchester.claranet
SB £35 DB £48 B £5 CC: MC Vi Am Swi Delt
🖂 ⊗ ☺ ☎ ⚘ 🕯 ☙ 🎠 ♫ ⚑ ♨
How to get there: Follow signs for Manchester
University on Oxford Road, continue until
Oxford Road becomes Wilmslow Road, and we
are off this on Park Cresecent.

New Central

144–146 Heywood Street, Manchester,
Lancashire, M8 0PD
Tel: 0161 205 2160 Fax: 0161 205 2169
Email: newcentral@talk21.com
SB £21.50 DB £35 D £4. CC: MC Vi
🐎 ☺ 🖵 P ⚘ 🕯 ☙ 🎠 ♫ ⚑ ♨ ⚲
How to get there: 1½ miles north of city centre,
off Cheetham Hill Road (A665). Look for Esso
service station on right. Heywood Street is
opposite on left.

Mawdesley, Lancashire

Mawdsley's Eating House & Hotel

★★★
Hall Lane, Ormskirk, Lancashire, L40 2QZ
Tel: 01704 822552 Fax: 01704 822096
Email: mawdsleyeh@aol.com
Web: www.mawdsleyeh.co.uk
SB £45 DB £55 B £5 L £10.50 D £10.50.
CC: MC Vi Am DC Swi Delt
⚓ ♿ 🖂 ☺ 🖵 ☎ P ⚘ 🕯 ☙ 🎠 ⚑ ♨ ☞ ♨ 👯
SPA ☂ 🎵
How to get there: From M6 J-27 follow signs to
Parbold. After ¼ mile, turn right (signed to
Wrightington). Follow signs to Eccleston. At
crossroads turn left, signed to Mawdesley.

Millom, Cumbria

Duddon Pilot

◆◆◆◆   ⚮ ❦
Devonshire Road, Millom, Cumbria, LA18 4JT
Tel: 01229 774116 Fax: 01229 774116
SB £25 DB £50 L £5 D £10.
⊗ ☺ 🖵 ☎ P ⚘ 🕯 ☙ 🎠 ♫ ⚑ ♨ 👯 👬 👫
How to get there: Exit M6 J-37, A590 to
Greenodd, followed by A5092 and A595 to
Millom.

Morecambe, Lancashire

Elms

★★★
Bare, Morecambe, Lancashire, LA4 6DD
Tel: 01524 411501 Fax: 01524 831979

Situated in its own landscaped gardens, the
recently refurbished Elms Hotel is perfect for
pleasure, business and conferences. Licensed
restaurant with excellent cuisine.
SB £53 DB £73 HBS £62 HBD £90 B £7.50
L £10.25 D £ 16.95. CC: MC Vi Am DC Swi Delt
⚓ ♿ ⚖ 🖂 🐎 ☺ 🖵 ☎ ⚘ P ⚘ 🕯 ☙ 🎠 ♫ ⚑ ♨
👯 👬
How to get there: Exit M6 J-34 for Morecambe
to large roundabout, 3rd exit onto Hall Drive
which joins onto Bare Lane, hotel on right.

Headway

★★★
East Promenade, Marine Road, Morecambe,
Lancashire, LA4 5AW
Tel: 01524 412525 Fax: 01524 832630
Email: admin@headway.net1.co.uk
Web: www.headwayhotel.co.uk
SB £37 DB £74 HBS £45 HBD £45 B £4.50
L £1.95 D £12.95. CC: MC Vi Am DC Swi Delt
♿ ⚖ 🖂 🐎 ☺ 🖵 ☎ P ⚘ 🕯 🎠 ♫ ⚑ ♨ 👯 👬
How to get there: Exit M6 J-34, A589.Turn left
by Broadway Hotel, 200m along Promenade.

Clarendon

★
Marine Road West, Morecambe,
Lancashire, LA4 4EP
Tel: 01524 410180 Fax: 01524 421616

Warwick Non Smoking Hotel

◆◆◆◆   ⚮
394 Marine Road East, Morecambe, LA4 5AN
Tel: 01524 418151 Fax: 01524 427235
SB £25 DB £50 HBS £35 HBD £60
⊗ ☺ 🖵 ⚘ 🕯 ☙ 🎠 ♫ ⚑ ♨ ⚲
How to get there: On East Promenade between
Broadway and Morecambe town hall.

Beach Mount

♦♦♦

395-6 Marine Road East, Morecambe,
Lancashire, LA4 5AN
Tel: 01524 420753 Fax: 01524 420753
Closed Nov-Mar
SB £24.75 DB £46.50 HBS £33.50 HBD £64
CC: MC Vi Am DC Delt

Hotel Prospect

♦♦♦

363 Marine Road, Morecambe,
Lancashire, LA4 5AQ
Tel: 01524 417819
Closed December to Easter
SB £24 DB £36 HBS £31 HBD £50 D £7.
CC: MC Vi DC Delt

How to get there: Exit M6 J34/35. Follow signs
to Lancaster/Morecambe. At Morecambe, follow
signs to East Promenade. Turn left at
Promenade. Hotel on left before Gala Bingo.

Channings

♦♦

455 Marine Road East, Bare, Morecambe,
Lancashire, LA4 6AD
Tel: 01524 417925 Fax: 01524 411794
Email: channings.hotel@ukgateway.net
Web: www.channingshotel.co.uk
SB £21.50 DB £39 B £4.50 D £5.50.
CC: MC Vi Am DC Swi Delt

How to get there: From the south, exit M6 J-34.
After 3½ miles, the hotel is situated on the
promenade directly opposite Bare Pool and
close to Happy Mount Park.

Moreton, Merseyside

Leasowe Castle

★★★

Leasowe Road, Moreton, Wirral,
Merseyside, CH46 3RF
Tel: 0151 606 9191 Fax: 0151 678 5551
Email: leasowe.castle@mail.cybase.co.uk
SB £54.50 DB £72 HBS £69.50 HBD £102
B £6.50 L £12.95 D £16.95.
CC: MC Vi Am DC Swi Delt

How to get there: Exit M53 J-1. Turn left off slip
road onto A551. Hotel on right after 3 minutes.
See advert on the right

Nantwich, Cheshire

Rookery Hall

★★★★

Main Road, Worleston, Nantwich, Cheshire,
Tel: 01270 610016 Fax: 01270 626027
Email: rookery@arcadianhotels.co.uk
Web: www.arcadianhotels.co.uk

Award-winning country house hotel set in 38
acres of peaceful countryside, offering 45
luxuriously-appointed bedrooms. Several
elegant lounges and a fine dining restaurant.
SB £95 DB £110 HBS £132.5 HBD £170
D £37.50. CC: MC Vi Am DC Swi

How to get there: M6 J-18, A54, A530, A51,
B5074. Hotel 1½ miles on right.

Leasowe Castle Hotel

This historic building circa 1595 and
converted to a hotel, only minutes from M53,
makes an ideal stopover for Wales and the
Lakes. The beautiful restaurant offers full à
la carte and table d'hote menus. Our 50
en-suite bedrooms have TV, telephone and
tea/coffee-making facilities, and two offer
four-poster beds.
A personal and friendly service is assured.

Leasowe Road, Moreton,
Merseyside CH46 3RF
Tel: 0151 606 9191 Fax: 0151 678 5551
Email: leasowe.castle@mail.cybase.co.uk

Northwest

Newby Bridge, Cumbria

Whitewater Hotel & Leisure Club

★★★
The Lakeland Village, Ulverston, Newby Bridge,
Cumbria, LA12 8PX
Tel: 01539 531133 Fax: 01539 531881
Email: smcintosh@btconnect.com
Web: www.whitewater-hotel.co.uk
SB £85 DB £120 HBS £100 HBD £70
B £6 L £5.50 D £19.
CC: MC Vi Am DC Swi Delt JCB

See advert below

Lyndhurst Country

◆◆◆
Lyndhurst, Newby Bridge, Ulverston,
Cumbria, LA12 8ND
Tel: 01539 531245
Email: lyndhurst@lyndhurstguesthouse.co.uk
Web: www.lyndhurstguesthouse.co.uk
SB £39 DB £42
How to get there: Lyndhurst is situated on A590
at its junction with the A592.

Northwich, Cheshire

Quality Hotel

★★★
London Road, Northwich, Cheshire, CW9 5HD
Tel: 01606 44443 Fax: 01606 42596
Email: admin@gb618.u-net.com
Web: www.qualityinn.com/hotel/gb618

SB £80.75 DB £102.50 HBS £59 HBD £59
CC: MC Vi Am DC Swi Delt
How to get there: Exit M6 J-19, A556 to
Northwich, A533 (London Road) to hotel.

Oldham, Lancashire

Hotel Smokies Park

★★★
Ashton Road, Bardsley, Oldham,
Lancashire, OL8 3HX
Tel: 0161 785 5000 Fax: 0161 785 5010
Email: sales@smokies.co.uk

Web: www.smokies.co.uk
SB £70 DB £80 HBS £87 HBD £114 B £7.50
L £5.95 D £10. CC: MC Vi Am DC Swi Delt
♿ ⅄ ⊗ ⌾ ⬚ ☎ ✆ **P** ✄ ⅂ℂ ☒ ♘ ⼐ ❦ ⚌
⚎ 'Ψ'
How to get there: On the A627 midpoint
between Oldham and Ashton-under-Lyne.

High Point
★★
Napier Street East, Oldham, OL8 1TR
Tel: 0161 624 4130 Fax: 0161 627 2757
SB £42 DB £53 HBS £52 HBD £73 B £5
L £10.95 D £11.95. CC: MC Vi Am Swi Delt
♿ ⬚ ⊗ ⌾ ⬚ ☎ **P** ✄ ⅂ℂ ♘ ⼐ ❦ ⚎
How to get there: Exit M62 J-20, A627M, A62 to
Manchester. Right off Manchester Street
roundabout, first left, right at top, right again.

Parbold, Lancashire

Lindley
★★
Lancaster Lane, Parbold, Lancashire, WN8 7AB
Tel: 01257 462804 Fax: 01257 464628

Penrith, Cumbria

North Lakes
★★★★ ℞
Ullswater Road, Penrith, Cumbria, CA11 8QT
Tel: 01282 414141 Fax: 01282 835586
Email: info@shireinns.co.uk
Web: www.shireinns.co.uk
SB £102 DB £122 CC: MC Vi Am DC Swi
⚘ ♿ ⅄ ⬚ ☇ ⊗ ⌾ ⬚ ☎ **P** ✄ ⅂ℂ ♘ ⼐ ❦
⚌ ⚎ 🆂🅿🅰 'Ψ' ⚡
How to get there: Exit M6 J-40 and follow signs
for Penrith.

Sharrow Bay
★★★ ℞ ℞ ℞ ℞
Lake Ullswater, Penrith, Cumbria, CA10 2LZ
Tel: 01768 486301 Fax: 01768 486349

Westmorland
★★★
Orton, Penrith, Cumbria, CA10 3SB
Tel: 01587 424351

Brantwood Country
★★
Stainton, Penrith, Cumbria, CA11 0EP
Tel: 01768 862748 Fax: 01768 890164

Norcroft Guest House
♦♦♦♦ ℣
Graham Street, Penrith, Cumbria, CA11 9LQ
Tel: 01768 862365 Fax: 01768 862365
Email: info@norcroftguesthouse.com
Web: www.norcroftguesthouse.com

Charming Victorian house. Convenient for M6
and only 5 minutes walk to town centre. Come
and sample our renowned warm welcome and
delicious home cooking.
SB £24.50 DB £39 HBS £30 HBD £25 D £5.50.
CC: MC Vi Swi Delt
♿ ⊗ ⌾ ⬚ **P** ✄ ⅂ℂ ♘ ⼐ ❦
How to get there: Left at town hall, left again
into Drovers Lane. Norcroft 400 yards.

Tymparon Hall
♦♦♦♦ ✍
Newbiggin, Stainton, Penrith, CA11 0HS
Tel: 01768 483236 Fax: 01768 483236
Email: margaret@peeearson.freeserve.co.uk
Web: www.peeearson.freeserve.co.uk

Closed Christmas.
Close to Lake Ullswater and M6 Junction 40. A
warm welcome, hearty breakfasts and
traditional dinners served. Peaceful rural setting
on village fringe.
SB £30 DB £50 HBS £42 HBD £74 B £6 D £12.
♘ ⊗ ⌾ **P** ✄ ⅂ℂ ♘ ⼐ ⅂ ❦
How to get there: A66 to Keswick. Right at sign
for Newbiggin. Hotel at end of village on right.

Limes Country

♦♦♦

Redhills, Stainton, Penrith, Cumbria, CA11 0DT
Tel: 01768 863343 Fax: 01768 867190
Email: jdhanton@aol.com
SB £29 DB £48 HBS £42 HBD £74 CC: MC Vi

How to get there: Exit M6 J-40, A66 left after ½ mile, then 400 yards. The Limes is on the right.

Woodland House

♦♦♦

Wordsworth Street, Penrith, Cumbria,
CA11 7QY
Tel: 01768 864177 Fax: 01768 890152
Email: enquiries@woodlandhouse.co.uk
Web: www.woodlandhouse.co.uk

Elegant red sandstone house with books and maps for walkers and nature lovers. Ideal base for exploring Eden Valley, Lakes and Pennines. A non-smoking hotel.
SB £29.50 DB £48 CC: MC Vi Swi Delt

How to get there: At the foot of Beacon Hill, near the town hall.

Preston, Lancashire

Novotel Preston

★★★

Reedfield Place, Walton Summit, Preston,
Lancashire, PR5 6AB
Tel: 01772 313331 Fax: 01772 627868
Email: h0838@accor-hotels.com
Web: www.novotel.com
SB £58 DB £63.50 HBS £71.50 HBD £85
B £8.50 L £6 D £13.95.
CC: MC Vi Am DC Swi Delt

How to get there: Exit M6 J-29. M65 J-1 off M65. 5 miles from Preston railway station.

Pickerings

★★★

Garstang Road, Catterall, Lancashire, PR3 0HA
Tel: 01995 600999 Fax: 01995 602100
Email: hotel@pickeringpark.demon.co.uk
Web: www.pickeringpark.com
SB £50 DB £60 HBS £65 HBD £90
B £10 L £4.75 D £15. CC: MC Vi Am Swi Delt

How to get there: Situated between J-32 and J-33 of the M6 at Garstang.

Swallow Hotel

★★★

Preston New Road, Samlesbury, Preston,
Lancashire, PR5 0UL
Tel: 01772 877351 Fax: 01772 877424

Brook House

★★

662 Preston Road, nr Chorley,
Clayton-Le-Woods, Lancashire, PR6 7EH
Tel: 01772 336403 Fax: 01772 337369
Email: enquiries@hotel-preston-chorley.co.uk
Web: www.hotel-preston-chorley.co.uk
SB £40 DB £50 B £5 D £10.
CC: MC Vi Am DC Swi Delt

How to get there: On the A6 ½ mile from J-29 M6, J-9 M61 and J-2 M65.

Claremont

★★

516 Blackpool Road, Ashton-on-Ribble,
Preston, Lancashire, PR2 1HY
Tel: 01772 729738 Fax: 01772 726274
Email: claremonthotel@btinternet.com
Web: www.claremonthotelpreston.co.uk
SB £39 DB £56 HBS £49 HBD £76 L £6.50
D £11.95. CC: MC Vi Am DC Swi Delt

How to get there: Exit M6 J-31, A59 for Preston. Right at roundabout, 4 miles along Blackpool Road. Hotel on right.

Tulketh

♦♦♦♦

209 Tulketh Road, Ashton-on-Ribble,
Preston, Lancashire, PR2 1ES
Tel: 01772 728096 Fax: 01772 723743
Closed Christmas to New Year
SB £37.50 DB £49.50 D £5.50.
CC: MC Vi Am DC Swi Delt

How to get there: Exit M6 J-31, left towards Preston. Right onto A5085. After 3 miles, left at St Andrew's church onto Tulketh Road.

Ramsbottom, Lancashire

Old Mill

★★★

Springwood Street, Ramsbottom, BL0 9DS
Tel: 01706 822991 Fax: 01706 822291
Email: oldmillhot@netscapeonline.co.uk
Web: www.oldmillhotel.co.uk
SB £45 DB £75 B £6 L £9.95 D £13.95.
CC: MC Vi Am DC Swi Delt Solo JCB Electron

How to get there: Close to M66 J-1.

Ravenglass, Cumbria

Muncaster Country Guest House

◆◆◆

Muncaster, Ravenglass, Cumbria, CA18 1RD
Tel: 01229 717693 Fax: 01229 717693
Closed December
SB £22 DB £44 HBS £34 HBD £68 B £5

How to get there: Opposite main entrance to
Muncaster Castle on A595.

Runcorn, Cheshire

Campanile

Travel Accommodation
Lowlands Road, Runcorn, Cheshire, WA7 5TP
Tel: 01928 581771 Fax: 01928 581730

Campanile hotels offer comfortable and
convenient budget accommodation and a
traditional French-style Bistro providing freshly
cooked food for breakfast, lunch and dinner. All
rooms en-suite with tea/coffee-making facilities,
DDT and TV with Sky channels.
SB £43.45 DB £48.40 HBS £50 HBD £65
CC: MC Vi Am DC Swi Delt

How to get there: Exit M56 J012, A557 towards
Runcorn. Follow signs for Runcorn railway
station.

Rydal, Cumbria

Rydal Lodge

◆◆◆

Rydal, Cumbria, LA22 9LR
Tel: 01539 433208

Saint Helens, Merseyside

Park View Guest House

◆◆

333/335 Prescot Road, St Helens, WA10 3HP
Tel: 01744 20491

Sale, Cheshire

Amblehurst

★★★

44 Washway Road, Sale, Cheshire, M33 1QZ
Tel: 0161 973 8800 Fax: 0161 905 1697

Belmore

★★★

143 Brooklands Road, Sale, Cheshire, M33 3QN
Tel: 0161 973 2538 Fax: 0161 973 2665

Salford, Manchester

Hazeldean

◆◆◆

467 Bury New Road, Kersall, Salford, M7 0NX
Tel: 0161 792 6667 Fax: 0161 792 6668

To make an on-line booking at an RAC
inspected Hotel or Guest Accommodation,
visit www.rac.co.uk/hotels

Northwest

Sandbach, Cheshire

Grove House

★★ 🐿🐿🐿

Mill Lane, Wheelock, Sandbach, CW11 4RD
Tel: 01270 762582 Fax: 01270 759465
Closed Christmas

Restaurant with rooms, family-owned and run.
Relaxing ambience, individually-styled rooms.
Excellent restaurant offering ambitious modern
cooking by chef-proprietor.
SB £47.50 DB £75 B £6.50 L £9.25 D £14.50.
CC: MC Vi Am Swi Delt

🐎🌐🧵💻☎️🅿️🧹🕯️🐕🎠🎋🐾♨️♒♒
How to get there: M6 J-17, A534, cross lights,
left at roundabout. Follow Wheelock signs.

Poplar Mount Guest House

♦♦♦

2 Station Road, Elworth, Sandbach, CW11 9JG
Tel: 01270 761268 Fax: 01270 761268
SB £22 DB £40 D £9. CC: MC Vi JCB

🧵💻🅿️🧹🕯️🎠🎋🐾
How to get there: On B5079. Opposite
Sandbach Railway Station.

Sawrey, Cumbria

Sawrey

★★

Far Sawrey, Ambleside, Cumbria, LA22 0LQ
Tel: 01539 443425 Fax: 01539 443425
Closed Christmas

An attractive two-storey, 18th-century inn built
in traditional Lake District style. Former stables
converted into a bar.
SB £29.50 DB £59 HBS £39.50 HBD £39.50
B £6.50 L £8.50 D £16.50. CC: MC Vi Swi Delt
♿🐎🧵💻☎️🅿️🧹🕯️🐕🎠🎋🐾♨️♒
How to get there: One mile from Windermere
car ferry on B5285 Hawkshead Road.

Buckle Yeat

♦♦♦♦

Buckle Yeat, Near Sawrey, Hawkshead,
Cumbria, LA22 0LF
Tel: 01539 436446 Fax: 01539 436446
Email: info@buckle-yeat.co.uk
Web: www.buckle-yeat.co.uk

Tastefully furnished guest house, all 7 rooms
ensuite with tea and coffee-making facilities.
Centrally heated and log fires. Ideally situated
for walking and touring. Open all year
SB £25 DB £50 CC: MC Vi Am Swi Delt
🐎🌐🧵💻🅿️🧹🕯️🎠🎋🐾
How to get there: Exit M6 J-36 to Windermere.
Cross Lake. Near Sawrey is second village.

West Vale Country House

♦♦♦♦ 🦋

Far Sawrey, Ambleside, Sawrey, LA22 0LQ
Tel: 01539 442817 Fax: 01539 488214
Children minimum age: 7
Closed November to February
SB £29 DB £52 HBS £41 HBD £76 D £11.
CC: MC Vi Swi Delt Electron JCB Solo
🌐🧵🅿️🧹🕯️🎠🎋🐾♨️🍴
How to get there: On the B5285 between
Hawkshead and the Ferry at Windermere.

Shap, Cumbria

Shap Wells

★★★

Shap, Cumbria, CA10 3QU
Tel: 01931 716628 Fax: 01931 716377

Email: manager@shapwells.com
Web: www.shapwells.com
Closed January to mid-February
SB £55 DB £80 HBS £51 HBD £85
B £6 L £9 D £16. CC: MC Vi Am Swi Delt JBC
How to get there: Exit M6 J-39 for Kendal. Left at A6 for Kendal. Hotel drive on left.

Silloth, Cumbria

Golf
★★
Criffel Street, Silloth, Cumbria, CA5 4AB
Tel: 016973 31438 Fax: 016973 32582

Skelmersdale, Lancashire

Quality Hotel Skelmersdale
★★★
Prescott Road, East Pimbo, Skelmersdale,

WN8 9PU
Tel: 01695 720401 Fax: 01695 50953
Email: admin@gb656.u-net.com
Web: www.choicehotels.com
SB £80.75 DB £102.50 HBS £97.50 HBD £136
B £9.75 L £16.75 D £16.75.
CC: MC Vi Am DC Swi Delt Solo
How to get there: M6 J-26, M58 J-5, left at roundabout, 100m left, hotel 300m on right.

Southport, Merseyside

Prince Of Wales
★★★★
Lord Street, Southport, Merseyside, PR8 1JS
Tel: 01704 536688 Fax: 01704 543488
Email: princeofwales@paramount-hotels.co.uk
SB £99 DB £115 HBS £72.50 HBD £62.50
B £8.95 L £8.95 D £17.50.
CC: MC Vi Am DC Swi Delt
How to get there: From North: M6 J-31, A59, A565 to Southport. South: M6 J-26, M58 J-3, A570 to Southport. Hotel in town centre.

Scarisbrick
★★★
Lord Street, Southport, Merseyside, PR8 1NZ
Tel: 01704 543000 Fax: 01704 533335
Email: scarisbrickhotel@talk21.com
Web: www.scarisbrickhotel.com
SB £ 65 DB £85 HBS £75 HBD £95
B £6 L £6 D £10. CC: MC Vi Am DC Swi Delt
How to get there: From South: exit M6 J-26, M58, A570. North: M6 J-31, A59 through Preston to A565.

Tree Tops
★★★ ☕☕
Southport Old Road, Formby, Southport, Merseyside, L37 0AB
Tel: 01704 572430 Fax: 01704 572430

Ideal for business or pleasure, situated just off the beaten track, in quiet and tranquil surroundings, offering top class dining in our country house restaurant.
SB £58 DB £95 B £7.50 L £11 D £13.
CC: MC Vi Am DC Swi Delt
How to get there: Follow A565 from Southport to Formby. Turn left onto Southport Old Road. At Woodvale, turn into Southport Old Road.

Metropole
★★
Portland Street, Southport, Merseyside, PR8 1LL
Tel: 01704 536836 Fax: 01704 549041
Email: metropole.southport@btinternet.com
Web: www.btinternet.com/~metropole.southport
SB £35 DB £60 HBS £47 HBD £84
CC: MC Vi Am Swi Delt
How to get there: 100m from Southport's Lord Street — 4 minute walk from railway station.

Ambassador

♦♦♦♦

13 Bath Street, Southport, PR9 0DP
Tel: 01704 543998 Fax: 01704 536269
Children minimum age: 3
Closed December 16 to January 14
SB £36 DB £50 D £10. CC: MC Vi

Rosedale

♦♦♦♦

11 Talbot Street, Southport, PR8 1HP
Tel: 01704 530604 Fax: 01704 530604
Email: rosedale.hotel@rapid.co.uk
Web: www.merseyworld.com/rosedale
Closed late December to early January
SB £25 DB £50 CC: MC Vi Delt

How to get there: From A570 to town centre
into Eastbank Street. Talbot Street is on left.

White Lodge

♦♦♦

12 Talbot Street, Southport, PR8 1HP
Tel: 01704 536320 Fax: 01704 536320
SB £25 DB £50 HBS £35 HBD £70

Whitworth Falls

♦♦♦

16 Lathom Road, Southport, PR9 0JH
Tel: 01704 530074
Email: whitworthfalls@rapid.co.uk
Web: www.whitworthfallshotel.co.uk
SB £25 DB £50 HBS £32.50 HBD £65
B £5 D £7.50.

How to get there: From centre, Lord St, north to
fire station, cross roundabout, 2nd left
(Alexandra Rd), and 4th right (Lathom Rd).

Stockport, Cheshire

Bredbury Hall

★★★

Dark Lane, Goyt Valley, Bredbury, SK6 2DH
Tel: 0161 430 7421 Fax: 0161 430 5079
Email: reservations@bredburyhallhotel.co.uk
Web: www.bredburyhallhotel.co.uk
SB £57.50 DB £80.50 HBS £74 HBD £113.50
B £8 L £7.50 D £16.50.
CC: MC Vi Am DC Swi Delt

How to get there: Exit M60 J-25. Follow the

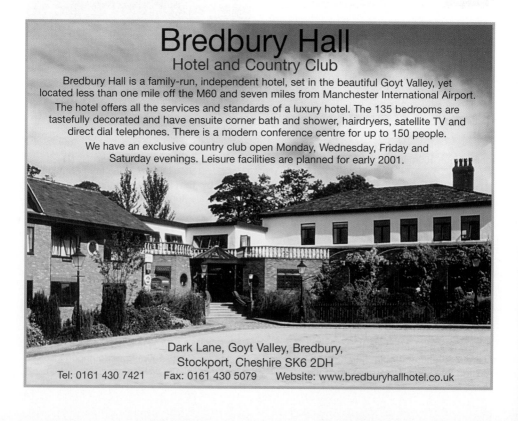

Bredbury Hall
Hotel and Country Club

Bredbury Hall is a family-run, independent hotel, set in the beautiful Goyt Valley, yet located less than one mile off the M60 and seven miles from Manchester International Airport.

The hotel offers all the services and standards of a luxury hotel. The 135 bedrooms are tastefully decorated and have ensuite corner bath and shower, hairdryers, satellite TV and direct dial telephones. There is a modern conference centre for up to 150 people.

We have an exclusive country club open Monday, Wednesday, Friday and Saturday evenings. Leisure facilities are planned for early 2001.

Dark Lane, Goyt Valley, Bredbury,
Stockport, Cheshire SK6 2DH
Tel: 0161 430 7421   Fax: 0161 430 5079   Website: www.bredburyhallhotel.co.uk

Bredbury Hall signs. Right at lights, then turn left after 400 yards into Osbourne Street.
See advert on facing page (below)

Tarporley, Cheshire

Willington Hall

★★★ ♟

Willington, Tarporley, Cheshire, CW6 0NB
Tel: 01829 752321 Fax: 01829 752596
Email: enquiries@willingtonhall.co.uk
Web: www.willingtonhall.co.uk
SB £67.50 DB £100 B £8 L £12 D £20.
CC: MC Vi Am Swi

How to get there: From Tarporley on A51, right at Bulls Head (Willington), then 1 mile on left.

Thornton Hough, Merseyside

Thornton Hall

★★★ ♟♟

Neston Road, Thornton Hough, L63 1JF
Tel: 0151 336 3938 Fax: 0151 336 7864

Ullswater, Cumbria

Heritage Hotels – Leeming House

★★★★ ♟♟

Watermillock, Penrith, Ullswater, CA11 0JJ
Tel: 0870 400 8131 Fax: 01768 486443

Patterdale

★★

Patterdale, Penrith, Cumbria, CA11 0NN
Tel: 01768 482231 Fax: 01768 482440
Closed January to February
SB £39 DB £70 HBS £50 HBD £100
B £6 D £17. CC: MC Vi Swi Delt

How to get there: Exit M6 J-40, A66 for Keswick, left at roundabout (A592). Right at T-junction. Continue through Glenridding to Patterdale.

Upholland, Lancashire

Holland Hall

★★★ ♟

6 Lafford Lane, Wigan, Upholland,
Lancashire, WN8 0QZ
Tel: 01695 624426 Fax: 01695 622433

Wallasey, Merseyside

Grove House

★★ ♟♟

Grove Road, Wallasey, Merseyside, L45 3HF
Tel: 0151 639 3947 Fax: 0151 639 0028

Warrington, Cheshire

Park Royal International

★★★★ ♟♟

Stretton Road, Stretton, Warrington,
Cheshire, WA4 4NS
Tel: 01925 730706 Fax: 01925 730740
Email: hotel@park-royal-int.co.uk
SB £62.50 DB £72.50 HBS £94 HBD £128
B £6.95 L £10.45 D £14.65.
CC: MC Vi Am DC Swi Delt

How to get there: Leave M56 and follow A49 towards Warrington. At first set of traffic lights turn right. The hotel is 200 yards on right.
See advert on following page

Paddington House

★★

514 Manchester Road, Warrington,
Cheshire, WA1 3TZ
Tel: 01925 816767 Fax: 01925 816651
Email: hotel@paddingtonhouse.co.uk
Web: www.paddingtonhouse.co.uk

Friendly, family-run Georgian hotel situated in its own grounds. Conveniently located close to junction 21 M6 and 2 miles from Warrington town centre. Antique-themed bar and restaurant.
SB £57.50 DB £70 HBS £67.50 HBD £90
CC: MC Vi Am DC Swi Delt Solo

How to get there: Exit M6 J-21. Follow signs for Warrington (A57). Continue along A57 for approximately 1 mile.

Northwest

The Park Royal International Hotel

A hotel which offers a standard of service and excellence which is unrivalled

★ A superb state-of-the-art Health and Leisure Spa which includes: 22m swimming pool, sauna, steam room, whirlpool bath, dance studio, gymnasium, solarium, 3 all-weather tennis courts.

★ The Retreat Beauty Centre: 6 beauty rooms including 1 hydrotherapy suite offering the ultimate in health & beauty.

Set in the charming village of Stretton in the heart of the Cheshire countryside, yet ideally located: Minutes from the M56 and M6 motorways • Manchester Airport 15 minutes • Liverpool 25 minutes • Chester 20 minutes.

An ideal venue for a relaxing short break.

★ Fully air-conditioned Royal Suite for up to 400 guests ★ Plus a selection of smaller suites ★
★ Award-winning AA Rosette Harequin Restaurant ★ 140 Deluxe ensuite bedrooms ★

Rates from only £52.50 per person, dinner, bed & breakfast — Call now for further details.

Stretton, Warrington WA4 4NS   Tel:01925 730706   Fax: 01925 730740
Email: hotel@park-royal-int.co.uk

Birchdale

◆◆◆ ✖️

Birchdale Road, Appleton, Warrington, Cheshire, WA4 5AW
Tel: 01925 263662 Fax: 01925 860607
Email: rfw@birchdalehotel.co.uk
Web: www.birchdalehotel.co.uk
SB £45 DB £60 CC: MC Vi DC Swi Delt
🐾🍳🖥🖨🅿🛎🕯🐴♨️🎱💈
How to get there: Situated off A49 at London Bridge Inn, 1½ miles from town centre. 2 miles from M56 and M6.

Wasdale, Cumbria

Wasdale Head Inn

◆◆◆◆ ♟️✖️

Wasdale, Gosforth, Cumbria, CA20 1EX
Tel: 01946 726229 Fax: 01946 726334
Email: wasdaleheadinn@msn.com
Web: www.wasdale.com
SB £45 DB £90 HBS £67 HBD £134
B £7.50 L £5 D £22. CC: MC Vi Am Swi Delt
🖼🐾❄️🍳🎱🅿🛎🕯🐴♨️💈
How to get there: From A595, turn into Gosforth village and take left fork for Wasdale. After 1 mile bear right to climb steep hill. Inn is another 9 miles along single-track road.

Wigan, Manchester

Kilhey Court

★★★★ ♟️♟️♟️
Chorley Road, Standish, Wigan, WN1 2XN
Tel: 01257 472100 Fax: 01257 422401

Quality Hotel

★★★
River Way, Wigan, Manchester, WN1 3SS
Tel: 01942 826888 Fax: 01942 825800
Email: admin@gb058.u-net.com
Web: www.choicehotels.com

SB £46 DB £60 HBS £50 HBD £120
B £6.95 L £5 D £16. CC: MC Vi Am DC Swi Delt
🔷♿🏋️🐾❄️🍳🖥🔔🅿🛎🕯🐴
♨️💈
How to get there: M6 J-25 or J-27.

To make an on-line booking at an RAC inspected Hotel or Guest Accommodation, visit www.rac.co.uk/hotels

Bel Air

★★

236 Wigan Lane, Wigan, Lancashire, WN1 2NU
Tel: 01942 241410 Fax: 01942 243967
Email: belair@hotelwigan.freeserve.co.uk
Web: www.belairhotel.co.uk
SB £39.50 DB £49.50 HBS £45 HBD £59.50
B £2.95 L £6.95 D £6.95.
CC: MC Vi Am Swi Delt

How to get there: Exit M6 J-27, A49 for Wigan.
Bel Air is on right before large roundabout and
Cherry Gardens public house.

Wigton, Cumbria

Gardeners Cottage

♦♦♦♦

Bank End, Hesket-Newmarket, Wigton,
Cumbria, CA7 8HR
Tel: 016974 78283

Wheyrigg Hall

♦♦♦

Wheyrigg, Wigton, Cumbria, CA7 0DH
Tel: 01697 361242 Fax: 01697 361020

Windermere, Cumbria

Lakeside

★★★★

Lakeside, Newby Bridge, Cumbria, LA12 8AT
Tel: 01539 531207 Fax: 01539 531699
Email: sales@lakesidehotel.co.uk
Web: www.lakesidehotel.co.uk

Overlooking nothing but the lake... Lakeside
Hotel is in the perfect location right on the
shores of Lake Windermere. Lake cruisers
depart directly from outside the hotel.
SB £110 DB £130 HBS £145 HBD £100

B £10 L £10 D £20. CC: MC Vi Am DC Swi Delt

How to get there: Exit M6 J-36, A590 to Newby
Bridge or follow signs for Lakeside Steamers.

Beech Hill

★★★

Newby Bridge Road, Bowness-on-Windermere,
Windermere, Cumbria, LA23 3LR
Tel: 01539 442137 Fax: 01539 443745
Email: beechhill@richardsonhotels.co.uk
Web: www.richardsonhotels.co.uk
SB £57 DB £94 HBS £69 HBD £118
B £8.50 L £5 D £27.50. CC: MC Vi Am Swi

How to get there: Exit M6 J-36, A591 to
Windermere. Left onto A592 for Newby Bridge.

Craig Manor

★★★

Lake Road, Windermere, Cumbria, LA23 3HR
Tel: 015394 88877 Fax: 015394 88878

Gilpin Lodge

★★★

Crook Road, Windermere, Cumbria, LA23 3NE
Tel: 01539 488818 Fax: 01539 488058
Email: hotel@gilpin-lodge.co.uk
Web: www.gilpin-lodge.co.uk
Children minimum age: 7

Friendly, relaxing, elegant hotel in 20 acres of
country gardens, moors and woodland, two
miles from Lake Windermere. Sumptuous
bedrooms. Exquisite food.
HBS £100 HBD £120 B £12.50
L £10 D £35.
CC: MC Vi Am DC Swi Delt JCB

How to get there: Exit M6 J-36. Take A590/A591
to the roundabout north of Kendal, then B5284
for 5 miles.

Northwest

Heritage Hotels – The Old England

★★★

Church Street, Bowness, Cumbria, LA23 3DF
Tel: 0870 400 8130 Fax: 01539 443432
SB £45 DB £90 HBS £65 HBD £130
B £11.95 L £12.95 D £22.50.
CC: MC Vi Am DC Swi Delt JCB

How to get there: Exit M6 J-36, A592 to
Windermere. Hotel next to lake on right.

Hillthwaite House

★★★

Thornbarrow Road, Windermere, LA23 2DF
Tel: 01539 443636 Fax: 01539 488660
Email: reception@hillthwaite.com
Web: www.hillthwaite.com
An extended 19th-century house, in elevated
position overlooking lake and fells. Swimming
pool, sauna, steam room, four-poster beds,
jacuzzi baths. Excellent restaurant.
SB £35 DB £70 HBS £49.50 HBD £99 B £10
L £10 D £17.50. CC: MC Vi Am DC Swi Delt

How to get there: Halfway between Windermere
and Bowness, left into Thornbarrow Road.
Hillthwaite House Hotel can be seen on skyline.

Holbeck Ghyll

★★★

Holbeck Lane, Windermere, Cumbria, LA23 1LU
Tel: 01539 432375 Fax: 01539 434743
Email: accommodation@holbeck-ghyll.co.uk
Web: www.holbeck-ghyll.co.uk
SB £85 DB £130 HBS £100 HBD £170 L £12.50
D £29.50. CC: MC Vi Am DC Swi Delt JCB

How to get there: Exit M6 J-36, A591 to
Windermere. Head for Ambleside, right after
Brockhole (Holbeck Lane, signposted
Troutbeck). Hotel is ½ mile on left.

Langdale Chase

★★★

Windermere, Cumbria, LA23 1LW
Tel: 01539 432201 Fax: 01539 432604
Email: sales@langdalechase.co.uk
Web: www.langdalechase.co.uk
SB £45 DB £90
L £14.50 D £28. CC: MC Vi Am DC Swi Delt

How to get there: Exit M6 J-36, A591 to
Windermere, then sign for Ambleside. Hotel is
¼ mile past Brockhole on left.

Lindeth Howe Country House

★★★

Lindeth Drive, Longtail Hill, Windermere,
Cumbria, LA23 3JF
Tel: 01539 445759 Fax: 01539 446368
Email: lindeth.howe@kencomp.net
Web: www.lakes-pages.co.uk
SB £43 DB £85 HBS £61 HBD £122
B £7 L £6.50 D £22.50.
CC: MC Vi Swi Delt JCB, Solo

How to get there: Exit M6 J-36, A591 at
roundabout, then first left onto B5284 for 6
miles, over crossroads to Longtail Hill. Hotel 200
yards on left (first drive).
See advert on facing page

Linthwaite House

★★★

Crook Road, Windermere, Cumbria, LA23 3JA
Tel: 01539 488600 Fax: 01539 488601
Email: admin@linthwaite.com
Web: www.linthwaite.com
SB £85 DB £90 HBS £79 HBD £59 B £13.50
L £10 D £39. CC: MC Vi Am DC Swi Delt

How to get there: Exit M6 J-36, A591 towards
Windermere, then B5284 through Crook.
Linthwaite is 6 miles on left, up private drive.
See advert on facing page

Low Wood

★★★

Windermere, Cumbria, LA23 1LP
Tel: 01539 433338 Fax: 01539 434072

Broadoaks Country House

★★

Bridge Lane, Troutbeck, Windermere, Cumbria,
LA23 1LA
Tel: 015394 45566 Fax: 015394 88766

Cedar Manor

★★

Ambleside Road, Windermere, Cumbria,
LA23 1AX
Tel: 01539 443192 Fax: 01539 445970
Email: cedarmanor@fsbdial.co.uk
Web: www.cedarmanor.co.uk
SB £40 DB £60 HBS £52 HBD £84
B £9 D £19.5. CC: MC Vi

How to get there: ¼ mile north of Windermere
on A591. Nearest motorway, J-36 on M6. Follow
signs for South Lakes.

Hideaway

★★ ℞

Phoenix Way, Windermere, Cumbria, LA23 1DB
Tel: 01539 443070 Fax: 01539 448664
Email: enquiries@hideaway-hotel.co.uk
Web: www.hideaway-hotel.co.uk
Closed January
SB £35 DB £60 HBS £48 HBD £84
L £5 D £10.95.
CC: MC Vi Am Swi Delt Solo JCB Maestro

🛋️ 🐕 ⊗ 🖁 🖥️ ☎ 🅿 ⚗ ⚘ 🐎 🎿 🏄 ♟️ ⛄

How to get there: Take A591 into Windermere,
turn off A591 into Phoenix Way. Hotel is 100m
on right down hill.
See advert on this page below

Hideaway Hotel

High all-round standards and personal service
by the proprietors Josephine and Henry
Gornall and their resident manager/chef
Alison. Our highly experienced chef John
cooks fresh food to perfection and the menu
is changed daily.
A central but quiet location makes this one of
the most sought after hotels in the area.

**Phoenix Way, Windermere,
Cumbria LA23 1DB**
Tel: 015394 43070   Fax: 015394 48664
Email: enquiries@hideaway-hotel.co.uk
Website: www.hideaway-hotel.co.uk

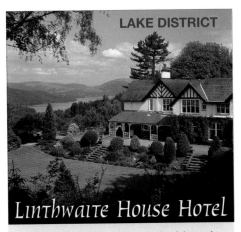

Northwest

Lindeth Fell

★★ ♞♞

Lyth Valley Road, Bowness-on-Windermere,
Cumbria, LA23 3JP
Tel: 01539 443286 Fax: 01539 447455
Email: kennedy@lindethfell.co.uk
Web: www.lindethfell.co.uk

One of the most beautifully situated hotels in
lakeland, Lindeth Fell offers a warm and friendly
atmosphere, superior accommodation and
superb modern English cooking, at outstanding
value.
SB £52 DB £90 HBS £69 HBD £140
B £8.50 L £6.95 D £23. CC: MC Vi Swi

How to get there: 1 mile south of Bowness-on-
Windermere on A5074.

The Beaumont

♦♦♦♦♦

Holly Road, Windermere, Cumbria, LA23 2AF
Tel: 01539 447075 Fax: 01539 447075
Email: thebeaumonthotel@btinternet.com
Web: www.lakesbeaumont.co.uk
Children minimum age: 10
SB £38 DB £34 CC: MC Vi Swi Delt JCB Solo

How to get there: Follow town centre signs
through one-way system, then take second left
into Ellerthwaite Road and then first left into
Holly Road.
See advert on this page below

Newstead

♦♦♦♦♦

New Road, Windermere, Cumbria, LA23 2EE
Tel: 01539 444485
Children minimum age: 7
DB £55

How to get there: Exit M6 J-36. Follow
A590/A591 to Windermere village. Newstead is
¼ mile on left.

Blenheim Lodge

♦♦♦♦

Brantfell Road, Bowness-on-Windermere,
Windermere, Cumbria, LA23 3AE
Tel: 01539 443440 Fax: 01539 443440
Email: blenheimlodge@supanet.com
Web: www.six-of-the-best.com
Children minimum age: 6
SB £30 DB £50 HBS £52 HBD £94 D £22.
CC: MC Vi Am Swi Delt

How to get there: Exit M6 J-36, A591 to
Windermere. Left to Bowness, cross mini-
roundabout, first left and first left again.

Fairfield

◆◆◆◆

Brantfell Road, Windermere, Cumbria,
LA23 3AE
Tel: 01539 446565 Fax: 01539 446565
Email: ray&barb@the-fairfield.co.uk
Web: www.the-fairfield.co.uk
Closed December to January

An attractive 200-year-old house set in a quiet,
secluded, well-matured garden. Close to the
village, lake, Fells & Dales Way. Superb value in
one of the most beautiful settings in Britain.
SB £32 DB £64 CC: MC Vi Swi Delt
🖨️ ⊗ ☺ 🖵 🅿 ⚘ ⁑🐎 🎠 ♯ 🐾 🍴
How to get there: From mini-roundabout in the
centre of Bowness village, take road towards
lake, turn left, then left again into Brantfell Road.

Fir Trees Guest House

◆◆◆◆

Lake Road, Windermere, Cumbria, LA23 2EQ
Tel: 01539 442272 Fax: 01539 442272

Green Gables

◆◆◆

37 Broad Street, Windermere, Cumbria,
LA23 2AB
Tel: 01539 443886
Email: greengables@fsbdial.co.uk
Web: www.lakes-pages.co.uk
SB £20
� ⊗ ☺ 🖵 ⚘ ⁑🐎 🎠 ♯ 🐾 🍴
How to get there: Opposite public car park in
Broad Street, turn left at last shop (Harry
Sharp's) at bottom of village centre.

Royal

◆◆◆

Royal Square, Bowness, Windermere,
Cumbria, LA23 3DB
Tel: 01539 443045 Fax: 01539 444990

Rockside Guest House

◆◆

Ambleside Road, Windermere, Cumbria,
LA23 1AQ
Tel: 01539 445343 Fax: 01539 445343
Email: suecoleman@aol.com
Web: www.rocksideguesthouse.fsnet.co.uk
Children minimum age: 5

Superb accommodation 100 yards from
Windermere village, train and bus station. Most
rooms en-suite with remote TV, telephone,
clock, radio, hairdryer etc. Parking for 12 cars.
Tours arranged if required.
SB £20 DB £38 B £5 CC: MC Vi JCB, Eurocard
🚶cross ⊗ ☺ 🖵 🅿 ⚘ ⁑🐎 🎠 ♯ 🐾 🍴
How to get there: Take Junction 36 off M6.
Proceed on route 591 to Windermere. In village
take 2nd left. Rockside is on corner.

Workington, Cumbria

Cumberland

★★★

Station Road, Workington, Cumbria, CA14 2XQ
Tel: 01900 64401 Fax: 01900 872400

Northwest

Wales

Holyhead
ANGLESEY
A5
A55
Llandudno
Conwy
Colwyn Bay
Rhyl
Flint
Bangor
A470
CLWYD
Caernarfon
A5
Betws-y-coed
Ruthin
Wrexham
A55
Snowdonia
Llangollen
Criccieth
Porthmadog
A5
Abersoch
A470
A494
GWYNEDD
POWYS
Dolgellau
A458
Welshpool
A487
Aberdyfi
A470
Newtown
Aberystwyth
A483
A44
Rhayader
Knighton
Aberaeron
A44
Llandrindod Wells
A487
ENGLAND
Cardigan
A482
DYFED
Builth Wells
Fishguard
A485
A40
Pembrokeshire
A40
Brecon
A40
A48
Carmarthen
POWYS
Milford Haven
A40
Pembroke
Abergavenny
Monmouth
Llanelli
A465
Merthyr Tydfil
GWENT
GLAMORGAN
Cwmbran
Chepstow
Swansea
Port Talbot
A470
M48
Newport
M4
M4
Cardiff
Barry

Glasgow
Edinburgh
Belfast
Dublin
Manchester
Birmingham
Cardiff
London

Trum y ddysgl, Snowdonia

From soaring granite mountains to gently undulating hills, often tainted by stains of old industry, Wales has a proud and rich national history, complemented by the warm hospitality shown to visitors. Hospitality was not always offered visitors. In AD 78 the Roman conquest of Celtic

Caernarfon Castle

Wales ended at the island of Anglesey in the northwest corner. After 1066 came the Normans, and then later the Plantagenet kings of England put the Welsh under the thumb towards the end of the medieval period. The turbulent history provides visitors with awe-inspiring architecture: from the cathedral of St David's in the southwest to the parallel chains of powerful castles along the western coast and eastern border with England: the Welsh Marches. The Welsh language, which still survives and is the first language in some parts of Wales, is to be found on most road signs and maps.

The interior thrills visitors with some of the most beguiling landscape to be found in Britain. Three parks, Snowdonia, the Pembrokeshire Coast and the Brecon Beacons, combine to present lush lowland valleys, bleak mountain moorland,

dramatic coastlines and stunning freshwater lakes. These not only suggest myriad leisure opportunities with spectacular scenery for walking, driving, mountain biking and watersports, but also provide a diverse habitat for some 1,100 species of plants and countless mammals, birds, insects and reptiles.

The major urban region is on the south coast, centred round Swansea and Cardiff. Both cities are witnessing a cultural revival as the old primary industries of coal-mining and steel-making have declined, to be replaced by tourism and commerce as the lifeblood. As a centre for shopping, Cardiff really can offer something for everyone: narrow Victorian streets with individual shops share the city with brand new giant shopping complexes.

Transport links to and from the south are excellent: The M4 motorway winds past Cardiff and Swansea to Llanelli, while ferries leave from Fishguard, Pembroke Dock and Swansea for Eire. The Heart of Wales railway line stretches from Swansea to the English border at Knighton and beyond. The single-carriage journey along a single-track line through tunnels, over viaducts and through some of the most breathtaking scenery in Wales is an experience not soon forgotten. Mid-Wales is served by the mountainous A44 from Worcester (don't miss Devil's Bridge just short of Aberystwyth), while the M6/M56 links to the northern coast roads. Visitors to the north of the Cardigan Bay area should not miss the unique fantasy village of Portmeirion, backdrop for many films and the TV series The Prisoner.

Guest houses in Wales offer excellent accommodation, a warm welcome and value for money, while larger hotels (mainly situated in the bigger cities of Swansea and Cardiff) offer efficient services at international standards.

Wales

Abercraf, West Glamorgan

Maes-y-Gwernen

♦♦♦♦

School Road, Abercraf, West Glamorgan,
SA9 1XD
Tel: 01639 730218 Fax: 01639 730765

Aberdovey, Gwynedd

Trefeddian

★★★

Aberdovey, Gwynedd, LL35 0SB
Tel: 01654 767213 Fax: 01654 767777
Email: tref@saqnet.co.uk
Closed January to February

The hotel is situated within the Snowdonia
National Park, with stunning views of Cardigan
Bay and 4 miles of unspoilt beaches just a short
walk away. The hotel is family run and has
disabled access.
SB £40 DB £55 HBS £59 HBD £79
B £10 L £13 D £20. CC: MC Vi Swi Delt
How to get there: ½ mile north of Aberdovey
village off A493, overlooking golf links and
Cardigan Bay.
See advert on facing page

Abergavenny, Gwent

Allt-Yr-Ynys

★★★

Walterstone, nr Abergavenny, Gwent,
HR2 0DU
Tel: 01873 890307 Fax: 01873 890539
Email: allthotel@compuserve.com
Web: www.allthotel.co.uk
SB £75 DB £100 HBS £90 HBD £70 B £8.50
L £10 D £20. CC: MC Vi Am Delt

How to get there: A456 Abergavenny/Hereford
road to Pandy. West at Pandy Inn. Right at
crossroads and follow signs.

Llansantffraed Court

★★★

Llanvihangel Gobion, nr Abergavenny, Gwent,
NP7 9BA
Tel: 01873 840678 Fax: 01873 840674
Email: mikemorgan@llch.co.uk
Web: www.llch.co.uk

A timeless landscape, steeped in history and
legend awaits at Llansantffraed. This majestic
country house offers the best of Welsh
hospitality. Spoil yourself.
SB £70 DB £88 HBS £85 HBD £70 B £8.50
L £10 D £25. CC: MC Vi Am DC Swi Delt
How to get there: From convergence of A465
and A40 at Abergavenny, B4598 to Usk. Hotel
gates on left after 4½ miles.

Abergele, Conwy

Kinmel Manor

★★★

St Georges Road, Abergele, Conwy, LL22 9AS
Tel: 01745 832014 Fax: 01745 832014
SB £52 DB £72 HBS £68 HBD £108 B £7.50
L £12.50 D £16. CC: MC Vi Am DC Swi Delt
How to get there: To west, Abergele turn-off to
roundabout. On roundabout, travelling east A55,
take Rhuddlan turn off to roundabout entrance.

Trefeddian Hotel

Standing prominently overlooking golf links, sand dunes and Cardigan Bay, 1½ miles north of Aberdyfi (Aberdovey) village, Trefeddian is set in its own grounds, and suitable for all the family. Trefeddian is renowned for friendly attentive service, excellent meals, an extensive wine list, and spacious lounges, affording relaxing holidays.

The hotel has an indoor swimming pool, tennis court, 9-hole pitch/putt, snooker room, children's indoor/outdoor play areas, sun terraces, and lift.

Trefeddian Hotel
Aberdovey,
Gwynedd LL35 0SB
Tel: 01654 767213
Fax: 01654 767777
Email: tref@saqnet.co.uk

Aberporth, Cardigan

Hotel Penrallt

★★★ ☕

Aberporth, Cardigan, SA43 2BS
Tel: 01239 810227 Fax: 01239 811375
Email: info@hotelpenrallt.co.uk
Web: www.hotelpenrallt.co.uk
SB £59 DB £96 HBS £79 HBD £136
B £8.95 L £10.50 D £20.
CC: MC Vi Am DC Swi Delt

How to get there: On A487 5 miles north of
Cardigan town, take B4333 signed Aberporth.
Hotel 1 mile on right.

Aberystwyth, Dyfed

Belle Vue Royal

★★★

Marine Terrace, Aberystwyth, Ceredigion, SY23 2BA
Tel: 01970 617558 Fax: 01970 612190
Email: reception@bellevueroyalhotel.fsnet.co.uk
Web: www.bellevueroyal.co.uk
SB £60 DB £90 HBS £77 HBD £124 B £8.50
L £13 D £22. CC: MC Vi Am DC Swi Delt

How to get there: On promenade overlooking
Cardigan Bay.

Conrah Country House

★★★ ☕☕

Chancery, Aberystwyth, Ceredigion, SY23 4DF
Tel: 01970 617941 Fax: 01970 624546
Email: hotel@conrah.freeserve.co.uk
Children minimum age: 5. Closed Christmas
SB £70 DB £100 HBS £87 HBD £67.50
B £13 L £15 D £24.
CC: MC Vi Am DC Swi Delt JCB Solo

How to get there: 3½ miles south of
Aberystwyth on A487.

Four Seasons

★★ ☕

Portland Street, Aberystwyth, Ceredigion, SY23 2DX
Tel: 01970 612120 Fax: 01970 627458
Email: reservations
        @fourseasonshotel.demon.co.uk
Web: www.smoothhound.co.uk/a07907.html
SB £55 DB £82 B £9.50 D £18.
CC: MC Vi Swi Delt

How to get there: In town centre, car park
entrance in Bath Street.

George Borrow

★★

Ponterwyd, Aberystwyth, Ceredigion, SY23 3AD
Tel: 01970 890230 Fax: 01970 890587
Email: georgeborrow@clara.net
Web: www.george-borrow.co.uk
SB £25 DB £50 HBS £35 HBD £70
B £5 L £5.50 D £11.95. CC: MC Vi Swi Delt

How to get there: Alongside A44, Aberystwyth
side of village of Ponterwyd, 15 mins from
Aberystwyth.

Glyn-Garth Guest House

◆◆◆◆

South Road, Aberystwyth, Ceredigion, SY23 1JS
Tel: 01970 615050 Fax: 01970 636835
Email: glyn-garth@southroad88.freeserve.co.uk
Children minimum age: 7
Closed Christmas to New Year
SB £21 DB £42

Plas Antaron

◆◆◆

Southgate, Aberystwyth, Ceredigion, SY23 1SF
Tel: 01970 611550 Fax: 01970 627084
SB £30 DB £50 HBS £40 HBD £70
B £4 L £5 D £10. CC: MC Vi Am Swi Delt

Queensbridge

◆◆◆

Promenade, Aberystwyth, Ceredigion,
SY23 2DH
Tel: 01970 612343 Fax: 01970 617452
SB £36 DB £55 B £7
CC: MC Vi Am DC Swi Delt

How to get there: At north end of promenade,
last hotel before Constitution Hill Cliff Railway.

Amlwch, Gwynedd

Trecastell

★★

Bull Bay, Amlwch, Gwynedd, LL68 9SA
Tel: 01407 830651 Fax: 01407 832114

Bala, Gwynedd

Plas Coch

★★

High Street, Bala, Gwynedd, LL23 7AB
Tel: 01678 520309 Fax: 01678 521135

Bangor, Gwynedd

Goetre Isaf Farmhouse

♦ ♦ ♦

Caernarfon Road, Bangor, Gwynedd, LL57 4DB
Tel: 01248 364541 Fax: 01248 364541
Email: bookings@fredw.com
Web: www.fredw.com
SB £18.50 DB £34 HBS £29 HBD £55 D £8.50.
How to get there: 2 miles outside Bangor on north side of Caernarfon Road A4087.

Barmouth, Gwynedd

Bontddu Hall

★★★

Bontddu, Dolgellau, Gwynedd, LL40 2UF
Tel: 01341 430661 Fax: 01341 430284
Email: reservations@bontdduhall.co.uk
Web: www.bontdduhall.co.uk
Closed November to February
SB £62.50 DB £100 HBS £86 HBD £75
L £9.50 D £16. CC: MC Vi Am DC Swi Delt JCB
How to get there: Off A470, A496 for Barmouth, 3 miles to Bontddu – hotel is on right hand side.

Beddgelert, Gwynedd

Royal Goat

★★★

Beddgelert, Gwynedd, LL55 4YE
Tel: 01766 890224 Fax: 01766 890422
Email: royal.goat@ukonline.co.uk
Web: web.ukonline.co.uk/royal.goat
SB £44 DB £74 HBS £63 HBD £112
B £7 L £10 D £20. CC: MC Vi Am DC Swi Delt
How to get there: In the centre of village.
See advert on the right

Tanronnen

★★

Beddgelert, Gwynedd, LL55 4YB
Tel: 01766 890347 Fax: 01766 890606
SB £40 DB £78 B £3 L £5 D £9.90.
CC: MC Vi Swi Delt
How to get there: Situated in village centre.

Looking for great dining? Look for RAC Hotels and Guest Accommodation displaying the RAC Dining Award symbol in this Guide.

Benllech, Anglesey

Bay Court

♦ ♦ ♦

Beach Road, Benllech, Tyn-y-Gongl, Anglesey, LL74 8SW
Tel: 01248 852573 Fax: 01248 852606
SB £23 DB £46 HBS £30 HBD £60
B £4.50 L £5.50 D £9.50.
CC: MC Vi Am DC Swi Delt
How to get there: A55 over Britannia Bridge. A5025 signposted Benllech. Right at crossroads in village towards beach.

Betws-y-Coed, Conwy

Royal Oak

★★★

Betws-y-Coed, Conwy, LL24 0AY
Tel: 01690 710219 Fax: 01690 710433
Email: glenn.evans@btinternet.com
SB £57 DB £86 HBS £73 HBD £118
CC: MC Vi Am DC Swi Delt
How to get there: On the main A5 London to Holyhead route, at village centre.

Royal Goat Hotel

A family owned establishment, The Royal Goat Hotel offers a combination of efficient service, good food and wine and spectacular scenery in the heart of the Snowdonia National Park. The hotel has an excellent reputation for good food and wine. A la carte and table d'hôte menus. Lift to all floors.

Beddgelert, Gwynedd LL55 4YE
Tel: 01766 890343 Fax: 01766 890422
Email: royal.goat@ukonline.co.uk
Website: www.ukonline.co.uk/royal.goat

Wales

Park Hill

★★

Llanrwst Road, Betws-y-Coed, Gwynedd,
LL24 0HD
Tel: 01690 710540 Fax: 01690 710540
Email: parkhill.hotel@virgin.net
Web: www.betws-y-coed.co.uk/acc/parkhill
Children minimum age: 6
SB £40 DB £55 HBS £55 HBD £83 L £5 D £15.
CC: MC Vi Swi Delt

How to get there: On A470 northbound from
Betws-y-Coed, ¹/₂ mile from A5/Waterloo Bridge
crossing.

Llannerch Goch Country House

◆◆◆◆

Capel Garmon, Betws-y-Coed, Conwy,
LL26 0RL
Tel: 01690 710261

Borth, Dyfed

Glanmor

◆◆

Borth, Dyfed, SY24 5JP
Tel: 01970 871689
SB £21 DB £42 HBS £31.50 HBD £63

How to get there: At northern end of Borth
seafront.

Brecon, Powys

Peterstone Court

★★★

Llanhamlach, Brecon, Powys, LD3 7YB
Tel: 01874 665387 Fax: 01874 665376
SB £85 DB £95 B £10 L £4 D £23.
CC: MC Vi Swi Delt

How to get there: A40 for Abergavenny, hotel is
approx 4 miles along on the right.
See advert on facing page

Usk Inn

◆◆◆◆

Station Road, Talybont on Usk, Brecon,
LD3 7JE
Tel: 01874 676251 Fax: 01874 676392
Email: stay@uskinn.co.uk
Web: www.uskinn.co.uk
Closed Christmas
SB £35 DB £60 B £6.95 L £7.95 D £15.95.

CC: MC Vi Am Swi JCB

How to get there: Just off the A40, 6 miles east
of Brecon, midway between canal and river.

Beacons

◆◆◆

16 Bridge Street, Brecon, Powys, LD3 8AH
Tel: 01874 623339 Fax: 01874 623339
Email: beacons@brecon.co.uk
Web: www.beacons.brecon.co.uk

This recently restored listed Georgian House
offers beautifully appointed bedrooms. The
candle-lit restaurant has fine food and wines.
Cosy cellar bar, elegant lounge and private
parking.
SB £25 DB £36 HBS £39.95 HBD £32.95
B £5 D £9.95. CC: MC Vi Swi Delt

How to get there: A40 west to centre, left, down
hill at lights, over bridge, hotel 100yds on right.

Maeswalter

◆◆◆

Heol Senni, nr Brecon, Powys, LD3 8SU
Tel: 01874 636629
Email: maeswalter@talk21.com
Children minimum age: 10

Maeswalter is a 300-year-old farmhouse in the
mountainous Brecon Beacons National Park.
Three tastefully decorated bedrooms. The lounge
features exposed timbers. Private suite available.

SB £20 DB £36 HBS £30.50 HBD £57 B £5 L £7
D £10.50.

🐕 ⊗ ⊚ 💻 **P** 🐎 🔧 🐴 ⛵

How to get there: A470 (Brecon to Merthyr).
Right onto A4215. After 2 miles left for Heol
Senni. Maeswalter 1½ miles on right.

Bridgend, Mid Glamorgan

Coed-y-mwstwr

★★★ 👤👤
Coychurch, Bridgend, Mid Glamorgan,
CF35 6AF
Tel: 01656 860621 Fax: 01656 863122

Bryngarw House

♦♦♦♦ 🔪
Bryngarw Country Park, Brynmenyn,
nr Bridgend, Mid Glamorgan, CF32 8UU
Tel: 01656 729009 Fax: 01656 729007

Burry Port, Carmarthenshire

George

♦♦♦♦
Stepney Road, Burry Port, Carmarthenshire,
SA16 0BH
Tel: 01554 832211
Children minimum age: 7
SB £28.50 DB £43 L £3.95 D £5.95.

⊚ 💻 🔧 🐴 ⛵ 👥

How to get there: M4 J-48. A484 to Burry Port.
At Jerusalem Chapel (on brow of hill) turn down
into town centre along Stepney Road.

Coasting Pilot Inn

♦♦♦
1 Bridge Street, Burry Port, Carmarthenshire,
SA16 0NR
Tel: 01554 833520 Fax: 01554 833520

Caernarfon, Gwynedd

Seiont Manor

★★★ 👤👤
Llanrug, Caernarfon, Gwynedd, LL55 2AQ
Tel: 01286 673366 Fax: 01286 672840
Web: www.arcadianhotels.co.uk
SB £95 DB £140 HBS £105 HBD £82.50
B £9.50 L £10.50 D £25.
CC: MC Vi Am DC Swi Delt

🔷 ⊘ ⊗ ⊚ 💻 ☎ **P** 🐎 🔧 🐴 ⛵ 👥 ⛲

🎿 ⛷

How to get there: A55 to Caernarfon. Hotel
3 miles outside Caernarfon on A4086.

Peterstone Court

If one was to dream of a haven of peace
and tranquility where one's every wish was
catered for and every desire anticipated,
Peterstone Court, an 18th-century
Georgian House Hotel, would surely be that
place. Cloaked in the breathtaking beauty
of the Brecon Beacons.

Llanhamlach, Brecon, Powys LD3 7YB
Tel: 01874 665387 Fax: 01874 665376

Cardiff

St David's

★★★★★ 👤👤
Havannah Street, Cardiff Bay, CF1 6SD
Tel: 029 2045 4045 Fax: 029 2031 3075
Email: pellis@thestdavidshotel.com
Web: www.rfhotels.com

Rocco Forte's five-star landmark: 136 bedrooms
(with private balconies), conference facilities and
award-winning restaurant, all overlooking Cardiff

Wales

Bay. Luxurious spa for marine hydrotherapy and pools.

SB £153.50 DB £183.50 HBS £178.50
HBD £208.50 B £10.50 L £14.50 D £20.
CC: MC Vi Am DC Swi Delt

How to get there: M4 J-33. A4232 for 9 miles. Leave dual carriageway by following signs to Techniquest. At roundabout, first left and immediate right into Havannah Street.

Angel
★★★★

Castle Street, Cardiff, CF1 2QZ
Tel: 029 2023 2633 Fax: 029 2039 6212
Email: angel@paramount-hotels.co.uk
Web: www.paramount-hotels.co.uk

Beautiful Victorian hotel situated in the heart of the city centre overlooking Cardiff Castle and Millennium Stadium. All rooms fully air-conditioned. Lovely restaurant with views of castle. Residents' car park.

SB £75 DB £105 HBS £90 HBD £135 B £8.95
L £12 D £17.50. CC: MC Vi Am DC Swi Delt

How to get there: City centre, facing Cardiff Castle.

Copthorne Cardiff-Caerdydd
★★★★

Copthorne Way, Culverhouse Cross, Cardiff, CF5 6DH
Tel: 029 2059 9100 Fax: 029 2059 9080
Email: sales.cardiff@mill-cop.com
Web: www.stay.with-us.com

In a picturesque setting just four miles from the city centre, this luxurious modern lakeside hotel offers you a warm welcome to Wales.

CC: MC Vi Am DC Swi

How to get there: M4 J-33. A4232, then exit to Culverhouse Cross. 4th exit to A48 Cowbridge at roundabout. Next left turn to hotel.

Hanover Hotel Cardiff Bay
★★★★

Schooner Way, Atlantic Wharf, Cardiff, CF10 4RT
Tel: 029 2045 7000 Fax: 029 2048 1491

HANOVER INTERNATIONAL

Imaginative design with a maritime theme throughout, this hotel provides quality accommodation and an exceptional leisure club. Close to the scenic Brecon Beacons.

CC: MC Vi Am DC

Jurys Cardiff

★★★★

Mary Ann Street, Cardiff, South Glamorgan,
CF10 2JH

Tel: 029 2034 1441 Fax: 029 2022 3742
Web: www.jurys.com
SB £60 DB £70 HBS £80 HBD £45 B £10.50
L £9.95 D £16.95. CC: MC Vi Am DC Swi Delt
♿ ♨ ⊗ ☺ ⌨ ☎ P ⚘ ⌖ 🎠 ♬ 🐎 ⚌
How to get there: M4 J-32. A470 to centre.
Left at lights on High Street. Hotel is on left.

Churchills

★★★

Llandaff Place, Cardiff Road, Llandaff, Cardiff,
CF5 2AD

Tel: 029 2040 1300 Fax: 029 2056 8347
Email: reservations@churchillshotel.co.uk
Web: www.churchillshotel.co.uk

Town-house hotel, near to the cathedral village
of Llandaff, within easy reach of the M4 and
minutes from the city centre. Weekend and
short break rates.
SB £75 DB £90 HBS £91.50 HBD £123
B £5.95 L £9.50 D £16.50.
CC: MC Vi Am DC Swi Delt
♿ ☺ ⌨ ☎ P ⚘ 🎠 ♬ 🐎 ⚌ ⚌⚌

Egerton Grey Country House

★★★ 🍴🍴

Porthkerry, Barry, nr Cardiff,
Vale of Glamorgan, CF62 3BZ

Tel: 01446 711666 Fax: 01446 711690
Email: info@egertongrey.co.uk
Web: www.egertongrey.co.uk
Beautiful old rectory set in a lush green valley
with outstanding views to the coast.
SB £75 DB £98.50 HBS £90 HBD £65 B £5.50
L £10 D £13.50. CC: MC Vi Am DC Swi Delt JCB
♿ ♨ 🐾 ⊗ ☺ ⌨ ☎ ⚘ P ⚘ 🎠 🐎 ♬
⚌⚌ ♙♙ 🍷
How to get there: M4 J-33. Signs to airport.
Left at small roundabout, signposted Porthkerry.
Left after 500 yards (following hotel signs).

Manor Parc

★★★ 🍴🍴🍴

Thornhill Road, Thornhill, Cardiff, CF14 9UA
Tel: 029 2069 3723 Fax: 029 2061 4624
SB £65 DB £95 CC: MC Vi Am Swi
♿ ♨ ☺ ⌨ ☎ P ⚘ 🎠 🐎 ♬ 🐎 ⚌ ♙♙ 🍷 ⚲
How to get there: Outskirts of Cardiff. Head for
Caerphilly on A469, Manor Parc on the left.

Quality Hotel

★★★

Merthyr Road, Tongwynlais, Cardiff, CF15 7LD
Tel: 029 2052 9988 Fax: 029 2052 9977
Email: admin@gb629@u-net.com
Web: www.qualityinn.com/hotel/gb629

Modern hotel, 8 miles from the city centre.
Ideally located for the business traveller with
motorway access and for the leisure guest to
explore Wales.
SB £92 DB £126 HBS £58 HBD £116
B £9.95 L £6.95 D £14.50.
CC: MC Vi Am DC Swi Delt
♿ ♿ ♨ ⚎ 🐾 ⊗ ☺ ⌨ ☎ ❄ ⚘ P ⚘ 🎠
♬ 🐎 ⚌ ♙♙ 🍸 🍷
How to get there: M4 J-32. A4054 exit for
Tongwynlais. Hotel is located on right.

Saint Mellons

★★★

Castleton, Cardiff, CF3 2XR
Tel: 01633 680355 Fax: 01633 680399
Email: stmellons@bestwestern.co.uk
Web: www.stmellonshotel.com
B £8 L £16 D £16. CC: MC Vi Am Swi Delt

How to get there: M4 J-28. Signs to A48 Cardiff.
After Castleton village, hotel signposted on left.

Sandringham

★★

21 St Mary Street, Cardiff, CF1 2PL
Tel: 029 2023 2161 Fax: 029 2038 3998
SB £48 DB £58 HBS £55 HBD £70
B £6 L £3.50 D £6.
CC: MC Vi Am DC Swi Delt JCB Solo

Campanile

Travel Accommodation

Caxton Place, Pentwynn, Cardiff, CF2 7HA
Tel: 029 2054 9044 Fax: 029 2054 9900

Typical Campanile Bistro

A comfortable hotel with 47 ensuite rooms,
colour TV and satellite channels, telephone and
welcome tray. With a friendly restaurant, bar and
free parking for our guests.
SB £41.95 DB £46.90 HBS £49 HBD £29.75
B £4.95 L £2.95 D £6.25.
CC: MC Vi Am DC Swi Delt

How to get there: M4 at J-30 (Cardiff). A4232 to
Pentwyn interchange. Follow the brown signs.

Marlborough Guest House

◆◆◆◆

98 Newport Road, Cardiff, CF2 1DG
Tel: 029 2049 2385

To make an on-line booking at an RAC
inspected Hotel or Guest Accommodation,
visit www.rac.co.uk/hotels

Albany Guest House

◆◆◆

191-193 Albany Road, Roath, Cardiff,
CF2 3NU
Tel: 029 2049 4121
Closed Christmas
SB £26 DB £36

How to get there: M4 J-29, or M48 at Cardiff
East, in lane for city centre. Right lights,
Roath Court is 500 yards on right.

Clare Court

◆◆◆

46-48 Clare Road, Grangetown, Cardiff, CF1 7RS
Tel: 029 2034 4839 Fax: 029 2066 5856
Email: clarecourthotelcardiff@hotmail.com
SB £28 DB £36 CC: MC Vi

How to get there: Close to city centre, and five
minutes walk from Cardiff Central rail station.

Cardigan, Dyfed

Castell Malgwyn

★★

Llechryd, Cardigan, Dyfed, SA43 2QA
Tel: 01239 682382 Fax: 01239 682644
Email: inquiries@malgwyn.co.uk
Web: www.castellmalgwyn.co.uk
SB £40 DB £80 HBS £54 HBD £54
B £9 L £14 D £ 20. CC: MC Vi Am DC Swi Delt

How to get there: Over River Teifi Bridge to hotel.

Penbontbren

★★ ☜

Glynarthen, Cardigan, Dyfed, SA44 6PE
Tel: 01239 810248 Fax: 01239 811129
Closed December 22-28
D £20. CC: MC Vi Am DC Swi Delt JCB

How to get there: A487 north from Cardigan,
second right 1 mile after Tan-y-groes.

Brynhyfryd Guest House

◆◆◆

Gwbert Road, Cardigan, Dyfed, SA43 1AE
Tel: 01239 612861 Fax: 01239 612861
Email: g.arcus@btinternet.com
Children minimum age: 8
SB £18 DB £40 HBS £27 HBD £58

How to get there: Down main street, left after
Spar shop on right. We are opposite tennis courts.

Carmarthen, Carmarthenshire

Capel Dewi Uchaf Country House

♦♦♦♦

Capel Dewi, Carmarthen, Carmarthenshire,
SA32 8AY
Tel: 01267 290799 Fax: 01267 290003
Email: uchaffarm@aol.com
Web: www.visit-carmarthenshire.co.uk/capel-dewi

Your stay with us is our pleasure. Enjoy a
relaxed and homely atmosphere with comfort
and good honest local fare, in a delightful
setting.
CC: MC Vi Swi

How to get there: M4 J-4. A48 to exit for
National Botanic Garden. B4310 to B4300, left.
Capel Dewi is ³/₄ mile on right.

Chepstow, Gwent

Beaufort, Chepstow

★★

Beaufort Square, Chepstow, Gwent, NP6 5EP
Tel: 01291 622497 Fax: 01291 627389
Email: info@beauforthotelchepstow.com
Web: www.beauforthotelchepstow.com
SB £49.50 DB £64.50 B £4 L £6 D £10.
CC: MC Vi Am DC Swi Delt

How to get there: Exit M48 after Old Severn
Bridge. A48 to lights. Left, and left again. Hotel
on right.

Colwyn Bay, Conwy

Hopeside

★★★

63 Princes Drive, Colwyn Bay, Conwy,
LL29 8PW
Tel: 01492 533244 Fax: 01492 532850

Norfolk House

★★★

Princes Drive, Colwyn Bay, Conwy, LL29 9PF
Tel: 01492 531757 Fax: 01492 533781

Quality Hotel Colwyn Bay

★★

Penmaenhead, Old Colwyn, Colwyn Bay,
Conwy, LL29 9LD
Tel: 01492 516555 Fax: 01492 515565
Email: colwynbayhotel@cwcom.net

On a cliff top overlooking the majestic sweep
of the bay, this splendid hotel offers a very high
standard of comfort and service. The Horizon
Restaurant serves excellent cuisine complemented by panoramic views. Conference facilities
up to 200.
SB £45 DB £59.50 HBS £55 HBD £90
B £7.50 L £4 D £15. CC: MC Vi Am DC Swi Delt

How to get there: Leave A55 at Llandulas exit,
follow A547 towards Old Colwyn.

Plas Rhos

♦♦♦♦♦

53 Cayley Promenade, Rhos-On-Sea,
Colwyn Bay, Conwy, LL28 4EP
Tel: 01492 543698

Whitehall

♦♦♦♦

Cayley Promenade, Rhos-on-Sea, Colwyn Bay,
Conwy, LL28 4EP
Tel: 01492 547296

Wales

Guide dogs   RaC

If a Hotel or Guest Accommodation
does not display this 'dogs welcome'
symbol in its listing, the hotelier may
still be happy to welcome guests with guide
dogs, and you should contact the property to
discover whether this will be a problem.

Northwood

♦♦♦

47 Rhos Road, Rhos-On-Sea, Colwyn Bay,
Conwy, LL28 4RS
Tel: 01492 549931
Email: mail@northwoodhotel.co.uk
Web: www.northwoodhotel.co.uk
SB £23 DB £46 HBS £31 HBD £62 B £6 L £5 D
£10. CC: MC Vi Am Swi Delt

How to get there: Opposite Tourist Information
Centre, 150yds up Rhos Road.

Rosehill Manor

♦♦♦

Queens Avenue, Colwyn Bay, Conwy, LL29 7BE
Tel: 01492 532993
Email: rosehill.manor@virgin.net
Children minimum age: 12
SB £25 DB £58

How to get there: West end of Colwyn Bay
immediately to the rear of Rydal School.

Conwy, Conwy

Old Rectory Country House

★★

Llanwrst Road, Llansanffraid Glan Conwy,
Conwy, LL28 5LF
Tel: 01492 580611 Fax: 01492 584555

Tir-y-Coed Country House

★★

Rowen, Conwy, LL32 8TP
Tel: 01492 650219 Fax: 01492 650219
Email: tirycoed@btinternet.com
Web: www.mkworld.net/tirycoed.htm
Closed November to February

Relax in a picturesque Snowdonia National Park
village amidst majestic scenery. Four miles from
the historic town of Conwy, within easy reach of
mountains, coast, castles and stately homes.

SB £28.25 DB £26.25 HBS £42.25 HBD £40.25
D £14.

How to get there: From B5106, take signposted
turning to Rowen (unclassified road). Hotel is on
fringe of village, about 60yds north of Post Office.

Sychnant Pass House

♦♦♦♦♦

Sychnant Pass Road, Conwy, LL32 8BJ
Tel: 01492 596868 Fax: 01492 596868
Email: bresykes@sychnant-pass-house.co.uk
Web: www.sychnant-pass-house.co.uk

Our country home is set in 2½ acres of natural
garden, surrounded by National Park land.
Large sitting rooms with log fires and comfy
sofas. See you soon!
SB £45 DB £60 HBS £60 HBD £90
L £10.95 D £15. CC: MC Vi Swi Delt

How to get there: Second left past visitors'
centre (Gate Street), proceed up hill for 2 miles.

Cowbridge, South Glamorgan

Bear

★★★

High Street, Cowbridge, South Glamorgan,
CF7 2AF
Tel: 01446 774814 Fax: 01446 775425

Criccieth, Gwynedd

Bron Eifion Country House

★★★

Criccieth, Gwynedd, LL52 0SA
Tel: 01766 522385 Fax: 01766 522003
Email: broneifion@criccieth.co.uk
Web: www.criccieth.co.uk/broneifion

A magnificent Baronial Mansion set in five acres
of glorious gardens and woodlands. Close to
the rugged mountains of Snowdonia. Friendly

service, fresh cuisine and a well-stocked wine cellar.
DB £71 B £10.50 L £11.95 D £21.95.
CC: MC Vi Am Swi Delt

🖼️🐾♨️💻☎️🚸🕯️🐴♬🛏️ 👥 👤👤

How to get there: On right ½ mile west on A497.

Lion
★★
Y Maes, Criccieth, Gwynedd, LL52 0AA
Tel: 01766 522460 Fax: 01766 523075

Gly-y-Coed
♦♦♦♦
Portmadoc Road, Criccieth, Gwynedd, LL52 0HL
Tel: 01766 522870 Fax: 01766 523341
Closed Christmas to New Year
SB £23 DB £46 HBS £33 HBD £66 D £10.
CC: MC Vi Am

♿🖼️🐴♨️♬💻☎️🅿️🚸🕯️🐴♬🐴🛏️👤👤👤

How to get there: Right side A497 facing sea.

Min-y-Gaer
♦♦♦♦
Porthmadog Road, Criccieth, Gwynedd, LL52 0HP
Tel: 01766 522151 Fax: 01766 523640
Email: info@minygaerhotel.co.uk
Web: www.minygaerhotel.co.uk
Closed November to February

A pleasant licensed hotel with delightful views of scenic coastline. Comfortable, non-smoking

bedrooms with colour TV and beverage facilities. An ideal base for touring Snowdonia. Car parking.
SB £22 DB £44
CC: MC Vi Am Delt

🖼️♨️♬💻🅿️🚸🕯️🐴♬🐴♬ 👤

How to get there: On A497 close to town centre, 300yds east of junction with B4411.

Crickhowell, Powys

Gliffaes Country House
★★★ 🦌🦌
Crickhowell, Powys, NP8 1RH
Tel: 01874 730371 Fax: 01874 730463
Email: calls@gliffaeshotel.com
Web: www.gliffaeshotel.com

A comfortable country house, spectacularly situated in 33 acres of magnificent grounds overlooking the River Usk. Fishing, relaxed atmosphere, imaginative menus and stunning walks.
SB £53 DB £112 HBS £77.50 HBD £56.15
CC: MC Vi Am DC

🔔♨️💻☎️🗝️🅿️👥👤👤 🍷🎣🔍🐟

Cwmbran, Gwent

The Parkway
★★★★
Cwmbrian Drive, Cwmbran, Gwent, NP44 3UW
Tel: 01633 871199 Fax: 01633 069160
SB £103.10 DB £124.65 HBS £119.80
HBD £158 B £9.40 L £9.45 D £17.95.
CC: MC Vi Am DC Swi Delt Solo

🔔♿🖼️🐾♨️♬💻☎️🗝️🅿️🚸🕯️🐴♬
👥 SPA 🍸✂️

How to get there: M4 J-25A (west), A4042. Take first exit at roundabout onto A4051. Take third exit at next roundabout, and then next right.
See advert on following page

Deganwy, Gwynedd

Deganwy Castle

★★

Station Road, Deganwy, Gwynedd, LL31 9DA
Tel: 01492 583555 Fax: 01492 583555
SB £35 DB £70 HBS £48 HBD £96
B £8 L £9.50 D £10. CC: MC Vi Am DC Swi Delt

How to get there: A55 from Chester until you reach Deganwy. Turn off approximately 40 miles from Chester.

Denbigh, Denbighshire

Cayo Guest House

◆◆◆

74 Vale Street, Denbigh, Denbighshire, LL16 3BW
Tel: 01745 812686
SB £19 DB £38 CC: MC Vi Am DC Swi Delt

How to get there: A525, follow signs to Denbigh. At traffic lights turn up hill into town. Look for supermarket on right. Hotel is a little way up on left.

The Parkway Hotel

Luxury 4-star hotel, designed and developed on a Mediterranean theme. The hotel boasts 70 ensuite bedrooms and extensive leisure facilities including a 15m level deck swimming pool, spa bath, sauna, steam room, solarium and gymnasium. 20 minutes from Cardiff and Bristol. Nearby attractions include Brecon Beacons and Wye Valley.

Cwmbrian Drive, Cwmbran, Gwent
NP44 3UW
Tel: 01633 871199   Fax: 01633 869160

Devils Bridge, Ceredigion

Hafod Arms

★★

Devil's Bridge, Aberystwyth, Ceredigion, SY23 3JL
Tel: 01970 890232 Fax: 01970 890394
Email: enquiries@hafodarms.co.uk
Web: www.hafodarms.co.uk
Children minimum age: 10
Closed December 15 to January 15
SB £35 DB £55 HBS £50 HBD £85 D £15.
CC: MC Vi Swi

How to get there: From Aberystwyth A4120 for 11 miles. From Llangurig, A44. Turn off left at Ponterwyd onto the A4120. Hotel 5 miles.

Dolgellau, Gwynedd

George III

★★

Penmaenpool, Dolgellau, Gwynedd, LL40 1YD
Tel: 01341 422525 Fax: 01341 423565
Email: reception@george-3rd.co.uk
Web: www.george-3rd.co.uk
SB £55 DB £94 B £7.50 L £12.95 D £25.
CC: MC Vi Swi Delt

How to get there: Left off A470 signs Tywyn, after approximately 2 miles turn right for Toll Bridge, then first left for hotel.

Royal Ship

★

Queen's Square, Dolgellau, Gwynedd, LL40 1AR
Tel: 01341 422209
SB £35 DB £60 B £4.50 L £5.95 D £9.95.
CC: MC Vi Swi

How to get there: Situated in town centre.

Clifton House

◆◆◆

Smithfield Square, Dolgellau, Gwynedd, LL40 1ES
Tel: 01341 422554 Fax: 01341 423580
Email: pauline@clifton-hotel.freeserve.co.uk
Web: www.clifton-hotel.freeserve.co.uk
Closed November
SB £36 DB £46 HBS £51 HBD £38 D £15.
CC: MC Vi Swi Delt

How to get there: Follow one way system right around to come up street facing hotel.

Fronoleu Farm

Tabor, Dolgellau, Gwynedd, LL40 2PS
Tel: 01341 422361 Fax: 01341 422023
SB £36.50 DB £56.50 B £6.50 L £6.45 D £8.45.
CC: MC Vi Swi

How to get there: From Dolgellau town centre,
follow road past hospital. Proceed up hill.
Follow Restaurant sign.

Fishguard, Dyfed

Fishguard Bay

★★★
Quay Road, Goodwick, Fishguard, Dyfed,
SA64 0BT
Tel: 01348 873571 Fax: 01348 873030
Email: mhar177485@aol.com
SB £45 DB £37.50 HBS £50 HBD £45
B £5 L £5 D £16. CC: MC Vi Am DC Swi Delt

How to get there: A40 from Haverfordwest to
Fishguard, follow signs for Ferry port. Proceed
straight over small roundabout, over railway
bridge and hotel is on right.

Abergwaun

★
Market Square, Fishguard, SA65 9HA
Tel: 01348 872077 Fax: 01348 875412
Web: www.abergwaun.com
SB £39.50 DB £58 B £4.50 L £6 D £6.
CC: MC Vi Am DC Swi Delt

How to get there: In the centre of Fishguard on
the A40/A487.

Harlech, Gwynedd

Castle Cottage

♦♦♦♦
Harlech, Gwynedd, LL46 2YL
Tel: 01766 780479 Fax: 01766 780479
Closed February
SB £29 DB £61 D £24. CC: MC Vi Swi Delt

How to get there: Just off Harlech High Street,
behind the Castle.

Haverfordwest, Dyfed

Hotel Mariners

★★
Mariner's Square, Haverfordwest, Dyfed,
SA61 2DU
Tel: 01437 763353 Fax: 01437 764258
SB £52.50 DB £72.50 D £17.
CC: MC Vi Am DC Swi Delt

How to get there: At town centre, up High Steet,
first right, Dark Street, leads to Mariners Square.

Wolfcastle Country

★★
Wolfcastle, Haverfordwest, Dyfed, SA62 5LZ
Tel: 01437 741688 Fax: 01437 741383
Email: andy741255@aol.com
Closed Christmas

In village of Wolf's Castle, equidistant from
Fishguard and Haverfordwest. Ideal location for
exploring Pembrokeshire National Park and
beaches. Conference facilities and 20 ensuite
bedrooms.
SB £43 DB £77 HBS £65 HBD £106
B £7 L £10 D £16. CC: MC Vi Am Swi Delt JCB

How to get there: On A40 6 miles from
Haverfordwest.

Holyhead, Anglesey

Anchorage

★★★
Four Mile Bridge, Holyhead, Anglesey, LL65 2EZ
Tel: 01407 740168 Fax: 01407 741599
Email: drylance@aol.com
Web: www.the-anchorage-hotel.co.uk
SB £50 DB £79.50 B £7 L £5 D £13.
CC: MC Vi Am Swi Delt

How to get there: A55 across Anglesey. Turn off,
head for Valley. Left at lights for Trearddur Bay.
Hotel is on left about 1½ miles from Valley.

Wales

HOLYHEAD

Superior ensuite bedrooms — Bars open and food served all day

The Bull Hotel
London Road, Valley
Holyhead
Isle of Anglesey

Tel: 01407 740351
Fax: 01407 342328

★★

The Valley Hotel
London Road, Valley
Holyhead
Isle of Anglesey

Tel: 01407 740203
Fax: 01407 740686

♦♦♦

Email: reservations@valley-hotel-anglesey.co.uk   Website: www.valley-hotel-anglesey.co.uk

Situated on the A5 (which runs parallel to A55) at Valley and only 4 miles from the ferry. Turn off at the last junction before Holyhead or, if arriving, at the first (or take A5 when leaving the port).

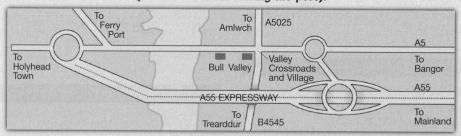

Restaurant open every evening and Sunday Lunchtimes at The Bull Hotel.
Private party rooms available by prior arrangement at The Valley.

Superior ensuite bedrooms with TV, tea/coffee makers, hair dryers, telephone.
Sheltered beer garden with play equipment.

Excellent base for touring Anglesey's magnificent sandy coves and beaches, touring North Wales, Bird Watching (nearby Bird Sanctuaries), golf, sailing, fresh and sea water fishing.

Bull

★★

London Road, Valley, Holyhead,
Isle of Anglesey, LL65 3DP
Tel: 01407 740351 Fax: 01407 742328
Email: reservations@valley-hotel-anglesey.co.uk
Web: www.valley-hotel-anglesey.co.uk
SB £37.50 DB £49.50 B £4.95 D £7.50.
CC: MC Vi Am Swi Delt

How to get there: On A5 3½ miles from
Holyhead at Valley (200 yards through traffic
lights). Exit for Valley from new motorway A55.
See advert on facing page

Valley

♦♦♦

London Road, Valley, Holyhead,
Isle of Anglesey, LL65 3DU
Tel: 01407 740203 Fax: 01407 740686
Email: reservations@valley-hotel-anglesey.co.uk
Web: www.valley-hotel-anglesey.co.uk
SB £37.50 DB £49.50 B £4.95 D £7.50.
CC: MC Vi Am Swi Delt

How to get there: From Holyhead, A5 signs for
Valley (not A55). At traffic lights at Valley.
See advert on facing page

Knighton, Powys

Knighton

★★★

Broad Street, Knighton, Powys, LD7 1BL
Tel: 01547 520530 Fax: 01547 520529
Email: knightonhotel@freeuk.com
Children minimum age: 12
SB £45 DB £65 HBS £61.50 HBD £98
B £7 L £12.50 D £16.50. CC: MC Vi Am Swi

How to get there: A4113 off A49 at Ludlow on
A388 or Shrewsbury-Llandrindod Wells road.
See advert on the right.

Lampeter, Ceredigion

Falcondale Country House

★★★

Falcondale Drive, Lampeter, Ceredigion,
SA43 7RX
Tel: 01570 422910 Fax: 01570 423559
Web: www.falcondalehotel.com
Closed late January
SB £60 DB £90 HBS £79 HBD £128
B £5.95 L £2.75 D £21. CC: MC Vi Swi Delt

How to get there: Hotel 500 yards west of Lampeter centre on A475, or 1 mile northwest on A482.
See advert on following page

Llanbedr, Gwynedd

Ty Mawr

★★

Llanbedr, Gwynedd, LL45 2NH
Tel: 01341 241440 Fax: 01341 241440

Friendly, family-run country house hotel and
pub, close to coast and mountains of
Snowdonia. Ten ensuite bedrooms. Relaxing

Wales

lounge and welcoming bar, with good local atmosphere. Restaurant serving homemade dishes. Log fires, CAMRA real ale. Lovely terrace and gardens with Bar-B-Q.
SB £37 DB £60 HBS £47 HBD £70
B £5 L £5 D £10. CC: MC Vi Swi Delt
🎣 🐴 🕭 🍵 🖳 🖵 P ⚿ ⍟ 🐎 🚶 🐾 ♨ ⛄ 🚹 ⚕
How to get there: From Barmouth on A496, turn right after bridge. Ty-Mawr is 100 yards on left.

Victoria Inn
♦♦♦♦   🍴 ✁
Llanbedr, Gwynedd, LL45 2LD
Tel: 01341 241213 Fax: 01341 241644
Email: brewery@frederic-robinson.co.uk
Web: www.frederic-robinson.com
SB £31.50 DB £61 B £6 L £4
CC: MC Vi Swi Delt
🐴 🕭 🍵 🖳 P ⚿ ⍟ 🐎 🚶 🐾 ⛄ 🚹
How to get there: Centre of Llanbedr on A496.

Llanberis, Gwynedd

Lake View
★★
Tan-y-Pant, Llanberis, Gwynedd, LL55 4EL
Tel: 01286 870422 Fax: 01286 872591

Falcondale
Country House Hotel

The Listed Italianate Mansion is set in 14 acres of the Teifi Valley with spectacular rural views. The family run hotel offers the highest levels of cuisine and prides itself on its friendly family atmosphere. Cycling, walking, fishing, golf, or just plain relaxation are all on offer.

Lampeter, Dyfed SA43 7RX
Tel: 01570 422910   Fax: 01570 423559
Website: www.falcondalehotel.com

Llandrindod Wells, Powys

Severn Arms
★★
Penybont, Llandrindod Wells, Powys, LD1 5UA
Tel: 01597 851224 Fax: 01597 851693
SB £28 DB £50
B £3.95 L £4.70 D £13.90.
CC: MC Vi Swi
🐴 🕭 🖳 🖵 ☎ P ⚿ ⍟ 🐎 🚶 🐾 🚹 🕯 ✁
How to get there: A488/A44 junction in Penybont, east of Llandrindod Wells.

Guidfa House
♦♦♦♦   🍴 ✁
Cross Gates, Llandrindod Wells, Powys, LD1 6RF
Tel: 01597 851241 Fax: 01597 851875
Email: guidfa@globalnet.co.uk
Web: www.guidfa-house.co.uk
Children minimum age: 10

Stylish Georgian house with an enviable reputation for its comfort, good food and service. Set in the very heart of Wales, offering an excellent base for touring both Wales and the Borders.
SB £31.50 DB £53 HBS £49 HBD £88 D £17.50.
CC: MC Vi Delt
🕭 🍵 🖳 P ⚿ ⍟ 🐎 🚶 🐾 🍴
How to get there: Centre of village of Crossgates, where A44 Kington to Rhayader road crosses A483 Builth Wells to Newtown road.

Three Wells Farm
♦♦♦♦   🍴 ✁
Chapel Road, Howey, Llandrindod Wells, Powys, LD1 5PB
Tel: 01597 824427 Fax: 01597 822484

Kincoed
♦♦
Temple Street, Llandrindod Wells, Powys, LD1 5HF
Tel: 01597 822656 Fax: 01597 824660

Llandudno, Conwy

Bodysgallen Hall

★★★ ♖♖♖♖

Llandudno, LL30 1RS

Tel: 01492 584466 Fax: 01492 582519

Email: info@bodysgallen.com

Web: www.bodysgallen.com

Children minimum age: 8

SB £123.50 DB £180 HBS £110 HBD £110

B £10.50 L £15.50 D £34. CC: MC Vi Swi Delt

♿ ⛟ ⊗ ⊜ ⌨ ☎ 🅿 ⚶ ⛦ 🐎 ♫ ❦ 🕿 ♨♨♨ ♨♨

SPA 🍸 🔍 🎵

How to get there: A55 to A470, towards
Llandudno. Hotel is 2 miles on the right.

Imperial

★★★ ♖

Vaughan Street, Llandudno, Conwy, LL30 1AP

Tel: 01492 877466 Fax: 01492 878043

The Risboro

★★★

Clement Avenue, Llandudno, Conwy, LL30 2ED

Tel: 01492 876343 Fax: 01492 879881

Ambassador

★★

Grand Promenade, Llandudno, LL30 2NR

Tel: 01492 876886 Fax: 01492 876347

SB £30 DB £55 HBS £45 HBD £85

B £8.25 L £6 D £14. CC: MC Vi Am Swi

♿ ♨♨ ⊜ ⌨ 🅿 ⚶ ⛦ 🐎 ♫ ❦ ♨♨♨ ♨♨

How to get there: A55 to A470, turn to
Promenade. Turn left at Promenade junction.
Hotel approximately 200 yds from pier.

Banham House

★★

2 St David's Road, Llandudno, LL30 2UL

Tel: 01492 875680 Fax: 01492 875680

SB £30 DB £48 HBS £41 HBD £71

B £4.50 L £11.50 D £11.50.

⊗ ⊜ ⌨ 🅿 ⚶ ⛦ 🐎 ♫ ❦ ♨♨ ♨

How to get there: From rail station, turn left. At
traffic lights, turn left again into Trinity Avenue.
Proceed until you reach St David's Road. Hotel
is at bottom left.

Belle Vue

★★

26 North Parade, Llandudno, LL30 2LP

Tel: 01492 879547 Fax: 01492 870001

SB £36 DB £62 HBS £48 HBD £86

L £2 D £12. CC: MC Vi Swi Delt

♨♨ ⛟ ⚓ ⊗ ⊜ ⌨ ☎ 🅿 ⚶ ⛦ 🐎 ♫ ❦ ♨♨ ♨

How to get there: A55 then A470 to Llandudno
onto seafront. Belle Vue at end near pier.

Branksome

★★

62/64 Lloyd Street, Llandudno, Conwy,
LL30 2YP

Tel: 01492 875989 Fax: 01492 875989

Dunoon

★★ ♖

Gloddaeth Street, Llandudno, Conwy,
LL30 2DW

Tel: 01492 860787 Fax: 01492 860031

Epperstone

★★

15 Abbey Road, Llandudno, Conwy, LL30 2EE

Tel: 01492 878746 Fax: 01492 871223

Small, select hotel, with car park, in award-
winning gardens. Spacious, comfortable rooms
portraying Edwardian elegance. Bedrooms
ensuite with excellent accessories. Convenient,
level walking. All amenities.

SB £28 DB £56 HBS £39 HBD £78

B £6.50 L £7.50 D £14. CC: MC Vi Am Swi Delt

♿ ⛟ ⚓ ⊗ ⊜ ⌨ ☎ 🅿 ⚶ ⛦ 🐎 ♫ ❦ ♨ ♨

How to get there: Corner of York and Abbey roads.

Esplanade

★★

Central Promenade, Llandudno, LL30 2LL

Tel: 01492 860300 Fax: 01492 860418

Email: info@esplanadehotel.co.uk

Web: www.esplanadehotel.co.uk

SB £20 DB £20 HBS £30 HBD £30

B £5 L £2 D £10. CC: MC Vi Am DC Swi Delt

♨♨ ⚓ ⊜ ⌨ ☎ 🅿 ⚶ ⛦ 🐎 ♫ ❦ ♨♨♨ ♨♨

How to get there: From A55 A470 to Llandudno.
To Promenade, towards pier. Esplanade on left.

Wales

Headlands

★★
Hill Terrace, Llandudno, LL30 2LS
Tel: 01492 877485
Children minimum age: 5
Closed January to February
SB £31 DB £62 HBS £40 HBD £80
🗺 🐕 🫖 💻 ☎ 🅿 ⚜ 🎠 🏇 🎠 ♨ ⚓

Marlborough

★★
South Parade, Llandudno, LL30 2LN
Tel: 01492 875846 Fax: 01492 876529
Email: nick@marlborough911.freeserve.co.uk
Web: www.northwales.uk.com
SB £22 DB £44 HBS £36 HBD £72
B £6 L £5 D £10.
CC: MC Vi Swi Delt
⬆ 🫖 💻 🅿 ⚜ 🎠 🏇 🎠 ⚓ 👥 🍷
How to get there: A55, A470 to Llandudno, to
Promenade, to pier, hotel left at pier T-junction.

Royal

★★
Church Walks, Llandudno, Conwy, LL30 2HW
Tel: 01492 876476 Fax: 01492 870210

St. Tudno Hotel

Without doubt one of the finest seaside
hotels on the coast of Britain, having
won a host of awards for excellence.
Elegantly and lovingly furnished, offering
the best in service and hospitality.
The Garden Room has a reputation as
one of the best restaurants in Wales.
Winner – Wine Award for Wales.
Lift. Car Park.

Promenade, Llandudno LL30 2LP
Tel: 01492 874411 Fax: 01492 860407
Email: sttudnohotel@btinternet.com
Website: www.st-tudno.co.uk

Sandringham

★★
West Parade, West Shore, Llandudno,
LL30 2BD
Tel: 01492 876513 Fax: 01492 872753
Email: sandringham@which.net
Web: sandringhamhotel-llandudno.co.uk
SB £34 DB £60 HBS £45 HBD £80
B £5 L £4.50 D £14.
CC: MC Vi Swi Delt
🫖 💻 ☎ 🅿 ⚜ 🎠 🏇 🎠 ⚓ 👥 👥
How to get there: A470 to Llandudno centre.
Left at Woolworths. Down dual carriageway
to seafront at West Shore. Hotel on left
corner.

Somerset

★★
Central Promenade, Llandudno, LL30 2LF
Tel: 01492 876540 Fax: 01492 863700
Email: favroy@somerset.freeserve.co.uk
Closed January to February
SB £39 DB £78 HBS £49 HBD £98
B £8.50 L £9.95 D £17.50.
CC: MC Vi Swi
⬆ 🐕 🫖 💻 ☎ 🅿 ⚜ 🎠 🏇 🎠 ⚓ 🍷
🎦 ♿

St Tudno

★★ 🏵 🏵 🏵
Promenade, Llandudno, LL30 2LP
Tel: 01492 874411 Fax: 01492 860407
Email: sttudnohotel@btinternet.com
Web: www.st-tudno.co.uk
SB £78 DB £95 HBS £113 HBD £82.50
B £15 L £13 D £25.
CC: MC Vi Am DC Swi Delt JCB
⬆ 🗺 🐕 ⊗ 🫖 💻 ☎ 📞 🅿 ⚜ 🎠 🏇 🎠 ⚓ 👥
🍷 🍾 🎦
How to get there: Opposite pier on
Promenade.
See advert on the left

Min-y-don

★
North Parade, Llandudno, LL30 2LP
Tel: 01492 876511 Fax: 01492 878169
Closed November to February
SB £25 DB £48 HBS £30 HBD £58
B £4.50 D £8.
CC: MC Vi Swi Delt
♿ 🫖 💻 🅿 ⚜ 🎠 🏇 🎠 ⚓ 🍷
How to get there: From Chester follow A55 to
Conwy and exit at Llandudno junction, taking
A470. Drive through Martyn Street onto
Promenade. Hotel is on North Parade opposite
the pier entrance.

Warwick

 ★

56 Church Walks, Llandudno, Conwy, LL30 2HL
Tel: 01492 876823

Lighthouse Little Gem

◆◆◆◆◆

Marine Drive, Great Orme's Head, Llandudno, LL30 2XD
Tel: 01492 876819 Fax: 01492 876668
Email: enquiries@lighthouse-llandudno.co.uk
Web: www.lighthouse-llandudno.co.uk
SB £70 DB £110 B £9 CC: MC Vi Swi

How to get there: Find Promenade. Enter Great Orme Scenic Route (Marine Drive). The Lighthouse is 2 miles on the right.

Carmel Private

◆◆◆◆

17 Craig-Y-Don Parade, Promenade, Llandudno, LL30 1BG
Tel: 01492 877643
Children minimum age: 4
Closed November to Easter
SB £16 DB £32 HBS £26 HBD £52

How to get there: A470 into Llandudno. By Links Hotel right at roundabout for the north. At second roundabout turn right. Hotel is on the right-hand side, overlooking the bay.

St Hilary

◆◆◆◆   🖎

Craig Y Don Parade, Promenade, Llandudno, LL30 1BG
Tel: 01492 875551 Fax: 01492 877538
Email: info@sthilaryhotel.co.uk
Web: www.sthilaryhotel.co.uk
Closed December to January
SB £22.5 DB £33 CC: MC Vi Am Swi Delt JCB
How to get there: On the Promenade, just 500yds from North Wales Theatre, towards Little Orme.

Cedar Lodge Guest House

◆◆◆

7 Deganwy Avenue, Llandudno, LL30 2YB
Tel: 01492 873330
Closed November to March
SB £25 DB £38 HBS £32 HBD £56
CC: MC Vi Swi
How to get there: From Promenade, turn left at St George's Hotel into Lloyd Street. Deganwy Avenue is then the third road on right. Cedar Lodge is on the right.

Hollybank Guest House

◆◆◆

9 St David's Place, Llandudno, Conwy, LL30 2UG
Tel: 01492 878521 Fax: 0870 0549854
Email: mike@hollybank-gh.demon.co.uk
SB £25 DB £21 HBS £35 HBD £31 B £4 D £10.

How to get there: From station, left at lights into Trinity Avenue. Third right into St David's Road and first right into St David's Place.

Minion

◆◆◆

21-23 Carmen Sylva, Llandudno, LL30 1EQ
Tel: 01492 877740
Children minimum age: 3
Closed November to March
SB £18 DB £36 HBS £27 HBD £54

Rosaire

◆◆◆

2 St Seiriols Road, Llandudno, LL30 2YY
Tel: 01492 877677
Closed November
SB £15.50 DB £16.50 HBS £22.50 HBD £24

Rosedene

◆◆◆   🖎

10 Arvon Avenue, Llandudno, Conwy, LL30 2DY
Tel: 01492 876491

Karden House

◆

16 Charlton Street, Llandudno, LL30 2AN
Tel: 01492 879347
SB £15 DB £30 HBS £21 HBD £42

How to get there: From station head for sea front, left after 300 yds to Charlton St. Hotel on left.

Llanelli, Dyfed

Hotel Miramar

★★

158 Station Rd, Llanelli, Carmarthenshire, SA15 1YH
Tel: 01554 773607 Fax: 01554 772454
Email: hotel-miramar@lineone.net
SB £24 DB £40 L £8.50 D £8.50.
CC: MC Vi Am DC Swi Delt

How to get there: M4 J48 to Llanelli. Hotel is adjacent to Llanelli railway station.

Wales

Southmead Guest House

♦♦

72 Queen Victoria Road, Llanelli,
Carmarthenshire, SA15 2TH
Tel: 01554 758588
SB £17 DB £30

How to get there: From Llanelli, head down side
of large theatre/cinema. House is 200yds on right.

Llanfairpwllgwyngyll, Gwynedd

Carreg Bran

★★★

Church Lane, Llanfairpwllgwyngyll, Gwynedd,
LL61 5YH
Tel: 01248 714224 Fax: 01248 715983

Llangammarch Wells, Powys

Lake Country House

★★★ ℞ ℞
Llangammarch Wells, Powys, LD4 4BS
Tel: 01591 620202 Fax: 01591 620457
Email: info@lakecountryhouse.co.uk
Web: www.lakecountryhouse.co.uk
SB £95 DB £135 HBS £125 HBD £195
B £10.50 L £17.50 D £30.
CC: MC Vi Am DC Swi Delt

How to get there: From Builth Wells west on
A483 six miles Garth. Hotel clearly signposted.

Llangollen, Clwyd

Bryn Howel

★★★ ℞
Llangollen, Clwyd, LL20 7UW
Tel: 01978 860331 Fax: 01978 860119

Hand

★★

Bridge Street, Llangollen, LL20 8PL
Tel: 01978 860303 Fax: 01978 861277
SB £25.00 DB £45 HBS £35 HBD £60 B £5.50
L £8.5 D £14.95. CC: MC Vi Am DC Swi Delt JCB

How to get there: From south A5 to Llangollen.
In Llangollen second right after Kwik Save.
From north A539 to Llangollen. Left over bridge,
left at lights. Second turn on left.

Tyn-y-Wern

★★

Maes Mawr Road, Llangollen, Clwyd, LL20 7PH
Tel: 01978 860252 Fax: 01978 860252
SB £32 DB £48
B £5 L £3.50 D £3.50.
CC: MC Vi Am DC Swi

How to get there: On A5 ½ mile east of centre.

West Arms

★★ ℞
Llanarmon-Dyffryn-Ceiriog, Llangollen,
LL20 7LD
Tel: 01691 600665 Fax: 01691 600622
Email: gowestarms@aol.com
Web: www.hotelwalesuk.com
SB £51.15 DB £91.30 HBS £70.95
HBD £130.90
B £8.95 L £15 D £21.90.
CC: MC Vi Swi

How to get there: Cross bridge, hotel on right.

Llanwddyn, Powys

Lake Vyrnwy

★★★ ℞
Llanwddyn, SY10 0LY
Tel: 01691 73692 Fax: 01691 73259
Email: res@lakevyrnwy.com
Web: www.lakevyrnwy.com
SB £80 DB £110 HBS £108 HBD £83
CC: MC Vi Am DC Swi Delt

How to get there: From Shrewsbury, A458 to
Welshpool, right onto B4393 just after Ford
(signposted to Lake Vyrnwy 28 miles).

Llanwrtyd Wells, Powys

Neuadd Arms

★

Llanwrtyd Wells, Powys, LD5 4RB
Tel: 01591 610236

Machynlleth, Powys

Ynyshir Hall

★★★ ℞ ℞ ℞ ℞
Machynlleth, Powys, SY20 8TA
Tel: 01654 781209 Fax: 01654 781366

Wynnstay

★★ ℞

Heol Maengwyn, Machynlleth, Powys,
SY20 8AE
Tel: 01654 702941 Fax: 01654 703884
Email: info@wynnstay-hotel.com
Web: www.wynnstay-hotel.com

Enjoy award winning chef Gareth Johns's
imaginative menus at this superb 18th-century
former coaching inn in the heart of the historic
market town. 23 well-appointed rooms, log fires,
all rooms ensuite.
SB £45 DB £70 HBS £57 HBD £48
B £5.50 L £6 D £14.95.
CC: MC Vi Am DC Swi Delt

Manorbier, Dyfed

Castlemead

★★ ℞

Manorbier, Dyfed, SA70 7TA
Tel: 01834 871358 Fax: 01834 871358
Email: castlemeadhot@aol.com
Web: www.castlemeadhotel.co.uk
SB £33 DB £60 HBS £45 HBD £90 D £13.
CC: MC Vi Swi Delt

How to get there: Bottom of village, above
beach. Car park on left.

Menai Bridge, Gwynedd

Gazelle

★

Glyn Garth, Menai Bridge, Gwynedd, LL59 5PD
Tel: 01248 713364 Fax: 01248 713167

Please mention the RAC Inspected guide
when you make your booking at an RAC
Hotel or Guest Accommodation.

Merthyr Tydfil, Mid Glamorgan

Castle

★★★

Castle Street, Merthyr Tydfil, CF47 8BG
Tel: 01685 386868 Fax: 01685 383898
Email: castlehotel.merthyrtydfil@virgin.net
SB £49 DB £63 HBS £55 HBD £38
B £4.95 L £4.95 D £8.95. CC: MC Vi Swi Delt

How to get there: Exit A470 at Merthyr junction
to centre. Hotel by Civic Centre and Law Courts
– a prominent five-storey building.

Tredegar Arms

♦ ♦

66 High Street, Dowlais Top, Merthyr Tydfil,
Mid Glamorgan, CF48 3PW
Tel: 01685 377467 Fax: 01685 377467

Milford Haven, Dyfed

Lord Nelson

★★

Hamilton Terrace, Milford Haven, Dyfed,
SA73 3AL
Tel: 01646 695341 Fax: 01646 694026

Belhaven House

♦ ♦

29 Hamilton Terrace, Milford Haven, Dyfed,
SA73 3JJ
Tel: 01646 695983 Fax: 01646 690787
Email: hbruceh@aol.com
Web: www.westwaleshotels.com
Closed December 22-29
SB £38.50 DB £50 B £5 D £5.
CC: MC Vi Am DC Swi Delt

How to get there: Opposite Cenotaph, A4076
overlooking marina. White building with red
canopy.

Mold, Clwyd

Beaufort Park

★★★

Altami Road, Mold, Flintshire, CH7 6RQ
Tel: 01352 758646 Fax: 01352 757132
SB £70 DB £85 CC: MC Vi Am DC Swi Delt

How to get there: Follow A55. Take A494
towards Mold. Second set of traffic lights on
the right.

Wales

Bryn Awel

★★

Denbigh Road, Mold, Clwyd, CH7 1BL
Tel: 01352 758622 Fax: 01352 758625

Morfa Nefyn, Gwynedd

Woodlands Hall

★★

Edern, Morfa Nefyn, Gwynedd, LL53 6JB
Tel: 01758 720425

Mumbles, Swansea

Norton House

★★★

Norton Road, Mumbles, Swansea, SA3 5TQ
Tel: 01792 404891 Fax: 01792 403210
Email: nortonhouse@btconnect.com
Children minimum age: 10

This elegant Georgian manor house is situated
¹/₂ mile from the picturesque village of Mumbles,
yet only 3 miles from the centre of Swansea.
Owned and managed by Jan and John Power.
SB £65 DB £75 D £16.50.
CC: MC Vi Am DC Swi Delt

How to get there: Norton House is off the A4067
Swansea to Mumbles. 1 mile after 'Welcome to
Mumbles' sign, turn right into Norton Road.

Coast House

♦♦♦

708 Mumbles Road, Mumbles, Swansea,
SA3 4EH
Tel: 01792 368702
Email: thecoasthouse@aol.com
SB £22 DB £42   Closed Christmas.

How to get there: M4 J-42. A283 to Swansea,
then A4067 to Mumbles Village. Coast House is
¹/₂ mile from shopping area, on right.

Narberth, Pembrokeshire

Highland Grange Farm

Robeston Wathen, Narberth, Pembrokeshire,
SA67 8EP
Tel: 01834 860952 Fax: 01834 860952
Email: info@highlandgrange.co.uk
Web: www.highlandgrange.co.uk
SB £21 DB £37 HBS £30 HBD £55

How to get there: 22 miles west of Carmarthen
on A40. Property last right before Bush Inn.
See advert on facing page bottom left

Neath, West Glamorgan

Castle

★★

The Parade, Neath, West Glamorgan, SA11 1RB
Tel: 01639 641119 Fax: 01637 641624
SB £55 DB £65 B £5.50 L £3.50 D £6.50.
CC: MC Vi Am DC Swi Delt

How to get there: Centre, 200yds past station.

New Quay, Ceredigion

Brynarfor

♦♦♦

New Road, New Quay, Ceredigion, SA45 9SB
Tel: 01545 560358 Fax: 01545 561204
Email: enquiries@brynarfor.co.uk
Web: www.brynarfor.co.uk
Closed November to February

Superb Victorian house, overlooking beaches
with panoramic views of mountains around
Cardigan Bay. You can spot our resident
dolphins. Visit our website: www.brynarfor.co.uk
D £6.50. CC: MC Vi

How to get there: A487 to Llanarth. B4342 New
Quay. Hotel left overlooking sea, before town.

Newport, Gwent

Celtic Manor Resort

★★★★★ ♕♕♕
Coldra Woods, Newport, Gwent, NP18 1HQ
Tel: 01633 413000 Fax: 01633 412910
Email: postbox@celtic-manor.com
Web: www.celtic-manor.com
B £13.95 L £17.95 D £23.
CC: MC Vi Am DC Swi Delt

How to get there: M4 J-24. At roundabout exit A48 towards Newport. Turn right after Alcatel offices.

Kings

★★★
Newport, Gwent, NP9 1QU
Tel: 01633 842020 Fax: 01633 244667
Email: kingshotel.wales@netscapeonline.co.uk
SB £72 DB £90 B £6 D £9.
CC: MC Vi Am DC Swi Delt

How to get there: M4 J-26, towards centre (A4051). At main roundabout third exit to hotel.
See advert below right

Inn At The Elm Tree

♦♦♦♦♦
St Brides, Wentlooge, Newport, NP10 8SQ
Tel: 01633 680225 Fax: 01633 681035
Email: inn@the-elmtree.freeserve.co.uk
Children minimum age: 10

Rural village close to capital. Enviable reputation for excellent cuisine. Luxury ensuite bedrooms, four-posters, waterbeds, jacuzzis – for those who appreciate the finer things in life.
SB £65 DB £75 L £5. D £7.
CC: MC Vi Am Swi Delt

How to get there: M4 at J-28. A48 to B4239. 2¹/₂ miles along to S-bend, Inn is on left.

Newtown, Powys

Elephant & Castle

★★

Broad Street, Newtown, Powys, SY16 2BQ
Tel: 01686 626271 Fax: 01686 622123
Email: info@theelephant.prestel.co.uk
Web: www.elephanthotel.co.uk
Closed Christmas
CC: MC Vi Am Swi Delt

How to get there: Turn for town centre at traffic lights by church to reach main street. The hotel is opposite the junction next to the river bridge.

Pembroke, Dyfed

Cleddau Bridge

★★★

Essex Road, Pembroke Dock, Dyfed, SA72 6UT
Tel: 01646 685961 Fax: 01646 685746

Lamphey Court

★★★ ℛ

Lamphey, Pembroke, Dyfed, SA71 5NT
Tel: 01646 672273 Fax: 01646 672480
Email: info@lampheycourt.co.uk
Web: www.lampheycourt.co.uk

An elegant Georgian mansion extensively refurbished with superb leisure centre. Ideally situated for local business area and exploring Pembrokeshire's coast with beautiful beaches. A Best Western hotel.
SB £70 DB £85 HBS £75 HBD £90
B £9.95 L £5.95 D £18.95.
CC: MC Vi Am DC Swi Delt

How to get there: M4 to Carmarthen and A477 to Pembroke. Turn left at Milton village. In Lamphey, turn at roadside hotel sign: entrance next to Lamphey Bishop's Palace.

Lamphey Hall

★★ ℛℛℛ

Lamphey, Pembroke, Dyfed, SA71 5NR
Tel: 01646 672394 Fax: 01646 672369

Wheeler's Old King's Arms

★★ ℛ

Main Street, Pembroke, Dyfed, SA7 4JS
Tel: 01646 683611 Fax: 01646 682335

Penarth, Mid Glamorgan

Glendale

♦♦♦ ℛ

10 Plymouth Road, Penarth, Mid Glamorgan, CF64 3DH
Tel: 029 20709269 Fax: 029 20709269
Web: www.infotel.co.uk

Family-run, well established, with large menu. Conveniently situated close to town centre and promenade (a 2 minute walk).
SB £52.50 DB £63.50
CC: MC Vi Am DC Swi Delt

How to get there: 1 mile A40, 2½ miles west of Crickhowell.

Port Talbot, West Glamorgan

Aberavon Beach

★★★

Neath, Port Talbot, Swansea Bay, West Glamorgan, SA12 6QP
Tel: 01639 884949 Fax: 01639 897885

Modern hotel close to M4 and 7 miles from centre of Swansea. Seafront location with views across Swansea bay. Comfortable bedrooms, elegant restaurant, full range of conference facilities.

SB £69 DB £79 HBS £74 HBD £99
B £5.50 L £8.50 D £11.
CC: MC Vi Am DC Swi Delt

How to get there: M4 J-41. A48 and follow
signs for Aberavon and Hollywood Park.

Porthcawl, Mid Glamorgan

Penoyre Guest House

♦♦♦♦
29 Mary Street, Porthcawl, CF36 3YN
Tel: 01656 784550 Fax: 01656 784550
SB £22.50 DB £45 HBS £31 HBD £62 D £8.50.
CC: MC Vi Am Swi Delt
Closed Christmas and New Year.

Porthmadog, Gwynedd

Hotel Portmeirion

★★★
Portmeirion, Gwynedd, LL48 6ET
Tel: 01766 770000 Fax: 01766 771331
Email: hotel@portmeirion-village.com
Web: www.portmeirion-village.com
Closed 3 weeks in January
SB £100 DB £140 HBS £118 HBD £88
B £10 L £11 D £33. CC: MC Vi Am DC Swi Delt

How to get there: Off A487 at Minffordd
between Penrhyndeudraeth and Porthmadog.

Rhyl, Denbighshire

Pier

♦♦♦
23 East Parade, Rhyl, Denbighshire, LL18 3AL
Tel: 01745 350280 Fax: 01745 350280
Closed December
SB £19 DB £38 HBS £26 HBD £52 D £7.

CC: MC Vi Am

Ruabon, Clwyd

Wynnstay Arms

★★
Ruabon, Clwyd, LL14 6BL
Tel: 01978 822187 Fax: 01978 820093

Ruthin, Denbighshire

Ruthin Castle

★★★
Corwen Road, Ruthin, Denbighshire, LL15 2NU
Tel: 01824 702664 Fax: 01824 705978
Email: reservations@ruthincastle.co.uk
Web: www.ruthincastle.co.uk
SB £82 DB £102 HBD £63.50 B £8 L £6.95
D £19.95. CC: MC Vi Am DC Swi

St David's, Dyfed

Warpool Court

★★★
St David's, Dyfed, SA62 6BN
Tel: 01437 720300 Fax: 01437 720676
Email: warpool@enterprise.net
Web: www.stdavids.co.uk/warpoolcourt
Closed January

Unrivalled views and large gardens. Imaginative
and creative food – fish a strong presence on
the menu. Various food awards. Close to
coastal path and sandy beaches.
SB £70 DB £122 HBS £87 HBD £156 B £8.50
L £15.50 D £37. CC: MC Vi Am DC Swi Delt

How to get there: From Cross Square, bear left,
follow hotel signs for approximately half a mile.

Wales

Old Cross

★★

Cross Square, St David's, Dyfed, SA62 6SP
Tel: 01437 720387 Fax: 01437 720394
Email: enquiries@oldcrosshotel.co.uk
Web: www.oldcrosshotel.co.uk
Closed January to February
SB £40 DB £72 HBS £55 HBD £103
B £7.50 L £4 D £18. CC: MC Vi Swi Delt
How to get there: In centre facing Cross Square.

St Non's

★★

Catherine Street, St David's, Dyfed, SA62 6RJ
Tel: 01437 720239 Fax: 01437 721839
Email: stnons@enterprise.net
Web: www.stdavids.co.uk/stnons
Closed November to December
SB £49 DB £76 HBS £71 HBD £120
B £8.50 L £4.95 D £4.95. CC: MC Vi Swi Delt
How to get there: From Cross Square, bear left
following hotel sign. After 500yds, hotel is on left.

Lochmeyler Farm

◆◆◆◆◆

Llandeloy, Pen-y-Cwm, nr Solva, St David's,
Dyfed, SA62 6LL
Tel: 01348 837724 Fax: 01348 837622
SB £20 DB £40 HBS £32.50 HBD £65
CC: MC Vi DC Swi Delt
How to get there: From Fishguard, A487
to Mathry, left to Llandeloy. From Haverfordwest
A487 to Pen-y-Cwm, right to Llandeloy.

Ramsey House

◆◆◆◆

Lower Moor, St David's, Dyfed, SA62 6RP
Tel: 01437 720321 Fax: 01437 720025
Email: ramseyho.stdavids@btinternet.com
Web: www.smoothhound.co.uk/hotels/
ramsey.htm

Mild climate and warm welcome make perfect
climate for year-round breaks. Non-smoking.
Award-winning Welsh cuisine/wines. Quiet,
convenient location for cathedral, coast,
walking, golf.
DB £54 HBD £82 D £15.
CC: MC Vi Swi Delt Connect JCB
How to get there: From centre of St Davids, left
down hill by HSBC bank, signposted Porthclais,
for 1/2 mile. Ramsey House last house on left.

Y Glennydd Guest House

◆◆◆

51 Nun Street, St David's, Dyfed, SA62 6NU
Tel: 01437 720576 Fax: 01437 720184

Saundersfoot, Dyfed

Merlewood

★★

St Brides Hill, Saundersfoot, Dyfed, SA69 9NP
Tel: 01834 812421 Fax: 01834 814886
Web: www.merlewood.co.uk
Closed November to February
SB £28 DB £50 HBS £38 HBD £70 B £5 D £10.
CC: MC Vi Swi Delt
How to get there: Hotel just out of Saundersfoot
centre, on right at top of St Bride's Hill.

Rhodewood House

★★

St Bride's Hill, Saundersfoot, Dyfed, SA69 9NU
Tel: 01834 812200 Fax: 01834 815005
Email: relax@rhodewood.co.uk
Web: www.rhodewood.co.uk
Closed January
SB £30 DB £50 HBS £40 HBD £70 B £5.95
L £5.95 D £11.95. CC: MC Vi Am DC Swi Delt
How to get there: From Carmarthen A40, A477,
B4316. Turn left. Hotel on left 1/2 mile further.

Woodlands

◆◆◆

St Brides Hill, Saundersfoot, Dyfed, SA69 9NP
Tel: 01834 813338 Fax: 01834 811480
Email: woodlands.hotel@virgin.net
Closed November to March
SB £24 DB £42 HBS £31 HBD £60
CC: MC Vi Swi Delt
How to get there: From centre of village, take
road to Tenby. 500yds up hill, hotel is on right.

Bay View

♦♦

Pleasant Valley, Stepaside, Saundersfoot,
Dyfed, SA67 8LR
Tel: 01834 813417
Closed October to March
SB £17.80 DB £38.50 HBS £22.85 HBD £48.60

How to get there: Off A477 to Stepaside.
Downhill to flats, turn left. After 50yds turn left.
¹/₂ mile on, turn left round chapel.

Swansea, West Glamorgan

Abercrave Inn

★★

145 Heol Tawe, Abercraf, Swansea, SA9 1XS
Tel: 01639 731002 Fax: 01639 730796

Beaumont Hotel

★★ 🐾

72–73 Walter Road, Swansea, SA1 4QA
Tel: 01792 643956 Fax: 01792 643044
Email: info@beaumonthotel.co.uk
Web: www.beaumonthotel.co.uk
SB £55 DB £65 HBS £70 HBD £95 D £10.
CC: MC Vi Am DC Swi Delt Eurocard

See advert on this page

Oaktree Parc

★★

Birchgrove Road, Birchgrove, Swansea, West
Glamorgan, SA7 9JR
Tel: 01792 817781 Fax: 01792 814542

St Anne's

★★

Western Lane, Mumbles, Swansea, West
Glamorgan, SA3 4EY
Tel: 01792 369147 Fax: 01792 360537
Email: enquiries@stannes-hotel.co.uk

Overlooked by Oystermouth Castle and with

spectacular views over Swansea Bay. Own
grounds, large private car park, quiet location in
the heart of Mumbles village.
SB £52 DB £69.50 HBS £65.75 HBD £48.50
L £10.95 D £13.75.
CC: MC Vi Am Swi Delt

How to get there: M4 J-42. A483 to Swansea,
then A4067 to Mumbles.
See advert on following page

Windsor Lodge

★★ 🐾

Mount Pleasant, Swansea, West Glamorgan,
SA1 6EG
Tel: 01792 642158 Fax: 01792 648996
SB £60 DB £70 HBS £80 HBD £110
B £8 L £15 D £20. CC: MC Vi Am DC Swi Delt
How to get there: M4 J-42. A483, right at traffic
lights after Sainsbury's, left at station, right after
second lights.

Wales

Woodside Guest House

♦♦♦♦ ✍

Oxwich, Gower, Swansea, SA3 1LS
Tel: 01792 390791
Email: david@oxwich.fsnet.co.uk
Closed December to January

Converted 200-year-old cottage with beamed
bar and inglenook fireplace. Close to the beach
and nature reserve, with ground floor
accommodation and conservatory.
SB £40 DB £50

How to get there: M4 J-42 for Swansea. A4118
Swansea to Portegnon. A mile past Penmaen
take unmarked road to Oxwich.

Overlooked by the historic Oystermouth Castle,
St. Anne's Hotel offers spectacular views over
Swansea Bay. Set in its own grounds with large
private car park, the hotel offers a quiet location in
the heart of Mumbles village. Ideally situated for
access to the Gower Peninsula and Swansea.

Western Lane, Mumbles, Swansea,
West Glamorgan SA3 4EY
Tel: 01792 369147   Fax: 01792 360537
Email: enquiries@stannes-hotel.co.uk

Alexander

♦♦♦ ✍

3 Sketty Road, Uplands, Swansea,
West Glamorgan, SA2 0EU
Tel: 01792 470045 Fax: 01792 476012
Email: alexander.hotel@swig-online.co.uk
Web: www.swig-online.co.uk/alexanderhotel
Children minimum age: 2
Closed Christmas to New Year
SB £34 DB £48 CC: MC Vi Am DC Swi Delt

How to get there: On A4118, in Swansea's
Uplands area. On left at start of Sketty Road
from Uplands.

Crescent Guest House

♦♦♦ ✍

132 Eaton Crescent, Uplands, Swansea,
West Glamorgan, SA1 4QR
Tel: 01792 466814 Fax: 01792 466814
Email: conveyatthecrescent@compuserve.com
Closed Christmas to New Year
SB £30 DB £50 CC: MC Vi Swi Delt

How to get there: From station, A4118 to
St James' Church, first left, first right into Eaton
Crescent.

Grosvenor House

♦♦♦ ✍

Mirador Crescent, Uplands, Swansea,
West Glamorgan, SA2 0QX
Tel: 01792 461522 Fax: 01792 461522
Email: grosvenor@ct6.com
Web: www.ct6.com/grosvenor
SB £30 DB £50 CC: MC Vi Am Swi Delt

How to get there: Off A4118, 1 mile west from
Swansea station, take 3rd right after St. James'
Church.

Rock Villa

♦♦♦

1 George Bank, Southend, Swansea, Wales,
SA3 4EQ
Tel: 01792 366794
Email: rockvilla@tinyworld.co.uk
Closed December 21 to January 3
SB £22 DB £44

How to get there: On A483 4½ miles Leisure
Centre, next to George restaurant and hotel.

Shoreline

◆ ◆ ◆

648 Mumbles Road, Mumbles, Swansea,
SA3 4QZ
Tel: 01792 366233
Web: www.shorelinehotel.co.uk
Closed Christmas

Recently refurbished family run hotel, situated
on the seafront in the beautiful village of
Mumbles, close to the city centre, ferry terminal
and the Gower Peninsula.
SB £35 DB £50 CC: MC Vi Am DC Swi Delt
🖨️ 🕮 🖵 🐎 🎠 ⛓️ 🎁 🍴 🍸
How to get there: M4 J-42, for Swansea, then
Mumbles. On main seafront, facing playground.

Talsarnau, Gwynedd

Hotel Maes-y-Neuadd

★ ★ 🍷 🍷 🍷

Talsarnau, Gwynedd, LL47 6YA
Tel: 01766 780200 Fax: 01766 780211
Email: maes@neuadd.com
Web: www.neuadd.com
SB £69 DB £127 HBS £70 HBD £123 B £9.50
L £9.50 D £27. CC: MC Vi Am DC Swi Delt
🔷 ⛓️ 🖨️ 🐎 🖵 ☎️ 🅿️ 🎁 🎠 🍴 🍸 🏕️ 🍸
How to get there: 3 miles northeast of Harlech,
signposted on an unclassed road off B4573.

Tenby, Dyfed

Atlantic

★ ★ ★ 🍷

The Esplanade, Tenby, Dyfed, SA70 7DU
Tel: 01834 842881
Email: enquiries@atlantic-hotel.uk.com
Web: www.atlantic-hotel.uk.com
Closed December 18 to January 15
SB £60 DB £84 CC: MC Vi Am Swi Delt
⛓️ 🕮 🖨️ 🐎 ⊗ ☕ 🖵 ☎️ 🅿️ 🎁 🎠 🍴 🍸
🏕️ 🍸 🔲

How to get there: Turn right at Esplanade. Hotel
halfway along on right.

Fourcroft

★ ★ ★

North Beach, Tenby, Dyfed, SA70 8AP
Tel: 01834 842886 Fax: 01834 842888
Email: chris@fourcroft-hotel.co.uk
Web: www.fourcroft-hotel.co.uk
SB £31 DB £62 HBS £47 HBD £94
B £8.50 L £5 D £16. CC: MC Vi Am DC Swi Delt
🔷 🕮 🐎 ⊗ 🖵 📞 🅿️ 🎁 🎠 🍴 🍸 🏕️ 👣
🆂🅿️🅰️ 🍷 🎿 🍸
How to get there: At seafront turn sharp left.
Fourcroft is 150yds along on left.

Heywood Mount

★ ★ ★

Heywood Lane, Tenby, Dyfed, SA70 8DA
Tel: 01834 842087 Fax: 01834 842087

St Brides

★ ★ ★

St Brides Hill, Saundersfoot, Dyfed, SA69 9NH
Tel: 01834 812304 Fax: 01834 811766
Email: andrew.evans9@virgin.net
B £11 L £7 D £18. CC: MC Vi Am DC Swi Delt
🎁 🍴 🍸 👣 🍸
How to get there: Saundersfoot is 4 miles
before Tenby on A477. Enter village, hotel
overlooks harbour on clifftop.

Greenhills Country

★ ★

St Florence, Tenby, Dyfed, SA70 8NB
Tel: 01834 871291 Fax: 01834 871948
Email: enquiries@greenhillshotel.co.uk
Web: www.greenhillshotel.co.uk
Closed December to March
SB £27 DB £54 HBS £39 HBD £78 D £12.
⛓️ ⊗ 🖵 🅿️ 🎁 🎠 🐎 🍴 🍸 👣 👣 🍸
How to get there: In St Florence, pass church
on right, left at hotel sign. Hotel 250yds on.

Royal Gate House

★ ★

North Beach, Tenby, Dyfed, SA70 7ET
Tel: 01834 842255 Fax: 01834 842441
Email: royal_gatehouse@hotmail.com
SB £42 DB £75 HBS £59 HBD £109
B £10 L £5.95 D £17.
CC: MC Vi Am DC Swi Delt
⛓️ 🕮 🖨️ 🐎 ⊗ 🖵 ☎️ 🅿️ 🎁 🎠 🐎 🍴 🍸 🏕️ 👣
🍸 🔲
How to get there: From M4, take A478 into
Tenby.

Wales

Broadmead

♦♦♦♦ 🐾 ✂ ⚑

Heywood Lane, Tenby, Dyfed, SA70 8DA
Tel: 01834 842641 Fax: 01834 845757
Closed November to March
SB £31 DB £62 HBS £44 HBD £88 D £14.
CC: MC Vi Am Swi Delt

♿🍳⌨☎🅿🛁🎠🔥🍽🍴

How to get there: Enter Tenby, right into
Serpentine Road, signs for Wildlife Park. Right
again into Heywood Lane.

Kinloch Court

✤

Queens Parade, Tenby, Dyfed, SA70 7EG
Tel: 01834 842777

Ashby House

♦♦♦ ✂

24 Victoria Street, Tenby, Dyfed, SA70 7DY
Tel: 01834 842867

Pen Mar

♦♦♦

New Hedges, Tenby, Dyfed, SA70 8TL
Tel: 01834 842435 Fax: 01834 842435
Email: penmar@jhurton.freeserve.co.uk
Web: www.s-h-systems.co.uk/a15498.html
SB £24 DB £48 HBS £35.60 HBD £71.20
B £5.50 D £11.50. CC: MC Vi DC Swi Delt

🚫🍳⌨🅿🛁🎠🔥🍽🏓🍴

How to get there: On A478 1 mile before Tenby.

Ripley St Mary's

♦♦♦

St Mary's Street, Tenby, Dyfed, SA70 7HN
Tel: 01834 842837 Fax: 01834 842837
Closed November to March
SB £24 DB £48 CC: MC Vi

⚑🚫🍳⌨🅿🛁🎠🔥🍽🍴

Castle View

♦♦

The Norton, Tenby, Dyfed, SA70 8AA
Tel: 01834 842666
SB £20 DB £20

🍳⌨🅿🛁🎠🔥🍽🍴

How to get there: To north beach onto Narberth
Road. Sea on left and hotel on right (front yellow
and green).

Trearddur Bay, Gwynedd

Beach

★★★

Lon St Fraid, Trearddur Bay, Gwynedd, LL65 2YT
Tel: 01407 860332 Fax: 01407 861140
SB £44.50 DB £70 HBS £51.50 HBD £89
L £5.45 D £13.95. CC: MC Vi Am DC Swi Delt

🐾🍳⌨☎🅿🛁🎠🔥🍽♿

How to get there: A5 to Valley crossroads. Left
on B4545 3 miles to Trearddur Bay. Hotel on right.

Trearddur Bay

★★★

Lon Isallt, Trearddur Bay, Gwynedd, LL65 2UW
Tel: 01407 860301 Fax: 01407 861181

Moranedd Guest House

♦♦♦

Trearddur Road, Trearddur Bay, Anglesey,
Gwynedd, LL65 2UE
Tel: 01407 860324 Fax: 01407 860324

Moranedd is a lovely guest house with a sun
patio overlooking three quarters of an acre of
garden in a quiet cul-de-sac, but only five
minutes stroll to the beach, shops, sailing and
golf clubs.
SB £20 DB £45

🐾🍳⌨🅿🛁🎠🔥🍽🍴

How to get there: A5 to Valley. Left at lights
onto B4545 to Trearddur. Past Beach Hotel,
right at second road through village. Second
house on left in Trearddur Road.

Tyn-y-Groes, Gwynedd

The Groes Inn

★★★ 🐾

Tyn-y-Groes, nr Conwy, Gwynedd, LL32 8TN
Tel: 01492 650545 Fax: 01492 650545

Tywyn, Gwynedd

Corbett Arms
★★
Tywyn, Gwynedd, LL36 9DG
Tel: 01923 822388 Fax: 01923 824906
SB £27 DB £54 HBS £36 HBD £72
B £6 L £6 D £10. CC: MC Vi Am Delt
How to get there: On A493 Dolgellau/Machynlleth.

Greenfield
★
High Street, Tywyn, Gwynedd, LL36 9AD
Tel: 01654 710354 Fax: 01654 710354
Closed January
SB £20 DB £40 HBS £27 HBD £54
B £3.25 L £3.95 D £6.95. CC: MC Vi Swi Delt
How to get there: In High Street opposite
Leisure Centre and Tourist Information Centre.

Usk, Gwent

Cwrt Bleddyn
★★★★ ♜♜♜
Llangybi, Usk, Gwent, NP15 1PG
Tel: 01633 450521 Fax: 01633 450220
Web: www.arcadianhotels.co.uk
SB £85 DB £105 HBS £100 HBD £140 B £9.50
L £9.95 D £24.50. CC: MC Vi Am DC Swi Delt

Welshpool, Powys

Buttington Country House   Little Gem
♦♦♦♦♦
Buttington, nr Welshpool, Powys, SY21 8HD
Tel: 01938 553351 Fax: 01938 553351
SB £50 DB £70 CC: MC Vi Swi
How to get there: 1¹/₂ miles from Welshpool,
turn off A483 at island. A458 to Shrewsbury,
over river bridge and level crossing. Right
opposite Green Dragon into Leighton. Hotel first
right next to church.

Lane Farm
♦♦♦♦
Criggion, Welshpool, Powys, SY5 9BG
Tel: 01743 884288 Fax: 01743 885126
Email: lane.farm@ukgateway.net
SB £25 DB £40

How to get there: On B4393 between Crew
Green and Llandrinio, 12 miles Shrewsbury,
9 miles Welshpool.

Wolfscastle, Dyfed

Stone Hall
♦♦♦
Welsh Hook, Wolfscastle, Dyfed, SA62 5NS
Tel: 01348 840212 Fax: 01348 840815

Wrexham, Clwyd

Llwyn Onn Hall
★★★ ♜♜
Cefn Road, Wrexham, Clwyd, LL13 0NY
Tel: 01978 261225 Fax: 01978 263233

Set in beautiful countryside just south of
Wrexham. This comfortable 17th century manor
house is a family-run hotel with 13 individually
furnished, ensuite bedrooms.
SB £64 DB £84 HBS £75 HBD £53
B £6.95 L £8.95 D £17.50.
CC: MC Vi Am DC Swi Delt
How to get there: Easily accessed from A483 and
near Wrexham town centre and industrial estate.

Wynnstay Arms
★★★
Yorke Street, Wrexham, Clwyd, LL13 8LP
Tel: 01978 291010 Fax: 01978 362138
SB £46.85 DB £53.80
B £6.95 L £9.95 D £12.95. CC: MC Vi Am DC
Swi Delt
How to get there: From A438, take left turn at
Ruthin, follow to T-Junction. Left again to
bottom of hill, right onto St Giles way. Left at
T-Junction, next left at roundabout.

Wales

Scotland

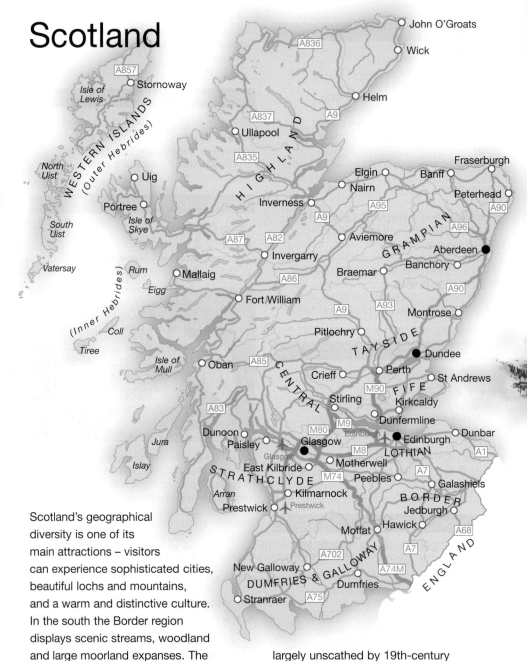

Scotland's geographical diversity is one of its main attractions – visitors can experience sophisticated cities, beautiful lochs and mountains, and a warm and distinctive culture. In the south the Border region displays scenic streams, woodland and large moorland expanses. The further north you go, the more rugged the landscape, culminating in the wild beauty of the Highlands and Islands, where Gaelic is still spoken, particularly in the Hebrides.

Edinburgh is the usual first port of call for visitors. Throughout the centuries, the city's innovative centres of learning, combined with the elegance of buildings largely unscathed by 19th-century industrialisation, earned Edinburgh the title of 'Athens of the North'. This reputation continues through the world-famous annual Edinburgh Festival, which is set against the dramatic backdrop of the looming castle and the glitter of Prince's Street. Other attractions include Holyrood House, Scott's Monument, the Royal Botanic Garden and

ORKNEY ISLANDS

Westray
Sanday
Lady Village
Eday
Rousay
Mainland   Stronsay
Dounby Shapinsay
Kirkwall   Kirkwall
Stromness   Gritley
Hoy
South
Ronaldsay
Burwick

SHETLAND ISLANDS

Haroldswick
Unst
Baltasound
Fetlar
Yell
Whalsay
Mainland
Bressay
Scalloway   Lerwick
Hoswick
Tolob   Sumburgh

Loch Lomond

Shetland
Islands

Orkney
Islands

Glasgow   Edinburgh

Belfast

Dublin   Manchester

Birmingham

Cardiff   London

the Museum of Childhood, not to mention the two famous bridges crossing the Firth of Forth.

Glasgow is Scotland's most populous city, with over a million inhabitants. Visually less grand than Edinburgh, Glasgow still has much to attract visitors, including the handsome Gothic Cathedral, the Theatre Royal, Hunterian Museum and Art Gallery, and the world famous Burrell Collection in Pollok Park, containing many famous pieces of art including works by Rembrandt, Boudin, Sisley and Cézanne.

Away from the Clyde-Forth valleys, Stirling and Perth are wrapped in history, St Andrews boasts one of Europe's finest universities, as well as being 'the home of golf', Dundee and Aberdeen each have their own unique characters, and between Fort William and Inverness you can travel the landscape that Macbeth knew.

For golfers, Scotland's numerous and wild links courses offer some of the game's best challenges and visitors from south of the border will be pleasantly surprised to find prices generally cheaper than in England. Trout and salmon fishing are also popular sports, and coarse fishing is common in southern Scotland. Hill walking, pony trekking, and skiing on snow or dry slopes are available, and in the summer, a visit to the Braemar Gathering of the Clans in the presence of the Royal Family is a magical experience, but prior booking is recommended.

Excellent airports and inexpensive flights serve the extremities of the Hebrides, Orkneys or Shetland Isles. Visitors should remember that Scotland has separate legal, educational and banking systems to those of England, Wales and Northern Ireland.

Scotland

Aberdeen

Copthorne

★★★★

122 Huntly Street, Aberdeen, AB10 1SU
Tel: 01224 630404 Fax: 01224 640573
Email: stuart.noble@mill-cop.com
Web: www.stay-with-us.com
SB £45 DB £50 HBS £60 HBD £98 B £12.50
L £9.95 D £18.50. CC: MC Vi Am DC Swi Delt

How to get there: From south, 2nd left at
roundabout, right at next. Follow Holburn Street
for 2 miles, onto Union Street, first left, 2nd right.

Burnett Arms

★★

25 High Street, Banchory, Kincardineshire,
AB31 5TD
Tel: 01330 824944 Fax: 01330 825553
Email: theburnett@totalise.co.uk
Web: www.burnettarms.co.uk
SB £40 DB £56 HBS £47 HBD £68
B £6 L £8 D £15. CC: MC Vi Am DC Swi Delt

How to get there: On A93 west of Aberdeen in
Banchory town centre. Northern side of street.
See advert on facing page

Jays Guest House

◆ ◆ ◆ ◆

422 King Street, Aberdeen, AB24 3BR
Tel: 01224 638295 Fax: 01224 638295
Email: alice@jaysguesthouse.co.uk
Web: www.jaysguesthouse.co.uk
Children minimum age: 12
SB £33.40 DB £56.70
CC: MC Vi Swi Delt JCB Solo

How to get there: From East End of Union
Street, turn left onto King Street and the Jays
Guest House is approx ³/₄ mile from this
junction.

Arkaig Guest House

◆ ◆ ◆

43 Powis Terrace, Aberdeen, Aberdeenshire,
AB25 3PP
Tel: 01224 638872 Fax: 01224 622189
Email: arkaig@netcomuk.co.uk
Web: www.arkaig.co.uk
SB £30 DB £44 HBS £39 HBD £31 D £9.
CC: MC Vi Swi Delt

How to get there: Situated on the A96
Aberdeen to Inverness road, ¹/₂ mile north of the
town centre.

Bimini Guest House

◆ ◆ ◆

69 Constitution Street, Aberdeen, AB2 1ET
Tel: 01224 646912 Fax: 01224 647006
Email: biminiabz@aol.com
Web: www.bimini.co.uk
SB £35 DB £50 CC: MC Vi

How to get there: 5 minute walk from town
centre, heading towards beachfront.

Cedars

◆ ◆ ◆

339 Great Western Road, Aberdeen, AB10 6NW
Tel: 01224 583225 Fax: 01224 585050
Email: reservations@cedars-private-hotel.
freeserve.co.uk
Web: www.cedars-private-hotel.freeserve.co.uk
SB £38 DB £52 CC: MC Vi Am Delt

How to get there: Great Western Road crosses
Anderson Drive, which is the city ring road.

Strathboyne Guest House

◆ ◆ ◆

26 Abergeldie Terrace, Aberdeen, AB1 6EE
Tel: 01224 593400

Aberfeldy, Perth & Kinross

Moness

★★★

Crieff Road, Aberfeldy, Perth & Kinross,
PH15 2DY
Tel: 01887 820446 Fax: 01887 820062
SB £27.50 B £8 L £5 D £15. CC: MC Vi Swi

How to get there: Follow A9 north from Perth.
Turn right at Ballinluig for Aberfeldy. Turn left at
the traffic lights in Aberfeldy. Moness is 200m
on left.

Weem

★★

Weem, Aberfeldy, Perth & Kinross, PH15 2LD
Tel: 01887 820381 Fax: 01887 820187

Aberlady, East Lothian

Kilspindie House

★★

Main Street, Aberlady, East Lothian, EH32 0RE
Tel: 01875 870682 Fax: 01875 587504

Abington, Lanarkshire

Abington

★★

Carlisle Road, Abington, Lanarkshire, ML12 6SD
Tel: 01864 502467 Fax: 01864 502223
Email: info@abington-hotel.ndirect.co.uk
Web: www.abington-hotel.ndirect.co.uk
SB £45 DB £65 HBS £58 HBD £39
B £7.95 L £6.95 D £12.95.
CC: MC Vi Am DC Swi Delt
How to get there: Exit M74 J-13. Follow signs
into village. Hotel is in village centre.

Aboyne, Aberdeenshire

Arbor Lodge

♦♦♦♦♦

Ballater Road, Aboyne, AB34 5HY
Tel: 01339 886951

Airdrie, Lanarkshire

Tudor Hotel

★★★

39 Alexandra Street, Airdrie,
Lanarkshire, ML6 0BA
Tel: 01236 764144 Fax: 01236 747589
SB £39.50 DB £59.50 B £3.95 L £4.95
D £11.95. CC: MC Vi Am Swi

Anstruther, Fife

Smugglers Inn

★★

High Street East, Anstruther, Fife, KY10 3DQ
Tel: 01333 310506 Fax: 01333 312706

Spindrift

♦♦♦♦

Pittenweem Road, Anstruther, Fife, KY10 3DT
Tel: 01333 310573 Fax: 01333 310573
Email: info@thespindrift.co.uk
Web: www.thespindrift.co.uk
DB £60 HBD £45 CC: MC Vi
How to get there: Approaching Anstruther from
the west, the Spindrift is first on the left. From
the east, it is last on the right.

The Burnett Arms Hotel

Historic coaching inn ideally situated for
touring Royal Deeside and the northeast of
Scotland. 18 miles from Aberdeen and 16 miles
from Dyce International Airport (ABZ).

Facilities include two function suites,
restaurant, two bars. Surrounding area of
Scotland renowned for its breathtaking beauty
and golf courses. Golf nearby.

25 High Street, Banchory AB31 5TD
Tel: 01330 824944   Fax: 01330 825553
Email: theburnett@totalise.co.uk
Website: www.burnettarms.co.uk

Arbroath, Angus

Hotel Seaforth

★★

Dundee Road, Arbroath, Angus, DD11 1QF
Tel: 01241 872232 Fax: 01241 877473
Email: hotelseaforth@ukonline.co.uk
SB £45 DB £58 B £7 L £4.95 D £7.95.
CC: MC Vi Am Swi Delt
How to get there: Hotel Seaforth is on the A92,
main road from Dundee to Aberdeen, facing
the sea.
See advert on following page

Kingsley House Guest House

♦♦

29/31 Market Gate, Arbroath, Angus, DD11 1AU
Tel: 01241 873933 Fax: 01241 873933

Ardbeg, Argyll & Bute

Ardmory House

★★

Ardmory Road, Ardbeg, Isle of Bute,
Argyll & Bute, PA20 0PG
Tel: 01700 502346

Scotland

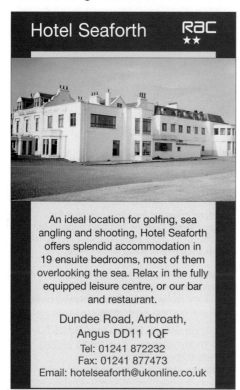
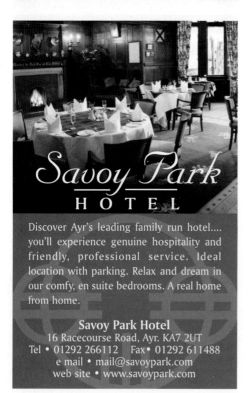
Arisaig, Inverness-shire

Arisaig

★★
Arisaig, Inverness-shire, PH39 4NH
Tel: 01687 450210 Fax: 01687 450310
Email: arisaighotel@dial.pipex.com
Web: www.arisaighotel.co.uk
SB £36 DB £72 L £2.50 D £12.
CC: MC Vi Swi Delt

How to get there: From south, A82 through Fort William, left onto A830. Arisaig is 35 miles further. Hotel is on right through village.

Auchencairn, Dumfries & Galloway

Balcary Bay

★★★ 🍴🍴
Auchencairn, Dumfries & Galloway, DG7 1QZ
Tel: 01556 640217 Fax: 01556 640272
Email: reservations@balcary-bay-hotel.co.uk
Web: www.balcary-bay-hotel.co.uk
Closed December to February

This 16th-century house occupies a beautifully secluded location on the shores of the Solway in southwest Scotland. Renowned for fine food and wines, in a unique setting.
SB £61 DB £108 HBS £70 HBD £124 B £12
L £11.50 D £25.75. CC: MC Vi Am Swi Delt JCB

How to get there: Exit M74, A75, A711 for Dalbeattie and Auchencairn. Left over bridge into Auchencairn and follow single-track Shore Road. Hotel on left.

Aviemore, Highland

Ravenscraig Guest House

◆◆◆
141 Grampian Road, Aviemore, PH22 1RP
Tel: 01479 810278 Fax: 01479 812742
Email: ravenscrg@aol.com
Web: www.aviemore.co.uk/ravenscraig

SB £18.25 DB £36.50 CC: MC Vi Swi Delt
🐾⊗☕🖵🅿️🛁🕯️🐴♬🐟
How to get there: At north end of main street through the village. 300m from Police Station.

Ayr, Ayrshire

Belleisle House
★★★
Doonfoot, Ayr, Ayrshire, KA7 4DU
Tel: 01292 442331 Fax: 01292 45325

Kylestrome
★★★
Miller Road, Ayr, Ayrshire, KA7 2AX
Tel: 01292 262474 Fax: 01292 260863

Quality Hotel Ayr
★★★
Burns Statue Square, Ayr, Ayrshire, KA7 3AT
Tel: 01292 263268 Fax: 01292 262293
Email: admin@gb624.u-net.com
Web: www.choicehotels.com

SB £80.75 DB £102.50 HBS £95.25
HBD £65.75 B £9.75 L £6 D £14.50.
CC: MC Vi Am DC Swi Delt
⚓♿♨🐾⊗☕🖵☎📞🅿️🛁🕯️🐴♬🐟 ♨♨♨ 👯 SPA 🍸
How to get there: From A77, take first exit off Holmston roundabout. Follow one-way system round to front of hotel.

Savoy Park
★★★ ♟♟
16 Racecourse Road, Ayr, Ayrshire, KA7 2UT
Tel: 01292 266112 Fax: 01292 611488
Email: mail@savoypark.com
Web: www.savoypark.com
SB £65 DB £80 HBS £80 HBD £110
CC: MC Vi Am Swi Delt
⚓🐾⊗☕🖵☎📞🅿️🛁🕯️🐴♬🐟 ♨♨♨ 👯
How to get there: From A77, at A70 crossover, take the turning for Ayr South. Follow signs for town centre then A719 Maidens Road. Hotel is on right.
See advert on facing page

Dunduff Farm
♦♦♦♦♦
Dunure, Ayr, Ayrshire, KA7 4LH
Tel: 01292 500225 Fax: 01292 500222

Ballachulish, Argyll & Bute

Lyn-Leven Guest House
♦♦♦♦
West Laroch, Ballachulish, PH39 4JP
Tel: 01855 811392 Fax: 01855 811600
Email: lynleven@amserve.net
Closed Christmas

SB £30 DB £48 HBS £39 HBD £66
CC: MC Vi Swi Delt Solo
♿🐾⊗☕🖵🅿️🛁🕯️🐴♬🐟 👯
How to get there: A82, left at Glencoe Hotel, 1 mile, Ballachulish left, Lyn-Leven signposted.

Ballater, Aberdeenshire

Darroch Learg
★★★ ♟♟♟
Braemar Road, Ballater, Aberdeen, AB35 5UX
Tel: 01339 755443 Fax: 01339 755252
Email: nigel@darroch-learg.demon.co.uk
Web: www.darroch-learg.demon.co.uk
Closed January
SB £62 DB £124 HBS £90 HBD £180
B £9 L £6.50 D £34. CC: Vi Am DC Swi Delt
♿🐕🐾⊗☕🖵☎🅿️🛁🕯️🐴♬🐟 👯
How to get there: On A93 leaving Ballater for Braemar on right as road climbs the hill.

Monaltrie
★★
5 Bridge Square, Royal Deeside, Ballater, Aberdeenshire, AB35 5QJ
Tel: 013397 55417 Fax: 013397 55180

Guide dogs

If a Hotel or Guest Accommodation does not display this 'dogs welcome' symbol in its listing, the hotelier may still be happy to welcome guests with guide dogs, and you should contact the property to discover whether this will be a problem.

Scotland

Glen Lui

♦♦♦♦

Invercauld Road, Ballater, Royal Deeside,
Aberdeenshire, AB35 5RP
Tel: 01339 755402 Fax: 01339 755545
Email: info@glen-lui-hotel.co.uk
Web: www.glen-lui-hotel.co.uk
SB £30 DB £30 HBS £39 HBD £39
CC: MC Vi Am Swi Delt

How to get there: From Aberdeen, through
Ballater, over bridge, left down Invercauld Road.
Drive to bottom of road, hotel is on the right.

Banchory, Aberdeenshire

Banchory Lodge

★★★

Dee Street, Banchory, AB31 5HS
Tel: 01330 822625 Fax: 01330 825019
Email: banchorylodgeht@btconnect.com
Closed 2 weeks in January
SB £55 DB £90 HBS £70 HBD £110
B £10 L £12.50 D £25. CC: MC Vi Am DC Swi

How to get there: A96 to Banchory. Left at
lights. Signs at end of driveway.

Raemoir House Hotel

This splendid country mansion is set in
an idyllic 3,500 acre estate, and situated
on beautiful Royal Deeside.
Twenty bedrooms, all ensuite, some with
four-poster beds, conference facilities,
tennis courts and golf course.

Raemoir House, Raemoir, Banchory
AB31 4ED
Tel: 01330 824884   Fax: 01330 822171
Email: raemoirhse@aol.com

Raemoir House

★★★

Banchory, AB31 4ED
Tel: 01330 824884 Fax: 01330 822171
Email: raemoirhse@aol.com
Web: www.raemoir.com
SB £50 DB £80 HBS £65 HBD £65 B £8.50
L £2.50 D £23.50. CC: MC Vi Am DC Swi

How to get there: From A93 to Banchory, right
onto A980, 1¹/₂ miles, hotel opposite T-junction.
See advert on this page (below)

Barrhead, Strathclyde

Dalmeny Park Country House

★★★

Lochilbo Road, Barrhead, Strathclyde, G78 1LG
Tel: 0141 881 9211 Fax: 0141 881 9214
Email: enquiries@maksu-group.co.uk
Web: www.maksu-group.co.uk
SB £70 DB £95 HBS £85 HBD £120 B £6.50
L £9.50 D £14. CC: MC Vi Am DC Swi Delt

How to get there: A736 through Barrhead for
Irvine. Hotel is on left as you leave Barrhead.

Beauly, Inverness-shire

Lovat Arms

★★★

Main Street, Beauly, Inverness-shire, IV4 7BS
Tel: 01463 782313 Fax: 01463 782862
Email: lovat.arms@cali.co.uk
Web: www.lovatarms.com
SB £35 DB £60 HBS £55 HBD £45
B £6 L £8 D £8. CC: MC Vi Swi Delt JCB

How to get there: A9 to Inverness and to Tore
roundabout. Left on A832, left on A862 to
Beauly, hotel at end of square.
See advert on facing page

Heathmount Guest House

♦♦♦♦

Station Road, Beauly, Inverness-shire, IV4 7EQ
Tel: 01463 782411
Closed Christmas and New Year
SB £20 DB £40 CC: MC Vi

How to get there: 20m from post office on main
road through Beauly village.

Biggar, Lanarkshire

Hartree Country House

★★★ ®
Biggar, Lanarkshire, ML12 6JJ
Tel: 01899 221027 Fax: 01899 221259

Shieldhill

★★★ ® ® ®
Quothquan, Biggar, Lanarkshire, ML12 6NA
Tel: 01899 220035 Fax: 01899 221092
Email: enquiries@shieldhill.co.uk
Web: www.shieldhill.co.uk
SB £75 DB £114 CC: MC Vi Swi Delt
⚐ 🖥 🐴 ⊗ 🖵 ☎ 🅿 🛂 🎡 🐎 🎋 🐕 🐝 ‼ 🎅
How to get there: B7016 from Biggar for
Carnwath. Left after 3 miles, 1¹/₂ miles on right.

Blairgowrie, Perth & Kinross

The Angus

★★★
46 Wellmeadow, Blairgowrie,
Perth & Kinross, PH10 6NQ
Tel: 01250 872455 Fax: 01250 875165
Email: info@theangus.freeserve.co.uk
Web: www.theangus.freeserve.co.uk
SB £45 DB £90 HBS £65 HBD £110
B £9 L £5 D £15. CC: MC Vi Am Swi Delt
🔥 ⚙ 🐴 🖵 ☎ 🅿 🛂 🎡 🐎 🎋 🐕 ‼ ⁝⁝ 🗽
How to get there: Situated in the centre of
Blairgowrie on the A93 overlooking the country
town centre.

Bonar Bridge, Sutherland

Kyle House

♦ ♦ ♦
Dornoch Road, Bonar Bridge, Sutherland,
IV24 3EB
Tel: 01863 766360/351370 Fax: 01863 766360
Email: kyle.hse@talk21.com
Children minimum age: 4. Closed Nov to Jan
SB £19 DB £30
⊗ ⚙ 🖵 🅿 🛂 🎡 🐎 🎋 🐕 ‼
How to get there: On A949, 4th house on left
after newsagents northbound. Also 4th house
on right entering village from east side.

Bothwell, Lanarkshire

Bothwell Bridge

★★★
89 Main Street, Bothwell, Lanarkshire, G71 8LN
Tel: 01698 852246 Fax: 01698 854686

Braemar, Aberdeenshire

Invercauld Arms

★★★
Braemar, Aberdeenshire, AB35 5YR
Tel: 01339 741605
Fax: 01339 741428
SB £83 DB £110 B £9 L £4
CC: MC Vi Am DC Swi Delt Eurocard Solo
🔥 ⚙ 🐴 ⊗ ⚙ 🖵 ☎ 🅿 🛂 🎡 🐎 🎋 🐕 ‼
🎅 ⁝⁝

Campbeltown, Argyll & Bute

Seafield

★★★ ®
Kilkerran Road, Campbeltown,
Argyll & Bute, PA28 6JL
Tel: 01586 554385 Fax: 01586 552741
SB £50 DB £80 B £8.50 L £5.50 D £15.
CC: MC Vi Am Swi
⚐ 🐴 ⊗ ⚙ 🖵 ☎ 🅿 🛂 🎅
How to get there: From A83 follow signs for
Ballycastle ferry terminal then follow road
around loch for about 500m.

Lovat Arms Hotel

Our Taste of Scotland Kitchen provides an
excellent variety of cuisine, much of it
produced on our own farm. Our bedrooms
are all furnished in clan tartans which adds
to the family atmosphere. The Garden and
Ceilidh rooms provide excellent areas for
small meetings and functions up to about
60 people.

Beauly, Nr. Inverness IV4 7BS
Tel: 01463 782313   Fax: 01463 782862
Email: lovat.arms@cali.co.uk
Website: www.lovatarms.com

Scotland

Westbank Guesthouse

♦♦♦

Dell Road, Campbeltown, Argyll & Bute,
PA28 6JG
Tel: 01586 553660 Fax: 01586 553660
SB £27 DB £46 CC: MC Vi Delt

How to get there: 30m past Heritage Centre (in
Southend direction), turn right into Dell Road.

Carnoustie, Angus

Letham Grange

★★★★ ℛℛ

Colliston, Angus, DD11 4RL
Tel: 01241 890373 Fax: 01241 890725
Email: lethamgrange@sol.co.uk
Web: www.lethamgrange.co.uk
SB £100 DB £145 B £3.50 L £5.95 D £16.
CC: MC Vi Am DC Swi Delt

How to get there: A92 to Arbroath, A933 for
Brechin. First right after Colliston, tourist signs.

Castle Douglas, Dumfries & Galloway

Douglas Arms

★★ ℛℛ

King Street, Castle Douglas,
Dumfries & Galloway, DG7 1DB
Tel: 01556 502231 Fax: 01556 504000
Email: doughot@aol.com
SB £37.50 DB £68.50 HBS £40 HBD £80
B £6.50 L £7 D £10. CC: MC Vi Am Swi Delt

How to get there: In centre of town on the main
street and close to the town clock tower.

Kings Arms

★★

St Andrews Street, Castle Douglas,
Dumfries & Galloway, DG7 1EL
Tel: 01556 502626 Fax: 01556 502097
Email: david@galloway-golf.co.uk
Web: www.galloway-golf.co.uk
SB £37 DB £58 HBS £45 HBD £75 B £5.50
L £7.50 D £12.50. CC: MC Vi Swi Delt

How to get there: From town clock, turn left.
Hotel 100 yards on left.

Craigadam

♦♦♦♦♦ ℛ ✍

Castle Douglas, Dumfries & Galloway, DG7 3HU
Tel: 01556 650233 Fax: 01556 650233

Comrie, Perth & Kinross

The Royal

★★★ ℛ

Melville Square, Comrie, PH6 2DN
Tel: 01764 679200

Crail, Fife

Croma

★

33–35 Nethergate Road, Crail, Fife, KY10 3TU
Tel: 01333 450239

Crieff, Perth & Kinross

Locke's Acre

★★

Comrie Road, Crieff, Perth & Kinross, PH7 4BP
Tel: 01764 652526 Fax: 01764 652526
Closed February
SB £28 DB £56 HBS £42 HBD £86
B £6.50 L £5.95 D £7.95. CC: MC Vi Swi

How to get there: A9 north for Perth, A822 to
Crieff. In Crieff, take A85 for Comrie,
Lochearnhead Road.

Gwydyr House

♦♦♦♦ ℛ

Comrie Road, Crieff, Perth & Kinross, PH7 4BP
Tel: 01764 653277 Fax: 01764 653277
Email: george.blackie@iclweb.com
Web: www.smoothhound.co.uk/hotels/
          gwydyr.html
SB £40 DB £60 HBS £51 HBD £82
B £7.95 D £12.95. CC: MC Vi

How to get there: On A85 Comrie Road, going
west from Crieff, opposite MacRosty Park.

Crinan, Argyll & Bute

Crinan

★★★ ℛℛℛ

Crinan, Argyll & Bute, PA31 8SR
Tel: 01546 830261 Fax: 01546 830292

Cumnock, Ayrshire

Royal

♦♦♦

1 Glaisnock Street, Cumnock, KA18 1BP
Tel: 01290 420822 Fax: 01290 425988

Cupar, Fife

Rathcluan

 ◆◆◆

Carslogie Road, Cupar, Fife, KY15 4HY
Tel: 01334 650000 Fax: 01334 650000

Dalmally, Argyll & Bute

Rockhill Farm & Guest House

◆◆◆

Rockhill, Ardbrecknish, Dalmally,
Argyll & Bute, PA33 1BH
Tel: 01866 833218

Denny, Falkirk

Topps Guest House

◆◆◆

Topps Farm, Fintry Road, Denny,
Falkirk, FK6 5JF
Tel: 01324 822471 Fax: 01324 823099
Web: www.thetopps.com

Scottish farmers Alistair and Jennifer welcome
you to their bungalow farmhouse. Stunning
panoramic views. 'Taste of Scotland' food is our
speciality. Disabled access to the house.
SB £32 DB £46 B £4.50 D £12. CC: MC Vi
♿ 🐾 ⊙ ⓢ 🖳 ☎ 🅿 ∻ ℜ ♿ ♿ ♿ 🎣
How to get there: From Glasgow, A80, A803 to
Denny, then B818, hotel 4 miles on right. From
Edinburgh, M9, M876, off at Denny sign, right at
lights, third right onto B818.

Dingwall, Ross-shire

National

★★

High Street, Dingwall, Ross-shire, IV15 9HA
Tel: 01349 862166 Fax: 01349 865178

Dornoch, Inverness-shire

Dornoch Castle

★★

Castle Street, Dornoch, Inverness-shire,
IV25 3SD
Tel: 01862 810216 Fax: 01862 810981

Drymen, Central

Buchanan Arms

★★★

Main Street, Drymen, Central, G63 0BQ
Tel: 01360 660588 Fax: 01360 660943

Dumfries, Dumfries & Galloway

Cairndale

★★★

English Street, Dumfries, Dumfries & Galloway,
DG1 2DF
Tel: 01387 254111 Fax: 01387 250555
Email: sales@cairndale.fsnet
Web: www.cairndalehotel.co.uk

Excellent leisure facilities. Regular weekend
entertainment (dinner dances, Ceilidhs, cabaret
nights) and conference facilities make the
Cairndale the number one choice in Dumfries.
Golfers particularly welcome.
SB £85 DB £105 HBS £64.50 HBD £44.50
B £6 L £8.95 D £17.50.
CC: MC Vi Am DC Swi Delt
⫢ 🐾 ⊙ ⓢ 🖳 ☎ 🅿 ∻ ℜ ♿ ♿ ⫳ ⫳
⫳ ∫
How to get there: Following main routes into
Dumfries, the hotel is on the northeast edge of
the town centre on English Street.

Scotland

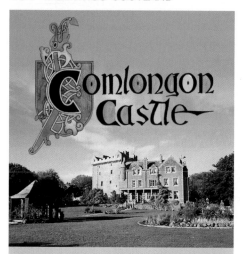

Comlongon Castle — a unique 120-acre estate containing a 13th-century keep. Edwardian mansion/hotel specialising in religious wedding ceremonies conducted by local ministers within restored Great Hall. Receptions and private functions catered for — all rooms contain four-poster beds and are ensuite.

Clarencefield, Dumfries DG1 4NA
Tel: 01387 870283   Fax: 01387 870266
Website: www.comlongon.co.uk

Hetland Hall Hotel

An elegant mansion set in 18 acres. The hotel offers excellent cuisine, superb bedrooms, gym, pool, sauna, steam room and toning beds. Includes a pitch and putt and helipad. Spectacular views and easy access to Gretna and Stranraer make the venue attractive for weekend and short breaks.

RAC
★★★

Best Western
★★★

Carrutherstown,
Dumfries & Galloway, DG1 4JX
Tel: 01387 840201   Fax: 01387 840211
Email: hetlandhallhotel@ic24.net
Website: www.hetlandhallhotel.ic24.net

Comlongon Castle
★★★
Clarencefield, Dumfries, DG1 4NA
Tel: 01387 870283 Fax: 01387 870266
Web: www.comlongon.com
Closed January
A unique restored 14th-century castle set in 120 acres of grounds, specialising in weddings and receptions daily. Celtic blessings performed for anniversaries.
SB £50 DB £100 L £7.50 D £28.
CC: MC Vi Am DC Swi
How to get there: At England/Scotland border, take A75 to Annan, then left onto B724. After 8 miles, at Clarencefield turn left down private drive.
See advert on the left

Hetland Hall
★★★
Carrutherstown, Dumfries, DG1 4JX
Tel: 01387 840201 Fax: 01387 840211
Email: hetlandhallhotel@ic.24.net
Web: www.hetlandhallhotel.ic.24.net
SB £55 DB £70 HBS £70 HBD £90
B £8.50 L £5.95 D £12.5.
CC: MC Vi Am DC Swi Delt
How to get there: On A75 Euroroute, 8 miles east of Dumfries.
See advert on the left

Huntingdon House
★★
18 St Mary's Street, Dumfries,
Dumfries & Galloway, DG1 1LZ
Tel: 01387 254893 Fax: 01387 262553
Email: acame4506@aol.com
Web: www.huntingdonhotel.co.uk
SB £40 DB £59 B £7.95 L £8.95 D £9.95.
CC: MC Vi Am DC Swi Delt
How to get there: M6 then M74 (A74) to North Carlisle. A75 to Dumfries. After Little Chef take second exit at roundabout and first exit at next roundabout onto A709.

Nith
★★
Glencaple, Dumfries & Galloway, DG1 4RE
Tel: 01387 770213 Fax: 01387 770568
SB £25 DB £45 B £5 L £5 D £5. CC: MC Vi Swi
How to get there: 5 miles from Dumfries on the B725 Glencaple road.

Franklea Guest House

◆ ◆ ◆

Castle Douglas Road, Dumfries, DG2 8PP
Tel: 01387 253004 Fax: 01387 259301

Dunbar, East Lothian

Bayswell

★★

Bayswell Park, Dunbar, East Lothian, EH42 1AE
Tel: 01368 862225 Fax: 01368 862225

Dundee

Swallow Hotel

★★★ 🍴

Kingsway West, Dundee, DD2 5JT
Tel: 01382 641122 Fax: 01382 568340

Beach House

◆ ◆ ◆ ◆

22 Esplenade, Broughty Ferry, DD5 2EQ
Tel: 01382 776614 Fax: 01382 420841
SB £38 DB £45 D £12. CC: MC Vi

🏌🎣🛌💻☎📞📺🅿🎿👫

How to get there: From Dundee station, 4 miles.

Dundonnell, Highland

Dundonnell

★★★ 🍴

Dundonnell, Highland, IV23 2QS
Tel: 01854 633204 Fax: 01854 633366

Dunfermline, Fife

Elgin

★★★

Charlestown, Dunfermline, Fife, KY11 3EE
Tel: 01383 872257 Fax: 01383 873044

King Malcolm

★★★

Queensferry Road, Wester Pitchorthie,
Dunfermline, Fife, KY11 5DS
Tel: 01383 722611 Fax: 01383 730865
Email: kingmalcolmhotel@hotmail.com
Web: www.peelhotel.com
B £8.95 L £9.95 D £16.50.
CC: MC Vi Am DC Swi Delt

🚗🛌💻☎🅿🎿👫👬〽

How to get there: Exit M90 J-2, A823 for
Dunfermline. Hotel on right at 3rd roundabout.

Pitbauchlie House

★★★

47 Aberdour Road, Dunfermline,
Fife, KY11 4PB
Tel: 01383 722282 Fax: 01383 620738
Email: info@pitbauchlie.com
Web: www.pitbauchlie.com

Situated in landscaped gardens, minutes from
M90. Conference, banqueting, bars and
restaurant facilities. Excellent food with the chef
taking advantage of Scotland's natural larder.
SB £66 DB £85 B £8.50 L £10 D £20.
CC: MC Vi Am DC Swi Delt

🚗🛌🖊🏌🎣💻☎📞🅿🎿🐴👫👬
👬 〽

How to get there: Exit M90 J-2, A823 towards
Dunfermline. Turn right onto B916. Hotel
situated ½ mile on right.

Halfway House

★★

Main Street, Kingseat, Dunfermline, Fife,
KY12 0TJ
Tel: 01383 731661 Fax: 01383 621274

Dunkeld, Perth & Kinross

Kinnaird

★★★ 🍴🍴🍴🍴

Kinnaird Estate, by Dunkeld, Perth & Kinross,
PH8 0LB
Tel: 01796 482440 Fax: 01796 482289
Email: enquiry@kinnairdestate.com
Web: www.kinnairdestate.com
Children minimum age: 12
HBS £300 HBD £345 B £15 L £30 D £45.
CC: MC Vi Am Swi

🚗🛌〽🏌💻☎📞🅿🎿🐴👫👬
🎣🎿🍴

How to get there: Travel north on A9 past Perth
and Dunkeld. Turn left onto B893. Hotel is 4
miles along on right.

Scotland

Atholl Arms

★★

Bridgehead, Dunkeld, Perth & Kinross, PH8 0AQ
Tel: 01350 727219 Fax: 01350 727219
Email: cdarbishire@aol.com
Children minimum age: 8
SB £45 DB £60 CC: MC Vi Am Swi Delt
How to get there: 12 miles north of Perth. After rail station on left, take first right into Dunkeld. First hotel over bridge on right.

Dunoon, Argyll & Bute

Argyll

★★

Argyll Street, Dunoon, Argyll & Bute, PA23 7NE
Tel: 01369 702059 Fax: 01369 704483
Email: info@argyll-hotel.co.uk
Web: www.argyll-hotel.co.uk
SB £50 DB £70 HBS £45 HBD £85 B £5
CC: MC Vi Am DC Swi Delt
How to get there: From Glasgow, M8 to Gourock for ferry to Dunoon. Hotel situated overlooks town's bandstand area and the Firth of Clyde.

Esplanade

★★

West Bay, Dunoon, Argyll & Bute, PA23 7HU
Tel: 01369 704070 Fax: 01369 702129
Web: www.end.co.uk
Closed November to March

Long-established, award-winning family run hotel situated on the traffic-free West Bay. Overlooking the River Clyde with easy access to the Western Highlands.
SB £41 DB £72 B £5.75 L £6.25 D £15.50.
CC: MC Vi Swi Delt

The Anchorage

♦♦♦♦♦

Shore Road, Ardnadam, Sandbank, Dunoon, Argyll & Bute, PA23 8QG
Tel: 01369 705108 Fax: 01369 705108

Ardtully

♦♦♦

297 Marine Parade, Hunters Quay, Dunoon, Argyll & Bute, PA23 8HN
Tel: 01369 702478

Small friendly hotel set in own grounds with outstanding views over the Clyde estuary and surrounding hills, close to amenities.
SB £30 DB £60 HBS £45 HBD £90
How to get there: On the coast road between Dunoon and Sandbank, 2 miles from Dunoon overlooking the Firth of Clyde at Hunters Quay. 200 yards from the Western Ferry Terminal.

Osborne

♦♦♦

44 Shore Road, Innellan, nr Dunoon, Argyll & Bute, PA23 7TJ
Tel: 01369 830445

East Kilbride, Lanarkshire

Bruce

★★★

35 Cornwall Street, East Kilbride, Lanarkshire, G74 1AF
Tel: 01355 229711 Fax: 01355 242216
Email: enquiries@maksu-group.co.uk
Web: www.maksu-group.co.uk
SB £75 DB £95 B £7.50 L £8 D £16.50.
CC: MC Vi Am DC Swi Delt
How to get there: Exit M74 J-5, A725 to East Kilbride. Follow signs to town centre into Cornwall Street, hotel is 200m on left.

Edinburgh

Balmoral

★ ★ ★ ★ ★ ℞ ℞ ℞
1 Princes Street, Edinburgh, EH2 2EQ
Tel: 0131 5562414 Fax: 0131 5573747
Web: www.rfhotels.com

RF Hotels' elegant five-star Balmoral Hotel offers 188 luxurious bedrooms (many with castle views), award-winning restaurants, health spa, pool and extensive function facilities.
SB £190 DB £230 HBS £215 HBD £280
B £16.75 L £25 D £25. CC: MC Vi Am DC Swi
How to get there: A8 to city centre, signs for Waverley rail station. Hotel is directly opposite.

Carlton

★ ★ ★ ★ ℞ ℞
North Bridge, Edinburgh, EH1 1SD
Tel: 0131 556 7277 Fax: 0131 556 2691

Royal Scot

★ ★ ★ ★ ℞
111 Glasgow Road, Edinburgh, EH12 8NF
Tel: 0131 334 9191 Fax: 0131 316 4507
Web: www.swallowhotels.com
To become Marriott, Summer 2001.
SB £125 DB £145 CC: MC Vi Am Swi
How to get there: From A1, A701, A702 or M8, take A720 to Gogar roundabout. Right, get into right-hand lane, hotel right over next lights.

Royal Terrace

★ ★ ★ ★
18 Royal Terrace, Edinburgh, EH7 5AQ
Tel: 0131 557 3222 Fax: 0131 557 5339
Email: reservations.royalterrace@principalhotels.
co.uk
SB £135 DB £170 HBS £155 HBD £210
CC: MC Vi Am Swi Delt

How to get there: Northeast from Princes Street, located off Leith Walk.

Barnton

★ ★ ★
562 Queensferry Road, Edinburgh, EH4 6AS
Tel: 0131 339 1144 Fax: 0131 339 5521
SB £89 DB £99 HBS £104 HBD £129
B £9 L £12 D £15. CC: MC Vi Am DC Swi Delt
How to get there: M8/M9 take A8, A902 (Maybury Road). Into Queensferry Rd, hotel left.

Braid Hills

★ ★ ★ ℞ ℞
134 Braid Road, Edinburgh, EH10 6JD
Tel: 0131 447 8888 Fax: 0131 452 8477
Email: bookings@braidhillshotel.co.uk
Web: www.braidhillshotel.co.uk

Magnificently situated only two miles from the city centre, yet a world away from the noise and congestion of the centre itself. An independently owned hotel.
SB £80 DB £135 HBS £95 HBD £165 B £8.95
L £8 D £16.95. CC: MC Vi Am DC Swi Delt
How to get there: From bypass, A702 to centre. Hotel is 1 mile on right-hand side.

Carlton Greens

★ ★ ★ ℞
2 Carlton Terrace, Edinburgh, EH7 5DD
Tel: 0131 556 6570 Fax: 0131 557 6680

Johnstounburn House

★ ★ ★ ℞ ℞
nr Dalkeith, Humbie, Edinburgh, EH35 5PL
Tel: 01875 833696 Fax: 01875 833626
SB £115 DB £150 HBS £135 HBD £190
B £12.50 L £7.50 D £35.
CC: MC Vi Am DC Swi Delt
How to get there: From A68 take B6368, signposted Haddington. Hotel on right.

Scotland

Jurys Edinburgh Inn

★★★

43 Jeffrey Street, Edinburgh, EH1 1DG
Tel: 0131 200 3300 Fax: 0131 200 0400
Email: info@jurys.com
Web: www.jurysdoyle.com
SB £71.50 DB £79 HBS £86.50 HBD £109
B £5.50 L £4.95 D £15. CC: MC Vi Am DC Swi

How to get there: At Waverley Station, exit onto
Market Street. Turn left. Hotel is situated two
minutes walk on right-hand side.

Norton House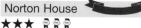

★★★ 🍴🍴🍴

Ingliston, Edinburgh, EH28 8LX
Tel: 0131 333 1275 Fax: 0131 333 5305
Email: events.nhh@arcadianhotels.co.uk
Web: www.arcadianhotels.co.uk
SB £125 DB £150 HBS £150 HBD £190 B £4.50
L £15.50 D £28. CC: MC Vi Am DC Swi Delt

How to get there: From Edinburgh, take A8 past
airport. Norton House is half a mile on the left.

Old Waverley

★★★

43 Princes Street, Edinburgh, EH2 2BY
Tel: 0131 556 4648 Fax: 0131 557 6316
Email:oldwaverleyreservations@paramount-
        hotels.co.uk
Web: www.paramount-hotels.co.uk

Standing on Princess Street, the hotel's
bedrooms, restaurant and lounges offer
stunning views of Edinburgh castle and Princess
Street gardens while being convenient for
Waverley station.
SB £111.50 DB £185 B £12.50 L £4.95 D £9.95.
CC: MC Vi Am DC Swi

How to get there: Follow signs to city centre
and Waverley Station. Directly opposite
Waverley Station & Scott's Monument.

Quality Hotel Commodore

★★★

Cramond Foreshore, Edinburgh, EH4 5EP
Tel: 0131 336 1700 Fax: 0131 336 4934

Allison House

★★ 🍴

15/17 Mayfield Gardens, Edinburgh, EH9 2AX
Tel: 0131 667 8049 Fax: 0131 667 5001
Email: enquiry@allisonhousehotel.com
Web: www.allisonhousehotel.com

Family-run hotel, one mile from city centre.
Twenty-two en-suite bedrooms, Murray's
restaurant, residents' bar, conference room and
private parking. Warm, friendly welcome awaits.
Theatre, golf and short breaks our speciality.
SB £35 DB £50 HBS £50 HBD £80
B £5.50 D £9. CC: MC Vi Am DC Swi Delt

How to get there: Situated on the south side of
Edinburgh, 1 mile from city centre on A701.

Iona

★★ 🍴

17 Strathearn Place, Edinburgh, EH9 2AL
Tel: 0131 447 5050 Fax: 0131 452 8574

Murrayfeld

★★

18 Corstorphine Road, Edinburgh, EH12 6HN
Tel: 0131 3371844 Fax: 0131 3468189
SB £59 DB £79 B £5 L £5 D £10.
CC: MC Vi Am Swi

How to get there: Situated on A8 running from
airport to city centre. Opposite Murrayfield
Rugby Stadium, 1 mile from zoo.

Orwell Lodge

★★

29 Polwarth Terrace, Edinburgh, EH11 1NH
Tel: 0131 229 1044 Fax: 0131 228 9492

Friendly and attentive service is a feature of this popular hotel. In quiet location close to the city centre. On bus route. Bar and restaurant. All rooms non-smoking.
SB £49 DB £75 B £8 L £6 D £12.
CC: MC Vi Am Swi

How to get there: From A702 turn into Gilmore Place (opposite Kings Theatre). 1 mile on left.

Royal Ettrick

★★

13 Ettrick Road, Edinburgh, EH10 5BJ
Tel: 0131 228 6413 Fax: 0131 229 7330

Thrums

★★

14 Minto Street, Edinburgh, EH9 1RQ
Tel: 0131 667 5545 Fax: 0131 667 8707
Closed Christmas
SB £35 DB £80 HBS £45 HBD £95
B £4.50 L £7.50 D £11.50. CC: MC Vi

How to get there: From Edinburgh South, take A7/A701 to Newington.

The Scotsman

❖

20 North Bridge, Edinburgh, Lothian, EH1 1YT
Tel: 0131 556 5565 Fax: 0131 652 3652

Dorstan   Little Gem

◆◆◆◆◆

7 Priestfield Road, Edinburgh, EH16 5HJ
Tel: 0131 667 5138 Fax: 0131 668 4644
Email: reservations@dorstan-hotel.demon.co.uk
Located close to the city centre's many attractions, this tastefully decorated Victorian

house exudes the warm hospitality of its proprietor Mairae Campbell.
SB £32 DB £72 D £17. CC: MC Vi Am Swi Delt

Grosvenor Gardens

◆◆◆◆◆

1 Grosvenor Gardens, Edinburgh, EH12 5JU
Tel: 0131 313 3415 Fax: 0131 346 8732
Email: info@stayinedinburgh.com
Web: www.stayinedinburgh.com
SB £40 DB £50 CC: MC Vi Swi Delt Solo

How to get there: From airport, left off A8 (Haymarket Terrace) into Roseberry Crescent. Grosvenor Gardens is the first street on the left.

The Lodge

◆◆◆◆◆

6 Hampton Terrace, West Coates, Edinburgh, EH12 5JD
Tel: 0131 337 3682 Fax: 0131 313 1700
Email: thelodgehotel@btconnect.com
Web: www.thelodgehotel.co.uk

Exclusive West End hotel offering finest quality accommodation and cuisine. Open fires in sumptuous lounge and cosy cocktail bar. Beautifully appointed non-smoking bedrooms. Car parking.
B £7.50 D £18.50. CC: MC Vi Am Swi Delt

How to get there: On A8, 1 mile west from city centre and railway station; 3 miles from airport.

Scotland

Adam

◆◆◆◆

19 Lansdowne Crescent, Edinburgh, EH12 5EH
Tel: 0131 337 1148

Almond House

◆◆◆◆

52 Glasgow Road, Edinburgh, EH12 8HW
Tel: 0131 467 4588

Ashlyn Guest House

◆◆◆◆

42 Inverleith Row, Edinburgh, EH3 5PY
Tel: 0131 552 2954 Fax: 0131 552 2954
Children minimum age: 7
SB £28 DB £55

Ben Doran Guest House

◆◆◆◆

11 Mayfield Gardens, Edinburgh, EH9 2AX
Tel: 0131 667 8488 Fax: 0131 667 0076
Email: info@bendoran.com
Web: www.bendoran.com

Luxurious Georgian guest house, beautifully
refurbished. Central, on bus routes close to
attractions and city centre. Free parking,
four-diamond amenities, non-smoking, views
and a warm welcome.
SB £35 DB £48 D £25. CC: MC Vi DC Delt
How to get there: On A701, 1 mile south of
Princes Street, 3 miles north of bypass (A720).
See advert on facing page

Corstorphine Guest House

◆◆◆◆

188 St Johns Road, Edinburgh, EH12 8SG
Tel: 0131 539 4237

Looking for great dining? Look for RAC Hotels
and Guest Accommodation displaying the
RAC Dining Award symbol in this Guide.

Ivy Guest House

◆◆◆◆

7 Mayfield Gardens, Edinburgh, EH9 2AX
Tel: 0131 667 3411 Fax: 0131 620 1422
Email: don@ivyguesthouse.com
Web: www.ivyguesthouse.com
How to get there: Located on A701 just over
1 mile from Princes Street.

Kew House

◆◆◆◆

1 Kew Terrace, Murrayfield, EH12 5JE
Tel: 0131 313 0700 Fax: 0131 313 0747
Email: kewhouse@worldsites.net
Web: www.kewhouse.com

Caring for the more discerning traveller,
this immaculate listed building is centrally
located with secure parking. Luxurious
bedrooms and peaceful residents bar ensures
a memorable stay.
SB £47 DB £75 L £7 D £7.
CC: MC Vi Am DC Swi Delt JCB
How to get there: Directly on A8 route 1 mile
west of Princes Street and on main route from
Edinburgh airport.

Roselea House

◆◆◆◆

11 Mayfield Road, Edinburgh, EH9 2NG
Tel: 0131 667 6115 Fax: 0131 667 3556

Abbotts Head Guest House

◆◆◆

40 Minto Street, Edinburgh, Lothian, EH9 2BR
Tel: 0131 668 1658 Fax: 0131 668 1658

Boisdale

◆◆◆

9 Coates Gardens, Edinburgh, EH12 5LG
Tel: 0131 337 1134 Fax: 0131 313 0048
SB £25 DB £60

Cumberland

♦♦♦

1 West Coates, Edinburgh, EH12 5JQ
Tel: 0131 337 1198 Fax: 0131 337 1022

Galloway

♦♦♦

22 Dean Park Crescent, Edinburgh, EH4 1PH
Tel: 0131 332 3672 Fax: 0131 332 3672
SB £25 DB £36
🐎🗨💻✗✗🐎🎠🛏🐕
How to get there: On A90, centre 10 mins walk.

Newington Guest House

♦♦♦

18 Newington Road, Edinburgh, EH9 1QS
Tel: 0131 667 3356 Fax: 0131 667 8307
Email: newington.guesthouse@dial.pipex.com
Web: www.newington-gh.co.uk
Children minimum age: 9
SB £32.50 DB £49 CC: MC Vi Swi Delt
🚗🐎⊗🗨💻📞P✗✗🐎🛏🐕🎠
How to get there: On A68/A7, main bus route.

Quaich Guest House

♦♦♦

87 St Johns Road, Edinburgh, EH12 6NN
Tel: 0131 334 4440 Fax: 0131 476 9002

SB £26 DB £52 CC: MC Vi Am Swi
⊗🗨💻P✗✗🐎🛏🐕
How to get there: From south, follow M6 to M74
to M8 and A8 to Edinburgh, into Glasgow Road
into St John's Road.

Averon City Centre Guest House

♦♦

44 Gilmore Place, Edinburgh, EH3 9NQ
Tel: 0131 229 9932
Email: info@averon.co.uk
Web: www.averon.co.uk
SB £26 DB £28 CC: MC Vi Am DC Swi Delt
♿🗨💻P✗✗🐎🛏🐕
How to get there: From Princes Street go up
Lothian Road and turn right at the Kings
Theatre.

Granville Guesthouse

♦♦

13 Granville Terrace, Edinburgh, EH10 4PQ
Tel: 0131 229 1676 Fax: 0131 229 4633

Kariba

♦♦

10 Granville Terrace, Edinburgh, Lothian,
EH10 4PQ
Tel: 0131 229 3773

Scotland

Edzell, Angus

Glenesk

★★★
High Street, Edzell, Angus, DD9 7TF
Tel: 01356 648319 Fax: 01356 647333
Email: gleneskhotel@btconnect.com
Web: www.gleneskhotel.co.uk
SB £55 DB £90 B £9 L £12 D £18.
CC: MC Vi DC Swi Delt

Erskine, Renfrewshire

Erskine Bridge Cosmopolitan

★★★
Erskine, Renfrewshire, PA8 6AN
Tel: 0141 812 0123 Fax: 0141 812 7642
Email: erskineres@cosmopolitan.com
Web: www.cosmopolitan-hotels.com
SB £54.50 DB £109
CC: MC Vi Am DC Swi Delt

How to get there: Exit M8 J-30, M898 to first
junction. Right at first roundabout, over 2nd,
left at 3rd, right at 4th.

Falkirk, Falkirk

Comfort Inn

★★
Manor Street, Falkirk, FK1 1NT
Tel: 01324 624066 Fax: 01324 611785

Falkland, Fife

Covenanter

♦♦♦
The Square, Falkland, Fife, KY15 7BU
Tel: 01337 857224 Fax: 01337 857163

For your complete reassurance, only RAC
Hotels and Guest Accommodation have been
assessed on your behalf by our team of
independent inspectors for quality, facilities
and service.

Forres, Moray

Ramnee

★★★ 🐾🐾🐾
Victoria Road, Forres, Moray, IV36 3BN
Tel: 01309 672410 Fax: 01309 673392
Email: ramneehotel@btconnect.com
SB £70 DB £95 HBS £95.50 HBD £146
B £8.50 L £10.50 D £20.50.
CC: MC Vi Am DC Swi Delt

How to get there: From A96 Inverness/Aberdeen
road at Forres, left onto Forres bypass east of
town. Hotel 500m on right.

Park

★★
Victoria Road, Forres, Moray, IV36 0BN
Tel: 01309 672611 Fax: 01309 672328

SB £45 DB £58 HBS £61 HBD £90
B £10 L £12.50 D £16. CC: MC Vi Am DC

How to get there: Enter Forres from the east
end of bypass. Park Hotel is first hotel on right.

Fort William, Highland

Inverlochy Castle

★★★★ 🐾🐾🐾🐾
Torlundy, Fort William, Highland, PH33 6SN
Tel: 01397 702177 Fax: 01397 702953
Email: info@inverlochy.co.uk
Web: www.inverlochy.co.uk
Closed January 7 to February 12
SB £180 DB £250 B £15 L £23 D £45.
CC: MC Vi Am Swi Delt

How to get there: Accessible from the A82 trunk
road from Glasgow to Fort William.

Moorings

★★★ 🐾🐾🐾
Banavie, Fort William, Highland, PH33 7LY
Tel: 01397 772797 Fax: 01397 772441
Email: reservations@moorings-fortwilliam.co.uk
Web: www.moorings-fortwilliam.co.uk
Sitting in the shadow of Ben Nevis, this award
winning hotel offers its guests a truly warm
welcome, with good food, cosy bedrooms and
friendly service.
SB £58 DB £48 HBS £83 HBD £73
B £8 D £21.
CC: MC Vi Am DC Swi Delt

How to get there: Follow A82 to Fort William

and turn onto A830, signposted Mallaig. Past canal bridge, turn right into Banauie.

Caledonian

★★

Achintore Road, Fort William, PH33 6RW
Tel: 01397 703117 Fax: 01397 700550
SB £75 DB £95 HBS £90 HBD £110
L £9.50 D £17.50. CC: MC Vi Am DC Swi Delt

How to get there: On the A82, 2 miles south of Fort William.

The Grand

★★ 🍴🍴

Gordon Square, Fort William, PH33 6DX
Tel: 01397 702928 Fax: 01397 702928
Email: thegrandhotel@compuserve.com
Web: www.grandhotel-scotland.co.uk
Closed January
B £7.95 L £9.95 D £16.95. CC: MC Vi
Am DC Swi Delt JCB Maestro Solo

How to get there: Town centre at the west end of the pedestrianised High Street.

Factor's House

♦ ♦ ♦ ♦ ♦

Torlundy, Fort William, Highland, PH33 6SN
Tel: 01397 702177 Fax: 01397 702953
Email: info@inverlochy.co.uk
Web: www.inverlochy.co.uk
CC: MC Vi Am Swi Delt

How to get there: On A82 from Glasgow.

Distillery House

♦ ♦ ♦ ♦

Nevis Bridge, North Road, Fort William,
Highland, PH33 6LH
Tel: 01397 700103 Fax: 01397 702980
Closed December to January
SB £35 DB £60 CC: MC Vi Am Swi

How to get there: From the north, turn right at second set of traffic lights. From the south, the hotel is on the left after Glen Nevis roundabout.

Fortingall, Perth & Kinross

Fortingall

★★

By Aberfeldy, Fortingall, PH15 2NQ
Tel: 01887 830367 Fax: 01887 830367

Gairloch, Ross-shire

Creag Mor

★★★ 🍴

Charleston, Gairloch, Ross-shire, IV21 2AH
Tel: 01445 712068 Fax: 01445 712044

Old Inn

♦ ♦ ♦ ♦

Gairloch, Ross-shire, IV21 2BD
Tel: 01445 712006 Fax: 01445 712445
Email: nomadscot@lineone.net
Web: www.theoldinn.co.uk

Galashiels, Borders

Kingsknowes

★★★ 🍴

1 Selkirk Road, Galashiels, Borders, TD1 3HY
Tel: 01896 758375 Fax: 01896 750377
Email: enquiries@kingsknowes.co.uk
SB £54 DB £80 HBS £66 HBD £104 B £8.50
L £10 D £15. CC: MC Vi Am DC Swi Delt

How to get there: From Edinburgh, or Junction 40 of M6, follow A7 to Glashiels. From Newcastle, follow A68 to Galashiels.

Scotland

Abbotsford Arms

★★

63 Stirling Street, Galashiels, TD1 1BY
Tel: 01896 752517 Fax: 01896 750744

Family hotel tastefully decorated. Small and
friendly with a reputation for good food, served
all day from 12 noon. Close to town centre.
SB £38 DB £58 B £5 L £9 D £12.
CC: MC Vi DC Swi Delt

How to get there: Centrally situated in town.

Gatehouse-of-Fleet, Dumfr. & Gallwy

Cally Palace

★★★★

Gatehouse-of-Fleet, DG7 2DL
Tel: 01557 814341 Fax: 01557 814522

Bank O'Fleet

♦♦♦

47 High Street, Gatehouse-of-Fleet, DG7 2HR
Tel: 01557 814302 Fax: 01557 814302
Email: info@bankofleethote.co.uk
Web: www.bankofleethotel.co.uk

An attractive hotel, resting in the heart of
picturesque and historic Galloway town,
Gatehouse-of-Fleet. The hotel has earned a
reputation for good food. Ideal for golf,
hillwalking and fishing.

SB £30 DB £47 HBS £42 HBD £35
B £4.25 L £5 D £6.25. CC: MC Vi Am

Glasgow

Millennium Hotel Glasgow

★★★★

George Square, Glasgow, G2 1DS
Tel: 0141 332 6711 Fax: 0141 332 4264

In an historic city centre location, this
refurbished town house offers a relaxed
environment with contemporary interiors,
complemented by fashionable conservatories
overlooking George Square.

Glynhill Hotel & Leisure Club

★★★

Paisley Road, Renfrew, PA4 8XB
Tel: 0141 886 5555 Fax: 0141 885 2838
Email: glynhillleisurehotel@msn.com
Web: www.glynhill.com

Ideal, convenient base for business executives
and tourists alike. Set in a quiet location with
two excellent restaurants, superb leisure club,
major conference centre and friendly and
efficient staff.
SB £64 DB £69 L £9.50 D £15.25.
CC: MC Vi Am DC Swi Delt

How to get there: Exit M8 J-27, A741 towards
Renfrew Cross. Hotel on right.

Jurys Glasgow

★★★

Great Western Road, Glasgow, G12 0XP
Tel: 003531 6070055 Fax: 003531 6609625
Email: dorothy_cusack@jurysdoyle.com
Web: www.jurysdoyle.com
CC: MC Vi Am DC

Kings Park

★★★

Mill Street, Rutherglen, Glasgow, G73 2AR
Tel: 0141 647 5491 Fax: 0141 613 3022
Email: enquiries@maksu-group.co.uk
Web: www.maksu-group.co.uk
SB £55 DB £80 HBS £70 HBD £100 B £6.50
L £6.75 D £18.50. CC: MC Vi Am DC Swi Delt

How to get there: From Glasgow, A730 for East
Kilbride. Hotel on left in suburb on Rutherglen.

MacDonald

★★★

Eastwood Toll, Giffnock, Glasgow, G46 6RA
Tel: 0141 638 2225 Fax: 0141 638 6231
SB £95 DB £115 B £9 L £6 D £9.
CC: MC Vi Am DC Swi Delt

How to get there: M77 J-3, A726 east 1½ miles.
Right after 2nd roundabout (Eastwood Toll).

Patio Hotel

★★★

1 South Avenue, Clydebank Business Park,
Glasgow, Clydebank, G81 2RW
Tel: 0141 951 1133 Fax: 0141 952 3713

Quality Hotel Glasgow

★★★

99 Gordon Street, Glasgow, G1 3SF
Tel: 0141 221 9680 Fax: 0141 226 3948
Email: admin@gb627.u-net.com
Web: www.choicehotels.com

SB £86.50 DB £112 HBS £101 HBD £141
B £9.50 L £7.95 D £14.50.
CC: MC Vi Am DC Swi Delt

How to get there: From M8 Westbound take
J-19 onto Argyle Street and left onto Oswald
Street. NCP car park on right.

Sherbrooke Castle

★★★

11 Sherbrooke Avenue, Glasgow, G41 4PG
Tel: 0141 427 4227 Fax: 0141 427 5685
Email: mail@sherbrooke.co.uk
Web: www.sherbrooke.co.uk
SB £65 DB £85 B £6.50 L £12.50 D £20.
CC: MC Vi Am DC Swi Delt

How to get there: Close to M77 J-1, M8 J-23
and J-22 from City and J-27 from aiport.

Stuart

★★★

2 Cornwall Way, East Kilbride, G74 1JR
Tel: 01355 221161 Fax: 01355 264410
SB £65 DB £80 B £5 L £7 D £14.
CC: MC Vi Am DC Swi Delt Solo JCB

How to get there: Exit M74 J-5 to East Kilbride,
then follow signs for town centre. Situated by
bus station and fire station.

Swallow Hotel

★★★

517 Paisley Road, Glasgow, G51 1RW
Tel: 0141 427 3146 Fax: 0141 427 4059
Children minimum age: 14
SB £70 DB £80 HBS £80 HBD £110
B £9.50 L £11.50 D £18.50.
CC: MC Vi Am DC Swi

How to get there: Exit M8 J-23, turn right into
Paisley Road West. Hotel located 400 yards on
right-hand side.

Scotland

Argyll

★★

973 Sauchiehall Street, Glasgow, G3 7TQ
Tel: 0141 337 3313 Fax: 0141 337 3283
Email: info@argyllhotelglasgow.co.uk
Web: www.argyllhotelglasgow.co.uk

Ideal location half a mile west of city centre.
Minutes' walk to SECC, Kelvingrove art
galleries/museum and Glasgow University.
Traditional bar/restaurant. Good value with
warm Scottish hospitality.
SB £56 DB £70 HBS £70 HBD £98 L £6 D £8.
CC: MC Vi Am Swi Delt

How to get there: Exit M8 J-18, ahead to 2nd
lights, right into Berkeley Street, right into
Elderslie Street, first left into Sauchiehall Street.

Dunkeld

★

10–12 Queen's Drive, Glasgow, G42 8BS
Tel: 0141 424 0160 Fax: 0141 423 4437

Angus

◆◆◆

970 Sauchiehall Street, Glasgow, G3 7TQ
Tel: 0141 357 5155 Fax: 0141 339 9469
Email: info@angushotelglasgow.co.uk
Web: www.angushotelglasgow.co.uk
SB £43 DB £56 CC: MC Vi Am Swi Delt

How to get there: Exit M8 J-18. At second set
of traffic lights, turn right into Berkeley Street.
At end turn right then first left into
Sauchiehall Street.

When booking at an RAC Hotel or Guest
Accommodation, please mention this Guide.

Kelvingrove

◆◆◆

944 Saucjiehall Street, Glasgow, G3 7TH
Tel: 0141 339 5011 Fax: 0141 339 6566
Email: kelvingrove.hotel@business.ntl.com
Web: www.kelvingrove-hotel.co.uk
SB £38 DB £58 CC: MC Vi Swi

How to get there: Exit M8 J-18, Charing Cross,
and then Kelvingrove.

Rennie Mackintosh

◆◆◆

218–220 Renfrew Street, Glasgow, G3 6TX
Tel: 0141 333 9992

McLays Guest House

◆◆

264–276 Renfrew Street, Charing Cross,
Glasgow, G3 6TT
Tel: 0141 3324796

Smith's

◆◆

963 Sauchiehall Street, Glasgow, G3 7TQ
Tel: 0141 339 6363/7674 Fax: 0141 334 1892
SB £20 DB £36

How to get there: 1/2 mile from city centre. Next
to the West End. (University) Taxi from city
centre approximately £4.

Charing X Guest House

◆

310 Renfrew Street, Glasgow, G3 6UW
Tel: 0141 332 2503 Fax: 0141 353 3047
Email: info@charing-x.com
Web: www.charing-x.com
SB £22 DB £38 CC: MC Vi Am DC Swi Delt

Gleneagles, Perth & Kinross

Cairn Lodge

★★ ♖♖♖
Orchil Road, Auchterarder, Gleneagles,
Perth & Kinross, PH3 1LX
Tel: 01764 662634 Fax: 01764 664866

Short breaks

Many Hotels and Guest Accommodation offer
special weekend rates and mid-week breaks.
If not quoted in the property's entry, call
RAC Hotel Reservations on 0870 603 9109
to find out what may be on offer.

Glenmoriston, Inverness-shire

Cluanie Inn

★★ ⊞

Glenmoriston, Inverness-shire, IV63 7YW
Tel: 01320 340238 Fax: 01320 340293
Email: cluanie@ecosse.net
Web: www.cluanie.co.uk

Lying between Loch Ness and the Isle of Skye, this newly refurbished Highland inn offers a range of facilities and services, the restaurants catering for every requirement. Children welcome. Dogs allowed.
SB £37.50 DB £85 B £3.50 L £7.50 D £14.50.
CC: MC Vi Am Swi

How to get there: The Cluanie Inn lies on the A87 halfway between Loch Ness and the Isle of Skye.

Grantown-on-Spey, Moray

Culdearn House

★★ ⊞⊞⊞

Woodlands Terrace, Grantown-on-Spey,
Morayshire, PH26 3JU
Tel: 01479 872106 Fax: 01479 873641
Email: culdearn@globalnet.co.uk
Web: www.culdearn.com
Children minimum age: 10. Closed Nov to Feb
HBS £65 HBD £130 B £10 D £25. CC: MC Vi
Am DC Swi Delt JCB

How to get there: Enter Grantown from southwest on A95. Turn left at 30mph sign.

Ravenscourt House

◆◆◆◆◆   ⊀ ⊱

Seafield Avenue, Grantown-on-Spey,
Moray, PH26 3JG
Tel: 01479 872286 Fax: 01479 873260
SB £35 DB £65 HBS £52 HBD £77
B £5 D £16.50.

How to get there: Turn left at Bank of Scotland. Ravenscourt is 200m on right-hand side.

The Pines

◆◆◆◆◆   ⊞ ⊀ ⊱ Little Gem

Woodside Avenue, Grantown-on-Spey, Moray,
PH26 3JR
Tel: 01479 872092 Fax: 01479 872092

Garden Park Guest House

◆◆◆◆   ⊀ ⊱

Woodside Avenue, Grantown-on-Spey,
PH26 3JN
Tel: 01479 873235
Children minimum age: 12
Closed November to February
SB £24 DB £48 HBS £36.50 HBD £73

How to get there: Corner of Forest Road and Woodside Avenue, off High Street.

Gretna, Dumfries & Galloway

Gretna Chase

★★★ ⊞

Gretna, Dumfries & Galloway, DG16 5JB
Tel: 01461 337517 Fax: 01461 337766

Solway Lodge

★★

Annan Road, Gretna, Dumfries & Galloway,
DG16 5DN
Tel: 01461 338266 Fax: 01461 337791
Web: www.solwaylodge.co.uk
SB £39.50 DB £59 B £8.50
CC: MC Vi Am DC Swi Delt

How to get there: From south, 2nd exit at roundabout ('Town Centre'), 200m on right.

Royal Stewart

★

Glasgow Road, Gretna, Dumfries & Galloway,
DG16 5DT
Tel: 01461 338210

Surrone House

◆◆◆   ⊀

Annan Road, Gretna, DG16 5DL
Tel: 01461 338341 Fax: 01461 338341
Email: surrone@aol.com
SB £40 DB £95 D £9.50.
CC: MC Vi Am Swi Delt

How to get there: On main road through Gretna, (not the bypass).

Scotland

Haddington, East Lothian

Brown's `Little Gem`

◆◆◆◆ ⬤ ⬤ ⬤
1 West Road, Haddington, East Lothian,
EH41 3RD
Tel: 01620 822254 Fax: 01620 822254

Hawick, Borders

Kirklands

★★
West Stewart Place, Hawick, Borders, TD9 8BH
Tel: 01450 372263 Fax: 01450 370404
SB £49.50 DB £75.50 B £4.95 L £6.95
D £10.95. CC: MC Vi Swi Delt
🐎⬤⬤⬤🖥☎📞P⬤⬤⬤⬤⬤⬤⬤⬤⬤⬤
How to get there: ½ mile north of Hawick High
Street, 200 yards west of A7.

Helensburgh, Argyll & Bute

Kirkton House `Little Gem`

◆◆◆◆◆ ⬤ ⬤ ⬤
Darleith Road, Cardross, Argyll & Bute, G82 5EZ
Tel: 01389 841951 Fax: 01389 841868
Email: rac@kirktonhouse.co.uk
Web: www.kirktonhouse.co.uk
Closed December to January

Near Loch Lomond and Glasgow Airport
(15 miles), in tranquil countryside with
panoramic Clyde views, with relaxed ambience
and home-cooked dinners by oil lamplight.
SB £40.50 DB £61.50 HBS £52.50 HBD £42.50
D £16. CC: MC Vi Am DC Swi Delt JCB
♿🐎⬤⬤🖥☎⬤P⬤⬤⬤⬤⬤⬤⬤
How to get there: Turn north off A814 at the
west end of Cardross Village, up Darleith Road.
Kirkton is ½ mile on right.

Howwood, Renfrewshire

Bowfield Hotel & Country Club

★★★ ⬤ ⬤
Lands of Bowfield, Howwood,
Renfrewshire, PA9 1DB
Tel: 01505 705225 Fax: 01505 705230

Inveraray, Argyll & Bute

Loch Fyne

★★★
Inveraray, Argyll & Bute, PA32 8XT
Tel: 01499 302 148 Fax: 01499 302 348

Invergarry, Inverness-shire

Glengarry Castle Hotel

★★★ ⬤ ⬤
Invergarry, Inverness-shire, PH35 4HW
Tel: 01809 501254 Fax: 01809 501207
Email: castle@clengarry.net
Web: www.glengarry.net
Closed December to February

Fine Victorian mansion in extensive wooded
grounds on the shores of Loch Oich. Privately
owned and personally managed by the
MacCallum family for over 40 years.
SB £55 DB £90 HBS £80 HBD £70
B £8 L £4.50 D £25. CC: MC Vi Swi Delt
⬤🐎⬤⬤🖥☎P⬤⬤⬤⬤⬤⬤⬤⬤⬤
How to get there: On A82 1 mile from Invergarry.

Craigard Guest House

◆◆◆ ⬤
Invergarry, Inverness-shire, PH35 4HG
Tel: 01809 501258 Fax: 01809 501258
Children minimum age: 12
SB £20 DB £40 D £15. CC: MC Vi Swi
⬤⬤🖥P⬤⬤⬤⬤⬤⬤⬤
How to get there: From the A82, take the A87.
Hotel is one mile out of village, on right.

Inverness, Inverness-shire

Inverness Marriott

★★★★ &

Culcabock Road, Inverness, IV2 3LP
Tel: 01463 257106 Fax: 01463 718480
Email: inverness@marriotthotels.co.uk
Web: marriott.com/marriott/invkm
SB £78 DB £78 B £6.50 L £11.50 D £24.
CC: MC Vi Am DC Swi Delt JCB Connect

How to get there: From south (A9) entering
Inverness take the slip road on the left marked
Culduthel and Kingsmills. Follow signs for
Kingsmills.

Loch Ness House

★★★ &

Glenurquhart Road, Inverness,
Inverness-shire IV3 6JL
Tel: 01463 231248 Fax: 01463 239327
Email: lnhhchris@aol.com

Friendly family-run 22-bedroom hotel.
Pleasantly situated beside Torvean golf course
and Caledonian canal. Excellent restaurant and
local pub. Scottish specialities.
SB £65 DB £110 HBS £82.50 HBD £140
B £9.50 D £18.50.
CC: MC Vi Am DC Swi Delt

How to get there: On A82 (Fort William). From
A9, left at Longman roundabout, follow A82
signs for 2½ miles.

Lochardil House

★★★ &

Stratherrick Road, Inverness, IV2 4LF
Tel: 01463 235995 Fax: 01463 713394
Email: lochardil@ukonline.co.uk
SB £75 DB £105 B £10 L £12 D £18.
CC: MC Vi Am DC Swi Delt

How to get there: Lochardil House is 1½ miles
from town centre.

Priory

★★★

The Square, Beauly, Inverness-shire, IV4 7BX
Tel: 01463 782309
SB £45 DB £85 B £3.50 L £5 D £12.50.
CC: MC Vi Am DC Swi Delt

How to get there: A9 to Tore roundabout. Follow
signs for Beauly. Hotel in village square.

Royal Highland

★★★

Station Square, Academy Street, Inverness,
Inverness-shire, IV1 1LG
Tel: 01463 231926 Fax: 01463 710705

A popular meeting place, welcomes non-
residents and offers breakfast, morning coffees,
home baking, buffet lunch, afternoon teas, high
teas and dinner in a friendly and restful
atmosphere.
SB £65 DB £99 HBS £77 HBD £123 B £6.50
L £5.50 D £12. CC: MC Vi Am DC Swi Delt JCB

How to get there: By Inverness railway station.

Alban House

♦♦♦♦

Bruce Gardens, Inverness, IV3 5EN
Tel: 01463 714301 Fax: 01463 714236
SB £30 DB £53 CC: MC Vi

Culduthel Lodge

♦♦♦♦ &

14 Culduthel Road, Inverness, IV2 4AG
Tel: 01463 240089 Fax: 01463 240089
Email: rac@culduthel.com
Web: www.culduthel.com
SB £45 DB £45 HBS £65 HBD £65 D £20.
CC: MC Vi Delt

How to get there: From centre, Castle Street
leads into Culduthel Road, Lodge is on right.

Westbourne Guest House

♦♦♦♦

50 Huntly Street, Inverness,
Inverness-shire, IV3 5HS
Tel: 01463 220700 Fax: 01463 220700
Email: richard@westbourne.org.uk
Web: www.westbourne.org.uk
SB £25 DB £40 CC: MC Vi Swi Delt
♿ 🐾 🌐 🍵 💻 🅿 🛎 🕯 🎠 ♨ 🦞
How to get there: Leave A9 at A82. Proceed
straight over 3 roundabouts, cross Friars Bridge.
Take first left into Wells Street, then into Huntly
Street.

Clisham House

♦♦♦

43 Fairfield Road, Inverness,
Inverness-shire, IV3 5QP
Tel: 01463 239965 Fax: 01463 239854
Email: clisham@dircon.co.uk
Web: www.clisham.dircom.co.uk
SB £25 DB £52
🌐 🍵 🅿 🛎 🕯 🎠 ♨ 🦞
How to get there: Cross Ness Bridge, right at
first set of traffic lights, then second left into
Fairfield Road.
See advert below

Clisham House   ♦♦♦

A non-smoking newly refurbished guest house
within walking distance of the town centre,
with a reputation for good food, warm
welcome and Highland hospitality none can
equal. All rooms are furnished to a high
standard with guests' comfort a priority.
Complimentary sandwiches provided for all.
Ample off-street parking.

43 Fairfield Road, Inverness IV3 5QP
Tel: 01463 239965   Fax: 01463 239854
Email: clisham@dircon.co.uk
Website: www.clisham.dircon.co.uk

St Ann's House

♦♦♦

37 Harrowden Road, Inverness,
Inverness-shire, IV3 5QN
Tel: 01463 236157 Fax: 01463 236157

Sunnyholm

♦♦♦

12 Mayfield Road, Inverness,
Inverness-shire, IV2 4AE
Tel: 01463 231336
Email: ago7195587@aol.com
Web: www.milford.co.uk/go/sunnyholm.html
Children minimum age: 2

Large sandstone bungalow set in a mature,
secluded garden, five minutes walk from the
town centre.
SB £28 DB £21
♿ 🌐 🍵 💻 🅿 🛎 🕯 🎠 ♨ 🦞
How to get there: From town centre, up Castle
Street onto Culduthel Road. At first set of lights,
left onto Mayfield Road. Sunnyholm is half-way
up on the right.

Inverurie, Aberdeenshire

Strathburn

★★★

Burghmuir Drive, Inverurie, Aberdeenshire,
AB51 4GY
Tel: 01467 624422 Fax: 01467 625133
Email: strathburn@btconnect.com
Web: www.strathburn-hotel.co.uk
SB £65 DB £90
B £8.75 L £10.95 D £17.75.
CC: MC Vi Am Swi Delt
🔥 ♿ 🌐 🍵 💻 📞 📶 🅿 🛎 🕯 🎠 ♨ 🦞
👪 👥
How to get there: From Aberdeen airport turn
right onto A96 towards Inverness for 10 miles.
Then at Blackhall roundabout (Safeway) turn
right. Turn right after 100m.

Isle of Arran, Ayrshire

Kinloch

★★★

Blackwaterfoot, Brodick, Isle of Arran, Ayrshire, KA27 8ET
Tel: 01770 860444 Fax: 01770 860447
Email: kinloch@cqm.co.uk
Web: www.kinloch-arran.com
SB £48.50 DB £97 HBS £64 HBD £128
B £9 L £7 D £16.50. CC: MC Vi Am DC Swi Delt

How to get there: Accessible from Ardrossan (Glasgow 25 miles) or Clonaig on Kintyre.

Isle of Mull, Argyll & Bute

Western Isles

★★★

Tobermory, Isle of Mull, PA75 6PR
Tel: 01688 302012 Fax: 01688 302297

Isle of Skye

Cuillin Hills

★★★

Portree, Isle of Skye, IV51 9LU
Tel: 01478 612003 Fax: 01478 613092
Email: office_w@cuillinhills.demon.co.uk
Web: www.cuillinhills.demon.co.uk

Spectacularly located with breathtaking views over Portree Bay to the Cuillin mountains. Award-winning restaurant; high standards of service and an informal and relaxing atmosphere.
SB £40 DB £80 HBS £66 HBD £132
CC: MC Vi Am Swi Delt

How to get there: Turn right 1/4 mile north of Portree off A855 and follow signs for the hotel.

Hotel Eilean Iarmain

★★

Isleornsay, Sleat, Isle of Skye, IV43 8QR
Tel: 01471 833332 Fax: 01471 833275
Email: bookings@eilean-iarmain.co.uk
Web: www.eileaniarmain.co.uk
SB £90 DB £120 B £10 L £15 D £31.
CC: MC Vi Am Swi Delt Solo

How to get there: A850, A851 8 miles, left at Isleornsay Road sign, hotel on harbour 1/2 mile.
See advert below

Royal

★★

Bank Street, Portree, Isle of Skye, IV51 9BU
Tel: 01478 612525 Fax: 01478 613198

Shorefield House

♦♦♦

Edinbane, Isle of Skye, IV51 9PW
Tel: 01470 582444 Fax: 01470 582414
Email: shorefieldhouse@aol.com
Web: www.shorefield.com
SB £28 DB £48 CC: MC Vi Delt

How to get there: From Portree, A87, A850 (Dunvegan), 9 miles to Lower Edinbane.

Scotland

Jedburgh, Borders

Ferniehirst Mill Lodge

♦ ♦ ♦

Jedburgh, Borders, TD8 6PQ
Tel: 01835 863279 Fax: 01835 863279
SB £23 DB £46 HBS £37 HBD £74
D £14. CC: MC Vi

How to get there: 2½ miles south of Jedburgh, 8 miles north of Scottish border, ⅓ mile off A68 on east side.

Kelso, Borders

Cross Keys

★★★

36-37 The Square, Kelso, Borders, TD5 7HL
Tel: 01573 223303 Fax: 01573 225792
Email: cross-keys-hotel@easynet.co.uk
Web: www.cross-keys-hotel.co.uk
CC: MC Vi Am DC Swi Delt

Ednam House

★★★ 🐎🐎

Bridge Street, Kelso, Borders, TD5 7HT
Tel: 01573 224168 Fax: 01573 226319

Kenmore, Perth & Kinross

Kenmore

★★★

The Quare, Kenmore, by Aberfeldy, PH15 2NU
Tel: 01887 830205 Fax: 01887 830262

Oldest Inn in Scotland (1572), conservation village in Highland Perthshire on the River Tay. Famous for golf and fishing, log fires and genuine Scottish hospitality.
SB £45 DB £90 HBD £140 B £8 L £8 D £15.
CC: MC Vi Am Swi

How to get there: On the banks of Loch Tay, at the mouth of the river.

Kilchrenan, Argyll & Bute

Taychreggan

★★★ 🐎🐎🐎

Taynuilt, Kilchrenan, Argyll & Bute, PA35 1HQ
Tel: 01866 833211/366 Fax: 01866 833244
Email: info@taychregganhotel.co.uk
Web: www.tacyhregganhotel.co.uk
Children minimum age: 14

Award-winning lochside hotel set amid breathtaking Argyll scenery. Excellent wine list, shamefully large malt whisky selection. Walk, fish or simply do nothing. Just peace and tranquility.
SB £105 DB £115 HBS £135 HBD £175
B £10 L £15 D £35. CC: MC Vi Am DC Swi Delt

How to get there: M8, A82 to Tyndrum, A85 to Taynuilt, then B845 to Kilchrenan.

Killiecrankie, Perth & Kinross

Dalnasgadh House

♦ ♦

Pitlochry, Killiecrankie, PH16 5LN
Tel: 01796 473237

Kingussie, Highland

Royal

★★

29 High Street, Kingussie, PH21 1HX
Tel: 01540 661898 Fax: 01540 661061
SB £30 DB £50 HBS £42 HBD £74
B £4 L £5.95 D £12. CC: MC Vi Am DC Swi Delt

How to get there: Just off A9, hotel is in the centre of the town on the High Street.

To make an on-line booking at an RAC inspected Hotel or Guest Accommodation, visit www.rac.co.uk/hotels

Kinross, Perth & Kinross

Green

★★★ ⋒

2 The Muirs, Kinross, KY13 7AS

Tel: 01577 863467 Fax: 01577 863180

Kirklands

★★

20 High Street, Kinross, KY13 7AN

Tel: 01557 863313

Kirkcaldy, Fife

Dean Park

★★★ ⋒

Chapel Level, Kirkcaldy, Fife, KY2 6QW

Tel: 01592 261635 Fax: 01592 261371

Beautifully appointed and professionally run hotel with custom-built conference facilities. Well situated for leisure activities (golf, fishing etc). Excellent table (RAC Dining Award) and cellar.

SB £59 DB £69 HBS £89

CC: MC Vi Am DC Swi Delt

⏚ ⑂ ⊔⊔ ⊜ ⊛ ⊙ ⊒ ☎ ⌔ 🄿 ⌗ ⌇ 🐴 ⅄ 🎿 ⅏ ⅏

How to get there: A92 Edinburgh-Dunfermline road to Kirkcaldy. Take A910 to first roundabout.

Kyle, Highland

Lochalsh

★★★

Ferry Road, Kyle of Lochalsh, IV40 8AF

Tel: 01599 534202

Email: mdmacrae@lochalsh-hotel.demon.co.uk

A family-owned hotel overlooking the Isle of Skye. An oasis of comfort and good living in the Scottish highlands, with 38 bedrooms — all en-suite.

SB £45 DB £70 B £9.95 L £10 D £22.

CC: MC Vi Am DC Swi Delt

⏚ ⊔⊔ ⌇ ⊛ ⊙ ⊒ ☎ 🄿 ⌗ ⌇ 🐴 ⅄ ⅏ ⅏ ⅏

How to get there: From south, turn left at Kyle traffic lights. Hotel 75m from lights.

Ladybank, Fife

Redlands Country Lodge

♦♦♦♦ ⋒ ⅏ ⅏

Pitlessie Road, Ladybank, Cupar, KY15 7SH

Tel: 01337 831091 Fax: 01337 831091

Closed December to January

SB £25 DB £50 HBS £37 HBD £75 CC: MC Vi

⌇ ⊛ ⊙ ⊒ 🄿 ⌗ ⌇ 🐴 ⅄ ⅏

How to get there: Under bridge at right of Ladybank Station, left. Hotel ½ mile further on.

Laide, Ross-shire

Sheiling

♦♦♦♦ ⅏ ⅏

Achgarve, Laide, Ross-shire, IV22 2NS

Tel: 01445 731487 Fax: 01445 731487

Email: annabell.maciver@talk21.com

Closed November to March

SB £24 DB £48

⊛ ⊙ ⊒ 🄿 ⌗ ⌇ 🐴 ⅄ ⅏

How to get there: From Laide post office 1½ miles for Metlon Udricle, left at Sheiling sign.

Langbank, Renfrewshire

Gleddoch House

★★★★ ⋒ ⋒

Langbank, Renfrewshire, PA14 6YE

Tel: 01475 540711 Fax: 01475 540201

Email: geddochhouse@ukonline.co.uk

SB £99 DB £150 B £12.50 L £20 D £35.

CC: MC Vi Am DC Swi Delt

⑂ ⌇ ⌇ ⊛ ⊙ ⊒ ☎ ⌔ 🄿 ⌗ ⌇ 🐴 ⅄ ⅏ ⅏ ⅏ ⅏ ⅏ ⅏

How to get there: From Glasgow, M8 to end, follow signs on B789 for 1 mile.

Largs, Ayrshire

Brisbane House

★★★ ☕☕

14 Greenock Road, Esplanade, Largs,
Ayrshire, KA30 8NF
Tel: 01475 687200
SB £70 DB £90 HBS £90 HBD £110
B £3.75 L £7.50 D £8.99.
CC: MC Vi Am DC Swi Delt Solo

How to get there: From Glasgow, follow the
Irvine Road to Loch Winnoch, follow signs for
Largs. Hotel is on right past main town.

Priory House

★★★ ☕☕☕

Broomfields, Largs, Ayrshire, KA30 8DR
Tel: 01475 686460 Fax: 01475 689070
Email: enquiries@maksu-group.co.uk
Web: www.maksu-group.co.uk
SB £65 DB £95 HBS £75 HBD £125
B £6.50 L £6.50 D £11.50.
CC: MC Vi Am DC Swi Delt

How to get there: Enter Largs on A78, turn into
John Street. Hotel is at end of road on seafront.

Lockerbie Manor
COUNTRY HOTEL

An idyllic haven of tranquility surrounded by
78 acres of woodland. Our 30-bedroom
18th-century former home of the Marquis of
Queensberry exudes comfort, warmth and a
genuine welcome. Retaining its original
features; the Adam fireplaces, coved ceilings,
chandeliers will take you back to a bygone era.

Located half mile off M74, junction 17.
Children, Pets welcome.

Boreland Road, Lockerbie DG11 2RG

Tel: 01576 202610   Fax: 01576 203046
Email: info@lockerbiemanorhotel.co.uk
Website: www.lockerbiemanorhotel.co.uk

Queen's

★★

North Promenade, Largs, Ayrshire, KA30 8QW
Tel: 01475 675311 Fax: 01475 675313
Email: queenshotel@ukonline.co.uk
SB £45 DB £80 HBS £55 HBD £100
B £5 L £5.95 D £9. CC: MC Vi Swi Delt

How to get there: 10 minute walk from Largs
pier, right on seafront next to Vikinggar.

Lochgilphead, Argyll & Bute

Stag

★★

Argyll Street, Lochgilphead, Argyll & Bute,
PA31 8NE
Tel: 01546 602496 Fax: 01546 603549

Tigh-Na-Glaic

◆◆◆◆

Crinan, By Lochgilphead, Argyll & Bute,
PA31 8SW
Tel: 01546 830245 Fax: 01546 830266

Lochinver, Sutherland

Inver Lodge

★★★ ☕☕☕

Lochinver, Sutherland, IV27 4LU
Tel: 01571 844496 Fax: 01571 844395
Email: stay@inverlodge.com
Web: www.inverlodge.com
Children minimum age: 7
Closed November to March
SB £80 DB £130 HBS £100 HBD £160 D £30.
CC: MC Vi Am DC Swi Delt JCB

How to get there: Left after tourist information
centre takes you onto private road to hotel.

Lochmaben, Dumfries & Galloway

Magdalene House

✤

Bruce Street, Lochmaben, Dumfries, DG11 1PD
Tel: 01387 810439 Fax: 01387 810439
Email: mckerrellofhillhouse@unkonline.co.uk
SB £33 DB £28 HBS £43 HBD £38 D £10.

How to get there: M74 to Lockerbie, then A709
to Lochmaben. Past the High Street, the road
turns left. Magdalene House is the first property
on the left.

Lockerbie, Dumfries & Galloway

Lockerbie Manor

★★★

Boreland Road, Lockerbie, Dumfries & Galloway, DG11 2RG
Tel: 01576 202610 Fax: 01576 203046
Email: info@lockerbiemanorhotel.co.uk
Web: www.lockerbiemanorhotel.co.uk
SB £48 DB £68 HBS £60 HBD £90
B £6 L £10 D £16.95. CC: MC Vi Am DC Swi

⏚ ♿ 🛏 🎣 🐾 ☕ 🖥 ☎ **P** 🐎 ℃ 🐴 🎠 🏇 ♨ 🍴 ⛄ 🍴 ℅ ⚐

How to get there: ½ mile from M74 J-17.
See advert on facing page

Mallaig, Highland

Morar

★★

Morar, Highland, PH40 4PA
Tel: 01687 462346 Fax: 01687 462212
Email: agmacleod@morarhotel.freeserve.co.uk
Web: www.road-to-the-isles.org.uk/morar-hotel
Children minimum age: 14
SB £35 DB £70 HBS £50 HBD £100 CC: MC Vi

⏚ 🎣 ☕ 🖥 **P** 🐎 ℃ 🐴 🎠 🏇 ♨ 🍴 ⛄

How to get there: On A830 in village of Morar.

West Highland

★★

Mallaig, Highland, PH41 4QZ
Tel: 01687 462210 Fax: 01687 462130

Markinch, Fife

Balbirnie House

★★★★ 🦌🦌🦌
Balbirnie Park, Markinch, Fife, KY7 6NE
Tel: 01592 610066 Fax: 01592 610529
Email: balbirnie@breathemail.net
Web: www.balbirnie.co.uk

A quite unique multi-award winning hotel which

combines understated luxury with superb service and outstanding value. Located 30 minutes equidistant from Edinburgh and St Andrews.
SB £125 DB £185 B £13.75 L £10 D £29.50.
CC: MC Vi Am DC Swi Delt

⏚ ♿ 🛏 🎣 🐾 ☕ 🖥 ☎ 📞 **P** 🐎 ℃ 🐴 🎠 🏇 ♨ 🍴 🍴

How to get there: M90 J-2a, A92 to Glenrothes. Across 3rd roundabout, right for Balbirnie Park.

Maybole, Ayrshire

Ladyburn ◀━

★★ 🦌🦌🦌
Ladyburn, Maybole, Ayrshire, KA19 7SG
Tel: 01655 740585 Fax: 01655 740580
Email: jhdh@ladyburn.freeserve.co.uk
Web: www.ladyburn.co.uk
SB £100 DB £150 HBS £120 HBD £200
B £10 L £15 D £30. CC: MC Vi Am

⏚ 🎣 ☕ ☕ 🖥 ☎ 📞 **P** 🍴 🍴

How to get there: A77, B7024 to Crosshill. Right at war memorial, 2 miles turn left. After a further ¾ mile, Ladyburn is on right.

Melrose, Borders

Dryburgh Abbey

★★★

St Boswells, Melrose, Borders, TD6 0RQ
Tel: 01835 822261 Fax: 01835 823945
Email: enquiries@dryburgh.co.uk
Web: www.dryburgh.co.uk

A red sandstone baronial mansion, breathtakingly set on the banks of the River Tweed. Family run and owned — fine food, wine and service await.
SB £55 DB £110 HBS £70 HBD £140
B £12 L £6.50 D £26. CC: MC Vi Am Swi Delt

⏚ ♿ 🛏 🎣 🐾 ☕ 🖥 ☎ **P** 🐎 ℃ 🐴 🎠 🏇 ♨ 🍴 📠 ⛄

How to get there: A68, B6404, B6356 then 2 miles to hotel entrance.

George & Abbotsford

★★

High Street, Melrose, Borders, TD6 9PD
Tel: 01896 822308 Fax: 01896 823363
Email: enquiries@georgeandabbotsford.co.uk
Web: www.georgeandabbotsford.co.uk
SB £50 DB £85 HBS £55 HBD £110
CC: MC Vi Am DC Swi Delt

How to get there: Midway up High Street.

Moffat, Dumfries & Galloway

Auchen Castle

★★★ ℞

Beattock, nr Moffat, DG10 9SH
Tel: 01683 300407 Fax: 01683 300667
Email: reservations@auchen-castle-hotel.co.uk
Web: www.auchen-castle-hotel.co.uk

An impressive 19th-century mansion house set
in 30 acres of beautiful gardens and woodlands,
overlooking our own private trout loch. A warm
welcome is assured.
SB £55 DB £60 D £17.45.
CC: MC Vi Am DC Swi Delt

How to get there: 1 mile north on B7076 from
A/M74 J-15 (Moffat turnoff).

Moffat House

❖

High Street, Moffat, Dumfries & Galloway,
Tel: 01683 220039 Fax: 01683 221288
Email: moffat@talk21.com
Web: www.moffathouse.co.uk
A Grade 'A' Listed hotel of 1751 offering superb
hospitality and food. Cooking awards being
gathered each year and refurbishments now
completed.
SB £50 DB £70 HBS £70 HBD £110
B £6.50 L £7 D £7. CC: MC Vi Am Swi Delt

How to get there: Exit M74 J-15 and travel 1
mile west into Moffat Square. Moffat House set
back from the square.

Famous Star

★★

44 High Street, Moffat, Dumfries & Galloway,
DG10 9EF
Tel: 01683 220156 Fax: 01683 221524
Email: tim@famousstarhotel.com
Web: www.famousstarhotel.com

Although the narrowest hotel, as seen in the
Guinness Book of Records – only 20 feet wide –
the interior and welcome are heart warming.
Excellent accommodation, real ales and good
homecooking restaurant.
SB £40 DB £56 HBS £48 HBD £144
B £4.95 L £4 D £5.
CC: MC Vi Am DC Swi Delt

How to get there: 2 miles from M74 J-15.
As you drive into Moffat town, The Star is the
first hotel on the right.

Well View

★ ♟ ♟ ♟
Ballplay Road, Moffat, Dumfries & Galloway,
DG10 9JU
Tel: 01683 220184 Fax: 01683 220088
Email: info@wellview.co.uk
Web: www.wellview.co.uk

Mid-Victorian villa set in half an acre of garden
and overlooking the town, with superb views of
surrounding hills.
SB £63 DB £100 HBS £88 HBD £76 B £10
L £15 D £30. CC: MC Vi Am Swi Delt Solo
🖼 🐾 ⊗ ☕ 🖵 🅿 ⚿ ⁑🕯 🐎 Ħ 🍴 ♨ 👁 ⚫ 🔱
How to get there: From Moffat, A708 for Selkirk,
$1/2$ mile left into Ballplay Rd, then 300yds on right.

Monymusk, Aberdeenshire

Grant Arms
♦ ♦
Monymusk, Aberdeenshire, AB51 7HJ
Tel: 01467 651226 Fax: 01467 651494

Motherwell, Lanarkshire

Dalziel Park Golf & Country Club
★★★
100 Hagen Drive, Dalziel Park, ML1 5RZ
Tel: 01698 862862 Fax: 01698 862863
Email: information@dalzielpark.co.uk
Web: www.dalzielpark.co.uk

Convenient base for touring and relaxation.
Midway between Glasgow and Edinburgh, near
Junction 6. Full country club facilities with
course, driving range, hairdressing and beauty
salon.
SB £41.95 DB £63.90 HBS £47 HBD £74
B £6.95 L £5.95 D £7.95. CC: MC Vi Swi Delt
🕭 ⚿ 🖼 🐾 ⊗ ☕ 🖵 ☎ 🅿 ⚿ ⁑🕯 🐎 Ħ 🍴 🐟
⚎⚎⚎ ⚎⚎⚎ ⚫ ⚬ ⌇
How to get there: From centre, along Merry
Street on A723 for Carfin, right into B7029..

Nairn, Inverness-shire

Alton Burn
★★
Alton Burn Road, Nairn, IV12 5ND
Tel: 01667 452051

Nethy Bridge, Inverness-shire

Nethybridge
★★
Nethy Bridge, Inverness-shire, PH25 3DP
Tel: 01479 821203 Fax: 01479 821686

Newton Stewart, Dumfries & Galloway

Kirroughtree House
★★★ ♟ ♟ ♟
Newton Stewart, DG8 6AN
Tel: 01671 402141 Fax: 01671 402425
Email: info@kirroughtreehouse.co.uk
Web: www.kirroughtreehouse.co.uk
Children minimum age: 10
Closed January to mid-February
SB £75 DB £150 HBS £100 HBD £200
B £10 L £14 D £30. CC: MC Vi Swi Delt
🖼 🐾 ☕ 🖵 ☎ 🅿 ⚿ ⁑🕯 🐎 Ħ 🍴 ⚎⚎⚎ ⚎⚎⚎ ⚲
How to get there: A75, A712, New Galloway
Road. Hotel driveway is 300m on left.

Crown
★★
101 Queen Street, Newton Stewart, DG8 6JW
Tel: 01671 402727 Fax: 01671 403374
SB £29.50 DB £50 HBS £39.50 HBD £70
B £5 L £3 D £10. CC: MC Vi Swi
🕭 🐾 ☕ 🖵 ☎ 🅿 ⚿ ⁑🕯 🐎 Ħ 🍴 ⚎⚎⚎ ⚎⚎⚎ ⚫

Galloway Arms
★★
54-56 Victoria Street, Newton Stewart,
Dumfries & Galloway, DG8 6DB
Tel: 01671 402653 Fax: 01671 402653

Scotland

Newtonmore, Inverness-shire

Glen
★★
Main Street, Newtonmore, Inverness-shire,
PH20 1DD
Tel: 01540 673203

North Berwick, East Lothian

Heritage Hotels – The Marine
★★★
Cromwell Road, North Berwick,
East Lothian, EH39 4LZ
Tel: 0870 400 8129 Fax: 01620 894480
Email: heritagehotels-north-berwick.marine@
forte-hotels.com
Web: www.heritagehotels.com
SB £45 DB £90 HBS £60 HBD £120
B £7.50 L £6.50 D £18.
CC: MC Vi Am DC Swi Delt
How to get there: From A1 City bypass, take
A198 for North Berwick. From A198 turn at
lights into Hamilton Road, North Berwick. Hotel
is second on right.

North Uist

Lochmaddy
★★
Lochmaddy, North Uist, HS6 5AA
Tel: 01876 500331 Fax: 01876 500210

Oban, Argyll & Bute

Alexandra
★★★
Corran Esplanade, Oban, Argyll & Bute,
PA34 5AA
Tel: 01631 562381 Fax: 01631 564497

Royal
★★★
Argyll Square, Oban, Argyll & Bute, PA34 4BE
Tel: 01631 563021 Fax: 01631 562811
SB £40 DB £80 HBS £60 HBD £120
B £8.50 D £15. CC: MC Vi Am Swi Delt
How to get there: The hotel is situated down
Oban's main street, near ferry, rail and bus
terminals.

Falls of Lora
★★
Connel Ferry, by Oban, Oban, PA37 1PB
Tel: 01631 710483 Fax: 01631 710694
Closed mid December to January

Overlooking Loch Etive, this owner-run hotel
has inexpensive family rooms to Luxury! The
cocktail bar has an open log fire and over 100
brands of whisky; there is an extensive Bistro
Menu.
SB £30 DB £39 B £9.50 L £8 D £17.50.
CC: MC Vi Am DC Swi Delt
How to get there: A82, A85. Hotel is 1/2 mile
past Connel signpost, 5 miles before Oban.

Foxholes
★★ ♔
Lerags, Oban, Argyll & Bute, PA34 4SE
Tel: 01631 564982 Fax: 01631 570890
Email: shirely.foxholes@tesco.net
Web: www.hoteloban.com
Closed December to February
SB £39.50 DB £55 HBS £53 HBD £86
CC: MC Vi Swi Delt JCB Solo
How to get there: Foxholes is 3 miles south of
Oban. From Oban take A816 for two miles, turn
right, one further mile.
See advert on facing page

King's Knoll
★★
Dunollie Road, Oban, Argyll & Bute, PA34 5JH
Tel: 01631 562536 Fax: 01631 566101

Lancaster
★★
Corran Esplanade, Oban, Argyll & Bute,
PA34 5AD
Tel: 01631 562587 Fax: 01631 562587
SB £27.50 DB £60 CC: MC Vi Swi
How to get there: The hotel is situated on the
seafront next to St Columba Cathedral.

Glenbervie Guest House

◆◆◆◆ ✑

Dalriach Road, Oban, Argyll & Bute, PA34 5JD
Tel: 01631 564770

Loch Etive House

◆◆◆◆ ✑✑

Connel, Oban, Argyll & Bute, PA37 1PH
Tel: 01631 710400 Fax: 01631 710680
Closed November to April
SB £25 DB £50 CC: MC Vi

How to get there: Off A85 in Connel, between
the village store and St Oran's Church.

Ronebhal Guest House

◆◆◆◆ ✑✑

Connel, by Oban, Argyll & Bute, PA37 1PJ
Tel: 01631 710310/813 Fax: 01631 710310
Email: ronebhal@btinternet.com
Web: www.argyllinternet.co.uk/ronebhal
Children minimum age: 7
Closed December to January
SB £19 DB £38 CC: MC Vi Delt

How to get there: Off A85 in Connel village, 4th
house after Connel Bridge junction.

Corriemar Guest House

◆◆◆

6 Corran, Esplanade, Oban, PA34 5AQ
Tel: 01631 562476 Fax: 01631 564339
Email: corriemar@tinyworld.co.uk
Web: www.corriemar.co.uk
Children minimum age: 3
SB £25 DB £44 CC: MC Vi

How to get there: A85 from Glasgow. Right-
hand lane into Oban at mini-roundabout, onto
seafront. Hotel is middle guest house.

Onich, Inverness-shire

Allt-Nan-Ros

★★★ ♖♖♖

Onich, nr Fort William, Inverness-shire,
PH33 6RY
Tel: 01855 821210 Fax: 01855 821462
Email: allt-nan-ros@zetnet.co.uk
Web: www.allt-nan-ros.co.uk
SB £45 DB £90 HBS £68 HBD £135
B £12.50 D £29.95. CC: MC Vi Am DC Swi Delt

How to get there: 2 miles north of Ballachulish
Bridge on main A82 Glasgow to Fort
William/Inverness road.

Foxholes Country Hotel

Foxholes nestles
peacefully in beautiful
grounds, in a secluded
glen, with magnificent
views from every
window. With only seven bedrooms, the
emphasis is on personal attention, good food
and friendly hospitality.
"Our aim is to spoil you"

Situated 3 miles south of Oban — The Gateway
to The Isles — ferries to Mull, Iona, Staffa, etc.

Lerags, Oban, Argyll PA34 4SE
Tel: 01631 564982   Fax: 01631 570890
Email: shirley.foxholes@tesco.net
Website: www.hoteloban.com

Onich

★★★ ♖♖♖♖

Onich, Inverness-shire, PH33 6RY
Tel: 01855 821214 Fax: 01855 821484
Email: reservations@onich-fortwilliam.co.uk
Web: www.onich-fortwilliam.co.uk

Surrounded by mountains, lochs and gardens,
this hotel offers the perfect setting for a relaxing
break. Award-winning cuisine specialising in
fresh local produce.
SB £58 DB £48 HBS £81 HBD £71
B £8 D £22. CC: MC Vi Am DC Swi Delt

How to get there: The Onich hotel is situated on
the A82 in the village of Onich, overlooking
Loch Linnhe, 12 miles south of Fort William.

Scotland

Perth, Perth & Kinross

Lovat

★★★

90-92 Glasgow Road, Perth, Perth & Kinross, PH2 0LT
Tel: 01738 636555 Fax: 01738 643123
Email: e-mail@lovat.co.uk
Web: www.scotlandhotels.co.uk
SB £45 DB £60 HBS £55 HBD £80
CC: MC Vi Am DC Swi Delt

How to get there: From A9 or M90 to Broxden roundabout follow A93 Perth for 1½ miles. Hotel is on right.

Murrayshall House

★★★

Scone, Perth, Perth & Kinross, PH2 7PH
Tel: 01738 551171 Fax: 01738 552595

Short breaks

RAC

Many Hotels and Guest Accommodation offer special weekend rates and mid-week breaks. If not quoted in the property's entry, call RAC Hotel Reservations on 0870 603 9109 to find out what may be on offer.

Queens Hotel

Ideally situated beside the rail and bus stations in the city centre with free, private car parking. There is a superb leisure club, the only one in Perth, with private facilities including pool, sauna, jacuzzi, steam room and gym. All rooms are ensuite with hospitality tray, hairdryer and satellite TV, etc. There are two restaurants and a bar for all types of dining.

Leonard Street, Perth PH2 8HB
Tel: 01738 442222   Fax: 01738 638496
Email: email@queensperth.co.uk
Website: www.scotlandhotels.co.uk

Quality Hotel Perth

★★★

Leonard Street, Perth, PH2 8HE
Tel: 01738 624141 Fax: 01738 639912
Email: admin@gb628.u-net.com
Web: www.choicehotels.com

SB £84.75 DB £96.75 HBS £100.85
HBD £137.50 B £9.75 L £5.75 D £15.80.
CC: MC Vi Am DC Swi Delt

How to get there: From M90/A90, turn left into Marshall Place, which runs into Kings Place, then Leonard Street. Adjacent to railway station.

Queen's

★★★

Leonard Street, Perth, Perth & Kinross, PH2 8HB
Tel: 01738 442222 Fax: 01738 638496
Email: email@queensperth.co.uk
Web: www.scotlandhotels.co.uk
SB £49 DB £70 HBS £59 HBD £90
CC: MC Vi Am DC Swi Delt

How to get there: From M90 follow A93 for Perth for 2 miles. Turn left and follow inner ring road. Hotel is on right.
See advert on the left

Salutation

★★

South Street, Perth, Perth & Kinross, PH2 8PH
Tel: 01738 630066 Fax: 01738 633598
Email: salutation@perth.fsnet.co.uk
SB £45 DB £80 HBS £50 HBD £90
B £5 L £3 D £14.50.
CC: MC Vi Am Swi Delt Solo Maestro

How to get there: Situated in the centre of Perth, M85 from Dundee, A9 from Inverness, A9 from Stirling/Glasgow, M90 from Edinburgh

Achnacarry Guesthouse

♦♦♦♦

3 Pitcullen Crescent, Perth, Perth & Kinross, PH2 7HT
Tel: 01738 621421 Fax: 01738 444110

Clunie Guest House

◆◆◆

12 Pitcullen Crescent, Perth, Perth & Kinross,
PH2 7HT
Tel: 01738 623625
Email: ann@clunieperth.freeserve.co.uk
SB £19 DB £38 CC: MC Vi Am
🚗☺⌒🖥️**P**♨〰🐎🎠╊🦞
How to get there: Situated on A94 Perth/Couper
Angus road. Exit M90 J-11, follow signs for A94.

Pitlochry, Perth & Kinross

Pine Trees

★★★ ☏☏
Strathview Terrace, Pitlochry, Perth & Kinross,
PH16 5QR
Tel: 01796 472121 Fax: 01796 472460
Email: info@pinetreeshotel.co.uk
Web: www.pinetreeshotel.co.uk
SB £50 DB £35 HBS £60 HBD £55
B £8.50 L £3.50 D £25.
CC: MC Vi Am DC Swi Delt
🔌🐕☺⌒🖥️☎**P**♨▦▥
How to get there: Travelling north, turn right into
Larchwood Road. Pine Trees is situated at the
top, on the left, just below the golf course.

Balrobin

★★
Higher Oakfield, Pitlochry, Perth & Kinross,
PH16 5HT
Tel: 01796 472901 Fax: 01796 474200
Email: balrobin@globalnet.co.uk
Web: www.milford.co.uk/go/balrobin.html
Children minimum age: 5
Closed November to February
SB £36 DB £79 HBS £42 HBD £51
B £inc D £16. CC: MC Vi
🚗🐕☺⌒🖥️**P**♨〰🐎🎠╊🦞▯
How to get there: From centre of town, follow
brown tourist signs.

Knockendarroch House

★★ ☏☏☏
Higher Oakfield, Pitlochry, Perth & Kinross,
PH16 5HT
Tel: 01796 473473 Fax: 01796 474068
Email: info@knockendarroch.co.uk
Web: www.knockendarroch.co.uk
Children minimum age: 10. Closed Nov to Feb
SB £59 DB £84 HBS £79 HBD £120
B £8.50 D £18. CC: MC Vi Am Swi Delt
♿🛏️☺⌒🖥️☎**P**♨〰🐎🎠╊🦞▦
How to get there: From A9 (Atholl Road),
Bonnethill Rd, Toberargan Rd, Higher Oakfield.

Port Askaig, Argyll & Bute

Port Askaig

★★
Port Askaig, Isle of Islay, Argyll & Bute,
PA46 7RD
Tel: 01496 840 245 Fax: 01496 840 295
Email: hotel@portaskaig.co.uk
Web: www.portaskaig.co.uk
Children minimum age: 5

This 400-year-old inn overlooks the
Sound-of-Islay, the picturesque harbour and
lifeboat station. Situated in own gardens.
The best of home-cooked food. Bars open
all day.
SB £31 DB £75 HBS £49 HBD £111
CC: MC Vi Swi Solo JCB
🚗⌒🖥️**P**♨〰🐎🎠╊🦞▦▥ ⁄.
How to get there: Harbourside at Port Askaig
ferry terminal. From Port Ellen terminal or from
Islay airport follow straight route through
Bowmore and Bridgend.

Port William, Wigtownshire

Corsemalzie House

★★★ ☏☏
Port William, Newton Stewart, Wigtownshire,
DG8 9RL
Tel: 01988 860254 Fax: 01988 860213
Email: corsemalzie@ndirect.co.uk
Web: www.corsemalzie-house.ltd.uk
Closed mid-January to February
SB £54.50 DB £80 HBS £64.50 HBD £100
CC: MC Vi Am Swi
🔌🚗☺⌒🖥️☎**P**♨〰🐎🎠╊🦞▦▥ 🐟
How to get there: From east on A75, left at
Newton Steward roundabout onto A714,
bypassing Wigtown. Turn right after crossing
bridge at Bladnoch.

Scotland

Portpatrick, Dumfries & Galloway

Fernhill

★★★ ⌂⌂
Heugh Road, Portpatrick,
Dumfries & Galloway, DG9 8TD
Tel: 01776 810220 Fax: 01776 810596
Email: fernhill@portpatrick.demon.co.uk
Web: www.mcmillanhotels.co.uk
B £10.50 L £12.50 D £22.50.
CC: MC Vi Am Swi Delt

How to get there: From Stanraer, take A77 to
Portpatrick. 100 yards past Portpatrick village
sign, turn right before war memorial. Hotel is
first on left.

Renfrew, Renfrewshire

Dean Park

★★★
91 Glasgow Road, Renfrew, PA4 8YB
Tel: 0141 304 9955 Fax: 0141 885 0681
Email: dpres@cosmopolitan-hotels.com
Web: www.cosmopolitan-hotels.com
SB £66 DB £86 B £7.50 L £6.95 D £12.95.
CC: MC Vi Am DC Swi Delt

How to get there: Exit M8 J-26, A8 for Renfrew
and Hillington. Hotel is located 200m on
Glasgow Road, on left.

Rockcliffe, Dumfries & Galloway

Clonyard House

★★
Colvend, Rockcliffe, by Dalbeattie,
Dumfries & Galloway, DG5 4QW
Tel: 01556 630372 Fax: 01556 630422
Email: nickthompson@clara.net
SB £40 DB £70 HBS £55 HBD £95
B £6 L £5 D £10.
CC: MC Vi Am Swi Delt JCB Solo

How to get there: On A710, 4 miles south of
Dalbeattie. Dalbeattie is 14 miles southwest of
Dumfries, on A711.

Rosebank, Lanarkshire

Popinjay

★★★ ⌂⌂
Rosebank, Lanarkshire, ML8 5QB
Tel: 01555 860441 Fax: 01555 860204

Rosyth, Fife

Gladyer Inn

★★
10 Heath Road, Ridley Drive, Rosyth, Fife,
KY11 2BT
Tel: 01383 419977 Fax: 01383 411728
Email: gladyer@aol.com
SB £39.50 DB £55 B £5 D £13.
CC: MC Vi Am Swi Delt

How to get there: Exit M90 J-1. Follow signs
into Rosyth. Go straight on at roundabout. Take
1st left.

St Andrews, Fife

Heritage Hotels – The Rusacks

★★★★ ⌂⌂
Pilmour Links, St Andrews, Fife, KY16 9JQ
Tel: 01334 474321 Fax: 01334 477896
Email: heritagehotels_standrews.rusacks@
forte-hotels.com
Web: www.heritage-hotels.com

Voted one of the top ten golfing hotels in the
world, our AA rosette-winning restaurant
overlooks the famous old course in St Andrews
and specialises in local game and seafood.

SB £55 DB £110 HBS £70 HBD £140
CC: MC Vi Am DC Swi Delt JCB

How to get there: Enter St Andrews on the A91.
Rusacks is 500 yards into town on the left,
adjacent to A91, with junction of M90 26 miles
away.

Scores

★★★
The Scores, St Andrews, Fife, KY16 9BB
Tel: 01334 472451 Fax: 01334 473947

Cleveden

3 Murray Place, St Andrews, Fife, KY16 9AP
Tel: 01334 474212 Fax: 01334 474212
Email: clevedenhouse@adl.com
SB £25 DB £50 CC: MC Vi DC Swi Delt

How to get there: Off main street, left at Tudor
Inn and park in car park, Murray Place.

West Park House

♦♦♦

5 St Mary's Place, St Andrews, Fife, KY16 9UY
Tel: 01334 475933 Fax: 01334 476734
Email: rosemary@westparksta.freeserve.co.uk
Closed December
DB £27 CC: MC Vi

How to get there: In centre of town.

St Andrews B&B

Lededdie Steading, St Andrews, Fife, KY15 5TY
Tel: 01334 840514 Fax: 01334 840833
Email: standrewsbb@talk21.com
Closed December to January
SB £28 DB £50

How to get there: From Cupar, B940 to
Pitscottie crossroads, left, next right. After 1
mile turn right up hill, entrance right before farm.

St Fillans, Perthshire

Four Seasons

★★★ 🐾🐾🐾
St Fillans, Perthshire, PH6 2NF
Tel: 01764 685333 Fax: 01764 685444
Email: info@thefourseasonshotel.co.uk
Web: www.thefourseasonshotel.co.uk
Closed February

The finest lochside location in the southern
Highlands. Contemporary cuisine using the best

ingredients available from Scotland's natural
larder, catering for the imaginative to more
traditional diner.
SB £36 DB £36 HBS £57 HBD £65
CC: MC Vi Swi Delt

How to get there: On the A85 at the west end of
St Fillans, and the east end of Lochearn.

Shetland Isles

Busta House

★★★ 🐾
Brae, Shetland Isles, ZE2 9QN
Tel: 01806 522506 Fax: 01806 522588

Shetland

★★★
Holmsgarth Road, Lerwick, ZE1 0PW
Tel: 01595 695515 Fax: 01595 695828
Email: robertsmith@mes.co.uk
Web: www.mes.co.uk/shetland-hotels
SB £73 DB £89 B £6.95 L £6.95 D £9.50.
CC: MC Vi Am DC Swi

How to get there: Opposite main P&O ferry
terminal for Lerwick.

Scotland

Glen Orchy House

♦♦♦♦ ✕

20 Knab Road, Lerwick, ZE1 0AX
Tel: 01595 692031 Fax: 01595 692031
Email: glenorchy.house@virgin.net
Web: www.guesthouselerwick.com
SB £38.50 DB £66 D £15. CC: MC Vi Delt JCB

🐎⊗🕭⏹❄🅿🛎✽🐴🎐🗻🦪i

How to get there: Follow main route until
Church/Knab Road/Annsbrae/Greenfield
junction. Turn right from south, straight ahead
from north, onto Knab Road.
See advert on previous page

Spean Bridge, Perthshire

Letterfinlay Lodge

★★ ▣

Lochlochy, Spean Bridge, Perthshire, PH34 4DZ
Tel: 01397 712622
SB £35 DB £70 HBS £55 HBD £110
B £7.50 L £5.50.

🐎🐎🕭⏹🕭🅿🛎✽🐴🎐🗻🦪♨♨ €∴

How to get there: 7 miles north of Spean
Bridge, on shore of Lochlochy on the A82.

Stirling, Stirlingshire

Stirling Highland

★★★★ ▣▣

Spittal Street, Stirling, Stirlingshire, FK8 1DU
Tel: 01786 272727 Fax: 01786 272829
Email: stirling@paramount-hotels.co.uk
Web: www.paramount-hotels.co.uk

SB £50 DB £55 HBS £60 HBD £65
CC: MC Vi Am DC Swi Delt

♿🛗🐎🕭⏹🕭🅿🛎✽🐴🎐🗻🦪📷♨♨♨
SPA 🍴🗲

How to get there: Take A84 into Stirling. Follow
signs for Stirling Castle. At Albert Hall, turn left
and left again, following signs to castle.

Golden Lion Milton

★★★

8–10 King Street, Stirling, Stirlingshire, FK8 1BD
Tel: 01786 475351 Fax: 01786 472755
SB £64 DB £90 B £6.50 D £12.50.
CC: MC Vi Am DC Swi Delt

🔄🛗⊗🕭⏹🕭🅿🛎✽🐴🎐🗻🦪♨♨

How to get there: In town centre, with car park
in Murray Place at rear of hotel: from rail station
turn left and left again into pedestrian precinct.
At Imperial Cancer, turn right into Car Park.

Royal

★★★ ▣

55 Henderson Street, Bridge of Allan,
Stirlingshire, FK9 4HG
Tel: 01786 832284 Fax: 01786 834377
SB £85 DB £130 HBS £105 HBD £160 B £6.95
L £6.95 D £22.50. CC: MC Vi Am DC Swi Delt

🔄🛗⊗🕭⏹🕭🅿🛎✽🐴🎐🗻🦪♨♨♨♨

How to get there: Exit M9 J-11. At large
roundabout, take fourth turning which is
signposted Bridge of Allan. Follow this road (A9)
into the village centre. Hotel is on left.

Strachur, Argyll & Bute

The Creggans Inn

★★★ ▣▣

Strachur, Argyll & Bute, PA27 8BX
Tel: 01369 860279 Fax: 01369 860637

Stranraer, Dumfries & Galloway

North West Castle

★★★★ ▣

Cairnryan Road, Stranraer, Dumfries & Galloway,
DG9 8EH
Tel: 01776 704413 Fax: 01776 702646
Web: www.mcmillanhotels.com
SB £55 DB £79 HBS £72 HBD £114
B £10.50 L £9.50 D £21. CC: MC Vi Swi

🔄♿🛗🖨🐎🕭⏹🕭🅿🛎✽🐴🎐🗻🦪♨♨♨
♨♨♨ SPA 🍴 €∴ 🗲

How to get there: Follow signs for Stena ferry
terminal and take the first left across from the
ferry terminal building.

Strathcarron, Ross-shire

Tigh an Eilean

★ ▣▣▣

Shieldaig, Strathcarron, Ross-shire, IV54 8XN
Tel: 01520 755251 Fax: 01520 755321

Strathpeffer, Highland

White Lodge

♦♦♦♦

Strathpeffer, Highland, IV14 9AL
Tel: 01997 421730

Strontian, Argyll & Bute

Strontian

★★ ♙

Acharacle, Strontian, Argyll & Bute, PH36 4HZ
Tel: 01967 402029 Fax: 01967 402314
Email: strontianhotel@supanet.com
Web: www.strontianhotel.supanet.com
SB £35 DB £52.50 HBS £47 HBD £76.50
B £5.50 L £5 D £12. CC: MC Vi Swi Delt
🐾🍴🖥☎📞P🐎🏇🐕🎣🥅🎣🛏 ♿

How to get there: From A82 take Corran ferry to
Ardgour. Turn left off ferry on A861. Hotel on
right as you enter Strontian.

Tain, Highland

Mansfield House

★★★ ♙♙♙

Scotsburn Road, Tain, Highland, IV19 1PR
Tel: 01862 892052 Fax: 01862 892260
Email: mansfield@cali.co.uk
Web: www.mansfield-house.co.uk
SB £65 DB £100 HBS £90 HBD £150 L £11.95
D £25. CC: MC Vi Am Swi Delt
⛵🚹🍴🐾🐕🍴🖥☎P🐎🏇🐕🎣🥅🎣
🛏🛏

How to get there: From south on A9, ignore first
entrance to Tain. Continue north for ¹/₂ mile
before turning right at signpost for police
station.

Morangie House

★★★ ♙

Morangie Road, Tain, Highland, IV19 1PY
Tel: 01862 892281 Fax: 01862 892872
Email: wynne@morangiehotel.com
Web: www.smoothhound.co.uk

Former Victorian mansion. Friendly staff, superb
food and good wines. Ideal for golfing breaks.
Under the personal supervision of the
proprietors. A very special place to visit.
SB £70 DB £90 HBS £90 HBD £135
B £7 L £8 D £20. CC: MC Vi Am DC Swi
⛵🚹🍴🐾🐕🍴🖥☎P🐎🏇🐕🎣🥅
🛏🛏

How to get there: Right off A9 at north end of
Tain. Hotel is first building on the right.

Royal

★★

High Street, Tain, Highland, IV19 1AB
Tel: 01862 892013 Fax: 01862 893450

Tarbert, Argyll & Bute

Stonefield Castle

★★★ ♙♙

Tarbert, Argyll & Bute, PA29 6YJ
Tel: 01880 820836 Fax: 01880 820929

Columba

★★ ♙♙

East Pier Road, Tarbert, Loch Fyne,
Argyll & Bute, PA29 6UF
Tel: 01880 820808 Fax: 01880 820808
Email: columbahotel@fsbdial.co.uk
Web: www.columbahotel.com
Closed Christmas
SB £35.95 DB £72 HBS £51.95 HBD £104
B £6 L £6 D £21.50. CC: MC Vi Am Swi Delt
🐾🍴🖥P🐎🏇🐕🎣🥅🎣🛏🛏 Ⓣ♿

How to get there: As you enter Tarbert on A83,
turn left around the harbour. Columba Hotel is
¹/₂ mile from junction.

Thurso, Highland

St Clair

★★

Sinclair Street, Thurso, Highland, KW14 7AJ
Tel: 01847 896481 Fax: 01847 896481

Ulbster Arms

★★ ♜

Halkirk, Highland, KW12 6XY
Tel: 01847 831641 Fax: 01847 831641
SB £43 DB £76 B £8 L £4.50 D £22.50.
CC: MC Vi Swi

How to get there: Halkirk is 109 miles north of
Inverness. Follow A9, then turn left onto A895.

Tongue, Sutherland

Ben Loyal

★★

Tongue, Sutherland, IV27 4XE
Tel: 01847 611216 Fax: 01847 611212
Email: thebenloyal@btinternet.com
Web: www.benloyal.co.uk
SB £35 DB £35 HBS £55 HBD £110
B £8 L £10 D £22.50. CC: MC Vi Swi

How to get there: From A9, to Bonar Bridge.
A836 north to A838. Left at junction into village.

Torridon, Highland

Loch Torridon

★★★ ♜♜♜

Torridon By Achnasheen, Highland, IV22 2EY
Tel: 01445 791242 Fax: 01445 791296
Email: enquiries@lochtorridonhotel.com
Web: www.lochtorridonhotel.com

Set in 58 acres of parkland at the foot of the
Torridon Mountains on the lochside, the hotel
offers real luxury in the Highlands.
SB £50 DB £80 HBS £56 HBD £88
B £15 L £5 D £38. CC: MC Vi Am DC Swi Delt

How to get there: From Inverness, follow signs
to Ullapool (A835). At Garve, left onto A832,
signs to Kinlochewe. Left onto A896: Torridon
10 miles. Pass Annat; hotel is on right.

Troon, Ayrshire

Marine

★★★★ ♜♜

8 Crosbie Road, Troon, Ayrshire, KA10 6HE
Tel: 01292 314444 Fax: 01292 316922
Email: marine@paramount-hotels.co.uk
Web: www.paramount-hotels.co.uk
B £3 L £4.50 D £18.
CC: MC Vi Am DC Swi Delt

How to get there: A77, A98 and A79 to
Prestwick airport. Right at B749. Hotel is on left
after golf courses.

South Beach

★★★ ♜

73 South Beach, Troon, Ayrshire, KA10 6EG
Tel: 01292 312033 Fax: 01292 318348
Email: info@southbeach.co.uk
Web: www.southbeach.co.uk
SB £50 DB £75 HBS £69.50 HBD £109
B £6 L £6.50 CC: MC Vi Am Swi

Ardneil

★★

51 St. Meddans Street, Troon, Ayrshire,
KA10 6NU
Tel: 01292 311611

Non smoking policy   RAC

Properties displaying this symbol in
the Guide have non smoking rooms
available for guests. However, smokers
should check in advance whether the Hotel or
Guest Accommodation displaying this symbol
actually allows smoking in any room.

Turnberry, Ayrshire

Turnberry

★ ★ ★ ★ ★ ☂ ☂ ☂

Turnberry, Ayrshire, KA26 9LT
Tel: 01655 331000 Fax: 01655 331706
Email: turnberry@westin.com
Web: www.turnberry.co.uk
Closed Christmas
SB £135 DB £175 HBS £184 HBD £275
L £25 D £49. CC: MC Vi Am DC Swi Delt

How to get there: 2 miles after Kirkoswald on
A77, turn right, signposted Turnberry.

Malin Court

★ ★ ★ ☂ ☂ ☂

Girvan, Turnberry, Ayrshire, KA26 9PB
Tel: 01655 331457 Fax: 01655 331072
Email: info@malincourt.co.uk
Web: www.malincourt.co.uk
SB £72 DB £104 HBS £85 HBD £130
B £6.50 L £5 D £12. CC: MC Vi Am DC Swi Delt

How to get there: A74, A719 to Turnberry.

West Wemyss, Fife

Belvedere

★ ★ ☂

Coxstool, West Wemyss, Fife, KY1 4SL
Tel: 01592 654167 Fax: 01592 655279

Whitebridge, Inverness-shire

Whitebridge

★ ★ ☂

Whitebridge, Inverness-shire, IV2 6UN
Tel: 01456 486226 Fax: 01456 486413
Email: whitebridgehotel@southlochness.
demon.co.uk
Web: www.southlochness.demon.co.uk
SB £30 DB £50 B £7.50 L £5 D £15.
CC: MC Vi Am DC Swi Delt JCB

How to get there: From A82 at Fort Augustus,
B862 9 miles. From Inverness, B862 24 miles.

Wick, Highland

Mackay's

★ ★

Union Street, Wick, Highland, KW1 5ED
Tel: 01955 602323 Fax: 01955 605930

Northern Ireland &

In recent years both Northern Ireland
and the Republic of Ireland (Eire)
have enjoyed increased tourism.
Eire underwent a renaissance in
the 1980s and 1990s, and
anyone who hasn't visited in

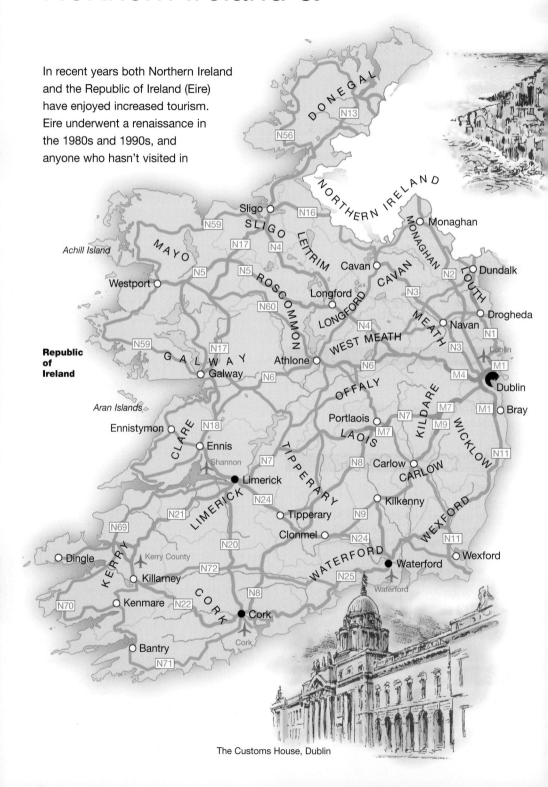

**Republic
of
Ireland**

DONEGAL
N13
N56

NORTHERN IRELAND

Sligo — N16
SLIGO
LEITRIM
Monaghan
MONAGHAN
N59
N17
N4
Cavan
CAVAN
N2
Dundalk
LOUTH
MAYO
Achill Island
N5
N5
Longford
N3
Westport
ROSCOMMON
LONGFORD
Drogheda
N60
N4
MEATH
Navan
N1
WEST MEATH
N3
Dublin
N59
N17
Athlone
N6
M4
M1
Dublin
GALWAY
Galway
N6
OFFALY
KILDARE
M7
M1
Bray
Aran Islands
Portlaois
N7
M7
M9
WICKLOW
Ennistymon
N18
LAOIS
N11
CLARE
Ennis
N8
Carlow
CARLOW
Shannon
N7
TIPPERARY
Limerick
N24
Kilkenny
WEXFORD
N21
LIMERICK
Tipperary
N9
N69
Clonmel
N24
N11
N20
WATERFORD
Wexford
Dingle
Kerry County
N72
Waterford
KERRY
Killarney
N25
N70
CORK
Waterford
Kenmare
N22
N8
Cork
Bantry
Cork
N71

The Customs House, Dublin

Republic of Ireland

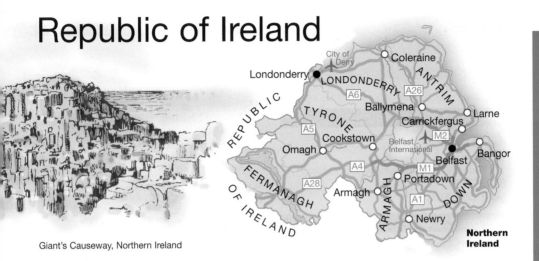

Giant's Causeway, Northern Ireland

recent years will see profound changes. Ireland has always been famed for its great natural beauty and the hospitality of its people, but now in addition to these qualities visitors will find the cities of Dublin and Belfast sporting a sophistication to rival any European city.

Belfast (derived from the Gaelic beal feirste, or 'mouth of the sandy ford') is a pleasant city to walk around, with plenty of parks, bars and restaurants along its Golden Mile, impressive Victorian Botanic Gardens, and a continuous series of exhibitions and concerts. Surrounded by hills, the beautiful Mountains of Mourne are only a short drive away. So too are the Glens of Antrim and the world famous Giant's Causeway, where a swathe of polygonal basalt rock columns sweep down to the sea. Northern Ireland is not a large province, and all parts are easily accessible within a couple of hours' drive from wherever you happen to be.

Dublin, capital of Eire, is a good place to start for any visitor to the south. With a third of the country's population – about a million – it is sizeable and a contrast to the rural nature of the rest of Eire. O'Connell Street is the main thoroughfare, but some of the most interesting places are to be found

elsewhere. Trinity College lies just a few hundred yards away across the River Liffey, Christ Church Cathedral and Dublin Castle are also within easy walking distance, and in Dublin Civic Museum you can trace the history of the city from Viking times.

The other major towns – Wexford, Waterford, Cork, Kilkenny, Limerick, Athlone – to name but a few, are full of traditional Irish warmth and hospitality. Whether near to a town or out in the countryside, the visitor will find plenty of first-rate accommodation to suit all budgets.

The Eirean country is comprised of wild boglands and small lakes left behind from the last ice age, beautiful mountain scenery, wild and craggy shorelines and above all a pervading greenness that gives the Emerald Isle its name. The many archaeological sites, such as Newgrange just north of Dublin, give the visitor an immediate sense of the island's long Celtic history. The west coast has a moody landscape accentuated by the wild Atlantic weather encountering its first land mass for over 2,000 miles, and it is in this region that Gaelic tradition survives best, along with the celebrated Irish traits of friendliness, warmth and good humour.

Ireland

Northern Ireland

Ballymena, Co. Antrim

Galgorm Manor
★★★★ ♟♟
136 Fenaghy Road, Ballymena, Co. Antrim,
BT42 1EA
Tel: 01226 881001

Bangor, Co. Down

Marine Court
★★★
The Marina, 18-20 Quay Street, Bangor,
Co. Down, BT20 5RD
Tel: 028 9145 1100 Fax: 028 9145 1200
Web: www.marinecourt.co.uk
B £7.50 L £5.95 D £8.95. CC: MC Vi Am Swi
⬙ ♿ ⚏ ☺ ☕ ▭ ☎ 🅿 ♨ ℃ ☂ ♫ ♨♨ ♀♀
'ϒ' 💷
How to get there: On Quay Street near central
pier on marina.
See advert below

Marine Court Hotel

Beautifully situated overlooking the Marina on
Bangor's seafront, this modern hotel is an ideal
location for business or pleasure. 52 spacious
bedrooms are tastefully fitted and have ensuite facilities.
Lord Nelson's Bistro offers an extensive menu,
while the Stevedore Restaurant offers both
à la carte and table d'hôte menus. Oceanis
Leisure Complex includes 18m swimming pool,
steam room and whirlpool. 12 superb golf
courses only 5 to 30 minutes drive.

The Marina, Bangor,
Co. Down BT20 5RD
Tel: 02891 451100   Fax: 02891 451200

Belfast

Hastings Europa
★★★★ ♟
Great Victoria Street,
Belfast, Co. Antrim,
BT2 7AP
Tel: 028 9032 7000
Fax: 028 9032 7800
Email: res@eur.hastingshotels.com
Web: www.hastingshotels.com
SB £117 DB £169 CC: MC Vi Am DC Swi Delt
⬙ ♿ ⚏ 🐾 ⊗ ☕ ▭ ☎ 🅿 ♨ ℃ ☂ ♫ ♨ ♨
♨♨ ♀♀

(HASTINGS EUROPA hotel logo)

Hastings Stormont
★★★★ ♟♟
Upper Newtonards Road,
Belfast, Co. Down,
BT4 1LP
Tel: 028 9065 8621
Fax: 028 9048 0240
Email: res@stor.hastingshotel.com
Web: www.hastingshotel.com
SB £122 DB £169 HBS £140 HBD £205
B £12 L £15 D £18. CC: MC Vi Am DC Swi Delt
♿ ⚏ ☺ ☕ ▭ ☎ 🅿 ♨ ℃ ☂ ♫ ♨ ♨♨ ♀♀
How to get there: From Belfast city centre,
follow A2 to Newtownards. Right at Stormont
Parliament Buildings.

(HASTINGS STORMONT hotel logo)

McCausland
★★★★ ♟
34–38 Victoria Street, Belfast, BT1 3GH
Tel: 028 9022 0200 Fax: 028 9022 0220
Email: info@mccauslandhotel.com
Web: www.slh.com
Closed Christmas

City centre location, luxury 60-bedroomed hotel
with restaurant and bar, conference and private
dining facilities. Sister property Hibernian Hotel
Dublin. Member of Small Luxury Hotels.
B £7.50 L £17.50 D £27.50.
CC: MC Vi Am DC Swi Delt

♿ ♨ ⊗ ☕ 🖥 ☎ 📞 📶 🅿 ⚬ ◖ 🐴 🦌 🎋 ♨ ⚏ ▥

How to get there: On Victoria Street between Anne Street and the Albert Clock Tower.

Dukes
★★★
65 University Street, Belfast, Co. Antrim, BT7 1HL
Tel: 01232 236666 Fax: 01232 237177

Jurys Inn Belfast
★★★
Fisherwick Place, Great Victoria Street, Belfast, BT2 7AP
Tel: +3531 6070055 Fax: +3531 6609625
Email: dorothy_cusack@jurysdoyle.com
Web: www.jurysdoyle.com
CC: MC Vi Am DC

♿ ♨ ☕ 🖥 ☎ 📞 📶 ⚬ ◖ 🐴 🦌 🎋 ♨ ⚏ ▥

Lansdowne Court
★★★
557 Antrim Road, Belfast, BT15 4EF
Tel: 028 9077 3317 Fax: 028 9037 0125
SB £60 DB £80 B £7.50 L £4.95 D £6.95.
CC: MC Vi Am Swi

⚓ 🦌 ☕ 🖥 ☎ 📞 🅿 ⚬ ◖ 🐴 🦌 🎋 ♨ ⚏ ▥

How to get there: Exit M2 at Fortwilliam. Take Shore Road. Turn right at Fortwilliam. Take Antrim Road exit. Hotel is on left.

Old Inn
★★★ ℞
Main Street, Crawfordsburn, Co. Down, BT19 1JH
Tel: 028 9185 3255 Fax: 028 9185 2775
Email: info@theoldinn.com
Web: www.theoldinn.com
SB £65 DB £85 HBS £88 HBD £131
B £8.50 L £5 D £15.25.
CC: MC Vi Am DC Swi Delt

⚓ ♿ 🦌 ☕ 🖥 ☎ 📞 🅿 ⚬ ◖ 🐴 🎋 ♨ ⚏ ▥

How to get there: A2 from Belfast towards Bangor. Three miles past Holywood, take B20 to Crawfordsburn. Hotel is on main street.

Culloden
℞ ℞
Bangor Road, Belfast, BT18 0EX
Tel: 028 9042 5223
Fax: 028 9042 6777
Email: gm@cull.hastingshotels.com
Web: www.hastingshotels.com

HASTINGS CULLODEN — hotel —

Northern Ireland's most prestigious luxury hotel, The Culloden stands in 12 acres of private grounds. The hotel has a unique air of elegance,

and guests can enjoy the facilities of the exclusive Elysium Health and Leisure Club.
SB £165 DB £210 HBS £195 HBD £270 B £15
L £10 D £30. CC: MC Vi Am DC Swi Delt

⚓ ♿ ♨ 🦌 🐴 ⊗ ☕ 🖥 ☎ 📞 🅿 ⚬ ◖ 🐴 🦌 🎋 ♨ ⚏ ▥ 🆂🅿🅰 🍸 🎾 🔍 ⛳

How to get there: A2 6 miles Belfast city centre, signposted Bangor.

Bushmills, Co. Antrim

Bushmills Inn
★★★ ℞ ℞
9 Dunluce Street, Bushmills, Co. Antrim, BT57 8QG
Tel: 028 2073 2339 Fax: 028 2073 2048
Email: roy@bushmillsinn.com
Web: www.bushmillsinn.com
SB £68 DB £98 L £10 D £23.85.
CC: MC Vi Am Swi

♿ 🦌 ⊗ 🖥 ☎ 📞 🅿 ⚬ ◖ 🐴 🎋 ♨ ⚏ ▥

How to get there: On A2 Antrim coast road. From Ballymoney, take B62, turn right onto B17 from Coleraine. Signs for Giants Causeway.

Carrickfergus, Co. Antrim

Dobbins Inn
★★
6-8 High Street, Carrickfergus, Co. Antrim, BT38 7AF
Tel: 028 9335 1905 Fax: 028 9335 1905
Email: info@dobbinsinnhotel.co.uk
Web: www.dobbinsinnhotel.co.uk
Friendly, family-owned 16th-century hotel with full bar, restaurant facilities and 15 comfortable

Ireland

bedrooms, all en-suite. Fully refurbished, regular evening entertainment and drinks promotions.
SB £44 DB £62 HBS £55 HBD £80
B £5 L £5 D £10.
CC: MC Vi Am Swi Delt

How to get there: Approximately 10 miles from Belfast City Airport, 15 miles from Belfast International Airport, 14 miles from port of Larne, 10 miles from port of Belfast.

Coleraine, Co. Londonderry

Brown Trout Golf & Country Inn

★★

Agivey Road, Aghadowey, Co. Londonderry,
BT51 4AD
Tel: 028 7086 8209 Fax: 028 7086 8878
Email: bill@browntroutinn.com
Web: www.browntroutinn.com
SB £60 DB £85 HBS £75 HBD £105
B £5 L £10 D £15. CC: MC

How to get there: On main road between Kilrea and Coleraine, where A54 intersects the B66, 7 miles from Coleraine.

Dunadry, Co. Antrim

Dunadry Inn

★★★★

2 Islandreagh Drive, Dunadry, Co. Antrim,
BT41 2HA
Tel: 028 9443 2474 Fax: 028 9443 3389

Dunmurry, Co. Down

Balmoral

★★★

Blacks Road, Dunmurry, nr Belfast, Co. Down,
BT10 0ND
Tel: 028 9030 1234 Fax: 028 9060 1455

Enniskillen, Co. Fermanagh

Killyhevlin

★★★

Killyhevlin, Dublin Road, Enniskillen,
Co. Fermanagh, BT74 6RW
Tel: 028 6632 3481 Fax: 028 6632 4726
Email: info@killyhevlin.com
Web: www.killyhevlin.com
SB £72.50 DB £105 B £7.95 L £14.50 D £22.50.
CC: MC Vi Am DC Swi

How to get there: On A4, east of Enniskillen, on main Dublin/Belfast road.

Feeny, Co. Londonderry

Drumcovitt House

♦♦♦♦

704 Feeny Road, Feeny, Co. Londonderry,
BT47 4SU
Tel: 028 7778 1224 Fax: 028 7778 1224
Email: drumcovitt.feeny@btinternet.com
Web: www.drumcovitt.com

Listed Georgian house. Centrally heated. Tour Sperrins, Donegal, Derry city, Giants Causeway. Walk farm lanes, Banagher Glen, Sperrin hills. Golf. Fish. Birdwatch. Relax. Enjoy.
SB £14 DB £38 HBS £34 HBD £68
B £5 L £10 D £13. CC: MC Vi Am Delt Eurocard

How to get there: From A6 Belfast-Derry road, 1/4 mile west of Dungiven take B74 to Feeny. After 3 miles, Drumcovitt is on right.

Hillsborough, Co. Down

White Gables

★★★

14 Dromore Road, Hillsborough, Co. Down,
BT26 6HS
Tel: 028 9268 2755 Fax: 028 9268 9532
CC: MC Vi Am DC Swi Delt

& 🚲 ⊗ 📟 ☎ 🅿 ⚄ ℃ 🐎 Ħ ✦ ♨ ⚏

How to get there: Join M2 to Belfast, then M1 west. Turn off J-7 to join A1 for Dublin. Through Hillsborough: hotel is approx ½ mile from centre of village.

Holywood, Co. Down

Beech Hill Country House Little Gem

♦♦♦♦♦   ⚓ ⚑

23 Ballymoney Road, Craigantlet,
Newtownards, Co. Down, BT23 4TG
Tel: 028 9042 5892 Fax: 028 9042 5892
Email: beech.hill@btinternet.com
Web: www.beech-hill.net
Children minimum age: 10

Stunning country house in peaceful Holywood Hills, with private parking and 3 beautifully decorated, comfortable en-suite bedrooms. 15 minutes from Belfast, Bangor, Newtownards and Dundonald.
SB £40 DB £30 CC: MC Vi
& 🐎 ⊗ 🍵 📟 ☎ 🅿 ⚄ ℃ 🐎 Ħ ✦

How to get there: A2 from Belfast. 4 miles from Holywood, right into Ballymoney Road, signed Craigantlet. Beech Hill is 1¾ miles on left.

Irvinestown, Co. Fermanagh

Mahon's

★★

Enniskillen Road, Irvinestown, BT94 1GS
Tel: 028 68621656 Fax: 028 6862 8344

Larne, Co. Antrim

Ballygally Castle

★★★
274 Coast Road,
Ballygally, Co. Antrim,
BT40 2QZ
Tel: 028 2858 3212
Fax: 028 2858 3681

Email: gm@bgc.hastingshotels.com
Web: www.hastingshotels.com
This genuine castle is ideally located on the scenic Antrim coast, only 20 miles from Belfast, and is an ideal base for touring the glens of Antrim and Giant's Causeway. This traditional hotel is full of character, and offers the best of Northern Ireland hospitality.
SB £65 DB £85 HBS £82 HBD £119

B £7 L £5 D £15. CC: MC Vi Am DC Swi Delt
⚄ ⊗ 🍵 📟 ☎ 🅿 ⚄ ℃ 🐎 Ħ ✦ ♨ ⚏

How to get there: 20 miles north of Belfast on Antrim coast road (M2 from Belfast, then A8 to Larne). 4 miles north of Larne on Antrim coast.

Derrin Guest House

♦♦♦
2 Princes Gardens, Larne, Co. Antrim,
BT40 1RQ
Tel: 028 2827 3269 Fax: 028 2827 3269
Email: info@derrinhouse.co.uk
Web: www.derrinhouse.co.uk
SB £19 DB £32 CC: MC Vi Am
🐎 ⊗ 🍵 📟 🅿 ⚄ ℃ 🐎 Ħ ✦

How to get there: Off Harbour highway (A8) for A2 coastal route. After lights at main street take first road on left.

Limavady, Co. Londonderry

Radisson Roe Park Hotel & Golf Resort

★★★★ ⛳ ⛳
Limavady, Co. Londonderry, BT49 9LB
Tel: 028 7772 2222 Fax: 028 7772 2313
Email: reservations@radissonroepark.com
Web: www.radissonroepark.com
SB £90 DB £130 HBS £109.50 HBD £169
CC: MC Vi Am DC Swi
& ⚏ 🚲 ⊗ 🍵 📟 ☎ 📞 🅿 ⚄ ℃ 🐎 Ħ ✦ 🕸
♨ ⚏ ♈ ⚓ ⚒ ⚐ 🎬

How to get there: On A2 Londonderry-Limavady Road, 16 miles Londonderry, 1 mile Limavady. Resort 10 miles Derry, 45 miles Belfast airport.

Londonderry, Co. Londonderry

Everglades

★★★★ ℛ

Prehen Road, Waterside,
Londonderry, BT47 2NH
Tel: 028 7134 6722
Fax: 028 7134 9200
Email: res@egh.hastingshotels.com
Web: www.hastingshotels.com

SB £85 DB £110 HBS £100 HBD £144
B £8 L £6 D £20. CC: MC Vi Am DC Swi

⏻⊗☎🖥☎🅿️🐎... ♨

How to get there: A6 to Londonderry. Signs for
Strabane/Omagh. Straight at lights at bridge.
Hotel second left.

Newcastle, Co. Down

Slieve Donard

★★★★

Downs Road, Newcastle,
Co. Down, BT33 0AH
Tel: 028 4372 3681
Fax: 028 4372 4830
Email: res@sdh.hastingshotels.com
Web: www.hastingshotels.com

Nestling at the foot of the mountains of Mourne,
the hotel stands in 6 acres of private grounds
and is the ideal setting in which to relax in style
and luxury.
SB £95 DB £140 B £8.50 L £16 D £23.
CC: MC Vi Am DC Swi

How to get there: From Belfast, A24 and follow
signs to Newcastle. From Dublin, R174 to
Newry then A2 and follow signs to Newcastle.

Burrendale Hotel & Country Club

★★★ ℛ ℛ

51 Castlewellan Road, Newcastle,
Co. Down, BT33 0JY
Tel: 028 4372 2599 Fax: 028 4372 2328
Email: reservation@burrendale.com
Web: www.burrendale.com

Nestling between the majestic Mourne
Mountains and the glimmering Irish Sea,
extensive leisure complex, conference and
banqueting facilities, a fine example of the best
in traditional hospitality.
SB £65 DB £99 HBS £80 HBD £130
B £5.75 L £9.95 D £15. CC: MC Vi Am DC Swi

How to get there: From Belfast, A24 to
Newcastle, then A50 Castlewellan Road.

Newtownabbey, Co. Antrim

Chimney Corner

★★

630 Antrim Road, Newtownabbey,
Co. Antrim, BT36 4RH
Tel: 028 9084 4925
Fax: 028 9084 4342
Email: info@chimneycorner.co.uk
Web: www.chimneycorner.co.uk
SB £45 DB £60 HBS £60 HBD £90
B £4.95 L £4.95 D £4.95.
CC: MC Vi Am DC Swi Delt

How to get there: Exit M2 at Mullusk slip road.
Take A6, hotel 1 mile on left-hand side of road.

Republic of Ireland

Achill Island, Co. Mayo

Achill Cliff House

◆◆◆◆

Keel, Achill Island, Co. Mayo
Tel: +353(0)98 43400 Fax: +353(0)98 43007
Email: achwch@anu.ie
Web: www.wejustloveit.com/ireland
SB £38 DB £28 HBS £55 HBD £48
B £5 L £5 D £15. CC: MC Vi Am Delt Laser
How to get there: Coming from Achill Sound,
hotel is on right-hand side of road in Keel.
See advert on the right

Adare, Co. Limerick

Adare Manor

★★★★★
Adare, Co. Limerick
Tel: +353(0)61 396566 Fax: +353(0)61 396124

Berkeley Lodge

◆◆◆◆

Station Road, Adare, Co. Limerick
Tel: +353(0)61 396857 Fax: +353(0)61 396857
Email: berlodge@iol.ie
Web: www.adare.org
Children minimum age: 2
SB £35 DB £50 CC: MC Vi
How to get there: Take N21 (Limerick) via
Killarney to Adare. Right at roundabout. Hotel is
fifth house on the right after petrol station.

Coatesland House Bed & Breakfast

◆◆◆◆

Killarney Road, Graigue, Adare, Co. Limerick,
Tel: +353(0)61 396372 Fax: +353(0)61 396833

Achill Cliff House

RAC Sparkling Diamond Guesthouse and
Restaurant. Excellent location. Spacious
bedrooms with magnificent scenery. Smoke-free.
Sauna for guest use. The restaurant commands
views of Minaun Cliffs and Atlantic Ocean over
Keel Beach. Fresh local produce — succulent
lamb, prime steak, oysters, lobsters, salmon and
mussels — served nightly in the fully licensed
restaurant. Excellent selection of fine wines.
Your host is happy to advise you on what to do.

Keel, Achill Island, Co. Mayo, Ireland
Tel: 098 43400   Fax: 098 43007
Email: achwch@anu.ie
Website: www."beourguest".com

Ardmore, Co. Waterford

Newtown Farm Guesthouse

❖
Newtown Farm, Grange Via Yougal, Ardmore,
Co. Waterford
Tel: +353(0)24 94143 Fax: +353(0)24 94054

Athlone, Co. Westmeath

Hodson Bay

★★★
Athlone, Co. Westmeath
Tel: +353(0)90 292444 Fax: +353(0)90 292688
Email: info@hodsonbayhotel.com
Web: www.hodsonbayhotel.com
SB £90 DB £118 B £9 L £11 D £20.
CC: MC Vi Am DC
How to get there: The hotel is located off the
N61 Roscommon road just 5 minutes from
Athlone Town, 90 minutes from Dublin
International Airport.
See advert on following page

Ireland

Athy, Co. Kildare

Coursetown Country House   `Little Gem`

♦♦♦♦♦   ✻ ❦

Stradbally Road, Athy, Co. Kildare
Tel: +353(0)507 31101 Fax: +353(0)507 32740
Children minimum age: 8. Closed Christmas

Large country house in 260 acre farm.
Bedrooms designed for maximum guest
comfort. Tastefully appointed fully accessible
wheelchair-friendly suite. Excellent breakfast
with homemade bread and preserves.
SB £35 DB £60 CC: MC Vi Am
♿ ✻ ⊗ ⑤ ▢ ☎ P ❦ ⅀ ♘ ♔ ☙
How to get there: Off N78 at Athy or N80 at
Stradally onto R428. Hotel is 3kms for Athy.

Hodson Bay Hotel

Fairytale Lakeside Location,
133 Deluxe Ensuite Bedrooms,
Award-Winning L'Escale Restaurant,
Lively Waterfront Bar, Garden Restaurant,
Leisure Centre, Swimming Pool,
Adjacent to Athlone Golf Club.

Athlone, Co. Westmeath, Ireland
Tel: +353 (0)902 80500
Fax:+353 (0)902 80520
Email: info@hodsonbayhotel.com
Website: www.hodsonbayhotel.com

Aughrim, Co. Wicklow

Brook Lodge

★★★★ ☗☗☗

Macreddin Village, Co. Wicklow
Tel: +353(0)402 36444 Fax: +353(0)402 36580
Email: brooklodge@macreddin.ie
Web: www.brooklodge.com

The perfect country house hotel, warm, friendly
and relaxed, deep in spectacular countryside
yet only an hour from South Dublin. Featuring
the sublime Strawberry Tree Restaurant.
SB £80 DB £116 HBS £107.50 HBD £171
B £8 L £12.50 D £27.50. CC: MC Vi Am DC
⚓ ♿ ⊞ ⇆ ✻ ⊗ ⑤ ▢ ☎ ☏ P ❦ ⅀ ♘ ♔ ☙
⚏ ⚌ ⁄ ♞
How to get there: South from Dublin, N11 to
Rathnew (29 miles), R752 to Rathdrum (8 miles),
R753 to Aughrim (7 miles), follow signs to
Macreddin Village (2 miles)

Ballinamore, Co. Leitrim

Riversdale Farmhouse

♦♦♦

Ballinamore, Co. Leitrim
Tel: +353 (0)78 44122 Fax: +353 (0)78 44813

Ballinasloe, Co. Galway

Haydens Gateway

★★★ ☗

Dunlo Street, Ballinasloe, Co. Galway
Tel: +353 (0)65 6823000 Fax: +353 (0)65 6823759
Email: cro@lynchhotels.com
Web: www.lynchhotels.com
SB £50 DB £75 HBS £62 HBD £100
B £4.70 L £6.25 D £15.60.
CC: MC Vi Am DC Access Laser
⚓ ♿ ⊞ ⊗ ⑤ ▢ ☎ ☏ P ❦ ⅀ ♘ ♔ ☙ ⚏
⚌ ⚏
How to get there: In the heart of Ballinasloe, just
30 minutes from Galway Airport (N6 road).

Ballingeary, Co. Cork

Gougane Barra

★★

Gougane Barra, Ballingeary, Co. Cork
Tel: +353(0)26 47069 Fax: +353(0)26 47226

Ballyconnell, Co. Cavan

Slieve Russell Golf & Country Club

★★★★ ⓡ

Ballyconnell, Co. Cavan
Tel: +353(0)49 26444 Fax: +353(0)49 26474

Ballyheigue, Co. Kerry

White Sands

★★★

Ballyheigue, Co. Kerry
Tel: +353(0)66 33357

Ballylickey, Co. Galway

Sea View House

★★★ ⓡ

Ballylickey, Bantry, Co. Galway
Tel: +353(0)27 50462 Fax: +353(0)27 51555
Email: seaviewhousehotel@eircom.net
Closed mid-November to mid-March
SB £50 DB £100 HBS £75 HBD £150
CC: MC Vi Am DC

♿ ⛽ ☎ P ⚅ ⚞ ⛾ ⨝ 🐎 🎋 ⛵ ⚏

How to get there: On main route N71, 3 miles
from Bantry, 7 miles from Glengariff.

Ballyvaughan, Co. Clare

Gregans Castle

★★★ ⓡⓡⓡ

Ballyvaughan, Co. Clare
Tel: +353(0)65 7077005 Fax: +353(0)65 7077111
Email: res@gregans.ie
Web: www.gregans.ie
Closed November to March
SB £126 DB £146 HBS £111 HBD £131
CC: MC Vi Am Delt

♿ ⛽ ☎ P ⚅ ⚞ ⛾ 🐎 🎋 ⛵ ⚏

How to get there: 3¹/₂ miles south of
Ballyvaughan village on N67.

Hylands

♣

Ballyvaughan, Co. Clare
Tel: +353(0)65 7077037 Fax: +353(0)65 7077131
Email: hylands@tinet.ie
Web: www.cmvhotels.com
Closed January
SB £57 DB £78 HBS £50 B £5 L £6 D £20.
CC: MC Vi Am DC

♿ ⛽ ⚅ ⛾ ☎ P ⚞ ⨝ 🐎 ⨝ ⛵ ⚏

How to get there: In the centre of Ballyvaughan
village.

Rusheen Lodge

♦♦♦♦ ⚞

Knocknagrough, Ballyvaughan, Co. Clare
Tel: +353(0)65 7077092 Fax: +353(0)65 7077152
Email: rusheenl@iol.ie
Web: www.rusheenlodge.com
Closed December to January
SB £50 DB £60 B £7.50 CC: MC Vi Am

⚅ ⛾ ☎ P ⚞ ⨝ 🐎 ⨝ ⛵

How to get there: From Ballyvaughan village,
N67 south for ³/₄ km. Rusheen Lodge on left.

Baltimore, Co. Cork

Casey's of Baltimore

★★ ⓡ

Baltimore, Co. Cork
Tel: +353(0)28 20197 Fax: +353(0)28 20509
Email: caseys@eircom.net
Web: www.baltimore-ireland.com/caseys
SB £65 DB £93 HBS £90 HBD £130
B £6 L £12 D £25. CC: MC Vi Am DC

⚅ ⛾ ☎ ☎ P ⚞ ⨝ 🐎 ⨝ ⛵ ⚏

How to get there: From Cork N71 to
Skibbereen. From Skibbereen R595 to
Baltimore. Hotel on R595 near Baltimore.

Bantry, Co. Cork

Westlodge

★★★

Bantry, Co. Cork
Tel: +353(0)27 50360 Fax: +353(0)27 50438
Email: reservations@westlodgehotel.ie
Web: www.westlodgehotel.ie
SB £48 DB £80 L £10.50 D £21.
CC: MC Vi Am DC

♿ ⛽ ⚅ ⛾ ☎ P ⚞ ⨝ 🐎 ⨝ ⛵ ⚏ 🌸
SPA ⚞ ⚞ ⚞

How to get there: Situated on Bantry Bay.

Ireland

The Mill

♦♦♦

Glengarriff Road, New Town, Bantry, Co. Cork
Tel: +353(0)27 50278 Fax: +353(0)27 50278
Email: bbthemill@eircom.net
SB £30 DB £45

How to get there: On N71, 1km from Bantry.

Blessington, Co. Wicklow

Downshire House

★★★

Blessington, Co. Wicklow
Tel: +353(0)45 865199 Fax: +353(0)45 865335

Bray, Co. Wicklow

Esplanade

★★★

Bray, Co. Wicklow
Tel: +353(0)1 2862056 Fax: +353(0)1 2866496
Email: roy@regencyhotels.com
Web: www.regencyhotels.com
Closed November to February

This 40 bedroom hotel is located overlooking the sea in the picturesque town of Bray, Co Wicklow. It is at the gateway to the 'Garden County of Ireland' and yet only 30 minutes from Dublin. The hotel boasts a new leisure studio with all up-to-the-minute equipment. The hotel has an excellent restaurant, Lacy's, and Victorian residents lounge with a particularly cosy atmosphere. The hotel also features private banqueting facilities for up to 130 persons.

SB £80 DB £120 B £7.95 D £18.75.
CC: MC Vi Am DC

How to get there: Bray is just south of Dublin off the M11.

Royal Hotel & Leisure Centre

★★★

Main Street, Bray, Co. Wicklow
Tel: +353(0)1 2862935 Fax: +353(0)1 2867373
Email: royal@regencyhotels.com
Web: www.regencyhotels.com

The hotel is on the main street of the coastal resort of Bray, Co Wicklow. It is 12km south of Dublin city, yet only a 30 minute DART (Dublin Area Rapid Transit) drive away. This 90-bedroom hotel offers fine dining facilities with the Dargle room restaurant and the hotel's banqueting suites that can cater for up to 250 persons. Quinns Lounge provides a lively atmosphere with entertainment featuring on a regular basis. Extensive free supervised car parking available.

SB £68 DB £80 B £6.95 L £6.95 D £16.95.
CC: MC Vi

How to get there: On main street in Bray, located off the Dublin to Wicklow route N11. Hotel 5 minutes from DART rail station.

Butterstown, Co, Waterford

Waterford Manor

Killotteen, Butlerstown, Co. Waterford
Tel: +353(0)51 377814 Fax: +353(0)1 354545

Cappoquin, Co. Wexford

Richmond House

♦♦♦♦ ⍟⍟

Cappoquin, Co. Wexford
Tel: +353(0)58 54278 Fax: +353(0)58 54988
Web: www.amireland.com/richmond
Closed Christmas to mid-January

Award-winning 18th century Georgian country house and fully licensed restaurant. Enjoy peace, tranquility and log fires combined with every modern comfort for discerning guests.
SB £60 DB £100 CC: MC Vi Am DC

How to get there: N72, ½ mile outside Cappoquin.

Caragh Lake, Co. Kerry

Caragh Lodge

★★ ⍟⍟⍟

Caragh Lake, Co. Kerry
Tel: +353(0)66 9769115 Fax: +3530)66 9769316
Email: caraghl@iol.ie
Web: www.caraghlodge.com
Children minimum age: 12
SB £85 DB £125 D £33. CC: MC Vi Am DC

How to get there: From Killorglin, N70 towards Glenbeigh. Left after 3 miles at signpost 'Caragh Lodge'. Left at end of road. Caragh Lodge is on right.
See advert on this page

Carlow, Co. Carlow

Barrowville Town House

♦♦♦♦♦

Kilkenny Road, Carlow Town, Co. Carlow
Tel: +353(0)50 343324
Fax: +353(0)50 241953
Five-diamond Georgian listed town house. Well appointed bedrooms. Traditional or buffet breakfast served in conservatory overlooking

gardens. Excellent location for golf or touring South-East/Midlands.
SB £30 DB £27.50 CC: MC Vi Am

How to get there: On N9 south side of Carlow town centre. Travelling south, hotel 50m past last traffic lights. From N80, turn off at first N9 sign.

Caragh Lodge

Victorian Lodge in award winning gardens. Antiques and log fires create the atmosphere for a drink before dinner. Ideal for golf, fishing or touring in Kerry.

Caragh Lodge, Caragh Lake,
Co. Kerry, Ireland
Tel: 066 9769115 Fax: 066 9769316
Email: caraghl@iol.ie
Website: www.caragh lodge.com

Ireland

Carrigaline, Co. Cork

Carrigaline Court
★★★★ ♟
Main Street, Carrigaline, Co. Cork
Tel: +353(0)21 371300 Fax: +353(0)21 371103

Carrigans, Co. Donegal

Mount Royd Country Home | Little Gem
◆◆◆◆ ♟
Carrigans, nr Derry, Co. Donegal
Tel: +353(0)74 40163 Fax: +353(0)74 40400
Email: gmgmartin@eircom.net
Closed Christmas
SB £25 DB £38
 ❂ ⌷ ☐ P ♟ ⁑ 🪑 ♬ ⇆
How to get there: From Londonderry A40. From
Lifford take N14 then R265. Hotel on R236.

Carrigbyrne, Co. Wexford

Woodlands House
◆◆◆
Carrigbyrne, Co. Wexford
Tel: +353(0)51 428287 Fax: +353(0)51 428287
Email: woodwex@eircom.net
Children minimum age: 5
Closed November to February

Beautiful countryside location only 30 minutes
from Rosslare on main Cork/Waterford road.
Recently refurbished. Ideal base for Wexford,
Waterford, Kilkenny. Golf, fishing, riding nearby.
SB £25 DB £38 D £6.95. CC: MC Vi
♟ ❂ ⌷ ☐ P ♟ ⁑ 🪑 ♬ ⇆
How to get there: Situated on the N25, Rosslare
to Waterford/Cork road, 30 minutes from
Rosslare, just past the Cedar Lodge Hotel.

Cashel, Co. Wexford

Cashel House
★★★ ♟ ♟ ♟
Cashel, Connemara, Co. Wexford
Tel: +353(0)95 31001 Fax: +353(0)95 31077
Children minimum age: 5. Closed January
SB £66.50 DB £133 HBS £100 HBD £200
B £15 L £15 D £37. CC: MC Vi Am
♟ ❂ 🐴 ⊗ ⌷ ☐ ☎ ☏ P ♟ ⁑ 🪑 ♬ ⇆ ♨
⚲ ♟
How to get there: 1 mile west of Recess. Turn
left off main Galway to Clifden road (N59).

Castlebar, Co. Mayo

Breaffy House
❖
Castlebar, Co. Mayo
Tel: +353(0)65 6866697 Fax: +353(0)65 6823759
Email: marketing@lynchotels.com
Web: www.lynchotels.com
SB £61 DB £100 HBS £77 HBD £65
B £6 L £8 D £17. CC: MC Vi Am DC
⚙ ♟ ⊥ ⊗ ⌷ ☎ P ♟ ⁑ 🪑 ♬ ⇆ ♨ ♨♨ 'Y'
How to get there: Take main Roscommon Road
out of Castlebar for 3km to Breaffy village.

Cavan, Co. Cavan

Hotel Kilmore
★★★ ♟
Dublin Road, Cavan, Co. Cavan
Tel: +353(0)49 4332288 Fax: +353(0)49 4332458
Email: kilmore@quinn-hotels.com
Web: www.quinn-group.com
SB £46 DB £72 HBS £65 HBD £55 B £7 D £20.
CC: MC Vi Am DC
♟ ❂ ⊗ ⌷ ☎ P ♟ ⁑ 🪑 ♬ ⇆ ♨♨ ♨♨
How to get there: N54 to Clones and Cavan (via
bypass). on towards Dublin. Hotel on left.

Clifden, Co. Galway

Sunnybank Guesthouse
Church Hill, Clifden, Co. Galway
Tel: +353(0)95 21437 Fax: +353(0)95 21976

Alcock & Brown Best Western
★★★ ♟ ♟
The Square, Clifden, Co. Galway
Tel: +353(0)95 21206 Fax: +353(0)95 21842
Email: alcockandbrown@eircom.net
Web: www.alcockandbrown-hotel.com

SB £45 DB £70 HBS £65 HBD £108 B £9 L £8
D £22. CC: MC Vi Am DC   Closed Dec 23-26.

How to get there: N6 Dublin to Galway, then
N59 to Clifden. Hotel is in centre of village.

Ardagh
★★★ 🅡🅡🅡
Ballyconneely Road, Clifden, Co. Galway
Tel: +353(0)95 21384 Fax: +353(0)95 21314
Email: ardaghhotel@eircom.net
Web: www.commerce.ie/ardaghhotel
Closed November to March
SB £75 DB £55 HBS £90 HBD £75
B £10 D £17.50. CC: MC Vi Am DC

How to get there: From Clifden follow signs to
Ballyconneely. Ardagh Hotel is 2 miles out of
Clifden.

Renvyle House
★★★ 🅡
Renvyle, Connemara, Co. Galway
Tel: +353(0)95 43511 Fax: +353(0)95 43515
Email: renvyle@iol.ie
Web: www.renvyle.com
Closed January to February

SB £30 DB £40 HBS £50 HBD £100
B £10 L £15 D £27.50. CC: MC Vi Am DC

How to get there: Take N59 west from Galway.
At recess turn right, at Kylemore turn left. At
Letterfrack turn right. Continue for 5 miles.

Station House
★★★
Clifden, Connemara, Co. Galway
Tel: +353(0)95 21699
Fax: +353(0)95 21667
Email: station@eircom.net
Web: www.stationhousehotel.com
Wonderfully nostalgic hotel development
situated in Clifden, the beautiful capital of
Connemara. A unique property which integrates

the old-world charm of the former Clifden
Railway Station buildings with superb modern
facilities. Definitely not to be missed!
SB £80 DB £55 HBS £95 HBD £75
B £8 L £8 D £21.

How to get there: N59 from Galway city.

Buttermilk Lodge Guest House
♦♦♦♦♦
Westport Road, Clifden, Co. Galway
Tel: +353(0)95 21951 Fax: +353(0)95 21953
Email: buttermilk@anu.ie
Web: www.connemara.net/buttermilk-lodge
Children minimum age: 5. Closed January
SB £25 DB £40 CC: MC Vi Laser

How to get there: From Galway, right at Esso
station; 400m on left. From Westport, on right
100m after 'Clifden' sign.

Mal Dua House   `Little Gem`
♦♦♦♦♦
Galway Road, Clifden, Connemara, Co. Galway
Tel: +353(0)95 21171 Fax: +353(0)95 21739
Email: info@maldua.com
Web: www.maldua.com
SB £26.25 DB £52.50
CC: MC Vi Am DC Laser Eurocard

How to get there: On the Galway Road (N59),
1¼km from Clifden.
See advert on following page

Ireland

Dún Rí Guest House

◆◆◆◆

Hulk Street, Clifden, Co. Galway
Tel: +353(0)95 21625 Fax: +353(0)95 21635
Email: dunri@anu.ie
Web: www.connemara.net/dun-ri
Children minimum age: 4
Closed November to February
SB £35 DB £50 CC: MC Vi

How to get there: Enter Clifden on N59, left
before Statoil Station, and on to Dún Rí.

Kingstown House

◆◆◆

Bridge Street, Clifden, Co. Galway
Tel: +353(0)95 21470

Benview House

◆◆

Bridge Street, Clifden, Co. Galway
Tel: +353(0)95 21256

Please mention the RAC Inspected guide
when you make your booking at an RAC
Hotel or Guest Accommodation.

Clonakilty, Co. Cork

Lodge and Spa

★★★★ 🍷🍷🍷
Inchydoney Island, Clonakilty, Co. Cork
Tel: +353(0)23 33143 Fax: +353(0)23 35229
Email: reservations@inchydoneyisland.com
Web: www.inchydoneyisland.com
SB £154 DB £263 HBS £130 HBD £205
B £14 L £20 D £40. CC: MC Vi Am DC

How to get there: N71 from Cork to Clonakilty.
At roundabout, follow signs for Lodge & Spa.

Clonmel, Co. Tipperary

Minella

★★★
Coleville Road, Clonmel, Co. Tipperary
Tel: +353(0)52 22385 Fax: +353(0)52 24381
Email: hotelminella@eircom.net
Web: www.hotelminella.ie
SB £75 DB £120 HBS £105 HBD £180
B £7 L £17 D £26. CC: MC Vi Am DC

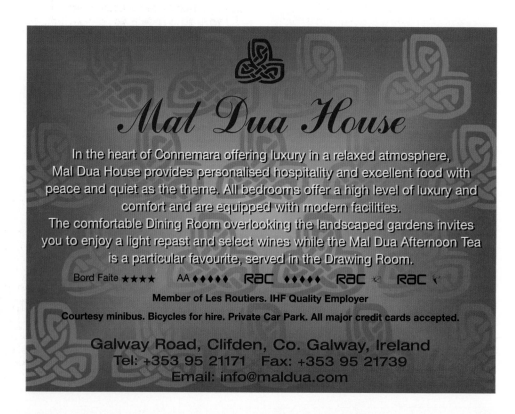

Cobh, Co. Cork

Waters Edge

★★★

next to Cobh Heritage Centre, Cobh, Co. Cork
Tel: +353(0)21 4815566 Fax: +353(0)21 4812011
Email: watersedge@eircom.net
Web: www.watersedgehotel.ie

Situated on the waterfront (next to Cobh
Heritage Centre), overlooking Cork Harbour. All
rooms ensuite. Most guest rooms with harbour
views. Our restaurant 'Jacob's Ladder' is
renowned for its seafood, steaks, ambience and
friendly staff.
SB £45 DB £35 B £5 L £8 D £18. CC: MC Vi DC
& 🐎 😊 🗏 🖵 ☎ 🔌 P 🏊 ♨ ⅲ ⅲ
How to get there: Cobh is 12 minutes from Cork
on R624, off N25. 20 minutes from Cork airport
and close to ferryport.

Cong, Co. Mayo

Ashford Castle

★★★★★ 🍴🍴🍴
Cong, Co. Mayo
Tel: +353(0)92 46003 Fax: +353(0)92 46260
Email: ashford@ashford.ie
Web: www.ashford.ie
SB £290 DB £365 HBS £338 HBD £463
B £14.50 L £25 D £42. CC: MC Vi Am DC
⅃ 🧺 🖵 ☎ 🔌 P🏊 ♨ 🎠 ☕ ♬ 🐎 👁 ⅲ ⅲ
SPA 🍴 ⛳ 🎣 🚶 ⛵
How to get there: N84 from Galway to Headford
(17 miles), straight through, taking the Cong
Road (10 miles).

Connemara, Co. Galway

Eldons

★★ 🍴🍴
Roundstone, Connemara, Co. Galway
Tel: +353(0)95 35933

The Anglers Return

♦♦

Toombeole, Roundstone, Connemara,
Co. Galway
Tel: +353(0)95 31091

Cork, Co. Cork

Hayfield Manor

★★★★ 🍴🍴🍴
Perrott Avenue, College Road, Cork, Co. Cork
Tel: +353(0)21 315600 Fax: +353(0)21 316839
Email: enquiries@hayfieldmanor.ie
Web: www.hayfieldmanor.ie

Experience unobtrusive yet attentive service at
Cork's only five-star (ITB) hotel. With a country
house ambience, luxurious guest rooms,
exclusive private leisure centre and award-
winning cuisine.
SB £180 DB £280 B £12 L £19.50 D £35.
CC: MC Vi Am DC
& ⅃ 😊 🖵 ☎ ❄ 🔌 P 🏊 ♨ 🎠 ♬ 🐎 👁 ⅲ
ⅲ 🍴 ⛳
How to get there: Travelling west from city
centre, take N70 for Killarney. Turn left at
university gates off Western Road. At top of
road turn right and immediately left; hotel at top
of avenue.

Jurys Cork

★★★★ 🍴🍴
Western Road, Cork, Co. Cork
Tel: +353(0)1 6070055 Fax: +353(0)1 6609625
Email: dorothy_cusack@jurysdoyle.com
Web: www.jurysdoyle.com
B £3.25 L £14 D £18. CC: MC Vi Am DC
& ⅃ 🖵 ☎ 🔌 P 🏊 ♨ 🎠 ♬ 🐎 ⅲ ⅲ 🍴
⛳ 🚶

Kingsley

★★★★ 🍴
Victoria Cross, Cork, Co. Cork
Tel: +353(0)21 4800500 Fax: +353(0)21 4800527

Silver Springs Moran

★★★★

Tivoli, Cork, Co. Cork
Tel: +353(0)21 4507533 Fax: +353(0)21 4507641
Email: silversprings@morangroup.ie
Web: www.morangroup.ie

Imposing 4-Star hotel in sylvan grounds. Five minutes drive to city centre, 15 minutes from Cork airport. 109 luxury en-suite bedrooms, choice of bars and restaurants. Excellent cuisine. Leisure centre and 9-hole golf course. SB £70 DB £78 L £14 D £22.50.
CC: MC Vi Am DC

How to get there: From airport, signs to N25, through Jack Lynch tunnel. First left and head for Cork centre. Turn left onto flyover, right at top; hotel is on left.

Bayview

★★★

Ballycotton, Co. Cork
Tel: +353(0)21 646746 Fax: +353(0)21 646075
Email: bayhotel@iol.ie
Web: www.bayview.com
Closed November to March
SB £82 DB £113 HBS £112 HBD £173
B £7 L £15 D £30.
CC: MC Vi Am DC

How to get there: At Castlemantyr on N25, turn onto the R632. Follow the signs for Ballycotton.

Jurys Inn Cork

★★★

Anderson's Quay, Cork, Co. Cork
Tel: +353(0)1 6070055 Fax: +353(0) 6609625
Email: dorothy_cusack@jurysdoyle.com
Web: www.jurysdoyle.com
CC: MC Vi Am DC

Fairy Lawn Guesthouse

♦♦♦♦

Western Road, Cork, Co. Cork
Tel: +353(0)21 4543444 Fax: +353(0)21 4544337
Email: fairylawn@holidayhound.com
Web: www.holidayhound.com/fairylawn.htm
SB £38 DB £55
CC: MC Vi Laser

How to get there: From city centre (Patrick Street) proceed to Capitol cineplex, right at lights onto Washington Street. Straight on past the gates of UCC and hotel is on right before next set of traffic lights.

Garnish House

♦♦♦♦

Western Road, Cork, Co. Cork
Tel: +353(0)21 4275111 Fax: +353(0)21 273872
Email: garnish@iol.ie

Web: www.garnish.ie
Garnish House offers a memorable stay. Our tastefully appointed rooms with optional ensuite jacuzzi and our extensive gourmet breakfast is certain to please. 24-hour reception.
SB £60 DB £80 B £10
CC: MC Vi Am DC

How to get there: N8 from Dublin and N22 from Kerry. Close to bus and rail stations, opposite Cork University, 20 min drive from Cork airport.

Lancaster Lodge

♦♦♦♦

Lancaster Quay, Western Road, Cork, Co. Cork
Tel: +353(0)21 251125 Fax: +353(0)21 425426
Email: info@lancasterlodge.com
Web: www.lancasterlodge.com
SB £60 DB £80   Closed December 24 and 25.
CC: MC Vi Am DC Swi Delt

How to get there: Located alongside Jurys Hotel on the western road in Cork. 5 minute walk to city centre.

Antoine House

♦♦♦

Western Road, Cork, Co. Cork
Tel: +353(0)21 273494 Fax: +353(0)21 273092

Killarney Guest House

♦♦♦

Western Road, Cork, Co. Cork
Tel: +353(0)21 270290 Fax: +353(0)21 271010

Roserie Villa

♦♦♦

Mardyke Walk, Off Western Road, Cork,
Co. Cork
Tel: +353(0)21 272958 Fax: +353(0)21 274087

St Kilda Guest House

♦♦♦

Western Road, Cork, Co. Cork
Tel: +353(0)21 273095 Fax: +353(0)21 275015

Crawford House

Western Road, Cork, Co. Cork
Tel: +353(0)21 4279000 Fax: +353(0)21 4279927
Email: crawford@indigo.ie
Web: www.crawfordhouse.com
SB £35 DB £50 CC: MC Vi Am
⊗ ⌚ ▭ ☎ 🕻 📶 P 🐎 ⅀ 🔥 ⋔ 🦢
How to get there: Ten-minute walk from centre.
Located opposite from University College, Cork.

Delgany, Co. Wicklow

Glenview

★★★ 🐾🐾
Glen-O-The-Downs, Delgany, Co. Wicklow
Tel: +353(0)1 2873399 Fax: +353(0)1 2877511

Dingle, Co. Kerry

Dingle Skellig

★★★ 🐾
Dingle, Co. Kerry
Tel: +353(0)66 9150200 Fax: +353(0)66 9151501
Email: dsk@iol.ie
Web: www.dingleskellig.com
Closed January to mid-February
SB £55 DB £90 HBS £80 HBD £140
B £9.95 D £29.95. CC: MC Vi Am DC
⚓ ⛵ 🍴 ⊗ ▭ ☎ P 🐾 📶 🐎 ⋔ 🦢 ⚙ ⅏ ▦
🏹 📶 ⅀
How to get there: Take R563 and R561 from
Killarney (or R559 from Tralee). Entering out-
skirts of town, hotel on left by Dingle Harbour.

Alpine House Guest House

♦♦♦♦   ⊁

Mail Road, Dingle, Co. Kerry
Tel: +353(0)66 9151250 Fax: +353(0)66 9151966
Email: alpinedingle@eircom.net
Web: www.alpineguesthouse.com
Children minimum age: 5

Newly renovated guest house. Beautifully
furnished bedrooms, all with spacious
bathrooms. Non-smoking. Private car park.
Town centre is 2 minute walk away.
SB £20 DB £18.50 CC: MC Vi Am
⊗ ⌚ ▭ ☎ P 📶 🐎 🔥 🦢
How to get there: On route N86 at entrance to
Dingle town. 2 minutes walk from town centre.

Ard Na Greine

♦♦♦♦   ⊁

Spa Road, Dingle, Co. Kerry
Tel: +353(0)66 9151113 Fax: +353(0)66 9151898
Children minimum age: 7
DB £24 CC: MC Vi
⊗ ⌚ ▭ ☎ P 📶

Bambury's Guesthouse

♦♦♦♦

Mail Road, Dingle, Co. Kerry
Tel: +353(0)66 9151244 Fax: +353(0)66 9151786
Email: bamburysguesthouse@eircom.net
Children minimum age: 4
SB £25 DB £30 CC: MC Vi
⊗ ⌚ ▭ ☎ P 📶 🐎 🔥 🦢
How to get there: On N86 into Dingle. Hotel is
situated after the Shell station as you enter
Dingle.

Guide dogs   RƎC

If a Hotel or Guest Accommodation
does not display this 'dogs welcome'
symbol in its listing, the hotelier may
still be happy to welcome guests with guide
dogs, and you should contact the property to
discover whether this will be a problem.

Ireland

Cleevaun House

◆◆◆◆

Ladys Cross, Milltown, Dingle, Co. Kerry
Tel: +353(0)66 9151108 Fax: +353(0)66 9152228
Email: cleevaun@iol.ie
Web: www.cleevaun.com
Children minimum age: 8
Closed mid-November to mid-March
SB £40 DB £45

How to get there: Route 559. First left off first
roundabout. Head for Sleahead. With water on
left, pass marina. Left at next roundabout.
Cross bridge. Cleevaun 500m on left.

Doyle's Town House

◆◆◆◆

John Street, Dingle, Co. Kerry
Tel: +353(0)66 9151174 Fax: +353(0)66 9151816
Email: adoyles@iol.ie
Web: www.doylesofdingle.com
Children minimum age: 8
Closed mid-November to mid-February
SB £60 DB £65 CC: MC Vi Am DC

How to get there: Enter Dingle and take right
turn at roundabout, right at next junction. Hotel
is situated uphill, 350m on left.

Greenmount House

◆◆◆◆

Upper John Street, Dingle, Co. Kerry
Tel: +353(0)66 9151414 Fax: +353(0)66 9157974
Email: mary@greenmounthouse.com
Web: www.greenmount.com
Children minimum age: 8
Closed December 20–27
SB £60 DB £80 CC: MC Vi Swi

How to get there: Enter Dingle and take right
turn at roundabout, right at next junction. Hotel
is situated uphill, 350m on left.

Milltown House

◆◆◆◆

Dingle, Co. Kerry
Tel: +353(0)66 9151372 Fax: +353(0)66 9151095
Email: milltown@indigo.ie
Web: indigo.ie/~milltown
Closed December 22–29
SB £65 DB £75 CC: MC Vi Am

How to get there: Leave Dingle on Sleahead
Drive Road. Take next two left turns. House less
than 1 mile west of Dingle town.

Book with RAC Hotel Reservations and check
the latest offers available. Call 0870 603 9109
and quote 'RAC Guide 2001'

Bolands

◆◆◆

Goat Street, Dingle, Co. Kerry
Tel: +353(0)66 9151426
Closed Christmas Day

A warm welcome awaits you in our family-run
guesthouse, with panoramic views of Dingle
Bay. All rooms are en-suite with direct dial
phones, TV, hairdryers, tea and coffee-making
facilities. Full breakfast menu.
DB £30 CC: MC Vi

How to get there: Situated on the upper part of
the main street near the Dingle hospital.

Donegal Bay, Co. Donegal

Sand House

★★★

Rossnowlagh, Donegal Bay, Co. Donegal
Tel: +353(0)72 51777 Fax: +353(0)72 52100

Donegal, Co. Donegal

Harvey's Point

★★★

Lough Eske, Donegal, Co. Donegal
Tel: +353(0)73 22208 Fax: +353(0)73 22352

Ardeevin

◆◆◆◆

Lough Eske, Barnesmore, Donegal, Co. Donegal
Tel: +353(0)73 21790 Fax: +353(0)73 21790

Rhu-Gorse

◆◆◆◆

Lough Eske, Donegal, Co. Donegal,
Tel: +353(0)73 21685 Fax: +353(0)73 21685
Email: rhugorse@iol.ie
Closed November to March
SB £27.50 DB £22.50 CC: MC Vi

How to get there: From Donegal, take N56 or N15. Follow signs to Harvey's Point and Lough Eske to crossroads (2³/₄ miles) then follow sign for Rhu-Gorse. House is on right after 2¹/₂ miles.

Dooega, Co. Mayo

Lavelles Sea Side House
♦ ♦ ♦
Achill Island, Dooega, Co. Mayo
Tel: +353(0)98 45116

Douglas, Co. Cork

Rochestown Park

Rochestown Road, Douglas, Co. Cork
Tel: +353(0)21 4892233 Fax: +353(0)21 4892178

Dromoland, Co. Clare

Clare Inn
★★★
Dromoland, Co. Clare
Tel: +353(0)65 6823000 Fax: +353(0)65 6823759
Email: cro@lynchhotels.com
Web: www.lynchhotels.com
SB £57 DB £90 HBS £70 HBD £115
B £6.50 L £11 D £16.50. CC: MC Vi Am Laser

How to get there: Just 10 minutes drive from Shannon International Airport on main Galway Road (N18) on the Dromoland Estate.

Dublin

Berkeley Court
★★★★★ 🐾
Lansdowne Road, Dublin 4
Tel: +353(0)1 6601711 Fax: +353(0)1 6617238
Email: joe_russell@jurys.com
Web: www.jurysdoyle.com
SB £220 DB £255 CC: MC Vi Am DC
How to get there: N11 into Donnybrook, right off Morehampton Road onto Waterloo Road, right into Pembroke Road. Continue through junction to corner of Shelbourne and Lansdowne Roads.

When booking at an RAC Hotel or Guest Accommodation, please mention this Guide.

Conrad International Dublin
★★★★★
Earlsfort Terrace, Dublin 2
Tel: +353(0)1676 5555 Fax: +353(0)1 676 5424
Email: sales@conrad-international.ie
SB £220 DB £260
CC: MC Vi Am DC
How to get there: Located in city centre, on the south side of St Stephen's Green, at the end of Leeson Street.

Merrion
★★★★★ 🐾🐾🐾🐾
Upper Merrion Street, Dublin 2
Tel: +353(0)1 2838277 Fax: +353(0)1 6030700
Email: cdeeny@merrionhotel.com
Web: www.merrionhotel.com
CC: MC Vi Am DC JCB

The Shelbourne Meridien
★★★★★ 🐾🐾🐾
St Stephens Green, Dublin 2
Tel: +353(0)1 6766471 Fax: +353(0)1 6616006

Burlington
★★★★
Upper Leeson Street, Dublin 4
Tel: +353(0)1 6070055 Fax: +353(0)1 6609625
Email: dorothy_cusack@jurysdoyle.com
Web: www.jurysdoyle.com
B £5.50 L £14 D £18.
CC: MC Vi Am DC Swi Delt
How to get there: N7 out of town. Up Naas Road to Newlands Cross, go right. At second set of lights turn left. Up that road for ¹/₄ mile and turn left.

Fitzpatrick Castle
★★★★
Killiney, Co. Dublin
Tel: +353(0)1 2305558 Fax: +353(0)1 2305466
Email: reservations@dublin.fitzpatricks.com
Web: www.fitzpatrickhotels.com
SB £118 DB £150 HBS £150 HBD £215
B £9 L £14 D £32.50.
CC: MC Vi Am DC   Closed December 24–25.
How to get there: Hotel is 1²/₃km from Dalkey. From Castle Street to Dalkey, turn left onto Dalkey Avenue. Hotel is on left. Dalkey village is 14¹/₂km south of Dublin city centre.

Ireland

Fitzwilliam

★★★★ ℛℛℛℛ
St Stephens Green, Dublin 2
Tel: +353(0)1 4787000 Fax: +353(0)1 4787878

Gresham

★★★★
23 Upper O'Connell Street, Dublin 1
Tel: +353(0)1 8746881

Behind the elegant façade lie luxury
bedrooms and spacious suites, an
award-winning restaurant and bars.
SB £220 DB £255
B £12.50 L £17 D £23.50.
CC: MC Vi Am DC Laser
How to get there: On Dublin's main
thoroughfare, O'Connell Street.

Herbert Park

★★★★ ℛℛ
Ballsbridge, Dublin
Tel: +353(0)1 6672200 Fax: +353(0)1 6672595

Jurys Ballsbridge

★★★★ ℛ
Ballsbridge, Dublin 4
Tel: +353(0)1 6070055 Fax: +353(0)1 6609625
Email: dorothy_cusack@jurysdoyle.com
Web: www.jurysdoyle.com
B £6 D £35. CC: MC Vi Am DC

Red Cow Moran

★★★★ ℛ
Naas Road, Dublin 22
Tel: +353(0)1 4593650 Fax: +353(0)1 4591588
Email: sales@morangroup.ie
Web: www.redcowhotel.com
Closed Christmas

Red Cow Moran Hotel combines classic
elegance with modern design. Each of the
hotel's 123 deluxe bedrooms are fully air-
conditioned. Guests have a choice of 3
restaurants and 4 bars and a nightclub in the
complex. Free parking.
SB £95 DB £140 L £15.50 D £25.
CC: MC Vi Am DC Lazer
How to get there: Drive towards city on M1 to
M50 southbound, cross toll bridge. Exit 9,
N7/The South. Hotel at top of slipway.

The Plaza

★★★★ ℛ
Belgard Road, Tallaght, Dublin 24
Tel: +353(0)1 462 4200 Fax: +353(0)1 462 4600

Butlers Town House

★★★★ Town House
44 Lansdowne Road, Ballsbridge, Dublin
Tel: +353(0)1 6674022 Fax: +353(0)1 6673960
Email: info@butlers-hotel.com
Web: www.butlers-hotel.com
SB £90 DB £120 B £10 CC: MC Vi Am DC
How to get there: Hotel is located on corner of
Shelbourne Road and Lansdowne Road in the
area of Ballsbridge, just south of the city centre.

Ashling

★★★
Parkgate Street, Dublin 8
Tel: +353(0)1 6772324 Fax: +353(0)1 6793783
Email: info@ashlinghotel.ie
Web: www.ashlinghotel.ie

SB £78 DB £98 B £7.50 L £12 D £18.
CC: MC Vi Am DC   Closed December 23-27.

How to get there: Easily found location by car/rail/bus. By car, take city centre route and briefly follow River Liffey westward.

Cassidys
★★★
Cavendish Row, Upper O'Connell Street, Dublin 1
Tel: +353(0)1 8780555 Fax: +353(0)1 78780687
Email: martin@cassidys.iol.ie
Web: www.cassidyshotel.com
Closed December 24–27
SB £65 DB £88 HBS £76 HBD £55
CC: MC Vi Am DC Laser

How to get there: Continue up O'Connell Street away from the river. Cassidys is located opposite famous Gate Theatre on Cavendish Row.
See advert below

Chief O'Neills
★★★
Smithfield Village, Dublin 7, Co. Dublin
Tel: +353(0)1 8173838 Fax: +353(0)1 8173839

Finnstown Country House
★★★
Newcastle Road, Lucan, Co. Dublin
Tel: +353(0)1 6280644 Fax: +353(0)1 6281088
Email: manager@finnstown-hotel.ie
Web: www.finnstown-hotel.ie
SB £95 DB £150 HBS £120 HBD £200
L £16 D £25. CC: MC Vi Am DC

How to get there: From Dublin, travel along South Quays, passing Heuston Station. Continue on N4. At traffic lights after Texaco garage, turn left. Hotel on right after two roundabouts.

Ireland

Hibernian

★★★ ℞℞℞

Eastmoreland Place, Ballsbridge, Dublin 4
Tel: +353(0)1 6687666 Fax: +353(0)1 6602655
Email: info@hibernianhotel.com
Web: www.slh.com
Closed Christmas

City centre location, luxury 40-bedroomed hotel
with award-winning restaurant, meeting room
and private dining facilities. Member of Small
Luxury Hotels.
B £8 L £15.95 D £29.50.
CC: MC Vi Am DC Swi Delt
How to get there: Turn right from Mespil Road
into Baggot Street Upper, left into Eastmoreland
Place. The Hibernian is at the end on the left.

Jurys Christchurch Inn

★★★

Christchurch Place, Dublin 8
Tel: +353(0)1 4540000 Fax: +353(0)1 4540012
Email: majella.carroll@jurys.com
Web: www.jurysdoyle.com
Closed Christmas
SB £66.50 DB £73 HBS £82.50 HBD £105
CC: MC Vi Am DC Laser
How to get there: Opposite Christchurch
Cathedral, at the top of Dame Street.

Jurys Green Isle

★★★

Naas Road, Dublin 22
Tel: +353(0)1 6070055 Fax: +353(0)1 6609625
Email: dorothy_cusack@jurysdoyle.com
Web: www.jurysdoyle.com
B £5.50 L £14 D £18. CC: MC Vi Am DC
How to get there: N7 out of Dublin. Up the
Naas Road until you come to Newlands Cross.
Right at the cross. At the second set of traffic
lights turn left and continue for about ¼ mile
and turn left.

Jurys Inn Custom House

★★★

Custom House Quay, Dublin 1
Tel: +353(0)1 6070055 Fax: +353(0)1 6609625
Email: dorothy_cusack@jurysdoyle.com
Web: www.jurysdoyle.com
CC: MC Vi Am DC

Jurys Montrose

★★★ ℞

Stillorgan Road, Dublin 4
Tel: +353(0)1 6070055 Fax: +353(0)1 6609625
Email: dorothy_cusack@jurysdoyle.com
Web: www.jurysdoyle.com
B £6.50 L £14 D £21. CC: MC Vi Am DC
How to get there: Take the right immediately
after Jurys Tara Hotel onto Trimelston Avenue.
After 1 mile, turn left at top (Maxo garage on
left). Montrose Hotel on left.

Jurys Skylon

★★★

Upper Drumcondra Road, Dublin 9
Tel: +353(0)1 6070055 Fax: +353(0)1 6609625
Email: dorothy_cusack@jurysdoyle.com
Web: www.jurysdoyle.com
B £6 L £15 D £21. CC: MC Vi Am DC
How to get there: From airport take M1 towards
city centre. Continue through Whitehall and
Griffith Avenue junctions onto Upper
Drumcondra Road. Hotel on right.

Jurys Tara

★★★

Merrion Road, Dublin 4
Tel: +353(0)1 6070055 Fax: +353(0)1 6609625
Email: dorothy_cusack@jurysdoyle.com
Web: www.jurysdoyle.com
B £6 L £6 D £21. CC: MC Vi Am DC
How to get there: Into Dublin off M50, follow
signs for the Stena Ferry to Blackrock. Turn left
at Blackrock; hotel is on seafront, on the left.

Longfields

★★★ ⍩⍩

10 Lower Fitzwilliam Street, Dublin 2
Tel: +353(0)1 6761367 Fax: +353(0)1 6761542
Email: lfields@indigo.com
Web: www.longfields.com

A centrally located, charming, intimate hotel with period furnishings and an excellent restaurant.
SB £87 DB £112 B £5.40 L £13.30 D £23.50.
CC: MC Vi DC

How to get there: From airport, follow signs for city centre then O'Connell Street. Around front of Trinity College to left, pass Shelbourne Hotel onto Baggot Street. At main junction of Lower and Upper Baggot streets, hotel first on left of Fitzwilliam Street.

Marine

★★★ ⍩

Sutton Cross, Sutton, Dublin 13
Tel: +353(0)1 8390000 Fax: +353(0)1 8390442
Email: info@marinehotel.ie
Web: www.marinehotel.ie.
SB £110 DB £165 B £9.50 L £15.50 D £28.
CC: MC Vi Am DC

Mount Herbert

★★★

Herbert Road, Lansdowne, Dublin 4
Tel: +353(0)1 668 4321 Fax: +353(0)1 660 7077
Email: info@mountherberthotel.ie
Web: www.mountherberthotel.ie
Gracious Victorian residence 5 minutes from city centre in Ballsbridge, Dublin's most exclusive area. 185 modern bedrooms, licensed restaurant, private car park, sauna/sunbed, conference centre, gift shop, picturesque gardens. Renowned for its warm and friendly atmosphere.

SB £54.50 DB £85 B £5.50 D £16.95.
CC: MC Vi Am DC

How to get there: From city centre, Nassau Street at Trinity College along Merrion Square, Mount Street, Northumberland Road. At Lansdowne Road turn left. Cross DART line, pass rugby stadium, cross bridge to hotel.

Royal Dublin

★★★

O'Connell Street, Dublin 1
Tel: +353(0)1 8733666 Fax: +353(0)1 8733120
Email: enq@royaldublin.com
Web: www.royaldublin.com
SB £105 DB £135 HBS £125 HBD £155
L £12 D £19.50. CC: MC Vi Am DC

How to get there: City centre, from O'Connell Bridge go north up O'Connell Street. Hotel at end of street on left.

Schoolhouse

★★★ ⍩

2-8 Northumberland Road, Ballbridge, Dublin 4
Tel: +353(0)1 6675014 Fax: +353(0)1 6675015
Email: school@schoolhousehotel.iol.ie
CC: MC Vi Am DC   Closed December 24–27.

The Court

★★★

Killiney Bay, Dublin
Tel: +353(0)1 2851622 Fax: +353(0)1 2852085

Uppercross House

★★★

26/30 Upper Rathmines Road 1, Dublin 6
Tel: +353(0)1 4975486 Fax: +353(0)1 4975486

Ireland

White Sands

★★★

Coast Road, Portmarnock, Co. Dublin
Tel: +353(0)1 8460003 Fax: +353(0)1 8460420
Email: info@whitesandshotel.ie
Web: www.whitesandshotel.ie
SB £70 DB £94 HBS £80 HBD £114
CC: MC Vi Am DC Laser

⚓ ♿ ⅃⅃ 🚲 ⊗ ☕ 🖥 ☎ 📞 🅿 🛎 🕯 🐴 Ħ 🐚
♨ ♨♨   Closed December 24–25.

How to get there: Take Belfast road from Dublin
Airport. Right at sign for 'Molahine' at 3rd
roundabout. Left at T–junction and follow
through to Portmarnock.
See advert below

Wynns

★★★

35–39 Lower Abbey Street, Dublin 1
Tel: +353(0)1 8745131
Fax: +353(0)1 8741556
Email: info@wynnshotel.ie
Web: www.wynnshotel.com

Ideal city-centre location close to fashionable
shops, restaurants, theatres, galleries and
places of interest. Conference, banqueting and
wedding facilities, small or large groups. Saints
and Scholars Bar and Peacock Restaurant.

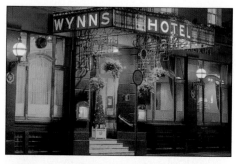

SB £75 DB £110 B £6 L £2.50 D £16.
CC: MC Vi Am DC

⚓ ⅃⅃ ⊗ ☕ 🖥 ☎ 🅿 🛎 🕯 🐴 Ħ 🐚 ♨ ♨♨

Regency North Star

★★

Amien Street, Dublin 1
Tel: +353(0)1 8881600 Fax: +353(0)1 8881604
Email: jamesmcgettigan@regencyhotels.com
Web: www.regencyhotels.com

The North Star Hotel is located in the city
centre, opposite the International Financial
Services Centre and adjacent to Dublin's
National Bus Depot. The hotel is within ten
minutes walk from Temple Bar, Dublin's left
bank area, St Stephens Green and Trinity

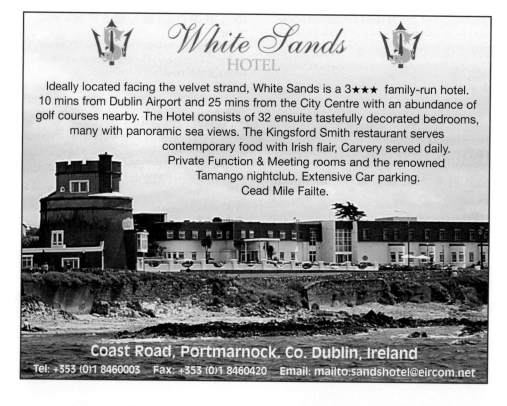

College, Ireland's oldest university. The hotel encompasses 130 newly appointed fully air-conditioned bedrooms, all with modern conveniences.
SB £100 DB £140 B £5 L £14 D £19.
CC: MC Vi Am DC

How to get there: Located opposite the International Financial Services Centre.

Park Lodge

7 North Circular Road, Dublin 7
Tel: +353(0)1 8386428

Parliament

Temple Bar, Dublin 2
Tel: +353(0)16708777 Fax: +353(0)1 6708787

Regency Airport

Swords Road, Whitehall, Dublin 9
Tel: +353(0)1 8373544 Fax: +353(0)1 8373174

Aberdeen Lodge

◆◆◆◆◆

53 Park Avenue, Ballsbridge, Dublin 4
Tel: +353(0)1 2838155 Fax: +353(0)1 2837877
Email: aberdeen@iol.ie
Web: www.halpinsprivatehotels.com
SB £70 DB £80 B £9.50 CC: MC Vi Am DC

How to get there: Minutes from city centre by DART or car. Take Merrion Road towards Sydney Parade DART station, then first left onto Park Avenue.
See advert on following page

Ariel House

◆◆◆◆◆

50–52 Lansdown Road, Ballsbridge, Dublin 4
Tel: +353(0)1 668 5512 Fax: +353(0)1 6685845

Cedar Lodge

◆◆◆◆◆

98 Merrion Road, Ballsbridge, Dublin 4
Tel: +353(0)1 6684410 Fax: +353(0)1 6684533
Email: info@cedarlodge.ie
Web: www.cedarlodge.ie
Children minimum age: 2

Edwardian house with fully-equipped modern bedrooms designed to the highest standard. 10 minutes from city centre, near airport and ferries.
SB £48 DB £68 CC: MC Vi Am

How to get there: From city centre (Nassau Street) continue onto Mount Street. Take Northumberland Road onto Ballsbridge; Jurys Hotel is on left. Cedar lodge opposite British Embassy on Merrion Road.

Glenogra

◆◆◆◆◆

64 Merrion Road, Ballsbridge, Dublin 4
Tel: +353(0)1 6683661 Fax: +353(0)1 6683698
Email: glenogra@indigo.ie
Closed Christmas to New Year
SB £55 DB £75 B £8 CC: MC Vi Am

How to get there: Opposite Four Seasons Hotel in Bullsbridge on main route from Dun Laoghaire car ferry.

Merrion Hall

◆◆◆◆◆

54 Merrion Road, Ballsbridge, Dublin 4
Tel: 01 6681426 Fax: 01 6684280
Email: merrionhall@iol.ie
Web: www.halpinsprivatehotels.com
SB £70 DB £80 B £9.50 CC: MC Vi Am DC

How to get there: Located in Ballsbridge, close to city centre on Merrion Road. Minutes from city centre by DART or bus.
See advert on following page

Ireland

66 Townhouse

◆◆◆◆　✕✎

66 Northumberland Road, Ballsbridge, Dublin 4
Tel: +353(0)1 6600471 Fax: +353(0)1 6601051
SB £50 DB £70　　Closed Dec 22 to Jan 6.
CC: MC Vi

♨ ▭ ☎ P ⚘ ⅀ ⛺ ♘ ♫ ⛵

How to get there: 66 Townhouse is south of
Trinity College/city centre on Diplomatic centre –
Ballsbridge Lansdowne Road area.

Baggot Court

◆◆◆◆

92 Lower Baggot Street, Dublin
Tel: +353(0)66 12819 Fax: +353(0)66 10253
Email: baggot@indigo.ie
Children minimum age: 8
SB £50 DB £80
CC: MC Vi Am

⊗ ♨ ▭ ☎ P ⚘ ⅀ ⛺ ♘ ♫ ⛵

How to get there: From O'Connell Street go
south on number 10 bus. Get off at Old
Convent. Directly opposite is Baggot Court.
See advert on following page

Charleville Lodge

◆◆◆◆　✕✎

268-272 North Circular Road,
Phisborough, Dublin 7
Tel: +353(0)1 8386633 Fax: +353(0)1 8385854
Email: charleville@indigo.ie
Web: www.charlevillelodge.ie
SB £50 DB £100 B £5
CC: MC Vi Am DC

♿ ▭ ☎ P ⚘ ⅀ ⛺ ♘ ♫ ⛵ ♨♨♨

How to get there: North from city centre
(O'Connell Street) to Phisborough, then take left
fork at St Peters Church.

Glenveagh Town House

◆◆◆◆　✕✎

31 Northumerland Road, Ballsbridge, Dublin
Tel: +353(0)1 6684612 Fax: +353(0)1 6684559

Hedigans

◆◆◆◆　✓

14 Hollybrook Park, Clontarf
Tel: +353(0)1 8531663 Fax: +353(0)1 8333337
Email: hedigans@indigo.ie
Closed Christmas to mid–January
SB £45 DB £70
CC: MC Vi

⊗ ♨ ▭ ☎ P ⚘ ⅀ ⛺ ♘ ♫ ⛵

How to get there: On Clontarf Road turn left
after Clontarf Motors. Up Hollybrook Road and
Hedigans is at the top.

Kilronan House

◆◆◆◆　✕✎ ✓

70 Adelaide Road, Dublin 2,
Tel: +353 (0)1 4755266 Fax: +353 (0)1 4782841
Email: info@dublinn.com
Web: www.dublinn.com

Exclusive Georgian house within walking
distance of St Stephen's Green, Trinity College
and most of Dublin's historic landmarks. Under
the personal supervision of owner Terry
Masterson.
SB £55 DB £90 CC: MC Vi Am DC

✕✎ ⊗ ♨ ▭ ☎ P ⚘ ⅀ ⛺ ♘ ♫ ⛵

How to get there: Drive down St Stephen's
Green east onto Earlsfort Terrace. Proceed onto
Adelaide Road. House is on right.

Kingswood Country House

◆◆◆◆　♞♞

Kingswood, Naas Road, Clondalkin, Co. Dublin
Tel: +353(0)1 4592428 Fax: +353(0)1 4592207
Email: kingswoodcountryhse@eircom.net
SB £50 DB £65 HBS £70 HBD £120
B £7 L £14 D £24. CC: MC Vi Am DC

⚔ ♞ ▭ ☎ P ⚘ ⅀ ⛺ ♘ ♫ ⛵ ♨♨♨ ♨♨♨

How to get there: From M50 Dublin ring road
take N7 exit. Hotel is 3 miles on N7 heading
south, clearly signposted.

Trinity Lodge　Little Gem

◆◆◆◆　✕✎ ✓ Little Gem

12 South Frederick Street, Dublin 2
Tel: +353(0)1 6795044 Fax: +353(0)1 6795223
Email: trinitylodge@eircom.net
Closed December 22 to January 2
SB £55 DB £110 CC: MC Vi Am DC

⊗ ♨ ▭ ☎ ✳ ☎ P ⚘ ⅀ ⛺ ♘ ♫ ⛵

How to get there: Lodge is situated in city
centre, beside Trinity College, off Nassau Street.

Ireland

Clifden Guesthouse

♦♦♦

32 Gardiner Place, Dublin 1
Tel: +353(0)1 8746364 Fax: +353(0)1 8746122
Email: tnt@indigo.ie
Web: www.clifdenhouse.com
SB £60 DB £80 CC: MC Vi

How to get there: From O'Connell Street (North End), drive round 3 sides of Parnell Square. Exit at the church. Clifden house is 400m further on.

Fitzwilliam

♦♦♦

41 Upper Fitzwilliam Street, Dublin 2
Tel: +353(0)1 6600448 Fax: +353(0)1 6767488

Harcourt Inn

♦♦♦

27 Harcourt Street, Dublin
Tel: +353(0)1 4783927

St Andrews House

♦♦♦

113 Lambay Road, Drumcondra, Co. Dublin
Tel: +353(0)1 8374684 Fax: +353(0)1 8570446
Email: andrew@dublinn.com
Web: www.dublinn.com/andrew

SB £40 DB £70

Herbert Lodge Guest House

♦♦

65 Morehampton Road, Donnybrook, Co. Dublin
Tel: +353(0)1 66 03403 Fax: +353(0)1 66 88794
Email: herbertl@indigo.ie
Children minimum age: 6
SB £40 DB £50 CC: MC Vi

See advert on the right

Blakes Townhouse

50 Merrion Road, Ballsbridge, Dublin 4,
Tel: +353(0)1 6688324 Fax: +353(0)1 6682280
Web: www.halpinsprivatehotels.com
SB £70 DB £80 B £9.5
CC: MC Vi Am DC

How to get there: Located in Ballsbridge, close
to city centre on the Merrion Road. Minutes
from city centre by DART or bus.
See advert on page 524

Eliza Lodge

23–24 Wellington Quay, Temple Bar, Dublin 2
Tel: +353(0)1 6718044 Fax: +353(0)1 6718362
Email: info@dublinlodge.com
Web: dublinlodge.com
Closed Christmas
SB £50 DB £85 B £4
CC: MC Vi Am

How to get there: Located at foot of Millennium
Bridge, second bridge after O'Connell Bridge.
25 minutes drive from Dublin Airport.
See advert on facing page

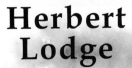

Ireland

Dun Laoghaire, Co. Dublin

Royal Marine

★★★

Dun Laoghaire, Co. Dublin
Tel: +353(0)1 2801911 Fax: +353(0)1 2801089

Victorian façade, 103-bedroom hotel set in an elegant four acres, overlooking Dublin's most prestigious site.
B £10 L £12 D £15.
CC: MC Vi Am DC Swi Delt Lazer

How to get there: Directly opposite Holyhead to Dun Laoghaire car ferry.

Tara Hall

◆◆

- ensuite rooms
- colour televisions
- tea/coffee-making facilities
- hairdryers
- off-road parking
- Full Irish breakfast
- smoking & non-smoking rooms

This refurbished Regency style house, once the former home of 'William Monk Gibbon' poet and writer, is nearby to the 'Joyce Tower' and Dun Laoghaire Harbour. The perfect retreat for the discerning traveller.

24 Sandycove Road
Dun Laoghaire
Co. Dublin
Tel/Fax: +353 (0)1 280 5120
Email: tarahall@indigo.ie

Kingston

★★

9–11 Haddington Terrace, Dun Laoghaire, Co. Dublin
Tel: +353(0)1 2801810

Tara Hall

◆◆

24 Sandycove Road, Dun Laoghaire, Co. Dublin
Tel: +353(0)1 2805120 Fax: +353(0)1 2805120
Email: tarahall@indigo.ie
Children minimum age: 5
SB £18 DB £45 CC: MC Vi

See advert below left

Dundalk, Co. Louth

Ballymascanlon House

★★★

Dundalk, Co. Louth
Tel: +353(0)42 9371124 Fax: +353(0)42 9371598
Email: info@ballymascanlon.com
Web: www.globalgolf.com/ballymascanlon
Closed December 24–27
SB £80 DB £114 HBD £80 B £9 L £14 D £27.
CC: MC Vi Am DC Laser

How to get there: 2 miles north of Dundalk, off main Belfast Road (on Carlingford Road).

Fairways

★★★

Dublin Road, Dundalk, Co. Louth
Tel: +353(0)42 9321500 Fax: +353(0)42 9321511
Email: info@fairways.ie
Web: www.fairways.ie
SB £65 DB £100 B £6 L £15 D £22.
CC: MC Vi Am DC Laser

How to get there: Three miles south of Dundalk and approximately 1 hour 15 mins from Dublin or Belfast.

Non smoking policy   RƎC

Properties displaying this symbol in the Guide have non smoking rooms available for guests. However, smokers should check in advance whether the Hotel or Guest Accommodation displaying this symbol actually allows smoking in any room.

Dunfanaghy, Co. Donegal

Arnolds

★★★ 🐾
Dunfanaghy, Co. Donegal
Tel: +353(0)74 36208 Fax: +353(0)74 36352
Email: arnoldshotel@eircom.net
Closed November to March

Nestled in the village of Dunfanaghy at the base of Horn Head, in the dramatic reaches of North Donegal, this family-run hotel is noted for its friendly atmosphere and good food.
SB £72.50 DB £105 B £8 D £25.
CC: MC Vi Am DC
How to get there: N56 northwest from Letterkenny. After 23 miles, hotel is on left as you enter village.

Dungarvan, Co. Waterford

Castle Farm   Little Gem

◆◆◆◆◆
Millsbreet, Cappagh, Dungarvan, Co. Waterford
Tel: +353(0)58 68049 Fax: +353(0)58 68099
Email: castlefm@iol.ie
Web: www.waterfordfarms.com/castlefarm
Closed November to February

Award winning restored wing of 15th century castle on large dairy farm. Excellent cuisine and elegant decor. Breakfast menu.

SB £27 DB £54 HBS £42 HBD £84 B £5 D £20.
CC: MC Vi Swi Delt
How to get there: Located 15km off N25.

Ennis, Co. Clare

West County Hotel

★★★
Clare Road, Ennis, Co. Clare
Tel: +353(0)65 6823000 Fax: +353(0)65 6823759
Email: cro@lynchhotels.com
Web: www.lynchhotels.com
SB £57 DB £91 HBS £70 HBD £116
B £7.50 L £10 D £14. CC: MC Vi Am DC Laser
How to get there: 15km from Shannon Airport, 15 minutes walk from Ennis town centre.

Temple Gate

The Square, Ennis, Co. Clare
Tel: +353(0)65 6823300 Fax: +353(0)65 6823322

Woodstock

Shanaway Road, Ennis, Co. Clare
Tel: +353(0)65 6846600 Fax: +353(0)65 6846611
Email: info@woodstockhotel.com
Web: www.woodstockhotel.com
Closed December 25–26.

Luxury 67-bedroomed hotel near Shannon with restaurant and bar, 18-hole golf course, health & leisure spa, and convention centre. Sister property Hibernian Hotel Dublin. Member of Small Luxury Hotels.
SB £75 DB £145 B £8 L £13.95 D £27.50.
CC: MC Vi Am DC Swi Delt
How to get there: From Limerick, follow N18 to Ennis. Take exit for Lahinch (N85). After 1km, turn left. Woodstock Hotel 1km further.

Ireland

Lahardan House

◆◆

Lahardan, Crusheen, Ennis, Co. Clare
Tel: +353(0)65 6827128 Fax: +353(0)65 6827319
Closed Christmas
SB £25 DB £38 HBS £39 HBD £66 CC: MC Vi
🐎⬜🍴☎🅿🛁🕯🐴🚶♿
How to get there: Take N18 north from Ennis,
N18 south from Galway. At railway bridge
beside Crusheen village, sign for Lahardan.

Ennistymon, Co. Clare

Grovemount House

◆◆◆◆

Lahinch Road, Ennistymon, Co. Clare
Tel: +353(0)65 7071431 Fax: +353(0)65 7071823
Email: grovemnt@gofree.indigo.ie
Closed November to April

SB £33 DB £50 CC: MC Vi
♿🍴⬜☎🅿🛁🕯🐴🚶♿
How to get there: Take N85 from Ennis to
Ennistymon, N67 to Lahinch. Grovemount House
is on the outskirts of Ennistymon on right.

Faithlegg, Co. Waterford

Faithlegg House

★★★★ ♟♟
Faithlegg, Co. Waterford
Tel: +353(0)51 382000 Fax: +353(0)51 380010

Fermoy, Co. Cork

Ballyvolane House

♣
Castlelyons, nr Fermoy, Co. Cork
Tel: +353(0)25 36349 Fax:+353(0)25 36781
Email: ballyvol@iol.ie
Web: www.ballyvolanehouse.ie
SB £62 DB £100 HBS £88 HBD £152
CC: MC Vi Am
🍴⬜🅿🛁🕯🐴🚶♿🍷
How to get there: From Cork, right off N8 at the
River Bride, just before Rath Cormac (R628).
Follow House signs.
See advert on facing page (top)

Galway, Co. Galway

Ardilaun House

★★★★ ♟
Taylors Hill, Galway, Co. Galway
Tel: +353(0)91 521433 Fax: +353(0)91 521546
Email: ardilaun@iol.ie
Web: www.ardilaunhousehotel.ie
SB £100 DB £150 HBS £125 HBD £200
B £8.50 L £14.50 D £25. Closed Dec 23–28.
CC: MC Vi Am DC Laser
♿♿🕯🐴🏊⬜☎📞🅿🛁🕯🐴🚶♿
📷🚶👥🏊🏊🎿🍴✂🖼
How to get there: N6 to Galway City West. Then
follow signs for N59 Clifden, then N6 for Salthill.
Taylor's Hill is en-route.

Glenlo Abbey

★★★★ ♟♟♟
Glenlo Abbey Hotel, Bushypark,
Co. Galway
Tel: +353(0)91 526666 Fax: +353(0)91 527800
Email: glenlo@iol.ie
Web: www.glenlo.com
B £12 L £8 D £28.50. CC: MC Vi Am DC
♿🕯📧🏊⬜☎📞🅿🛁🕯🐴🚶♿👥👥
🍴🖐
How to get there: 4 km from Galway city centre
on the N59 to Clifden.
See advert on facing page (bottom)

Park House

★★★★
Forster Street, Eyre Square, Galway,
Co. Galway
Tel: +353(0)91 564924 Fax: +353(0)91 569219
Email: parkhousehotel@eircom.net
SB £95 DB £155 B £8.95 D £25.95.
CC: MC Vi Am DC Laser
♿🕯🍴⬜☎📞🅿🛁🕯🐴🚶♿👥👥
How to get there: Follow all signs for city centre.

Hotel is situated on Forster Street, off Eyre Square. Car park is at rear of hotel.
See advert on following page (top)

Brennans Yard
★★★
Lower Merchants Road, Galway, Co. Galway
Tel: +353(0)91 568166 Fax: +353(0)91 568262
Email: brennansyard@eircom.net
Web: www.hotelboot.com
SB £65 DB £105
CC: MC Vi Am DC Swi Delt

How to get there: From Eyre Square, turn left after the Great Southern Hotel. Turn right. At the end of the road turn right and stay in right-hand lane. Turn right and immediately right again.

Flannerys Best Western
★★★
Dublin Road, Galway, Co. Galway
Tel: +353(0)91 55111

Galway Ryan Hotel & Leisure Club
★★★
Dublin Road, Galway, Co. Galway
Tel: +353(0)91 753181 Fax: +353(0)91 753187
Email: ryan@indigo.ie
Web: www.ryan-hotel.com

A modern hotel, with well-furnished rooms, situated in the suburbs of Galway city.
SB £140 DB £160 B £10 L £8 D £17.
CC: MC Vi Am DC

How to get there: Follow the signs for Galway East when approaching Galway from Dublin.

Imperial
★★★
Eyre Square, Galway, Co. Galway
Tel: +353(0)91 63033

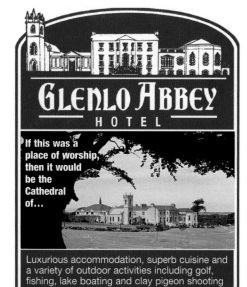
Ireland

Park House Hotel

An oasis of luxury and calm situated in the city centre of Galway. Award-winning hotel and restaurant – "Hotel of the Year Ireland 2000 – Les Routiers". Park Room Restaurant – Bord Failte Awards of Excellence over many years. Les Routiers Plat d'Or 2000. Private, secure residents car park.

Forster Street, Eyre Square, Galway
Tel: 353 91 564924   Fax: 353 91 569219
Email: parkhousehotel@eircom.net

Jurys Galway Inn

★★★
Quay Street, Galway, Co. Galway
Tel: +353(0)91 66444 Fax: +353(0)91 568415
Email: enquiry@jurys.com
Web: www.jurys.com
B £6.50 L £4 D £15.95. CC: MC Vi Am DC

How to get there: Hotel in centre of Galway, 8–10 minute walk from bus and rail stations.

Galway Bay Golf & Country Club

Oranmore, Co. Galway
Tel: +353(0)65 6866697 Fax: +353(0)65 6823759
Email: marketing@lynchotels.com
Web: www.lynchotels.com
SB £61 DB £100 HBS £77 HBD £65
B £7 L £4 D £19. CC: MC Vi Am DC

How to get there: In Oranmore village follow the signs for Maree. At the new church take first exit to the right. Galway Bay Hotel is 5–10 minutes down this road.

Glandore, Co. Cork

Marine

Glandore, Co. Cork
Tel: +353(0)28 33366

Glin, Co. Limerick

Glin Castle

★★★ ♟♟
Glin, Co. Limerick
Tel: +353(0)68 34173 Fax: +353(0)68 34364
Email: knight@iol.ie
Web: www.glincastle.com
Children minimum age: 10
Closed December to March
SB £190 DB £190 B £15 L £12 D £33.
CC: MC Vi Am DC

How to get there: On N69 32 miles west of Limerick, 4 miles east Tarbert/Killimar car ferry.
See advert on the left

Gorey, Co. Wexford

Marlfield House

★★★ ♔♔♔

Gorey, Co. Wexford
Tel: +353(0)55 21124 Fax: +353(0)55 21572
Email: info@marlfieldhouse.ie
Web: www.marlfieldhouse.com
Closed mid–December to January

Set in 36 acres of magnificent gardens and filled with numerous antiques, Marlfield's true Irish hospitality and cuisine have gained it world acclaim.
SB £95 DB £170 HBS £133 HBD £245
B £12 L £25 D £38. CC: MC Vi Am DC
How to get there: Outside Gorey on Courtown road.

Woodlands Country House

♦♦♦♦♦

Killinierin, Gorey, Co. Wexford
Tel: +353(0)402 37125 Fax: +353(0)402 37133
Email: woodlands@iol.ie
Web: www.woodlandscountryhouse.com
Closed October to March

Woodlands Country House, built in 1836, is set in 1½ acres of lawns and garden courtyard. Old stone buildings, noted for tranquility, ideal base for touring southeast Ireland. Listed in many quality guides.
SB £35 DB £25 CC: MC Vi
How to get there: 1 mile N11, 2½ miles north Gorey.

Howth, Co. Dublin

Deer Park Hotel & Golf Courses

★★★

Howth, Co. Dublin
Tel: +353(0)1 8322624 Fax: +353(0)1 8392405
Email: sales@deerpark.iol.ie
Web: www.deerpark-hotel.ie
SB £80 DB £120 HBS £105 HBD £170
B £6 L £15 D £25. CC: MC Vi Am DC
How to get there: From Dublin, follow coast road via Fairview and Clontarf. Through Cutton Cross and take third right.
See advert on following page (top)

Kenmare, Co. Kerry

Park Hotel Kenmare

★★★★ ♔♔♔

Kenmare, Co. Kerry
Tel: +353(0)64 41200 Fax: +353(0)64 41402
Email: info@parkkenmare.com
Web: www.parkkenmare.com
Closed November 5 to December 23 and January 2 to April 13

Deluxe country house hotel in Ireland's Lake District. Set on 12 acres of terraced gardens overlooking Kenmare Bay, the park is one of Ireland's most luxurious and comfortable retreats.
SB £149 DB £264 B £15.50 L £8.50 D £44.
CC: MC Vi Am DC
How to get there: Located at the top of Kenmare.

Ireland

SB £271.15 DB £271.15 HBS £306.85
HBD £342.55 B £14.45 L £12.75 D £35.70.
CC: MC Vi Am DC

How to get there: From Kenmare, take N71
towards Clengarriff. Turn left after suspension
bridge.

Dromquinna Manor
★★★
Blackwater Bridge, Kenmare, Co. Kerry
Tel: +353(0)64 41657 Fax: +353(0)64 41791
Email: info@dromquinna.com
Web: www.dromquinna.com
SB £45 DB £50 HBD £56 B £8.50 D £21.50.
CC: MC Vi Am DC Swi

How to get there: 3km from Kenmare town on
the Sneem Road (Ring of Kerry).
See advert on facing page (below)

Kilkee, Co. Clare

Ocean Cove
★★★
Kilkee Bay, Kilkee, Co. Clare
Tel: +353(0)65 6823000 Fax: +353(0)65 6823759
Email: cro@lynchhotels.com
Web: www.lynchhotels.com
SB £56 DB £88 HBS £68 HBD £114
B £5 L £9 D £16.50. CC: MC Vi Am Laser

How to get there: On the main N67–N68 road,
the Ocean Cove Hotel overlooks the Atlantic
Ocean and offers commanding views of the bay.

Halpins
♦♦♦♦
Kilkee, Co. Clare,
Tel: +353(0)65 9056032 Fax: +353(0)65 9056317
Email: halpins@iol.ie
Web: www.halpinsprivatehotels.com
Closed December to February
SB £40 DB £60 B £9.50 L £10.50 D £16.
CC: MC Vi Am DC

How to get there: In the centre of Kilkee.
Shannon Airport 50-minute drive away on N67,
Killimer Car Ferry 10 miles away.
See advert on page 524

When booking at an RAC Hotel or Guest
Accommodation, please mention this Guide.

Kilkenny, Co. Kilkenny

Kilkenny River Court
★★★★
The Bridge, John Street, Kilkenny, Co. Kilkenny
Tel: +353(0)56 23388 Fax: +353(0)56 23389
Email: krch@iol.ie
Web: www.kilrivercourt.com
SB £120 DB £180 HBS £145 HBD £240
CC: MC Vi Am

How to get there: Kilkenny Castle is a landmark:
hotel is situated directly opposite across river.
Entrance under archways at bridge in city centre.

Mount Juliet
★★★★
Thomastown, Co. Kilkenny
Tel: +353(0)56 73000 Fax: +353(0)56 73019
Email: info@mountjuliet.ie
Web: www.mountjuliet.com

A beautiful 18th century house situated in a
1,500-acre sporting estate which includes a
Jack Nicklaus golf course.
B £8.50 L £8.50 D £30. CC: MC Vi Am DC

How to get there: Thomastown is on the N9
Dublin to Waterford Road.

Hotel Kilkenny
★★★
College Road, Co. Kilkenny
Tel: +353(0)56 62000 Fax: +353(0)56 65984
Email: kilkenny@griffingroup.ie
Web: www.griffingroup.ie
SB £60 DB £110 HBS £85 HBD £80
L £12 D £25. CC: MC Vi Am DC

How to get there: N9 to Kilkenny. When
approaching Kilkenny, go left at the roundabout,
onto the ring road. Hotel is located at bottom of
the ring road on the right.

Ireland

Kilkenny Ormonde

Ormonde Street, Kilkenny, Co. Kilkenny
Tel: +353(0)56 23900 Fax: +353(0)56 23977
Email: info@kilkennyormonde.com
Web: www.kilkennyormonde.com
SB £85 DB £125 CC: MC Vi DC Laser

How to get there: Off High Street and adjacent
to 24-hour car park.
See advert on facing page (top)

Shillogher House

♦♦♦♦

Callan Road, Kilkenny, Co Kilkenny,
Tel: +353(0)56 63249 Fax: (0)56 64865

Chaplins

♦♦♦

Castlecomer Road, Kilkenny, Co. Kilkenny,
Tel: +353 (0)56 52236
Closed Christmas
SB £18.25 DB £36.50 CC: MC Vi
How to get there: On N77 Alhy–Dublin road.

Killarney, Co. Kerry

Aghadoe Heights

★★★★
Killarney, Co. Kerry
Tel: +353(0)64 31766 Fax: +353(0)64 31345
Email: aghadoeheights@eircom.net
Web: www.aghadoeheights.com
SB £110 DB £170 L £25 D £39.50.
CC: MC Vi Am DC Laser
How to get there: N22 from Cork for Tralee.
Leave Killarney for Tralee, follow signs for
Aghadoe Heights Hotel. Left turn after 2 miles.
See advert on facing page (bottom)

Dunloe Castle

★★★★
Killarney, Co. Kerry
Tel: +353(0)64 44111 Fax: +353(0)64 44583
Email: sales@kih.liebherr.com
Web: www.iol.ie/khl
Closed October to April

SB £114 DB £132 B £10.50 L £17 D £32.
CC: MC Vi Am DC Laser

How to get there: Six miles outside of Killarney,
facing the Gap of Dunloe. Follow signs for
Killorglin on entering Killarney.

Killarney Park

★★★★
Killarney, Co. Kerry
Tel: +353(0)64 35555 Fax: +353(0)64 35266
Email: info@killarneyparkhotel.ie
Web: www.killarneyparkhotel.ie
Closed December
SB £240 DB £240 HBS £270 HBD £300
B £15 L £12 D £30.
CC: MC Vi Am DC
How to get there: N22 from Cork to Killarney. At
first roundabout, take first exit. At second
roundabout, take first exit. Killarney Park Hotel
is second entrance on left.

Muckross Park

★★★★
Muckross Village, Killarney, Co. Kerry
Tel: +353(0)64 31938

Killarney Ryan

★★★
Cork Road, Killarney, Killarney, Co. Kerry,
Tel: +353(0)64 31555 Fax: +353(0)64 32438

A modern hotel set within
extensive grounds, featuring a
leisure centre, sports hall, tennis
courts, crazy golf and play areas.
An ideal location from which to
enjoy Ireland's most famed beauty
spots.
SB £85 DB £140 B £10 D £20.
CC: MC Vi Am DC Laser
How to get there: On N22 2km
from Killarney town centre.

Ireland

The Cahernane

★★★

Muckross Road, Killarney, Co. Kerry
Tel: +353(0)64 31895 Fax: +353(0)64 34340

White Gates

★★★

Muckross Road, Killarney, Co. Kerry
Tel: +353(0)64 31164

Earls Court House `Little Gem`

♦♦♦♦♦

Woodlawn Junction, Muckross Road,
Killarney, Co. Kerry
Tel: +353(0)64 34009 Fax: +353(0)64 34366
Email: earls@eircom.net
Web: www.earlscourt-killarney.ie
Closed December to February
SB £70 DB £80 CC: MC Vi Am

How to get there: Take Muckross Road from
Killarney. After Shell station, take a left and
Earls Court House is third house on your left.
See advert below

Earls Court House
RAC Small Hotel Of The Year 1998

A magical 4-star hideaway five minutes walk
from town centre. Antique furnishings,
log fires, fresh flowers and home baking.
Superior rooms with individual themes,
full bathroom, TV, ice, phones, individual
balconies, private parking.

Woodlawn Jnct. Muckross Road.
Killarney
Tel: +353 64 34009   Fax: +353 64 34366
Email: earls@eircom.net
Website: www.killarney-earlscourt.ie

Foley's Townhouse

♦♦♦♦♦

23 High Street, Killarney, Co. Kerry
Tel: +353(0)64 31217 Fax: +353(0)64 34683
SB £49.50 DB £82.50 B £8.50 L £9 D £20.
CC: MC Vi Am

How to get there: Town centre location on right-
hand side of High Street (when travelling north,
direction Tralee).

Fuchsia House

♦♦♦♦♦

Muckross Road, Killarney, Co. Kerry
Tel: +353(0)64 33743 Fax: +353(0)64 36588

Kathleens Country House

♦♦♦♦♦

Tralee Road (N22), Killarney, Co. Kerry
Tel: +353(0)64 32810 Fax: +353(0)64 32340
Email: info@kathleens.net
Web: www.kathleens.net
Children minimum age: 10
Closed November to February

Family-run guest house where traditional
hospitality and personal attention are a way of
life. All bedrooms en-suite with telephone, TV,
tea/coffee facilities. Easy to get to! Hard to
leave!
SB £75 DB £90 CC: MC Vi Am

Gleann Fia

♦♦♦♦

Deerpark, Killarney, Co. Kerry
Tel: +353(0)64 35035 Fax: +353(0)64 35000

Killarney Villa

◆◆◆◆

Cork/Mallow Road (N72), Killarney, Co. Kerry
Tel: +353(0)64 31878 Fax: +353(0)64 31878
Email: killarneyvilla@circom.net
Web: www.kerry.insight.com/killvilla
Children minimum age: 6
Closed November to April
SB £25 DB £44

How to get there: N22 from Killarney. After first roundabout continue for 1¹/₃ miles to signposted junction. Bear left for 300 yards. Villa on right.

Ross Castle Lodge

◆◆◆◆

Ross Road, Killarney, Co. Kerry
Tel: +353(0)64 36942 Fax: +353(0)64 36942
Email: rosscastlelodge@killarneyb-and-b.com
Web: www.killarneyb-and-b.com

Situated on the edge of Killarney town in a magical woodland setting bordering lakes, National Park and golf course. Elegant, spacious bedrooms. A walker's paradise.
DB £40 CC: MC Vi

How to get there: 100m past Cineplex Cinema, turn right at Esso garage. House is on left immediately after Ross Golf Club.

Ashville Guest House

◆◆◆

Rock Road, Killarney, Co. Kerry
Tel: +353(0)64 36405
Fax: +353(0)64 36778
Email: ashvillehouse@eircom.net
Web: www.kerry-insight.com/ashville
Spacious, family-run guest house, two minutes walk from the town centre, situated on the main Tralee road (N22). Private car park. Comfortably furnished en-suite bedrooms. Your ideal touring base.
SB £30 DB £40 CC: MC Vi

How to get there: On main Tralee road (N22), two minutes walk from town centre.

Purple Heather

◆◆

Gap of Dunloe, Beaufort, Killarney, Co. Kerry
Tel: +353(0)64 44266 Fax: +353(0)64 44266
Email: purpleheather@eircom.net
SB £25.50 DB £19 CC: MC Vi

How to get there: From Killarney take road to Fossa. At Fossa turn left to Hotel Dunloe Castle. At hotel turn left and continue straight ahead for one mile.

Killinick, Co. Wexford

Danby Lodge

◆◆◆◆

Rosslare Road, Killinick, Co. Wexford
Tel: +353(0)53 58191 Fax: +353(0)53 58191

Killorglin, Co. Kerry

Grove Lodge

◆◆◆◆

Killarney Road, Killorglin, Co. Kerry
Tel: +353(0)66 9761157 Fax: +353(0)66 9762330
SB £30 DB £60 CC: MC Vi DC

How to get there: N72, 300m from Killorglin Bridge, on the Killarney exit from Killorglin.

Ireland

Kilmallock, Co. Limerick

Flemingstown House

◆◆◆◆◆ ✳️ ⚐

Kilmallock, Co. Limerick
Tel: +353(0)63 98093 Fax: +353(0)63 98546
Email: flemingston@keltec.ie
Web: www.ils.ie/flemingstown
Closed December to February

Approached by a long avenue, this 18th century farmhouse is the ideal location for relaxation and gourmet food combined. Ideal base for touring the south of Ireland.
SB £35 DB £50 HBS £50 HBD £90
CC: MC Vi
⊗ ⊜ ▭ ₽ ✳️ ✆ ☃ ♘ ⊞ ❦
How to get there: On R512 Kilmallock–Kilfinane road and 4km from R515 Tipperary–Killarney road.

Kinsale, Co. Cork

Trident

★★★

World's End, Kinsale, Co. Cork
Tel: +353(0)21 772301 Fax: +353(0)21 774173
Email: info@tridenthotel.com
Web: www.tridenthotel.com
Closed Christmas
SB £58 DB £38 HBS £83 HBD £63
B £6.50 D £20.
CC: MC Vi Am
⟁ ⟁ ⌱ ⊜ ▭ ☎ ₽ ✳️ ✆ ☃ ♘ ⊞ ❦ ⁂ ⁑ 'Ψ'
How to get there: Take R600 to Kinsale from Cork. The Trident is located at the end of Pier Road on the waterfront.

Old Bank House

◆◆◆◆ ✳️ ⚐

11 Pearse Street, Kinsale, Co. Cork
Tel: +353(0)21 4774075 Fax: +353(0)21 4774296
Email: oldbank@indigo.ie
Web: indigo.ie/~oldbank
Children minimum age: 10

The Old Bank House is a Georgian residence of great character and charm, which has been consistently voted one of the 'Top 100 Places to Stay in Ireland' every year since 1990. Gourmet Irish breakfast cooked to order each morning by Master Chef Michael Riese. A warm welcome awaits you from Michael, Marie and Katy Riese.
SB £120 DB £120 CC: MC Vi Am
⌱ ▭ ☎ ✳️ ✆ ☃ ♘ ⊞ ❦ ↾
How to get there: At start of Kinsale town, on right by Post Office. 11km on R600 from Cork airport.

Rivermount House

◆◆◆◆ ✳️

Knocknabinny, Kinsale, Co. Cork
Tel: +353(0)21 778033

Deasys Guest House

◆◆◆

Long Quay House, Long Quay, Kinsale, Co. Cork
Tel: +353(0)21 774120 Fax: +353(0)21 4774563
Closed December

SB £50 DB £80 CC: MC Vi

How to get there: R600 from Cork to Kinsale. Hotel on right as you enter Kinsale, just before supermarket and post office.

Knock, Co. Mayo

Belmont

★★★

Knock, Co. Mayo
Tel: +353(0)94 88122 Fax: +353(0)94 88532
Email: belmonthotel@tinet.ie
Web: www.belmonthotel.ie
SB £42 DB £65 HBS £57.50 HBD £95
B £4.80 L £4.50 D £6.50. CC: MC Vi Am DC

How to get there: In the village of Knock on N17 between Galway and Sligo.

Limerick, Co. Limerick

Castletroy Park

★★★★

Dublin Road, Limerick, Co. Limerick
Tel: +353(0)61 335566 Fax: +353(0)61 331117
Email: sales@castletroy-park.ie
Web: www.castletroy-park.ie
SB £102 DB £122 B £9 L £15.50 D £26.
CC: MC Vi Am DC

How to get there: On main N7 Dublin road, 3 miles from Limerick and 25 minutes from Shannon International Airport.

Jurys Limerick

★★★★

Ennis Road, Limerick, Co. Limerick
Tel: +353(0)1 6070055 Fax: +353(0)1 6609626
Email: dorothy_cusack@jurysdoyle.com
Web: www.jurysdoyle.com
B £6 L £13 D £17. CC: MC Vi Am DC

Limerick Inn

★★★★

Ennis Road, Limerick, Co. Limerick
Tel: +353(0)61 326666 Fax: +353(0)61 326281
Email: limerick-inn@limerick-inn.ie
Web: www.limerick-inn.ie
Closed Christmas
SB £IR118.50 DB £158 B £8.50 L £14 D £16.
CC: MC Vi Am DC

How to get there: N7 Dublin to Limerick, then N18 for Shannon, hotel 3 miles from city centre.

Limerick Ryan

★★★★

Ennis Road, Limerick, Co. Limerick
Tel: +353(0)61 453922 Fax: +353(0)61 326333
Email: ryan@indigo.ie
Web: www.ryan-hotels.com

A Georgian building dating back to 1780 which has been recently restored to its former elegance.
SB £137 DB £181 HBS £162
HBD £206 B £10.75 L £6.90
D £23.70. CC: MC Vi Am DC

How to get there: Limerick Ryan Hotel is on N18 Ennis Road.

South Court

★★★★

Adare Road, Raheen, Raheen, Limerick, Co. Limerick
Tel: +353(0)65 6823000
Fax: +353(0)65 6823759
Email: cro@lynchhotels.com
Web: www.lynchhotels.com
SB £109 DB £187 HBS £121 HBD £212
B £10 D £20.
CC: MC Vi Am DC Laser

How to get there: On main Cork/Killarney road (N20), the South Court Hotel offers an ideal base for touring the Shannon region.

Ireland

Jurys Inn Limerick

★★★

Lower Mallow Street, Limerick, Co. Limerick
Tel: +353(0)61 207000 Fax: +353(0)61 400966
Email: fiona_cleary@jurysdoyle.com
Web: www.jurysdoyle.com
Closed Christmas
SB £61.50 DB £68 HBS £25 HBD £25
B £6.50 L £9 D £15.95.
CC: MC Vi Am DC Laser

How to get there: From north: follow signs N7. Into city centre at top of O'Connell St. Take left at bottom of street beside Shannon Bridge.

Woodfield House

★★★

Ennis Road, Limerick, Co. Limerick
Tel: +353(0)61 453022 Fax: +353(0)61 326755
Email: woodfield@eircom.net
Web: www.woodfieldhousehotel.com
SB £59 DB £99   Closed December 24–25.
CC: MC Vi Am DC Laser

How to get there: Situated 1 mile outside city centre on north side of Limerick, on main Shannon road.

Clifton House

♦♦♦

Ennis Road, Limerick, Co. Limerick
Tel: +353(0)61 451166 Fax: +353(0)61 451224
Email: cliftonhouse@eircom.net
SB £35 DB £50 CC: MC Vi

How to get there: Clifton House is on Ennis Road, opposite Woodfield House Hotel, and near Gaelic Grounds. Within city limits.

Lisdoonvarna, Co. Clare

Kincora House

♦♦♦♦

Lisdoonvarna, Co. Clare
Tel: +353(0)65 7074300
Fax: +353(0)65 7074490
Email: kincorahotel@eircom.ie
Web: www.kincora-hotel.com
Children minimum age: 12
Closed November to February
Award-winning country inn, built in 1860 and recently refurbished. Excellent cuisine. Art gallery showing contemporary works. Feature garden. Near cliffs of Moher and the Burren.
SB £30 DB £45 B £6 L £8 D £15. CC: MC Vi

How to get there: From Lisdoonvarna town centre, take the Doolin Road. Hotel is on first junction 1/4 km from town centre.

MacRoom, Co. Cork

Castle

★★

Main Street, MacRoom, Co. Cork
Tel: +353(0)26 41074 Fax: +353(0)26 41505
Email: castlehotel@eircom.net
Web: www.castlehotel.ie
Closed December 25–27
SB £59 DB £78 B £4.50 L £8.50 D £18.50.
CC: MC Vi Am DC

How to get there: On N22, 25 miles from Cork and 30 miles from Killarney.

Malahide, Co. Dublin

The Grand

★★★★

Malahide, Co. Dublin
Tel: +353(0)1 8450000 Fax: +353(0)1 8168025
Email: sstone@thegrand.ie
Web: www.thegrand.ie
Closed Christmas
SB £125 DB £171.60 HBS £143 HBD £190
CC: MC Vi Am DC

How to get there: From Dublin airport, take N1. Proceed north, pass 3 roundabouts; at 4th take 3rd exit for Malahide. At T-junction turn left; hotel 1km ahead at end of village.

Mallow, Co. Cork

Longueville House

★★★ 🍴🍴🍴
Mallow, Co. Cork
Tel: +353(0)22 47156 Fax: +353(0)22 47459
Email: info@longuevillehouse.ie
Web: www.longuevillehouse.ie
Closed January to February
SB £95 DB £135 HBS £120 HBD £185
B £15 D £36. CC: MC Vi Am DC
🛏️☺️🛁🖥️☎️🔌📠☕♨️🐴♬🎬⛵♒
👥🍽️
How to get there: 3 miles west of Mallow, via
the N72 to Killarney. Turn right at Ballyclough
junction; hotel entrance is 200m further.

Springfort Hall Country House

★★★
Mallow, Co. Cork
Tel: +353(0)22 21278 Fax: +353(0)22 21557

Maynooth, Co. Kildare

Moyglare Manor

★★★ 🍴🍴🍴
Maynooth, Co. Kildare
Tel: +353(0)1 6286357 Fax: +353(0)1 6285405
Email: info@moyglaremanor.ie
Web: www.moyglaremanor.ie
Children minimum age: 12
SB £110 DB £180 B £9 L £22.50 D £30.
CC: MC Vi Am Laser
♿🛏️🖥️☎️🔌📠☕♨️🐴♬⛵♒👥
How to get there: Travelling west on N4/M4, exit
for Maynooth. Travelling through town, turn left
at T-junction. Keep right at Catholic church.
Hotel is after 2km.

Midleton, Co. Cork

Ballymaloe House

★★★ 🍴🍴
Shangarry, Middleton, Co. Cork
Tel: +353(0)21 4652531 Fax: +353(0)21 4652021
Email: res@ballymaloe.ie
Web: www.ballymaloe.ie
Closed December 23–27
A large family-run country house on a 400-acre
farm, featuring home and local produce.
Situated 20 miles southeast of Cork, 3 miles
from the coast.
SB £80 DB £160 L £24 D £37.50.
CC: MC Vi Am DC Swi Delt
♿☎️📠☕♨️🐴♬⛵👥👥🥂♒
How to get there: From Cork, N25 to Midleton,

then the Ballycotton Road via Cloyne
(signposted from Midleton).

Rathcoursey House

❖
Ballinacurra, nr Midleton, Co. Cork
Tel: +353(0)1 4613418 Fax: +353(0)1 4613393

Mountshannon, Co. Clare

Mountshannon

★★
Main Street, Mountshannon, Co. Clare
Tel: +353(0)61 927162

Naas, Co. Kildare

Harbour View

★★
Limerick Road, Naas, Co. Kildare
Tel: +353(0)45 879145 Fax: +353(0)45 874002

Ireland

New Ross, Co. Wexford

Creacon Lodge

♦♦♦♦ ℞

New Ross, Co. Wexford
Tel: +353(0)51 421897 Fax: +353(0)51 422560
Email: creacon@indigo.ie
Web: www.creaconlodge.com

Country House Hotel set amidst the peace and tranquility of the countryside. 45 minutes drive from Rosslare. 10 en-suite bedrooms. Fully licensed bar. Renowned restaurant.
SB £45 DB £70 HBS £60 HBD £100 D £17.50.
CC: MC Vi

How to get there: From Wexford take N25 to New Ross. Just before reaching New Ross turn left on R733. After 5km, turn left for Creacon Lodge.

Oakwood House

♦♦♦♦

Ring Road, Mountgarrett, New Ross,
Co. Wexford
Tel: +353(0)51 425494 Fax: +353(0)51 425494

Newmarket-on-Fergus, Co. Clare

Dromoland Castle

★★★★★ ℞℞

Newmarket-on-Fergus, Co. Clare
Tel: +353(0)61 368144 Fax: +353(0)61 363355
Email: sales@dromoland.ie
Web: www.dromoland.ie
Children minimum age: 12
B £13 L £20 D £40.
CC: MC Vi Am DC Swi Delt

How to get there: From Dublin, take N7 to Limerick, then N18 from Limerick to Dromoland Castle (approx 19 miles).
See advert on facing page

Oranmore, Co. Galway

Moorings Restaurant & Guest House

♦♦♦

Oranmore, Co. Galway
Tel: +353(0)91 790462 Fax: +353(0)91 790462
SB £35 DB £50 D £25.
CC: MC Vi Am Swi

How to get there: From roundabout on approach road from Dublin/Cork/Limerick into Oranmore village. At T-junction turn right; Moorings is on right on main street.

Oughterard, Co. Galway

Ross Lake House

★★★ ℞

Rosscahill, Oughterard, Co. Galway
Tel: +353(0)91 550109 Fax: +353(0)91 550184

Portlaoise, Co. Laois

Ivyleigh House Little Gem

♦♦♦♦♦

Bank Place, Portlaoise, Co. Laois
Tel: +353(0)502 22081 Fax: +353(0)502 63343
Email: ivyleigh@gofree.indigo.ie
dinah@ivyleigh.com
Web: www.ivyleigh.com
Children minimum age: 8. Closed Dec 22 to Jan 2.

SB £46 DB £72
CC: MC Vi

How to get there: Ivyleigh, luxurious listed Georgian accommodation, excellent service and superb breakfast cuisine. Golf, Slieve Blooms, equestrian centre, fishing, and 100 yards from train station. Art centre and theatre. Excellent base for touring Ireland.

Portmagee, Co. Kerry

Moorings

◆◆◆◆

Portmagee Village, Co. Kerry
Tel: +353(0)66 9477108 Fax: +353(0)66 9477220
Email: moorings@iol.ie
Web: www.moorings.ie
Closed November to February
SB £38 DB £30 HBS £60 HBD £52
CC: MC Vi

How to get there: Follow Ring of Kerry road —
Killarney to Caherciveen. Three miles outside
Caherciveen, right for Portmagee. The Moorings
is in centre of village.

Portsalon, Co. Donegal

Croaghross

◆◆◆◆

Portsalon, Letterkenny, Co. Donegal
Tel: +353(0)74 59548 Fax: +353(0)74 59548
Email: jkdeane@croaghross.com
Web: www.croaghross.com
Closed November to February

SB £26 DB £56 HBS £40 HBD £42 B £4 D £14.
CC: MC Vi Laser

How to get there: From Letterkenny, drive to
Ramelton and turn right just before Milford onto
R246. Proceed through Kerrykeel to Portsalon.
Take small road opposite golf club entrance.

Portumna, Co. Galway

Shannon Oaks Hotel and Country Club

★★★★

St Joseph's Road, Portumna, Co. Galway
Tel: +353(0)509 41777 Fax: +353(0)509 41357
Email: sales@shannonoaks.ie
Web: www.shannonoaks.ie
The Shannon Oaks Hotel and Country Club is a
4-Star multiactivity hotel located in the picturesque
village of Portumna by the shores of Lough Derg.
SB £56 DB £72 HBS £78.50 HBD £117
B £7.50 L £11.50 D £22.50. CC: MC Vi Am DC

How to get there: Shannon Oaks Hotel and
Country Club is located on St Joseph's Road in
the village of Portumna.

Ireland

Rathmullan, Co. Donegal

Rathmullan House

★★★ ⓡ ⓡ ⓡ
Rathmullan, Letterkenny, Co. Donegal
Tel: +353(0)74 58188 Fax: +353(0)74 58200
Email: info@rathmullanhouse.com
Web: www.rathmullanhouse.com
Closed January to mid–February
SB £66 DB £132 HBS £93.50 HBD £187
B £7.50 L £5 D £30. CC: MC Vi Am DC Delt
♿ ⊞ ⊗ ⊚ ▭ ☎ ℙ ♨ ℃ 🐎 ♩ 🦀 👁 ⅲ
🔍 ⓢ
How to get there: From Belfast airport, follow A6
to Derry. N13 to Letterkenny, and on arrival turn
right into Ramelton. After bridge turn right to
Rathmullan. Hotel is situated 500m north of
village.

Roscommon, Co. Roscommon

The Abbey

★★★
Roscommon, Co. Roscommon
Tel: +353(0)903 26505 Fax: +353(0)903 26021

The Abbey Hotel, set in its own private grounds,
is ideally situated for the touring holidaymaker.
Excellent restaurant and spacious comfortable
accommodation that compare favourably with
the best international standards.
SB £55 DB £100 B £7.50 L £15 D £25.
CC: MC Vi Am DC
♨ ♿ ⊞ ⊚ ▭ ☎ ℙ ♨ ℃ 🐎 ♩ 🦀 ⅲ ⅲ
How to get there: The hotel is on the Galway
Road (N63), southern side of Roscommon town
in town itself.

Rosslare, Co. Wexford

Kelly's Resort

★★★★ ⓡ
Rosslare, Co. Wexford
Tel: +353(0)53 32114 Fax: +353(0)53 32222
Email: kellyhot@iol.ie
Web: www.kellys.ie
Closed December 10 to February 23

Renowned resort hotel. Fine food and wine,
indoor/outdoor amenities. Extensive leisure and
beauty complex. Special spring–autumn activity
midweeks, 2-day weekends and 5-day
midweeks.
SB £60 DB £77 L £14 D £24.
CC: MC Vi Am
♿ ↟ ▭ ☎ ℒ ℙ ♨ ℃ 🐎 ♩ 👁 ⅲ SPA ⵝ ╱
🔍 ⓢ
How to get there: From Dublin airport, N11 to
Rosslare, signposted South-East (Gorey,
Enniscorthy, Wexford, Rosslare). The hotel is in
Rosslare Strand.

Churchtown House

♦♦♦♦♦ ⓡ ⵝ ⵒ
Tagoat, Rosslare, Co. Wexford
Tel: +353(0)53 32555 Fax: +353(0)52 32577
Email: churchtown.rosslare@indigo.ie
Web: www.churchtown-rosslare.com
Children minimum age: 10
SB £50 DB £95 D £20.
CC: MC Vi Am
♿ ⊗ ▭ ☎ ℙ ♨ ℃ 🐎 ♩ 🦀 ⅰ
How to get there: ½ mile from N25 on the K736
at Tagoat. Turn between pub and church in
village.

Rosslare Harbour, Co. Wexford

Ferryport House

Rosslare Harbour, Co. Wexford
Tel: +353(0)53 33933 Fax: +353(0)53 33033

Roundstone, Co. Galway

Roundstone House

★★ ♛♛
Roundstone, Roundstone, Connemara,
Co. Galway,
Tel: +353(0)95 35864 Fax: +353(0)95 35944
Email: diar@eircom.net
Closed November to April 1
SB £50 DB £63 B £6 D £25. CC: MC Vi
⟨icons⟩
See advert on the right

Heatherglen House

♦♦♦ ♟
Roundstone, Co. Galway,
Tel: +353(0)95 35837 Fax: +353(0)95 35837

Skerries, Co. Dublin

Redbank House & Restaurant

♦♦♦ ♛♛
6-7 Church Street, Skerries, Co. Dublin
Tel: +353(0)1 8490439 Fax: +353(0)1 8491598
Email: redbank@eircom.net
Web: www.redbank.ie
Closed Christmas

Now listed for protection, confirming the
McCoys' sense of style, having converted this
old bank into one of Ireland's finest restaurants
and guest houses, featuring the catch of the
day at Skerries Pier.
SB £45 DB £70 HBS £70 HBD £140
B £5 L £22 D £28.
CC: MC Vi Am DC Swi Delt Laser
⟨icons⟩
How to get there: 20 minutes off the N1
Dublin to Belfast road. From the south,
through the village of Lusk. From the north,
turn to left at Balbriggam and follow coast
road.

Roundstone House Hotel

RAC ★★ ♛♛

Situated in the delightful, scenic fishing village
of Roundstone on the west coast of Ireland —
overlooking the Atlantic and the Twelve Bens
mountain range of Connemara. Owned and
successfully managed by the Vaughan family
for 40 years. All twelve bedrooms are ensuite
and our dining room is renowned for fine food
and good wine.

Roundstone, Connemara, Co. Galway
Tel: 095 35863   Fax: 095 35944

Spiddal, Co. Galway

Suan na Mara

♦♦♦♦♦ ♛♟♟
Stripe, Furbo, Spiddal, Co. Galway
Tel: +353(0)91 591512 Fax: +353(0)91 591632

Straffan, Co. Kildare

Kildare Hotel & Country Club

★★★★★ ♛♛♛
Straffan, Co. Kildare
Tel: +353(0)1 6273333 Fax: +353(0)1 6273312
Email: ann.cronin@kclub.ie
Web: www.kclub.ie
SB £327 DB £344 HBS £382 HBD £554
B £17 L £25 D £55.
CC: MC Vi Am DC Swi
⟨icons⟩
How to get there: N7 south as far as the Kill
crossing, turn right at traffic lights. Resort is
5 miles, and is well signposted from that
point.

Ireland

Tahilla, Co. Kerry

Tahilla Cove Country House

♦♦♦♦

Tahilla, nr Sneem, Co. Kerry
Tel: +353(0)64 45204 Fax: +353(0)64 45104

Thomastown, Co. Kilkenny

Belmore Country Home

♦♦♦

Jerpoint Church, Thomastown, Co. Kilkenny
Tel: +353(0)56 24228
Closed Christmas

Charming country home on family farm featuring a warm welcome, spacious en-suite rooms and own fishing for guests. Golf and many other activities and attractions locally. Open all year except Christmas.
SB £26.50 DB £40 CC: Eurocheque
🐎 P 🛇 🕯 🐴 🎋 🐾 🍷 🥂
How to get there: Turn off main N9 road near Jerpoint Abbey, towards Stoney Ford/Mount Juliet. House signposted to right — second entrance.

Tralee, Co. Kerry

Ballyseede Castle

★★★ ♜ ♜ ♜

Ballyseede, Tralee, Co. Kerry
Tel: +353(0)66 7125799 Fax: +353(0)66 7125287
SB £100 DB £180 B £10 D £30.
CC: MC Vi DC
🔹 🔄 🛇 🖥 ☎ P 🛇 🕯 🐴 🎋 🐾 🎯 🎯
How to get there: Located off the N21 from Limerick and the N22 from Cork.

Meadowlands

★★★ ♞

Oakpark, Tralee, Co. Kerry
Tel: +353(0)66 7180444 Fax: +353(0)66 7180964
Email: medlands@iol.ie
SB £75 DB £120 B £7.50 L £12.95 D £25.
CC: MC Vi

🔹 ᛁᛁ 🔄 🛇 🖥 ☎ ❄ P 🛇 🕯 🐴 🎋 🐾 🎯 🎯
How to get there: 1km from Tralee town centre on the main N69.

Barnagh Bridge Guesthouse

♦♦♦♦ ✍

Cappaclogh, Camp, Tralee, Co. Kerry
Tel: +353(0)66 7130145 Fax: +353(0)66 7130299
Email: bbguest@eircom.net
Children minimum age: 10
Closed November to March
SB £28 DB £40 CC: MC Vi Am
🛇 🛇 🖥 ☎ P 🛇 🕯 🐴 🎋 🐾
How to get there: Leave N86 at Camp. Follow Conor Pass Road, R560, for 1 mile.

Glenduff House

♦♦♦♦ ✍

Kielduff, Tralee, Co. Kerry
Tel: +353(0)66 7137105 Fax: +353(0)66 7137099
Email: glenduffhouse@eircom.net
Web: www.tralee-insight.com/glenduff
Closed November to mid-March

A beautiful family-run Period House set in 6 acres, 5 miles from Tralee. Refurbished to its original character with fine antiques and paintings. Five en-suite rooms ideal for golfing, touring etc.
SB £32 DB £64 CC: MC Vi
🔄 🖥 ☎ P 🛇 🕯 🐴 🐾 🎯
How to get there: From Tralee take route to race course off N21 at Clash roundabout and continue for 4¹/₂ miles.

Tramore, Co. Waterford

Glenorney

◆◆◆◆ ⌀

Newtown, Tramore, Co. Waterford
Tel: +353(0)51 381056 Fax: +353(0)51 381103

Tullamore, Co. Offaly

Moorhill Country House

Moorhill, Clara Road (N80), Tullamore,
Co. Offaly
Tel: +353(0)5 0621395

Upper Newcastle, Co. Galway

Westwood House

✤

Dangan, Upper Newcastle, Co.Galway
Tel: +353(0)91 521442 Fax: +353(0)91 521400

Waterford, Co. Waterford

Dooley's

★★★

The Quay, Waterford, Co. Waterford
Tel: +353(0)51 873531 Fax: +353(0)51 870262
Email: hotel@dooleys-hotel.ie
Web: www.dooleys-hotel.ie

Family-run hotel situated on the quay in
Waterford. High levels of comfort and personal
service. Stay here and you won't be
disappointed.
SB £80 DB £110 B £8.50 L £17 D £25.
CC: MC Vi Am DC

⌂ ⅙ ⊪ 🗐 ⊗ ☺ ⬚ ☎ ⬧ ⅗ ⅔ ⅞ ♘ 🗡 ♥
♨ ⅢⅠ

How to get there: Located in Waterford City on
the quayside. Follow W25 route to the city
centre.

Granville

★★★ ⊛

Meacher Quay, Waterford, Co. Waterford
Tel: +353(0)51 305555 Fax: +353(0)51 305566
Email: stay@granville-hotel.ie
Web: www.granville-hotel.ie
SB £60 DB £100
B £8.50 L £13.50 D £25.
CC: MC Vi Am DC

⌂ ⊪ ⊗ 🗐 ☎ ⬧ ☐ ⅗ ⅔ ♘ 🗡 ♥ ⅢⅠ Ⅲ

How to get there: City centre, on the quay
opposite clocktower.
See advert below

Jurys Waterford

★★★

Ferrybank, Waterford, Co. Waterford,
Tel: +353(0)1 6070055 Fax: +353(0)1 6609625
Email: dorothy_cusack@jurysdoyle.com
Web: www.jurysdoyle.com
B £5 L £13 D £17. CC: MC Vi Am DC

⊪ ☺ 🗐 ☎ ☐ ⅗ ⅔ ♘ 🗡 ♥ ☜ ⅢⅠ Ⅲ SPA ⅄
♨ 🗐

Ireland

Diamond Hill Country House

◆◆◆

Milepost, Slieverue, Co. Waterford
Tel: +353(0)51 832855 Fax: +353(0)51 832254
Closed December 24–26
SB £30 DB £27.50 CC: MC Vi
♿♨☎🖥☎🅿️♨🎠🛏️🦞
How to get there: Situated less than a mile from
Waterford city, off the N25 Rosslare-Waterford
road.

Villa Eildon

◆◆◆ ⚜♞

Belmont Road/Rosslare Road, Ferrybank,
Ferrybank, Waterford, Co. Waterford
Tel: +353(0)51 832174
Children minimum age: 7
Closed November to April
DB £38
⊗🅿️♨🎠🛏️🦞
How to get there: 2km from Waterford Bridge on
Rosslare Road (N25) — 4th house on right, after
Ferrybank Church.

Please mention the RAC Inspected guide
when you make your booking at an RAC
Hotel or Guest Accommodation.

Castlecourt Hotel
Conference & Leisure Centre

Located in the heart of Westport town
a haven for Irish Culture and Tradition

140 Deluxe Bedrooms
Sumptuous Cuisine
Swimming pool & Leisure Centre
Lively Harbour Lights Bar
Championship Golf Courses

"For a Holiday to Remember"

Castlebar Street, Westport, Co Mayo
Tel: 098 25444   Fax: 098 28622
Email: castlecourt@anu.ie
Website: www.castlecourthotel.com

Waterville, Co. Kerry

Brookhaven

◆◆◆ ⚜

New Line Road, Waterville, Co. Kerry
Tel: +353(0)66 9474431 Fax: +353(0)66 9474724
Email: brookhaven@esatclear.ie
Web: www.euroka.com/waterville/brookhaven
Closed December to February
SB £40 DB £56
⊗♨🖥☎📞🅿️♨🎠🛏️🦞
How to get there: Located on the Ring of Kerry
route, 1km on the north side of the village of
Waterville.

Westport, Co. Mayo

Castlecourt

★★★

Castlebar Street, Westport, Co. Mayo
Tel: +353(0)98 25444 Fax: +353(0)98 28622
Email: castlecourt@anu.ie
Web: www.castlecourthotel.ie
SB £45 DB £110 L £11.95 D £18.95.
CC: MC Vi
🔱♿🛗♨🖥☎🅿️♨🎠🛏️🦞🕷🍴♨♨ SPA
🍴💈
How to get there: Approaching from the main
Castlebar Road (N5), the Castlecourt Hotel is
located at the first set of traffic lights.
See advert on the left

Hotel Westport

★★★

Newport Road, Westport, Co. Mayo
Tel: +353(0)98 25122 Fax: +353(0)98 26739
Email: sales@hotelwestport.ie
Web: www.hotelwestport.ie
SB £85 DB £70 B £8.50 L £12.95 D £23.95.
CC: MC Vi Am DC
♿🛗🍴♨🖥☎📞🅿️♨🎠🛏️🦞♨♨
🍴💈
How to get there: N5 to Castlebar, N60 to
Westport. At end of Castlebar Street turn right
before the bridge. Turn right at lights and take
immediate left at hotel signpost. Follow to end
of road.

Wexford, Co. Wexford

Ferrycarrig

★★★★ ⌿⌿

Ferrycarrig Bridge, Wexford, Co. Wexford
Tel: +353(0)53 20999 Fax: +353(0)53 20982
Email: ferrycarrig@griffingroup.ie
Web: www.griffingroup.ie
SB £70 DB £120 HBS £98 HBD £88 D £28.
CC: MC Vi Am DC

⌘ ⌐ ♒ ⌂ ▢ ☎ ☏ **P** ♘ ⌁ ⌓ ♞ ⛢ ♋ ⌣ ⚎
⚎⚎ ⟦SPA⟧ ⌥ ⌐

How to get there: Travelling on N11 from
Enniscorthy to Wexford town, the hotel is
2 miles from Wexford on the Enniscorthy Road,
overlooking the River Slavey estuary.

Cedar Lodge

★★★ ⌿

Carrigbyrne, Newbawn, New Ross,
Co. Wexford
Tel: +353(0)51 428386 Fax: +353(0)51 428222
Email: cedarlodge@tinet.ie
Web: www.prideofeirehotels.com
Closed January
The Cedar Lodge is a charming country hotel
and restaurant situated beneath the slopes of
Carrigbyrne Forest and within easy driving of
Wexford's fine beaches.

SB £70 DB £115 HBS £95 HBD £165
B £10 L £15 D £25. CC: MC Vi Am DC
⌘ ⌐ ⌂ ▢ ☎ ❄ **P** ♘ ⌁ ⌓ ⛢ ♋ ⚎⚎ ⚎⚎⚎

How to get there: On the N25 road between
Wexford and New Ross.

Ireland

Talbot

★★★

Trinity Street, Wexford, Co. Wexford
Tel: +353(0)53 22566 Fax: +353(0)53 23377
Email: talbotwx@eircom.net
Web: www.talbothotel.ie

Superior three-star hotel established in 1905. Completely refurbished with all modern amenities — 99 en-suite bedrooms, central location, private parking, business and leisure facilities.

SB £70 DB £110 HBS £90 HBD £75
CC: MC Vi Am

How to get there: From Dublin and Rosslare, take N11, following signs for Wexford. Hotel is in town centre, on quay.

White's

★★★

George Street, Wexford, Co. Wexford
Tel: +353(0)53 22311 Fax: +353(0)53 45000

Whitford House

★★★

New Line Road, Wexford, Co. Wexford
Tel: +353(0)53 43444 Fax: +353(0)53 46399
Email: whitford@indigo.ie
Web: www.whitford.ie
Closed December 23 to January 16
SB £41 DB £69 HBS £59 HBD £101
B £6 L £10 D £18.
CC: MC Vi Am Laser

How to get there: Situated 2 miles from Wexford Town, 10 miles from Rosslare Port, easy access to N11 and N25.

See advert on previous page

Ballinkeele House

John and Margaret Maher's distinguished country mansion with a striking pillared portico provides the most civilized and stylish base for a spell of relaxation.
The original oils and prints hang on the walls, the furniture is very grand and the five ensuite bedrooms (non-smoking) offer abundant space and comfort. Meals really are something to look forward to: Margaret is a fine cook, and her delicious dinners (book by noon) are served by candlelight in the lovely dining room

Ballinkeele House, Ballymurn, Enniscorthy, Co. Wexford, Ireland
Tel: 053 38105   Fax: 053 38468
Email: info@ballinkeele.com   Website: www.ballinkeele.com

Ballinkeele House

♦♦♦♦

Ballymurn, Enniscorthy, Co. Wexford
Tel: +353(0)53 38105 Fax: +353(0)53 38468
Email: info@ballinkeele.com
Web: www.ballinkeele.com
Children minimum age: 5
Closed November 12 to February 28
SB £57 DB £90 HBS £83 HBD £142 CC: MC Vi

How to get there: Take N11 north to Oilgate village and turn right at signpost.
See advert on facing page

Darral House

♦♦♦♦

Spanell Road, Wexford, Co. Wexford
Tel: +353(0)53 24264

Wicklow, Co. Wicklow

Rathsallagh House

★★★

Dunlavin, Co. Wicklow
Tel: +353(0)45 403112 Fax: +353(0)45 403343
Email: info@rathsallagh.com
Web: www.rathsallagh.com
Closed Christmas
SB £110 DB £210 HBS £145 HBD £245
L £20 D £35. CC: MC Vi Am DC Swi

Tinakilly House

★★★

Rathnew, Wicklow, Co. Wicklow
Tel: +353(0)404 69274
Fax: +353(0)404 67806
Email: reservations@tinakilly.ie
Web: www.tinakilly.ie
SB £122 DB £148 D £39. CC: MC Vi Am DC

How to get there: N11/M11 (Dublin-Wicklow-Wexford road) to Rathnew village. At roundabout, follow R750 to Wicklow Town. Entrance to hotel is 500m from village.

Youghal, Co. Cork

Ahernes Little Gem

♦♦♦♦♦

163 North Main Street, Youghal, Co. Cork
Tel: +353(0)24 92424 Fax: (0)24 93633

Channel Islands & Isle Of Man

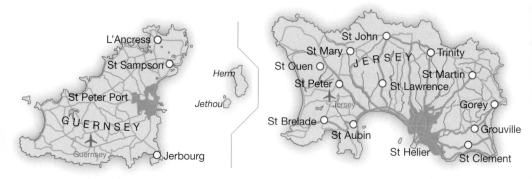

The Channel Islands of Jersey, Guernsey, Sark and Alderney lie 15 miles off the French coast, but are part of the British Isles. Their culture is a unique mix of British and French, and each island has its own parliament. During the

Second World War, the islands became the only part of the British Isles to be occupied by Germany, and this legacy remains an important interest to visitors.

Jersey – largest of the islands – boasts over 30 sandy beaches and miles of cliffs. At St Ouen's Bay the five-mile beach plays host to walkers, swimmers, surfers and some of the world's highest tides. Jersey's capital, St Helier, is popular with shoppers because visitors do not have to pay VAT and the island's respected jewellery trade is long-established. Jersey has an outstanding variety of eating places, and the visitor is spoilt for choice. St Helier is connected to Poole in Dorset, and Guernsey, or for visitors who remember their passports, St Malo in France.

Next largest in area, Guernsey's granite cliffs in the south rise to 90 metres above the sea and provide some of the UK's most spectacular coastal scenery. Of the island's 27 beaches and bays, the ones to be

found in the north of the island are most accessible. The capital, St Peter Port, is a bustling fishing and ferry port connecting to Jersey, England and France. Attractions include the German Underground Hospital, Forte Grey Maritime Museum, Hauteville House where Victor Hugo – exiled from France – wrote part of 'Les Misérables', and numerous craft centres.

Manx Electric
Railway Tram

To get away from the bustle of traffic, try Alderney or Sark, where there are no cars. Frequent 40-minute flights depart from Heathrow and Gatwick to Jersey and Guernsey, and frequent ferries get you around Alderney and Sark. Ferries from the mainland take about four hours. With plenty of high quality, friendly hotels on the islands, there is something to suit virtually any budget.

The Isle of Man – measuring a bare 31 by 13 miles – lies midway between England, Scotland, Ireland and Wales. Part of the British Isles but not of the United Kingdom, this small country has a huge variety of scenery and natural beauty. Over 100 miles of coastline enclose a land of wooded valleys, open moorland and meandering rivers, dominated by the central mountain range that climbs to 620 metres at Snaefell.

Roman and Norman invasions of Britain had little effect on the island, which remained Celtic until Viking rule during the 9th century. In coming together, these cultures created the Tynwald, the unique form of government that survives to this day.

Situated on the east coast, Douglas is the Isle of Man's capital, centre of government and the main port. For the visitor, Douglas provides a useful base for exploring the rest of the island, as well as being home to

several excellent museums, including Manx National Heritage. The famous Manx Electric Railway winds its spectacular path from Douglas northwards to Ramsey, using original tramcars from 1893, the year it opened. Seven miles along, the small town of Laxey is the eastern terminus of Britain's only electric mountain railway, the narrow-gauge Snaefell Mountain Railway. Built in just seven months in 1895, its track climbs from Laxey to the peak of Snaefell. You can also visit the popular Laxey Wheel, a 22-metre wheel once used to pump water from underground.

To the west, visit Peel, with its magnificent sandy beach, towering castle ruins and 13th-century cathedral. The small island of St Patrick's guards the harbour and is said to be the place where Christianity first landed in the isles, in the guise of the great Irish saint.

Just off Port St Mary on the south coast lies the Calf of Man, an island nature reserve owned by the Manx National Trust. Open to the public in summer, boat trips allow visitors access to seals, the rich variety of bird life on the island and enormous basking sharks in the waters.

Kirk Michael
A10
A17
A3
Ramsey
Maughold
Snaefell
A4
A2
Peel
A3
Laxey
St John's
A18
A24
Onchan
Douglas
A36
Manx Electric Railway
Port Soderick
Port Erin
Ronaldsway
Calf of Man
Port St Mary
Castletown

Guernsey

Old Government House

★★★★ ♨

Ann's Place, St Peter Port, Guernsey,
GY1 4AZ
Tel: 01481 724921 Fax: 01481 724429
Email: ogh@guernsey.net
Web: www.oghhotelguernsey.com

£2.5m refurbishment programme has made this
one of the island's premier hotels. 68 ensuite
bedrooms and suites, award-winning restaurant,
two bars and heated outdoor pool.
SB £70 DB £115 HBS £86 HBD £73.50 B £9.50
L £5 D £18.75. CC: MC Vi Am DC Swi Delt
♿ 〓 ◎ 〓 ▢ ☎ ☎ P ♨ 〽 ⚐ ♞ ♉ ⚘ ⚑ ♨
How to get there: From airport, left, left at 2nd
lights, through two more, right at next. Left at
first filter, right at next. Through three sets of
lights, right into Ann's Place, just before 4th set.

Saint Pierre Park

★★★★ ♨♨♨

Rohais, St Peter Port, Guernsey, GY1 1FD
Tel: 01481 728282 Fax: 01481 712041
Email: mail@stpierrepark.co.uk
Web: www.stpierrepark.co.uk

Set in 45 acres of its own parkland, 9-hole
par-3 golf course designed by Tony Jacklin,
3 all-weather tennis courts and a wide range of
leisure facilities, hair and beauty salon.
SB £130 DB £170 HBS £144 HBD £198
B £9.50 L £8 D £8. CC: MC Vi Am DC Swi

◈ ⚐ ◎ 〓 ▢ ☎ P ♨ 〽 ⚐ ♞ ♉ ⚘ ⚑ ⚑ ♨
🅂🅿🄰 'Ÿ' ⚐ ⚲ ⚐ ♨
How to get there: 10 minutes' drive from airport
and harbour front. Hire cars provide free maps.

Best Western Hotel de Havelet

★★★ ♨♨

Havelet, St Peter Port, Guernsey, GY1 1BA
Tel: 01481 722199 Fax: 01481 714057
Email: havelet@sarniahotels.com
Web: www.havelet.sarniahotels.com
SB £50 DB £84 HBS £60 HBD £104 D £16.
CC: MC Vi Am DC Swi
◎ ⚐ ☎ P ♨ 〽 ⚐ ♞ ♉ ⚘ ⚑ ⚑ ♨
How to get there: From airport, left for St Peter
Port. At bottom of Val de Terres hill, left up
Havelet Hill (signposted). Hotel on right of hill.

Green Acres

★★★ ♨

Les Hubits, St Martins, Guernsey, GY4 6LS
Tel: 01481 235711 Fax: 01481 235971
Email: greenacres@guernsey.net
Web: www.greenacreshotelguernsey.net
Closed November to March
SB £32 DB £64 HBS £42 HBD £84
CC: MC Vi Am Swi Delt
♿ ◎ ◎ ⚐ ☎ P ♨ 〽 ⚐ ♞ ♉ ⚘ ⚑ ⚑ ♨
How to get there: Follow hotel signs from the
three main roads that surround Les Hubits area
in the south-east corner of Guernsey.

Hotel Bon Port

★★★ ♨♨

Moulin Huet Bay, St Martins, GY4 6EW
Tel: 01481 239249 Fax: 01481 239596
Email: mail@bonport.com
Web: www.bonport.com

Spectacular views over Moulin Huet Bay, the
famous Peastacks, Saints Bay and Jersey.
Excellent food and views in the restaurant,
health suite, atrium and stunning grounds.
SB £30 DB £60 HBS £47.50 HBD £95 B £7.50
L £2.55 D £7.50. CC: MC Vi Am Swi Delt
◈ ♿ ◎ ⚐ ☎ P ♨ 〽 ⚐ ♞ ♉ ⚘ ⚑ ⚑ 'Ÿ' ♨
How to get there: From airport, signs to Bon Port.

L'Atlantique

★★★ ♖ ♖

Perelle Bay, St. Saviours, Guernsey, GY7 9NA
Tel: 01481 264056 Fax: 01481 263800
Email: patrick@perellebay.com
Web: www.perellebay.com
Closed November to March
SB £45 DB £77 HBS £58 HBD £51.50
B £6.55 D £17.95. CC: MC Vi Swi Delt

How to get there: Right from airport to west
coast, right, along coast for 1½ miles.

La Favorita

★★★ ♖

Fermain Bay, Guernsey, GY4 6SD
Tel: 01481 235666 Fax: 01481 235413
Email: info@favorita.com
Web: www.favorita.com
Closed January to February

Former country house overlooking bay and sea.
St Peter Port in easy walking distance. Indoor
pool and comfortable lounges with an open fire
help make La Favorita an ideal 'Pied à Terre'.
SB £58.50 DB £95 HBS £69.50 HBD £61.50
B £6 L £10.50 D £15.
CC: MC Vi Am DC Swi Delt Cheque Cash

How to get there: Follow signs for Fermain Bay
at junction of Sausmarez/Fort roads.

Le Chalet

★★★ ♖

Fermain Bay, St Martins, Guernsey, GY4 6SD
Tel: 01481 235716 Fax: 01481 235718
Email: chalet@sarniahotels.com
Web: www.chalet.sarniahotels.com
Closed mid-October to mid-April
SB £40 DB £60 HBS £50 HBD £80
CC: MC Vi Am DC Swi

How to get there: From airport, left, signs for
St Martins. After Sausmarez Manor, follow signs
for Fermain Bay and Le Chalet.

Les Rocquettes

★★★ ♖

Les Gravee, St Peter Port, GY1 1RN
Tel: 01481 722146 Fax: 01481 714543
Email: rocquettes@sarniahotels.com
Web: www.rocquettes.sarniahotels.com
SB £42 DB £60 HBS £50 HBD £80 D £15.
CC: MC Vi Am DC Swi Delt

How to get there: Left from airport, left at 2nd
lights, through next lights, over roundabout,
right at 4th lights, left at filter, left at next filter
into Les Gravees. Hotel on right.

Moores

★★★ ♖

Le Pollet, St Peter Port, Guernsey, GY1 1WH
Tel: 01481 724452 Fax: 01481 714037
Email: moores@sarniahotels.com
Web: www.moores.sarniahotels.com
SB £50 DB £70 HBS £60 HBD £90 B £6.50
L £9.50 D £15.50. CC: MC Vi Am DC Swi

How to get there: From airport, signs to St Peter
Port along seafront. On North Esplanade left
into Lower Pollet and continue to hotel on right.

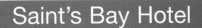

Channel Islands

Peninsula

★★★ ☗☗

Les Dicqs, Vale, Guernsey, GY6 8JP
Tel: 01481 48400 Fax: 01481 48706

St Margaret's Lodge

★★★ ☗

Forest Road, St Martins, Guernsey, GY4 6UE
Tel: 01481 255757 Fax: 01481 237594
Email: smlhotel@gtonline.net
Web: www.smlodge.com

Whatever the occasion – romantic weekend, anniversary, birthday or business trip – St Margaret's Lodge has just the right facilities to make your stay a special one.
SB £23.50 DB £39 HBS £40.50 HBD £50.50
B £6 L £6.50 D £10.50. CC: MC Vi Am Swi Delt
☗ ⊞ ☗☗☗☗☗☗☗☗☗☗☗☗☗☗☗☗
☗☗
How to get there: On main road to airport.

Saints Bay

★★★ ☗☗

Icart Point, St Martins, Guernsey, GY4 6JG
Tel: 01481 238888 Fax: 01481 235558
Web: www.saintsbayhotel.com
SB £31 DB £29.50 HBS £43.50 HBD £42
CC: MC Vi Am DC Swi
☗☗☗☗☗☗☗☗☗☗☗☗☗☗☗☗
☗☗
See advert on previous page

Grange Lodge

★★ ☗

The Grange, St Peter Port, Guernsey, GY1 1RQ
Tel: 01481 725161 Fax: 01481 724211

Hotel Hougue du Pommier

★★ ☗☗

Castel, Guernsey, GY5 7FQ
Tel: 01481 256531 Fax: 01481 256260
Email: hotel@houguedupommier.guernsey.net
Web: www.hotelhouguedupommier.com
SB £33 DB £66 HBS £13 L £5.50 D £16.50.

CC: MC Vi Am DC Swi
☗☗☗☗☗☗☗☗☗☗☗☗☗☗☗☗☗
How to get there: From Cobo Bay, take the road inland to Route de Hougue du Pommier. Ten minutes' drive from St Peter Port and 20 minutes from the airport.

Sunnycroft

★★ ☗

5 Constitution Steps, St Peter Port, Guernsey, GY1 2PN
Tel: 01481 723008
Closed November to March

Situated on an old stepped street in centre of town, with views of harbour and other islands. A character hotel with atmosphere and good food.
SB £40 DB £80 HBS £48 HBD £96
B £6 D £13.50. CC: MC Vi
☗☗☗☗☗☗☗☗☗☗☗☗☗
How to get there: Constitution Steps are just past Salvation Army building in Clifton.

La Galaad

◆◆◆ ☗☗

Rue des Francais, Castel, Guernsey, GY5 7FH
Tel: 01481 257233 Fax: 01481 253028
Closed November to April
SB £22 DB £44 HBS £37 HBD £74
D £9.50. CC: MC Vi
☗☗☗☗☗☗☗☗☗☗

Marine

◆◆◆

Well Road, St Peter Port, Guernsey, GY1 1WS
Tel: 01481 724978 Fax: 01481 711729
Web: www.hotel-guernsey.com
SB £16.95 DB £33.90 B £5
CC: MC Vi Delt Eurocard and JCB
☗☗☗☗☗☗☗☗
How to get there: Well Road is situated just off Glatengy Esplanade, opposite Queen Elizabeth II Marina. Just 5 minutes walk from ferry and town.

Jersey

Atlantic

★★★★ 🏆🏆🏆

Le Mont de La Pulente, St Brelade, Jersey,
JE3 8HE
Tel: 01534 744101 Fax: 01534 744102
Email: atlantic@itl.net
Web: www.slh.com/atlantic
Closed January to February.

In private local ownership since 1970, this
four-star luxury hotel is the sole Channel Islands
member of Small Luxury Hotels of the World.
SB £125 DB £160 L £16.50 D £25.
CC: MC Vi Am DC Swi Delt

How to get there: From the A13 take the B35 to
Le Mont de la Pulente. Hotel sign is on the right.

Hotel La Place

★★★★ 🏆

Route Du Coin, La Haule, St Brelade, Jersey,
JE3 8BT
Tel: 01534 744261 Fax: 01534 745164
Email: hotlaplace@aol.com
Web: www.jersey.co.uk/hotels/laplace
SB £74 DB £108 B £8.95 L £13.50 D £26.
CC: MC Vi Am DC Swi Delt

How to get there: Approaching St Aubin from
St Helier, at La Haule Manor turn right. Take
second left then first right. 200 yards on right.

L'Horizon

★★★★ 🏆🏆🏆

St Brelades Bay, St Brelades, Jersey, JE3 8EF
Tel: 01534 743101 Fax: 01534 746269
Email: lhorizon@hotellhorizon.com
Web: www.hotellhorizon.com
Jersey's leading hotel, L'Horizon nestles at the
centre of St Brelade's Bay. The hotel has 107
rooms and suites, of which 65 are sea-facing.
Guests can choose from three restaurants, each

with individual style and character.

Longueville Manor

★★★★ 🏆🏆🏆

St Saviours, Jersey, JE2 7WF
Tel: 01534 725501 Fax: 01534 731613
Email: longman@ih.net
Web: www.longuevillemanor.com

Stunning 18th-century Norman manor, set in a
16-acre wooded valley. Luxurious bedrooms,
award-winning restaurant and beautiful gardens.
Member of Relais & Châteaux.
SB £172.50 DB £225 HBS £187.50 HBD £255
B £12.50 L £17 D £42.50.
CC: MC Vi Am DC Swi Delt

How to get there: From airport, A1 to St Helier
and then A3 towards Gorey. Longueville Manor
is situated approximately 1 mile on the left.

St Brelade's Bay

★★★★ 🏆🏆

Jersey, JE3 8EF
Tel: 01534 746141 Fax: 01534 747278
Closed October to April
SB £60 DB £60 HBS £75 HBD £75
B £7.50 L £15 D £25. CC: MC Vi

How to get there: Located in the southwest of
the island.

Apollo

★★★

St Saviours Road, St Helier, Jersey,
Tel: 01534 725441 Fax: 01534 722120
Email: huggler@psilink.co.je
Web: www.huggler.com
SB £59 DB £99 HBS £67 HBD £119
L £11 D £11. CC: MC Vi Am DC Swi

How to get there: Take St Helier Ring Road. On St Saviours Road heading towards town centre, turn left onto Mountpleasant Road to hotel.

Beau Couperon

★★★

Rozel Bay, St Martin, Jersey, JE3 6AN
Tel: 01534 865522 Fax: 01534 865332
Email: beaucouperon@southernhotels.com
Web: www.jerseyhols.com/beaucouperon
Closed November to March.
SB £72 DB £96 HBS £87.50 HBD £126.40
B £4.95 L £9.90 D £15. CC: MC Vi Swi Delt

How to get there: From St Helier, follow signs for St Martin. At St Martin's church turn right, directly followed by a left turn. Follow signs towards Rozel bay.

Beaufort

★★★

Green Street, St Helier, Jersey, JE2 4UH
Tel: 01534 721023 Fax: 01534 722120
Email: huggler@psilink.co.je
Web: www.huggler.com
SB £65 DB £99 HBS £73 HBD £115 B £7.25
L £10 D £14.85. CC: MC Vi Am DC Swi

How to get there: From airport or harbour proceed to St Helier. Go under flyover and through tunnel. Turn left at roundabout after tunnel. Hotel is 150yds down road on left.

Beausite

★★★

Grouville Bay, Grouville, Jersey, JE3 9DJ
Tel: 01543 857577 Fax: 01543 857211
Email: beausite@jerseymail.co.uk
Web: www.southernhotels.co.uk
Closed November to February
SB £32.80 DB £65.65 HBS £40.95 HBD £81.90
B inc D £10.95. CC: MC Vi Am DC Swi Delt

How to get there: A1 east to A17 to A3 towards Gorey. The hotel is on the left at Grouville.

Bergerac

★★★

Portelet Bay, St Brelades, Jersey, JE3 8AT
Tel: 01534 745991 Fax: 01534 743010
Email: southern@itl.net
Web: southernhotels.com
Closed November to early March.
SB £33.50 DB £67 HBS £40.95 HBD £81.90
B £4.95 D £10.95. CC: MC Vi Am DC Swi Delt

How to get there: From the airport, head towards St Brelades then St Aubin. Turn right at Woodbine Corner and follow signs.

Chateau La Chaire

★★★

Rozel Bay, St Martin, Jersey, JE3 6AJ
Tel: 01534 863354 Fax: 01534 865137
Email: res@chateau-la-chaire.co.uk
Web: www.chateau-la-chaire.co.uk
Children minimum age: 7

A charming Victorian house, beautifully decorated and furnished. Set in terraced, wooded gardens. 14 bedrooms, all ensuite.
SB £90 DB £105 HBS £105 HBD £130
B £7 L £13 D £27.50.
CC: MC Vi Am DC Swi Delt

Chateau de la Valeuse

★★★

St Brelades Bay, Jersey, JE3 8EE
Tel: 01534 746281 Fax: 01534 747110
Email: chatval@itl.net
Web: user.super.net.uk/~chatval
Children minimum age: 5
Closed November to March
This small hotel of character overlooks our own award winning gardens and beautiful swimming pool. The 34 bedrooms are all ensuite, and the terrace and balconies decorated with window boxes.

SB £32 DB £32 HBS £43 HBD £43
B £6.50 L £12.50 D £18. CC: MC Vi Swi Delt
How to get there: Go into St. Brelades Bay and turn towards Churchill Memorial Park. Continue on and hotel is on left.

Lobster Pot
★★★ 🍴🍴
La Route De L'Etacq, St Ouen, Jersey, JE3 2DL
Tel: 01534 482888 Fax: 01534 481574

Mermaid
★★★
PO Box 38, St. Peter, Jersey, JE4 9N4
Tel: 01534 721023 Fax: 01534 722120
Email: huggler@psilink.co.je
Web: www.huggler.com
SB £45 DB £84 HBS £53 HBD £98
L £11 D £11. CC: MC Vi Am DC Swi
How to get there: Turn right from roundabout by airport. Take next left into hotel grounds and proceed to hotel.

Moorings
★★★ 🍴🍴
Gorey Pier, Gorey, Jersey, JE3 6EW
Tel: 01534 853633 Fax: 01534 857618

Old Court House
★★★ 🍴
Gorey Village, Grouville, Jersey, JE3 9FS
Tel: 01534 854444 Fax: 01534 853587
Email: ochhotel@itl.net
Web: www.vikingtravel.co.uk/ochhotel
Closed November to March
SB £33.50 DB £67 HBS £41 HBD £82
CC: MC Vi Am DC Swi Delt JCB Solo

Pomme d'Or
★★★ 🍴
Liberation Square, St Helier, Jersey, JE1 3UF
Tel: 01534 878644 Fax: 01534 437781
Email: pomme@seymourhotels.com
Web: www.seymourhotels.com

Jersey's best known hotel is ideally located at the heart of St Helier's shopping and financial district. The Pomme d'Or overlooks the island's marina and offers outstanding service.
SB £68 DB £136 HBS £82.50 HBD £165
B £7 L £10 D £11.
CC: MC Vi Am DC Swi Delt

Revere
★★★
Kensington Place, St Helier, Jersey, JE2 3PA
Tel: 01534 611111 Fax: 01534 611116
Email: reservations@revere.co.uk
Web: www.revere.co.uk
B £5 CC: MC Vi Am DC Swi Delt
How to get there: 15 minutes from the airport by car.

Royal
★★★
David Place, St Helier, Jersey, JE2 4TD
Tel: 01534 726521 Fax: 01534 724035
SB £67.50 DB £110 HBS £77.50 HBD £130
B £7.95 L £9.95 D £15.50.
CC: MC Vi Am DC Swi Delt
How to get there: Follow signs for the ring road, then Rouge Bouillon A14. Turn right at roundabout and right at traffic lights into Midvale Road. Past two lights, hotel is on left corner at lights.

Royal Yacht

★★★

Weighbridge, St Helier, Jersey, JE2 3NF
Tel: 01534 720511 Fax: 01534 767729
Email: theroyalyacht@mail.com
SB £46.50 DB £93 HBS £59 HBD £118
L £10.50 D £12.50.
CC: MC Vi Am Swi Delt

How to get there: On the weighbridge beside
bus station, 5 minutes walk from Fort Regent
leisure centre and the main shopping area.

Silver Springs

★★★

St Brelade, Jersey, JE3 8DB
Tel: 01534 46401 Fax: 01534 46823

Beau Rivage

★★

St Brelade's Bay, Jersey, JE3 8EF
Tel: 01534 45983 Fax: 01534 47127

Dolphin

★★ 🐾🐾

Gorey Pier, Gorey, Jersey, JE3 6EW
Tel: 01534 853370 Fax: 01534 855343

Dixcart Bay Hotel

The haunt of Victor Hugo, Swinburne and
Mervyn Peake, Sark's oldest hotel offers
comfortable ensuite accommodation, good
food, log fires and gentle hospitality.

In a world of its own, this converted farm
longhouse is surrounded by 40 acres of
woodlands leading to the sheltered bay of
Dixcart.

Isle of Sark, Channel Islands GY9 0SD
Tel: 01481 832015
Email: dixcart@itl.net
Website: www.dixcart.guernseyci.com

Hotel Savoy

★★

Rouge Bouillon, St Helier, Jersey, JE2 3ZA
Tel: 01534 727521 Fax: 01534 768480
Email: logo-hotel@psilink.co.uk
Closed December to January
SB £25 DB £44 HBS £32 HBD £58 B £5.50
D £11.50. CC: MC Vi Am DC Swi Delt

How to get there: Located opposite St Helier
police station.

Sarum

★★ 🐾

19–21 New St John's Road, St Helier, Jersey,
JE3 3LD
Tel: 01534 758163 Fax: 01534 731340
Email: sarum@jerseyweb.demon.co.uk
Web: www.jersey.co.uk/hotels/jwh/sarum
Children minimum age: 16
SB £34.50 DB £54 B £7
CC: MC Vi Am Swi Delt

How to get there: The hotel is located to the
western side of St Helier, less than ½ mile from
the town centre.

White Heather

★★

Rue de Haut, Millibrook, St Lawrence, Jersey,
JE3 1JQ
Tel: 01534 720978 Fax: 01534 720968
Children minimum age: 3
Closed November to April

Ideally situated between St Helier and
St Aubin's beach. Close to all amenities in a
quiet location, the hotel offers good catering
and comfort in a friendly atmosphere.
SB £24 DB £42 HBS £28 HBD £49 D £8.25.
CC: MC Vi DC

How to get there: On A1 between St Helier and
St Aubin, take A11, turn right at the school.

Bon Air

♦♦♦♦ ✠ ✞

Coast Road, Pontac, St Clements, Jersey,
JE2 6SE
Tel: 01534 855324 Fax: 01534 857801
Closed November to February
DB £50

🛏 💻 **P** ⚘ ✗ ℃ 🐎 ♄ 🐕 ❢ 🗲

Millbrook House

♦♦♦♦ ✠

Rue de Trachy, Millbrook, St Helier, Jersey,
JE23 3JN
Tel: 01534 733036 Fax: 01534 724317
Closed October to April

Peace, quiet and character, where the air is
clear and traditional values are maintained.
Ten acres of grounds, car park, 27 ensuite
rooms, memorable food and wines.
SB £36 DB £72 HBS £42 HBD £84
CC: MC Vi Am Swi

ᵫ ⊥⊥ 🛏 💻 ☎ **P** ⚘ ✗ ℃ 🐎 ♄ 🐕 ❢ ⌇
How to get there: 1½ miles west from St Helier
off A1.

Bryn-Y-Mor

♦♦♦

Route de la Haule, St Aubins Bay, Jersey,
JE3 8BA
Tel: 01534 20295 Fax: 01534 24262

Hotel des Pierres

♦♦♦

Greve de Lecq Bay, St Ouen, Jersey, JE3 2DT
Tel: 01534 481858 Fax: 01534 481858
Email: despierres@jerseyhols.com
Web: www.jerseyhols.com
B £4.85 D £9.85. CC: MC Vi Swi Delt

⊛ 🛏 💻 **P** ⚘ ✗ ℃ 🐎 ♄ 🐕 ❢ 🍸
Closed December 15 to January 11.

Sark

Aval Du Creux

★★★ ℞

Harbour Hill, Sark, Channel Islands, GY9 0SB
Tel: 01481 832036 Fax: 01481 832368

Dixcart Bay

❖

Isle of Sark, Channel Islands, GY9 0SD
Tel: 01481 832015 Fax: 01481 832164
Email: dixcart@itl.net
Web: www.dixcart.guernseyci.com
SB £30 DB £60 HBS £42 HBD £84 B £4
CC: MC Vi Am DC Swi Delt

🐎 🛏 💻 ☎ ⚘ ✗ ℃ 🐎 ♄ 🐕 ⫴⫴ 🍴
How to get there: From top of Harbour Hill take
avenue through centre of village. Turn left,
following signs to Dixcart Hotel.
See advert on facing page

Isle of Man

Mount Murray Country Club

★★★★ ℞ ℞

Santon, Isle of Man, IM4 2HT
Tel: 01624 661111 Fax: 01624 611116
Email: hotel@enterprise.net
Web: www.mountmurray.com
SB £79 DB £99 B £6.50 L £6.95 D £14.94.
CC: MC Vi Am DC Swi Delt

ᵫ ⊥⊥ 🖥 ⊛ 🛏 💻 ☎ 📞 **P** ⚘ ✗ ℃ 🐎 ♄ 🐕 ☠
⫴⫴ ⫴⫴ 🆂🅿🅰 🍸 ⚒ ◿ ⚲ ⌇ 🗲
How to get there: From airport take main road
to Douglas. Turn left at Santon, hotel is
signposted.

Ascot

★★★ ℞

7 Empire Terrace, Douglas, Isle Of Man,
IM2 4LE
Tel: 01624 675081 Fax: 01624 661512

Cherry Orchard

★★★

Bridson Street, Port Erin, Isle Of Man, IM9 6AN
Tel: 01624 833811 Fax: 01624 833583

Isle of Man

The Empress
★★★
Central Promenade, Douglas, Isle Of Man, IM2 4RA
Tel: 01624 661155 Fax: 01624 673554

Port Erin Royal
★★★
Promenade, Port Erin, Isle of Man, IM9 6LH
Tel: 01624 835503 Fax: 01624 835402
Email: rac@porterinhotels.com
Web: www.porterinhotels.com
Closed December to January
SB £28 DB £56 HBS £37 HBD £74
B £5.95 L £1.95 D £12.95.
CC: MC Vi Swi Delt

How to get there: Take road signs from either the sea terminal or airport marked 'Port Erin and the South'. Hotel on the upper promenade facing the sea.
See advert above

Welbeck
★★★
Mona Drive, off Central Promenade, Douglas, Isle of Man, IM2 4LF
Tel: 01624 675663 Fax: 01624 661545
Email: welbeck@isle-of-man.com
Web: www.isle-of-man.com/tourism/
        accommodation/welbeck/index.htm
SB £44 DB £57 B £7 CC: MC Vi Am Swi Delt

How to get there: From the south, go along Promenade. Take first left after Crescent Leisure Centre. Follow road to the right. We are on crossroads of Mona/Empress Drive.

Port Erin Imperial
★★
Promenade, Port Erin, Isle of Man, IM9 6LH
Tel: 01624 835503 Fax: 01624 835402
Email: rac@porterinhotels.com
Web: www.porterinhotels.com
Closed December to January
SB £25 DB £50 HBS £33 HBD £66
B £5.95 D £11.95. CC: MC Vi Swi Delt

How to get there: Follow directions from either the sea terminal or airport marked 'Port Erin and the South'. Hotel on the upper promenade facing the sea.
See advert on the left

Rutland
★★
Queens Promenade, Douglas, Isle of Man, IM2 4NS
Tel: 01624 621218 Fax: 01624 611562
Closed November to March
SB £23 DB £46 HBS £31.50 HBD £63 D £9.50.
CC: MC Vi Am DC Swi

How to get there: Centrally situated on the promenade 5 minutes' drive from sea terminal, 20 minutes from airport.

Travelling abroad?

2 ways we can look after you.

If you're going abroad, don't forget to protect yourself against illness, accidents and your car breaking down. With our Travel Insurance and European Motoring Assistance, you'll have the reassurance of knowing we'll be there when you need us.

Travel Insurance

From just £9.00, you'll be covered for the costs of illness, accident, delays and loss of belongings.

- Choose between Standard and Extra Cover
- Choose from single trip or annual cover
- Cover for medical expenses of up to £10 million
- Upgrade for winter sports available.

European Motoring Assistance

If you're taking your car to the continent, you can't afford to be without this valuable cover. In the event of a breakdown, one phone call will bring us to your rescue.

- Choose from 2 levels of cover: Standard Cover (worth up to £2,500 of assistance) Additional Cover (worth up to £3,500 of assistance)
- You're covered as soon as you leave home.

Call 0800 55 00 55

Lines open 8am to 9pm Mon to Fri, 9am to 5pm on Sat and quote GUI2

Distance Chart

To find the distance from one town to another, follow the horizontal and vertical columns until they intersect.

The upper figures are miles and the lower *italic* figures are kilometres - for example the distance from Perth to York is 249 miles or *401* kilometres

Aberdeen	445 420 493 471 505 221 588 125 569 149 145 439 105 327 383 341 517 340 235 496 686 82 360 547 228 319
	716 676 793 758 813 356 947 201 916 240 233 707 169 526 616 549 832 547 378 798 1104 132 579 880 367 513
Aberystwyth	114 125 214 105 224 292 320 201 430 320 111 486 169 199 104 211 129 257 276 317 386 159 201 325 195
	183 201 344 169 360 478 515 323 692 515 179 782 272 320 167 340 208 414 444 510 621 256 323 523 314
BIRMINGHAM	81 100 103 196 194 292 157 392 292 148 458 113 90 93 117 80 207 166 275 337 76 128 297 130
	130 161 166 315 312 470 253 631 470 238 737 182 145 150 188 129 333 267 443 542 122 206 478 209
Bristol	169 45 277 202 373 76 486 373 206 539 194 183 161 122 161 299 252 185 419 161 76 378 222
	272 72 466 325 600 122 782 600 332 867 312 295 259 196 259 481 406 298 674 259 122 608 357
Cambridge	190 264 125 345 249 479 372 270 505 145 85 194 54 165 241 62 337 390 120 148 379 165
	306 425 201 555 401 771 599 435 813 233 137 312 87 266 388 100 543 628 193 238 610 266
CARDIFF	289 238 385 121 485 385 216 549 238 233 165 157 183 325 262 233 440 194 121 390 244
	465 383 620 195 781 620 348 884 373 335 272 253 295 523 422 375 708 312 195 628 393
Carlisle	389 96 353 206 96 231 262 119 191 120 301 119 57 289 461 144 152 324 101 121
	626 154 568 332 154 372 422 192 307 193 484 192 92 465 742 232 245 521 163 195
Dover	462 248 596 488 360 622 260 202 299 71 276 358 174 356 534 245 143 496 282
	744 399 959 786 580 1001 418 325 481 114 444 576 280 573 859 394 230 798 454
EDINBURGH	450 144 44 333 158 202 258 216 390 215 110 366 559 43 235 438 124 194
	724 232 71 536 254 325 415 348 628 346 177 589 900 69 378 705 200 312
Exeter	560 449 282 618 270 247 237 181 236 364 308 112 492 237 105 454 287
	901 723 454 995 435 398 381 291 380 586 496 180 792 381 169 731 462
Fort William	101 438 66 329 399 329 510 329 253 504 661 97 348 541 195 330
	163 705 106 530 642 530 821 530 407 811 1064 156 560 871 314 531
Glasgow	330 166 215 291 216 397 215 148 385 556 50 248 433 84 217
	531 267 346 468 348 639 346 238 620 895 80 399 697 135 349
Holyhead	474 176 216 102 269 124 272 311 403 371 168 293 338 204
	763 283 348 164 433 200 438 501 649 597 270 472 544 328
Inverness	360 427 382 550 373 268 529 720 116 393 598 262 352
	579 687 615 885 600 431 852 1159 187 632 963 422 566
Leeds	68 75 189 40 92 176 401 254 33 232 220 24
	109 121 304 64 148 283 645 409 53 373 354 39
Lincoln	129 131 84 159 105 367 312 46 204 298 75
	208 211 135 256 169 591 502 74 328 480 121
Liverpool	202 35 168 220 366 266 72 239 221 99
	325 56 270 354 589 428 116 385 356 159
LONDON	185 286 114 285 433 159 77 402 207
	298 460 183 459 718 256 124 647 333
MANCHESTER	132 185 354 263 38 221 220 64
	212 298 570 423 61 356 354 103
Newcastle upon Tyne	264 484 155 125 324 158 84
	425 779 249 201 521 254 135
Norwich	436 430 146 206 403 181
	702 692 235 332 649 291
Penzance	604 368 223 569 410
	974 592 359 916 661
Perth	306 479 154 249
	492 771 248 401
Sheffield	199 263 217
	320 423 349
Southampton	445 258
	716 415
Stranraer	222
	357
York	

Inverness
Aberdeen
Fort William
Perth
Glasgow
EDINBURGH
Londonderry
Stranraer
Newcastle upon Tyne
Carlisle
Donegal
BELFAST
York
Sligo
Leeds
Liverpool MANCHESTER
Galway
Athlone
Lincoln
DUBLIN
Holyhead
Sheffield
Limerick
Norwich
Rosslare
BIRMINGHAM
Killarney
Cork Waterford
Aberystwyth
Cambridge
LONDON
CARDIFF
Bristol
Southampton
Dover
Exeter
Penzance

KEY TO MAPS

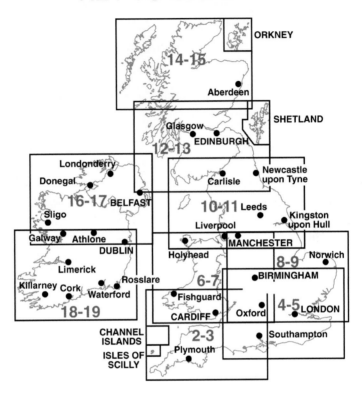

ORKNEY

14-15

Aberdeen

SHETLAND

Glasgow
EDINBURGH

12-13

Londonderry

Donegal

Newcastle
upon Tyne

Carlisle

16-17 BELFAST

10-11 Leeds

Sligo

Liverpool

Kingston
upon Hull

Galway Athlone

MANCHESTER

DUBLIN

Holyhead

Norwich

Limerick

8-9

Rosslare

BIRMINGHAM

Killarney Cork

6-7

Waterford

Fishguard

4-5 LONDON

18-19

CARDIFF

Oxford

CHANNEL
ISLANDS

2-3

Southampton

ISLES OF
SCILLY

Plymouth

LEGEND

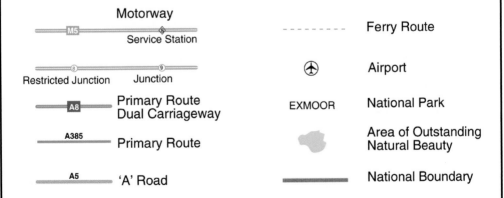

M5 Motorway / Service Station	---------- Ferry Route
Restricted Junction Junction	✈ Airport
A8 Primary Route Dual Carriageway	EXMOOR National Park
A385 Primary Route	Area of Outstanding Natural Beauty
A5 'A' Road	National Boundary

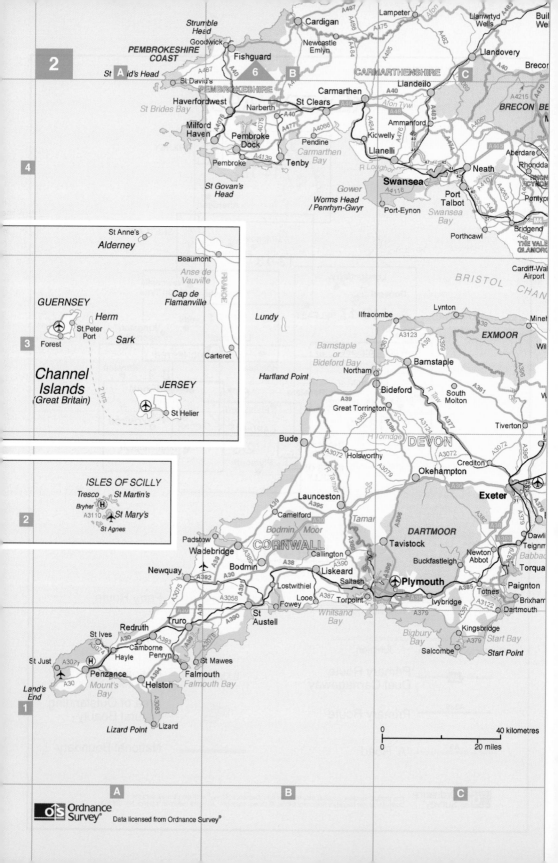

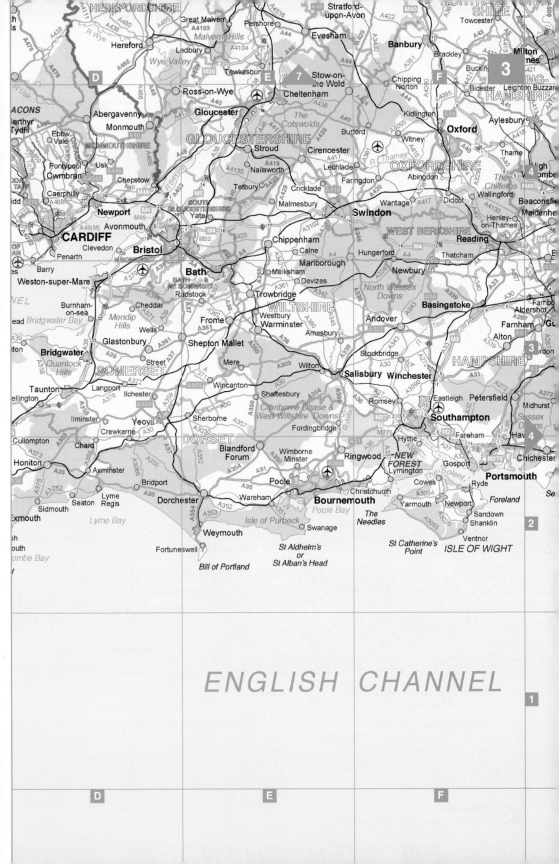

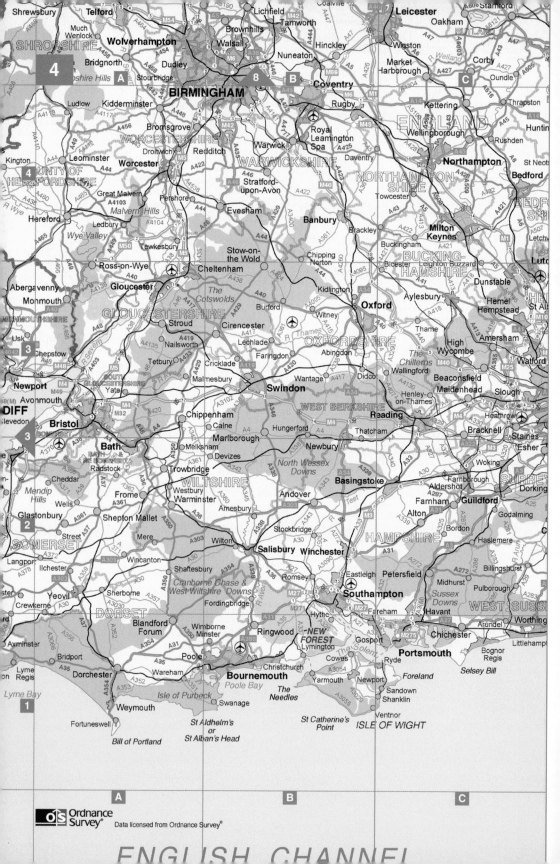

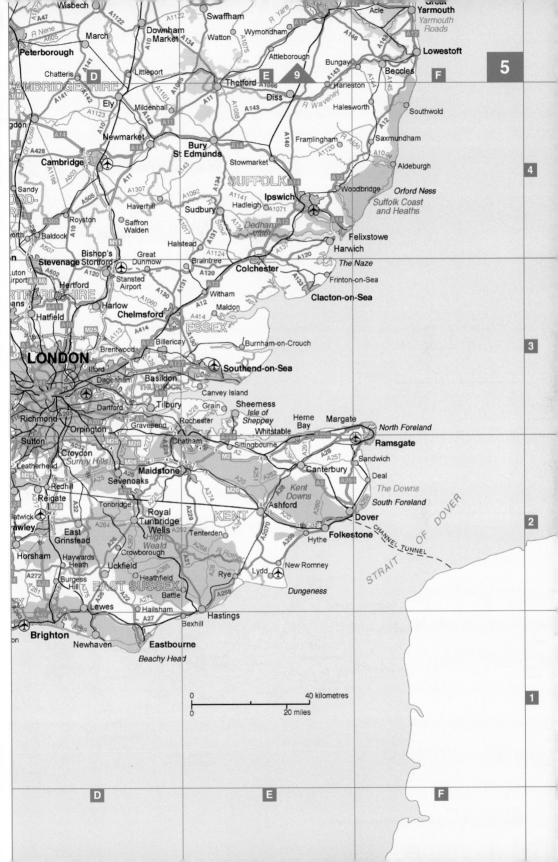

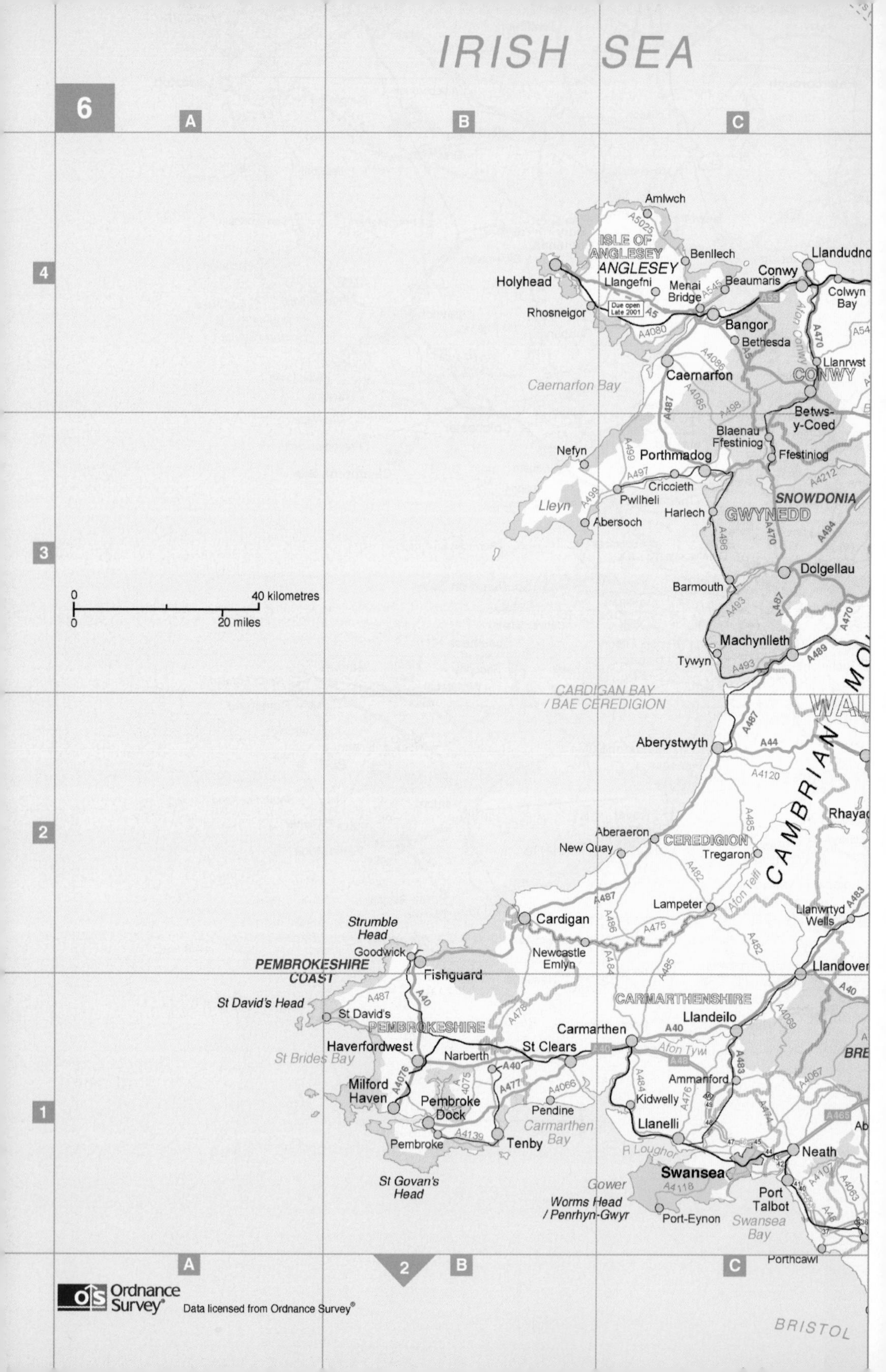

IRISH SEA

6

A   B   C

4

Amlwch

ISLE OF
ANGLESEY
ANGLESEY
Benllech
Conwy Llandudno
Holyhead Llangefni
Menai Beaumaris Colwyn
Bridge Bay
Rhosneigor Due open
Late 2001 Bangor CONWY
Bethesda Llanrwst

Caernarfon Bay Caernarfon Betws-
y-Coed
Blaenau
Ffestiniog Ffestiniog
Nefyn Porthmadog
SNOWDONIA
Criccieth GWYNEDD
3 Lleyn Pwllheli Harlech
Abersoch
Dolgellau
Barmouth
Machynlleth
Tywyn

CARDIGAN BAY
/ BAE CEREDIGION WAL
Aberystwyth A44
Rhayad

Aberaeron CAMBRIAN MO
New Quay CEREDIGION
2 Tregaron
Lampeter Llanwrtyd
Wells
Cardigan
Strumble Llandover
Head Newcastle
Goodwick Emlyn
PEMBROKESHIRE CARMARTHENSHIRE
COAST Fishguard
St David's Head Llandeilo BRE
St David's PEMBROKESHIRE Carmarthen
Haverfordwest St Clears Ammanford
St Brides Bay Narberth Ab
Milford Kidwelly
1 Haven Pembroke Pendine Llanelli
Dock Carmarthen Neath
Pembroke Tenby Bay
R Loughor
St Govan's Swansea Port
Head Gower Talbot
Worms Head Port-Eynon Swansea
/ Penrhyn-Gwyr Bay
Portcawl
A   2   B   C

0 ___ 40 kilometres
0 ___ 20 miles

Ordnance Survey
Data licensed from Ordnance Survey

BRISTOL

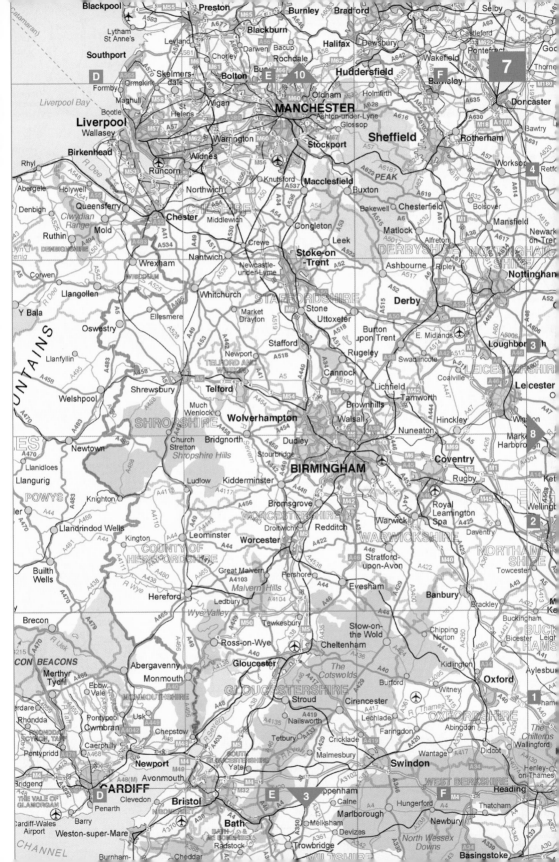

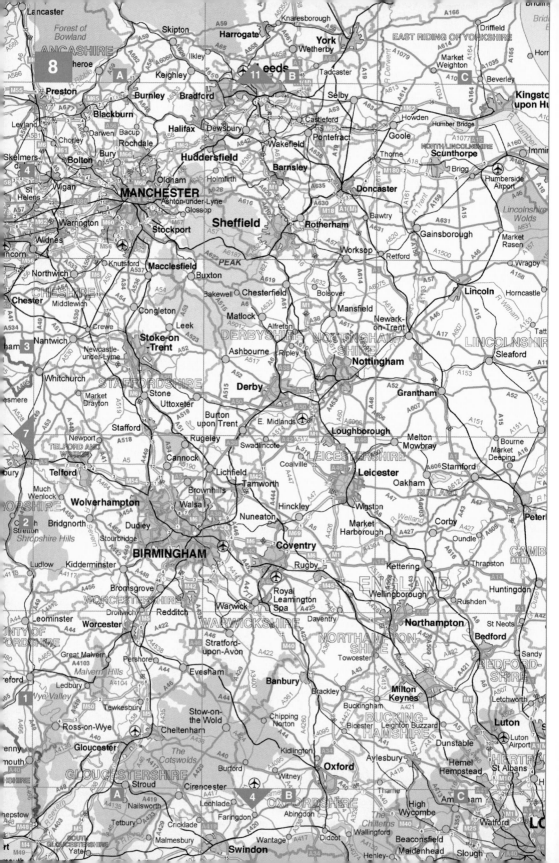

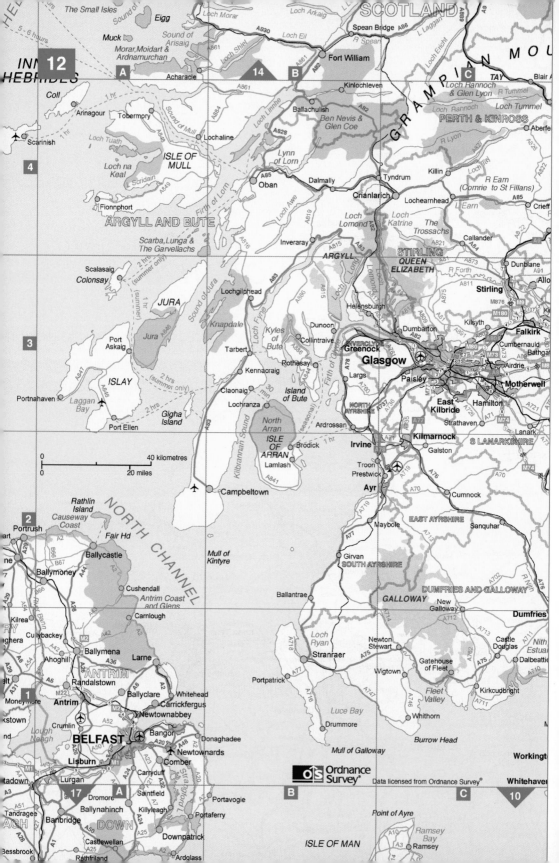

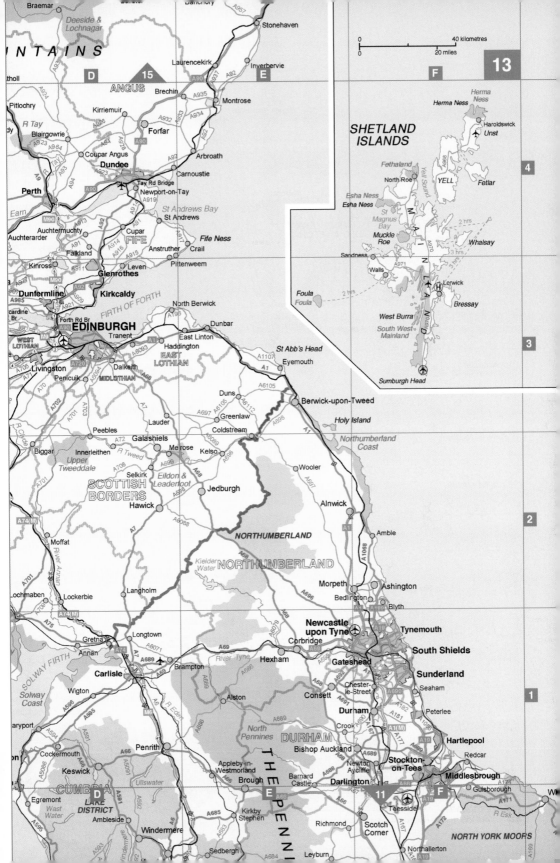

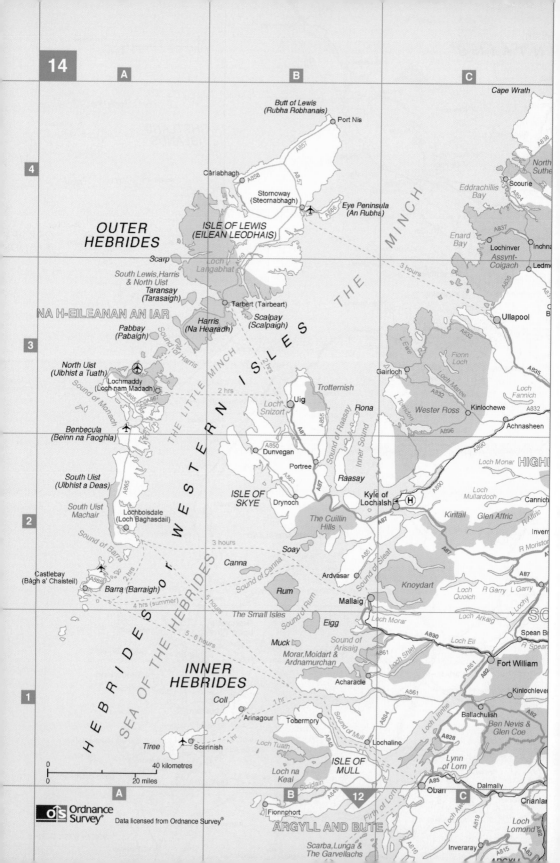

A   B   C

4

Northern Ireland based upon the Ordnance Survey map with the sanction of
The Controller of Her Majesty's Stationery Office, Crown copyright reserved.
OSNI Permit No. 1602

0 ──────── 40 kilometres
0 ──────── 20 miles

Tory Island
Bloody
Foreland
Horn
Head
Dunfanaghy
Falcarrag
Derry Veagh
Mountains
Aran
Island
R257
R259
N56
Burtonport
R254
Lette
Dunglow
R252
R250
R261
R252
Glenties
Ballybofe
Ardara
R262
R253
R263
N56
Blue Stack
Mountains
N15
Killybegs
Donegal

Benwee
Head
Ballintra
Pettigo
Ballyshannon
Bundoran
Beleek
Lower
Lough Erne
Lough
Melvin
FER
Donegal Bay
N15
R280
A47
A40

Belmullet
R313
Ballycastle
Killala
Bay
R314
Killala
R315
Manorhamilton
N16
Sligo
LETRIM
Crossmolina
R314
N59
SLIGO
Dromahair
A4
Nephin Beg
Range
Ballina
N26
Tobercurry
N17
Ballymot
R284
Swanlinbar
A32
Lough
Conn
Foxford
N26
N5
Swinford
Charlestown
Lough
Allen
Ballycc
Drumshanbo
MAYO
R312
R310
N5
R293
R295
R285
Achill
Island
R319
R317
Castlebar
Kiltamagh
R375
N5
Ballaghadereen
Boyle
Carrick-on-
Shannon
Killsh
Clare
Island
Clew Bay
N60
N5
Knock
N17
N83
R361
ROSCOMMON
R370
R368
R202
Mohill
Arva
Westport
R330
Ballyhaunis
N191
Roosky
R198
Louisburgh
R335
Partry
Mountains
Claremorris
R323
Castlerea
R367
Strokestown
N60
R194
Longford
N59
Lough
Mask
R331
R327
Lanesborough
N5
R371
LONGFORD
Leenaun
Ballinrobe
N84
N83
Ballymoe
R364
IRELA
Clifden
Maumturk
Mountains
R345
Cong
R332
Dunmore
R362
Glenamaddy
N60
Roscommon
Lough
Ree
Ballymaho
R341
R336
R340
R333
Tuam
N63
Mountbellew
Bridge
R363
N61
Ballymaho
N55
R390
R392
Slyne
Head
Oughterard
N59
Headford
N17
R Clare
R339
R357
R358
Athlone
WESTMEA
Carraroe
N59
R347
GALWAY
R359
R360
N6
Moate
N55
Spiddle
Galway
R336
Athenry
Ballinasloe
R Shannon
N6
N60

18

Black
Head
Craughwell
N6
Shannonbridge
144
R436
Clara
Aran Islands
R477
N67
R480
Ballyvaghan
N66
Loughrea
R355
R356
R357
OFFALY
Tullamore
N62
Lisdoonvarna
R476
Gort
R353
N65
Portumna
N52
R421
Banagher

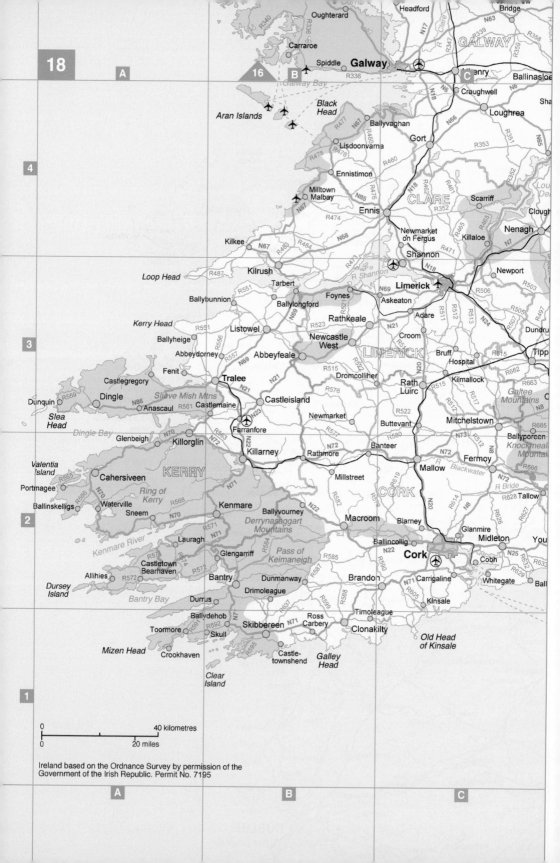

A · B · C

4

3

2

1

Oughterard
Headford
Bridge

Carraroe
Spiddle
Galway

16

Galway Bay

Black
Head

Aran Islands

Ballyvaghan

Lisdoonvarna

Ennistimon

Milltown
Malbay

Ennis

Kilkee

Kilrush

Tarbert

Loop Head

Ballybunnion

Ballylongford

Foynes

Kerry Head

Listowel

Rathkeale

Ballyheige

Abbeydorney

Abbeyfeale

Newcastle
West

Fenit

Tralee

Castlegregory

Dingle

Slieve Mish Mtns

Anascaul

Castlemaine

Castleisland

Dunquin

Slea
Head

Dingle Bay

Glenbeigh

Killorglin

Killarney

Valentia
Island

Cahersiveen

KERRY

Portmagee

Ring of
Kerry

Millstreet

Ballinskelligs

Waterville

Sneem

Kenmare

Macroom

Lauragh

Derrynasaggart
Mountains

Ballyvourney

Blarney

Glengarriff

Pass of
Keimaneigh

Ballincollig

Dursey
Island

Allihies

Castletown
Bearhaven

Bantry

Cork

Bantry Bay

Durrus

Drimoleague

Brandon

Ballydehob

Dunmanway

Toormore

Skull

Skibbereen

Ross
Carbery

Clonakilty

Mizen Head

Crookhaven

Castle-
townshend

Galley
Head

Old Head
of Kinsale

Clear
Island

GALWAY

Craughwell

Loughrea

Gort

CLARE

Scarriff

Clough

Nenagh

Newmarket
on Fergus

Killaloe

Newport

Shannon

Limerick

Askeaton

Adare

Croom

LIMERICK

Dromcolliher

Bruff

Hospital

Kilmallock

Newmarket

Rath
Luirc

Buttevant

Mitchelstown

Rathmore

Banteer

Fermoy

Mallow

Blackwater

CORK

Tallow

Glanmire

Midleton

Carrigaline

Cobh

Whitegate

Kinsale

Timoleague

Dundru

Tipp

Galtee
Mountains

Ballyporeen

Knockmeal
Mountai

You

Ball

40 kilometres

20 miles

Ireland based on the Ordnance Survey by permission of the
Government of the Irish Republic. Permit No. 7195

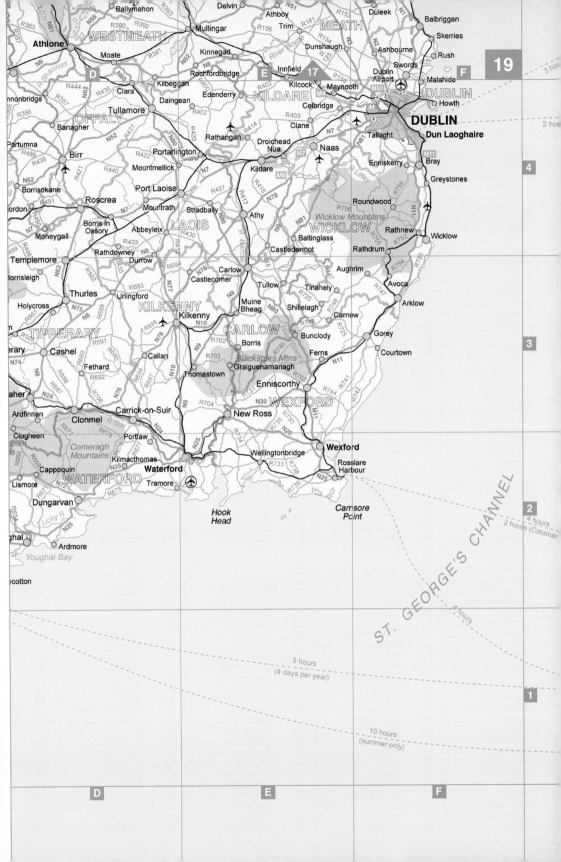

INDEX TO GREAT BRITAIN